A Study Book for the

NEBOSH National General Certificate

Technician Member (Tech IOSH)

This category recognises the qualifications and competence needed by professionals working in a range of operational health and safety roles. To become a Technician, you must have a suitable level of experience in a health and safety role, as well as an IOSH accredited qualification.

Students on a course of study towards Tech IOSH will find this **Essential Health and Safety Guide** particularly useful in developing the knowledge requirements for an IOSH accredited qualification at this level.

RMS Publishing Limited

Victoria House, Lower High Street, Stourbridge, DY8 1TA

First Published February 2003.

First Edition Revised April 2003.

Second Edition February 2004.

Third Edition September 2005.

Fourth Edition December 2006.

Fifth Edition January 2008.

Sixth Edition January 2011.

Cover design by Graham Scriven.

Printed and bound in Great Britain by Stephens and George Print Group, Merthyr Tydfil.

ISBN-13: 978-1-906674-07-6

Editor's Notes

Diagrams and photographs

This 6th Edition has been thoroughly revised, reformatted and updated and provides an excellent reference for those with management responsibilities for health and safety in the workplace. We have taken particular care to support the text with over three hundred photographs and schematics. The photographs have been selected to be illustrative of both good and bad work practices and should always be considered in context with supporting text. I am sure that students will find this a useful aid when trying to relate their background and experience to the broad based NEBOSH General Certificate syllabus. They will give an important insight into some of the technical areas of the syllabus for those who may not have a strong technical background.

Where diagrams/text extracts are known to be drawn from other publications, a clear source reference is shown and RMS wishes to emphasise that reproduction of such diagrams/text extracts within the Study Book is for educational purposes only and the original copyright has not been infringed.

Legal requirements

The Study Book has at its heart the fact that health and safety should be managed as a risk. However, as one of the risks to a business is the risk of prosecution, care has been taken to relate topics to current legislation. Legislation is referred to in context in the various elements that comprise the Study Book, it reflects the syllabus of the NEBOSH General Certificate and is targeted to meet the needs of students studying to this level. In addition, the Study Book has a section dedicated to legislation, and here the student will find a useful summary of the legislation required for this award.

Syllabus

Each element of the Study Book has an element overview that sets out the learning outcomes of the element, the content and any connected sources of reference and/or relevant statutory provisions. The Study Book reflects the order and content of the NEBOSH General Certificate syllabus, because of this the student can be confident that the Study Book reflects the themes of the syllabus. The syllabus is structured in a very useful way, focusing on hazards, their control and core management of health and safety principles. Note: Unit NGC1 (Elements 1-5) also fulfils the study requirements for Unit NGC1 of the unitised NEBOSH Fire Safety and Risk Management and Construction Certificates.

National Vocational Qualification

We are confident that those working towards national vocational qualifications will find this Study Book a useful domain knowledge reference source for NVQ Level 3 in Occupational Health and Safety.

Tech IOSH

Students on a course of study leading towards **Tech IOSH** will find this Essential Health and Safety Guide valuable in developing the knowledge requirements for an IOSH accredited qualification at this level.

Acknowledgements

Managing Editor: Ian Coombes.

Member of the Safety Groups UK (SGUK) Management Committee. Former NEBOSH examiner, NEBOSH Director, member of NEBOSH Council, member of the IOSH Professional Committee and Chair of the IOSH Initial Professional Development Committee.

RMS Publishing wishes to acknowledge the following contributors and thank them for their assistance in the preparation of the 6th Edition General Certificate study book: Geoff Littley, Barrie Newell, Nick Attwood, Kris James and Design and Development Co-ordinator Julie Skett.

RMS publishing offer a series of excellent reference publications, to enable students to develop the knowledge requirements necessary to achieve IOSH accredited awards leading to Graduate membership (Grad IOSH):

Publication	Edition	13-digit ISBN	EAN
A Study Book for the NEBOSH National Certificate in Construction Safety and Health	Second	978-1-900420-89-1	9781900420891
A Study Book for the NEBOSH Certificate in Fire Safety and Risk Management	Third	978-1-906674-05-2	9781906674052
A Study Book for the NEBOSH National Certificate in Environmental Management	First	978-1-906674-03-8	9781906674038
A Study Book for the NEBOSH Certificate in the Management of Health and Well-being	First	978-1-906674-06-9	9781906674069
Study Books for the NEBOSH National Diploma in Occupational Safety and Health:			
■ (Unit A) Managing Health and Safety	Third	978-1-906674-02-1	9781906674021
■ (Unit B) Hazardous Agents in the Workplace	Third	978-1-900420-98-3	9781900420983
■ (Unit C) Workplace and Work Equipment	Third	978-1-906674-01-4	9781906674014
A Study Book for the NEBOSH International General Certificate	First	978-1-900420-90-7	9781900420907
Controlling skin exposure (BOHS)	First	978-1-906674-00-7	9781906674007

Contents

Figure List (including tables and quotes)

Element 5

UNIT NGC2 - CONTROLLING WORKPLACE HAZARDS

Element 1

Element 2

Element 3

Element 4

Element 5

Element 6

Element 7

Element 8

RELEVANT STATUTORY PROVISIONS

List of abbreviations

LEGISLATION

CAOR	Control of Artificial Optical Radiation at Work Regulations 2010
CAR	Control of Asbestos Regulations 2006
CDM	Construction (Design and Management) Regulation 2007
CHIP4	Chemicals (Hazard Information and Packaging for Supply) Regulations 2009
CHPR	Construction (Head Protection) Regulations 1989
CLAW	Control of Lead at Work Regulations 2002
CNWR	Control of Noise at Work Regulations 2005
COSHH	Control of Substances Hazardous to Health (Amendment) Regulations 2004
CSR	Confined Spaces Regulations 1997
CUR	Road Vehicles (Construction and Use) Regulations 1986
CVWR	Control of Vibration at Work Regulations 2005
CMCHA	Corporate Manslaughter and Corporate Homicide Act 2007
DPA	Data Protection Act 1998
DSE	Health and Safety (Display Screen Equipment) Regulations 1992
DSEAR	Dangerous Substances and Explosive Atmospheres Regulations 2002
EARR	Health and Safety (Enforcing Authority for Railways and Other Guided Transport systems) Regulations 2006
EHSPS	Employer's Health and Safety Policy Statements (Exception) Regulations 1975
ELCI	Employer's Liability (Compulsory Insurance) Act 1969
EPCA	Employment Protection (Consolidation) Act 1978
EPS	Equipment and Protective Systems Intended for Use in Potentially Explosive Atmospheres Regulations 1996.
EWR	Electricity at Work Regulations 1989
FAR	Health and Safety (First-Aid) Regulations 1981
FSA	Fire (Scotland) Act 2005
FSSR	Fire Safety (Scotland) Regulations 2006
HASAWA	Health and Safety at Work etc Act 1974
HSCER	Health and Safety (Consultation with Employees) Regulations 1996
HSOA	Health and Safety (Offences) Act 2008
HWR	Hazardous Waste (England and Wales) Regulations 2005
IA	Interpretation Act 1978
IER	Health and Safety (Information for Employees) Regulations 1989
IRR	Ionising Radiation Regulations 1999
LOLER	Lifting Operations and Lifting Equipment Regulations 1998
MAR	Health and Safety (Miscellaneous Amendments) Regulations 2002
MHOR	Manual Handling Operations Regulations 1992
MHSWR	Management of Health and Safety at Work Regulations 1999
PPER	Personal Protective Equipment at Work Regulations 1992
PUWER	Provision and Use of Work Equipment Regulations 1998
RIDDOR	Reporting of Injuries, Diseases and Dangerous Occurrences Regulations 1995
RRFSO	Regulatory Reform (Fire Safety) Order 2005
RTA	Road Traffic Act 1988, 1991
RVLR	Road Vehicles Lighting Regulations 1989
SMSR	Supply of Machinery (Safety) Regulations 1992
SRSC	Safety Representatives and Safety Committees Regulations 1977
SSSR	Health and Safety (Safety Signs and Signals) Regulations 1996
SWASR	Special Waste Amendment (Scotland) Regulations 2004
SWR	Special Waste Regulations 1996
TWA	Transport and Works Act 1992
WAH	Work at Height Regulations 2005
WHSWR	Workplace (Health, Safety and Welfare) Regulations 1992

GENERAL

AA	Automobile Association
ABS	Active Breaking Systems
AC	Alternating Current
ACOP	Approved Code of Practice
ACTS	Advisory Committee on Toxic Substances.
A&E	Accident and Emergency Services
AIDS	Acquired Immune Deficiency Syndrome
APF	Assigned Protection Factor
BBVs	Blood Borne Viruses
BMGVs	Biological Monitoring Values
BSI	British Standards Institution
CAT	Cable Avoidance Tool
CBI	Confederation of British Industry
CEN	European Standards
CFCs	Chlorofluorocarbons

CITB	Construction Industry Training Board
CO^2	Carbon Dioxide
CORGI	Council for the Registration of Gas Installers
CPL	Classification, Labelling and Packaging of Substances and Mixtures Regulation
CPR	Cardio Pulmonary Resuscitation
CPS	Crown Prosecution Service
CTS	Carpal Tunnel Syndrome
dB	Decibel
DC	Direct Current
DETI	Department of Enterprise, Trade and Investment
DVLA	Driver and Vehicle Licensing Agency
EA	Environmental Agency
EAT	Employment Appeal Tribunal
EC	European Community
EEF	Engineering Employers Federation
EFAW	Emergency First Aid at Work
EHO	Environmental Health Office
EHSRS	Essential Health and Safety Requirements
ELCI	Employers' liability compulsory insurance
EMAS	Employment Medical Advisory Service
ET	Employment Tribunal
ETA	Event Tree Analysis
EU	European Union
EWR	Electricity at Work
FAW	First Aid at Work
FGD	Flue Gas Desulphurisation
FLT	Forklift Truck
FMEA	Failure Mode and Effect Analysis
FRA	Fire Risk Assessment
FTA	Fault Tree Analysis
HAVS	Hand-arm Vibration Syndrome
HAZOP	Hazard and Operability Studies
HEPA	High-Efficiency Particulate Arrester
HIV	Human Immunodeficiency Virus
HML	High, Medium and Low values
HMSO	Her Majesty's Stationary Office
HPA	Health Protection Agency
HSC	Health and Safety Commission
HSE	Health and Safety Executive
HSG	Health and Safety Guidance
HV	High Voltage
ICC	Incident Contact Centre
IEE	Institute of Electrical Engineers
ILO	International Labour Organisation
IOSH	Institute of Occupational Safety and Health
IPC	Integrated Pollution Control
IT	Information Technology
KPI	Key Performance Indicator
LAAPC	Local Authority Air Pollution Control
LEV	Local Exhaust Ventilation
LFS	Labour Force Survey
LPG	Liquified Petroleum Gas
LTEL	Long Term Exposure Limit
LV	Low Voltage
MDI	Methylene Bisphenyl Di-isocyanate
MEWP	Mobile Elevated Work Platform
MSDs	Musculoskeletal disorders
MSF	The Manufacturing , Science and Finance Union
MSW	Municipal Solid Wastes
NVQ	National Vocational Qualifications
ORR	Office of Rail Regulation
OSH	Occupational Safety and Health
PAT	Portable Appliance Testing
PCV	Passenger Carrying Vehicle
PNA	Predicted Noise Attenuation
PPE	Personal Protective Equipment
PPM	Parts Per Million
PTW	Permit to Work
QSA	Qualified Security Assessor
RCD	Residual Current Device
RCSs	Risk Control Systems
REACH	Registration, Evaluation, Authorisation and restriction of Chemicals

RES	Representatives of Employment Safety
RH	Relative Humidity
RPA	Radiation Protection Advisors
RPE	Respiratory Protective Equipment
SDS	Safety Data Sheet
SEPA	Scottish Environmental Protection Agency
SNR	Single Number Rating values
SR	Safety Representatives
SSW	Safe System of Work
STEL	Short Term Exposure Limit
SVQ	Scottish Vocational Qualification
SWL	Safe Working Load
TDI	Toluene Di-isocyanate
TUC	Trade Union Congress
TWA	Time Weighted Average
UV	Ultra Violet
VCM	Vinyl Chloride Monomer
VWF	Vibration White Finger
WATCH	Working on Action to Control Chemicals
WBV	Whole Body Vibration
WEL	Workplace Exposure Limits
WHO	World Health Organisation
WRULD	Work Related Upper Limb Disorder

UNIT NGC1
MANAGEMENT OF HEALTH AND SAFETY

Element

1

Foundations in health and safety

Learning outcomes

On completion of this element, candidates should be able to demonstrate understanding of the content through the application of knowledge to familiar and unfamiliar situations. In particular they should be able to:

1.1 Outline the scope and nature of occupational health and safety.

1.2 Explain the moral and financial reasons for promoting good standards of health and safety in the workplace.

1.3 Explain the legal framework for the regulation of health and safety including sources and types of law.

1.4 Explain the scope, duties and offences of employers, managers, employees and others under the Health and Safety at Work etc. Act 1974.

1.5 Explain the scope, duties and offences of employers, managers, employees and others under the Management of Health and Safety at Work Regulations.

1.6 Outline the legal and organisational health and safety roles and responsibilities of clients and their contractors.

Content

Sources of reference

The Management of Health and Safety at Work (ACOP) (L21), HSE Books ISBN 0-7176-2488-9

Successful Health and Safety Management (HSG65), HSE Books ISBN 0-7176-1276-7

Health and Safety Executive 'Ready Reckoner' website at www.hse.gov.uk/costs

Leading health and safety at work (INDG 417) HSE Books, ISBN 978 0 7176 6267 8

Managing Health and Safety in Construction (ACOP) (HSG224), HSE Books ISBN 0-7176-2139-1

Health and Safety in Construction (Guidance) (HSG150rev), HSE Books ISBN 0-7176-0716-X

OHSAS 18001 Occupational health and safety management systems - Requirements

Relevant statutory provisions

The Health and Safety at Work etc. Act (HASAWA) 1974

The Interpretation Act (IA) 1978

The Management of Health and Safety at Work Regulations (MHSWR) 1999 (as amended)

The Construction (Design and Management) Regulations (CDM) 2007

Corporate Manslaughter and Corporate Homicide Act (CMCHA) 2007

1.1 - The scope and nature of occupational health and safety

The multi-disciplinary nature of health and safety

Health and safety is a fundamental aspect of managing an organisation as it impacts on all the functions within the organisation, just as quality might. Health and safety embraces a number of disciplines reflecting the scope of its influence, including finance, insurance, health, personnel, production, design, purchase and information technology (IT).

The obstacles to success with health and safety are the same as with other business objectives, with an additional obstacle being that the main operational requirements of the organisation will tend (unless the organisation has the balance correct) to take priority, whether this is construction, manufacture or health care. Organisations tend to focus on the immediate costs of implementing health and safety rather than the benefits that can be gained from doing so. The constant struggle to balance often complex, conflicting demands and behavioural issues with protecting profits (or those wanting to budget) by not spending unnecessarily is something that those wishing to improve health and safety face daily. The organisation may divert resources from health and safety needs to deal with competing issues such as quality improvement.

Successful organisations are realising the need to take an inclusive approach to heath and safety that balances effort between the four primary issues - service, quality, health and safety, and environment - by implementing technical, procedural and behavioural solutions.

Meanings of and distinctions between common terms

HEALTH, SAFETY, WELFARE AND ENVIRONMENTAL PROTECTION

Health

"A state of well being"

The term 'health' has been defined as a state of well being. It includes well being in a physiological and psychological sense. In occupational terms this would include not suffering from noise-induced deafness, mental fatigue or stress. There is an element of overlap with the terms 'safety" and 'health'; for example, it would be clear that someone who has experienced a fall could sustain a physical injury such as a broken bone (a safety issue). In addition, it would not be a surprise if someone observed that the injured party had a 'poor state of health' for the period that the injury affected them. Maintaining health includes attention to the various health hazards (agents) in the working environment that can affect the worker and others, for example, chemical and biological agents.

Safety

"Absence of danger of physical harm"

The term 'safety' is considered to be the absence of danger of physical harm to people. The term would extend to other things that could be harmed in the workplace such as equipment, structures and materials. Attention to safety matters would typically deal with factors that can cause this type of harm, such as a fall from height, fire, electricity, and moving plant and machinery.

Welfare

"Facilities for workplace comfort"

The term 'welfare' relates to the provision of workplace facilities that maintain the basic well being and comfort of the worker, such as eating, washing, toilet facilities and first aid.

Environmental protection

"A measure used to prevent harm to the environment of the world"

The term 'environmental protection' relates to measures that are specifically focused on maintaining the general environment of the world. As such it focuses on such things as protection of plant life including flora and fauna, animals, birds and marine life, and the quality of water, land and air. Though the protection does not focus on the worker or other people directly by protecting the environment, people obtain a benefit.

1.2 - The moral and financial reasons for promoting good standards of health and safety

General argument

There are three good reasons for preventing accidents in the workplace:

1) Moral

Injury accidents result in a great deal of pain and suffering for those affected. Clearly, we must all do that we can to avoid this.

2) Legal

It is a legal requirement to safeguard the health and safety of employees and others that might be affected by the organisation's operations.

3) Financial

Accidents at work cost a great deal of money, especially when we add in damage accidents (particularly when they interrupt production, downgrade the quality of our products or impair the environment).

Costs can be enormous - and perhaps already are many times larger than most individuals consider.

The size of the problem

Health and Safety Executive (HSE) statistics reveal that 152 workers were killed at work during the year 2009/10. The construction industry (42%) and agriculture (38%) accounted for most of these. Falls from height, being struck by a vehicle and being struck by a falling object account for approximately 50% of all fatal injuries.

More than 121,000 other injuries (including more than 26,000 major injuries) were reported under the Reporting of Injuries Diseases and Dangerous Occurrences Regulations (RIDDOR) 1995 and, about 28,500,000 days were lost in total due to work-related ill-health and injury. Slipping and tripping accounts for 41% of all major injuries. The second most common type of major injuries is those sustained whilst lifting, handling or carrying. These types of injury account for 36% of all "3 day" injuries.

Accidents and ill health are costly to workers and their families. They can also impact significantly on organisations because, in addition to costs of personal injuries, they may incur far greater costs from damage to property or equipment, and lost business time such as production.

The Health and Safety Executive (HSE) reported the following statistics for 2009/10, the latest available at time of going to press.

ILL-HEALTH

- **1.3 million** (1.2 2008/9) working people suffered from a work-related illness during the year, of which 555,000 (552,000 2008/9) were new cases.
- **2,249** (2,156 in 2007) people died of mesothelioma (2008), and thousands more from other occupational cancers and lung diseases.

INJURIES

- **152** (180 2008/9) workers were killed at work, a rate of 0.5 (0.6 2008/9) per 100 000 workers.
- **121,430** (131,895 2008/9) other injuries to employees were reported under RIDDOR 1995, a rate of 473 (502.2 2008/9) per 100,000 employees.
- **233,000** (246,000 2008/9) reportable injuries occurred, according to the Labour Force Survey, a rate of 840 (870 2008/9) per 100,000 workers.

WORKING DAYS LOST

- **28.5 million** (29.3 million 2008/9) days were lost overall, equivalent to 1.2 (1.24 2008/9) days per worker, 23.4 million (24.6 million 2008/9) due to work-related ill-health and 5.1 million (4.7 million) due to workplace injury.

Societal expectations of good standards of health and safety

Society expects and demands that we provide a safe and healthy work environment, without harm to employees, contractors, the self-employed and the general public. This would include any major impact on the local or global community from a disaster.

Societal opinion tends to fall into two parts:

- Strategic, influenced by the general mass of public concerning its tolerance of specific workplace hazards or situations (e.g. display screen equipment or major disasters).
- Local influences tend to surround acceptability or unacceptability of the practices of a specific organisation. This is most acute following an accident and has had the effect of causing closure of some smaller organisations.

The business case for health and safety

INSURED AND UNINSURED COSTS

Many case studies over recent years have illustrated the difference between insured costs and uninsured costs. It has been shown that uninsured costs were often between 8 and 36 times greater than the costs of insurance premiums.

The following 'Accident Costs Iceberg' represents the ratio of insured to uninsured costs incurred by the main contractor (1:11) during the building of a supermarket.

HSE studies found that uninsured costs outweighed insured costs by up to 36 times.

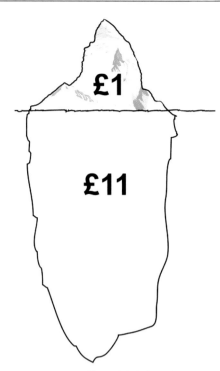

INSURED COSTS

- Employer's Liability
- Public / Third party liability
- Contractors all risks
- Plant and building damage
- Tools and equipment

UNINSURED COSTS

- Product and materials damage
- Emergency supplies
- Production delays
- Overtime and temporary labour
- Investigation time
- Supervisors' time diverted

Figure 1-1-1: Costs incurred by the main contractor (1:11) during the building of a supermarket. *Source: RMS/HSG96.*

Direct costs

- Insurance.
- Court costs.
- Fines.
- Lost time of injured employee and continued payments to employee.
- Damage to the equipment, tools, property and plant or to materials.

Indirect costs

- Lost time by other employees who stop work or reduce performance.
  - Out of curiosity.
  - Out of sympathy.
- • Weakened morale.
- Lost time by supervisor or other managers.
  - Assisting injured employee.
  - Investigating the cause of the accident.
  - Arranging for the injured employee's production to be continued by some other employee.
  - Selecting or training a new employee to replace an injured employee.
- • Preparing accident reports, attending hearings, inquests courts.
- Interference with production leading to failure to fill orders on time, loss of bonuses, penalty payments and similar losses.

The HSE have published a series of four case studies to illustrate just how much accidents at work could cost a company. The industries chosen were from a wide range of activities. The following table illustrates the losses identified.

		Total loss	*Annualised loss*	*Representing*
1	Construction site	£245,075	£700,000	8.5% tender price
2	Creamery	£243,834	£975,336	1.4% operating costs
3	Transport company	£48,928	£195,712	1.8% of operating costs 37% of profits
4	Oil platform	£940,921	£3,763,684	14.2% of potential output

Figure 1-1-2: Sample costs of accidents.　　　　　　　　　　　　　　*Source: The costs of accidents at work, HSG96, HSE Books.*

EMPLOYERS' LIABILITY INSURANCE

Employers' liability compulsory insurance (ELCI) enables businesses to meet the costs of compensation and legal fees for employees who are injured or made ill at work through the fault of their employer.

Under the Employers' Liability (Compulsory Insurance) Act 1969, an employer must have ELCI and be insured for at least £5 million per individual claim. Most insurers automatically provide cover of at least £10 million. ELCI must cover all employees in England, Scotland, Wales and Northern Ireland.

An employer who has been issued with a certificate must display one or more copies of it at each place of business at which he employs any employee of the class or description to which such certificate relates and keep copies for at least 40 years.

The purpose of employer's liability insurance is to satisfy a legal requirement for employers to carry such insurance so that an employee who is harmed due to the fault of his/her employer is assured of receiving compensation that the employer might otherwise have insufficient resources to pay. At a time of increases in the number of claims and size of awards, and the consequent rise in premiums, this type of insurance is exerting significant pressure on employers to improve their standards of health and safety.

The Health and Safety Executive (HSE) is responsible for enforcing the law on ELCI. Employers can be fined up to £2,500 for each day that they do not have appropriate insurance.

Employers' liability compulsory insurance is designed to protect employees who have suffered a personal loss. Separate provision will need to be considered for the many costs associated with a workplace accident that may not, depending on the policies carried, be covered by insurance. Compensation to injured employees is covered as a legal requirement and is paid in full by the insurer. Any excess agreed between the employer and the insurance company will have to be paid by the employer to the insurance company, as will any increase in the insurance premium that could follow a serious accident.

Other costs that may be incurred relate to:

- Production delays.
- Damaged goods and equipment.
- Accident investigation.
- Loss of expertise or experience.

- Hiring and training replacement staff.
- Loss of goodwill and reputation.
- Clean-up operations.
- Possible fines and associated legal fees.

HSE research shows that uninsured costs generally far exceed insured costs.

1.3 - The legal framework for the regulation of health and safety

Role of the European Union in harmonising standards

The Council of the European Commission can, under the Treaty of Rome, issue Directives. These are to harmonise the laws of the member states, including those covering occupational health and safety.

Representatives of the member states meet to agree on the content of draft Directives. When they are agreed, they are presented to the European Parliament for ratification. The Directives impose a duty on each member state to make legislation to conform to the Directive and to enforce such legislation. The Directives are legally binding on the governments. Framework Directives set out the overall objectives and deal with individual objectives of Daughter Directives. In the UK the Directives are translated into Regulations. For example, we have the Working Time Directive translated into the Working Time Regulations.

The Single European Act identified the need to eliminate technical barriers to trade, such as the differing legal health and safety standards throughout the Community. The approach is to develop a philosophy of essential health and safety requirements and harmonisation Directives that establish those essential health and safety requirements. Further to this, there is recognition in the Act to encourage improvements in the working environment.

Meaning of criminal law

Criminal law is the principal means by which the government identifies and criminalises behaviour that is considered wrong, damaging to individuals or to society as a whole or is otherwise unacceptable. The criminal justice system is the mechanism by which action is taken to deal with those suspected of committing offences. The criminal justice system refers to the whole process from the initial investigation of a crime through to acquittal or to conviction and sentence in the criminal courts.

Normally, the prosecution (Crown) must prove guilt to the standard of "beyond reasonable doubt". However, in the case of the Health and Safety at Work etc Act (HASAWA) 1974 this requirement is modified by a duty placed on the accused to show that they were in compliance with the requirement that they were accused of breaching (Section 40). This differs from the traditional criminal stance where the accused has no need to prove compliance and the emphasis is on the prosecution bringing sufficient evidence to convince the court of the non-compliance. This does not take away the over-all burden of proof for the prosecution to establish the case beyond reasonable doubt, in relation to the facts of the case, but this will clearly depend on the employer's ability to illustrate that compliance existed.

Structure of criminal courts

MAGISTRATES COURT

Magistrates' Courts are mostly staffed by lay magistrates who are not legally qualified and sit part-time. Stipendiary magistrates sit in large towns and are paid a stipend (a form of salary). Lay magistrates sit two or usually three to a court, a stipendiary magistrate sits alone. The Magistrates' Court deals with minor (summary) health and safety offences.

Appeal from this court is usually to the Crown Court, but in some cases might be to the High Court (on a point of law). In addition, the Magistrates Court will consider indictable cases to determine whether there is sufficient evidence to support a charge.

THE CROWN COURT

The Crown Court tries all serious (indictable) criminal health and safety offences, with a judge and a jury. It hears appeals and deals with committals for sentencing from magistrates' courts where they find they do not have sufficient power of punishment to match the crime.

From the Crown Court appeal on criminal matters is made to the Criminal Division of the Court of Appeal. As with the Magistrates Court, an appeal on a point of law may also be made to a Divisional Court of the Queen's Bench division (High Court).

THE HIGH COURT

The High Court is staffed by judges (Justices of the High Court) who must be persons who have had right of audience in the High Court for at least ten years or a Circuit judge who has held office for at least two years.

In hearing a case for the first time a High Court judge sits alone. A Divisional Court of two or more High Court judges sits to hear appeals from Magistrates and Crown Courts.

THE COURT OF APPEAL

The Court of Appeal is divided into Criminal and Civil Divisions.

The Court consists of 35 Lords Justices of Appeal. Normally, three judges will sit together to hear appeals from the Crown Court. It does not conduct a complete rehearing of the case but reviews the record of the evidence in the lower court and the legal arguments put before it. It may uphold or reverse the earlier decision or order a new trial. A majority decision is given and dissenting judgements are stated.

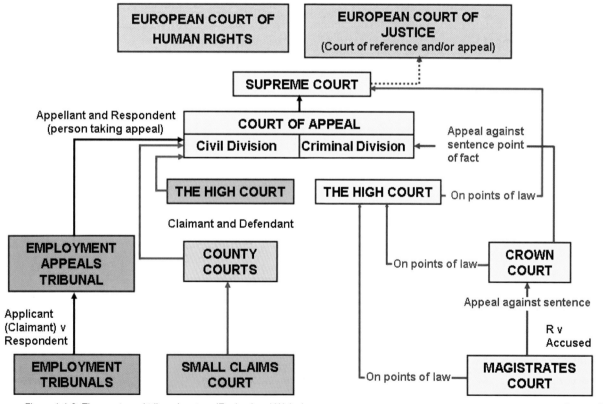

Figure 1-1-3: The courts and tribunal system (England and Wales). Source: RMS.

THE SUPREME COURT

The Supreme Court replaced the House of Lords in October 2009, in the form of 12 Justices, independently appointed to maintain the highest standards set by the Appellate Committee.

The Court hears appeals on arguable points of law of the greatest public importance, for the whole of the United Kingdom in civil cases, and for England, Wales and Northern Ireland in criminal cases. The court is an independent institution, presided over by independently appointed Law Lords (Justices). Appeals are heard by a panel of at least three Justices.

The Supreme Court operates explicitly separate from both Government and Parliament. To emphasise the distinction between politics and legislation, it is housed in the historic Middlesex Guildhall on London's Parliament Square - opposite the Houses of Parliament and alongside Westminster Abbey and the Treasury.

Criminal law liabilities

THE ROLES AND FUNCTIONS OF EXTERNAL AGENCIES

Health and safety executive

The Health and Safety Executive (HSE) is a national regulatory body responsible for promoting the cause of better health and safety at work. The Board of the HSE is responsible for both health and safety strategy and compliance. As such it provides consultation and drafting of proposed legislation and approved codes of practice, as well as enforcing authority services. Its enforcing officers, where possible, take a monitoring role in the workplace but, where necessary, have a wide range of powers that enable them to enforce compliance. They will set out requirements orally or in writing as they see fit. If a more formal approach is required they will issue an enforcement notice or take steps to prosecute. In England and Wales they can take their own case in a Magistrates Court. Their field of responsibility is for the more technical workplaces such as construction, manufacturing, power generation, railways and farms. They also enforce the law in local authorities' workplaces. They are agents of the crown. Health and Safety Awareness Officers work in conjunction with the HSE enforcement staff. They have no enforcement powers but are usually trained to a minimum of NEBOSH National General Certificate level. They contact employers and visit workplaces, increasing awareness of health and safety. The HSE produces many guidance documents and provides information on its website to assist in promoting better health and safety at work.

The Health and Safety Executive influences the health and safety performance of an organisation in many ways. These may include:

- The provision of information such as guidance notes, leaflets, codes of practice, statistics.
- Campaigns for reducing noise at work and campaigns aimed at particular business sectors.
- Carrying out health and safety inspections with follow up visits to ensure compliance with the advice given.
- Carrying out accident investigations and investigations following receipt of complaints.
- Giving advice and assistance to employers on how to comply with their statutory duties.
- Taking enforcement action such as the issue of improvement or prohibition notices or instigating criminal proceedings.
- Establishing adverse publicity such as the Public Register of Enforcement Notices displayed on the HSE website.

Health and safety executive for Northern Ireland (HSENI)

HSENI is an executive Non-Departmental Public Body sponsored by the Department of Enterprise, Trade and Investment (DETI). HSENI is the lead body responsible for the promotion and enforcement of health and safety at work standards in Northern Ireland. As with other parts of the UK the HSENI shares responsibility with the district councils who also enforce the Health and Safety at Work (Northern Ireland) Order 1978.

HSENI's role is:

> *"To ensure that risks to people's health and safety arising from work activities are effectively controlled".*

Figure 1-1-4: HSENI mission. *Source: HSENI.*

HSENI's functions include:

- Promotion of workplace health and safety messages and themes to targeted sectors and groups.
- Communication of practical workplace health and safety information and advice.
- Improving compliance with health and safety standards through inspection and investigation activities.
- Maintaining the health and safety at work regulatory framework for Northern Ireland.

Local authorities

Local authorities have a similar remit to the HSE and HSENI, except that they do not develop and establish law, they only enforce the law in simpler workplaces such as offices, shops and restaurants. Their enforcing officers (Environmental Health Officers - EHO) enforce health and safety law in HSE premises. The local authority appoints their enforcing officers.

Office of Rail Regulation (ORR)

The Office of Rail Regulation has a similar role and function to the HSE, but its remit is limited to rail operations.

Fire authorities

The fire authorities have a similar role to the HSE and Local Authority enforcing officers, but for the narrow risk of fire. The fire authority enforcing officers are employees appointed by local authorities, and have the responsibility for enforcing the Regulatory Reform (Fire Safety) Order (RRFSO) 2005 in the majority of premises. Under the Fire and Rescue Act (FRA) 2004 they are also responsible for promoting community fire safety, with the aim of preventing deaths and injuries in the home and reducing the impact of fire on the community as a whole. In addition, they provide plans and arrangements for fighting fires and rescuing people from incidents, such as road accidents.

Environment agency/Scottish environment protection agency

The Environment Agency (EA)/Scottish Environment Protection Agency (SEPA) took over the responsibilities of HMIP, the NRA and the Waste Regulatory Authorities on April 1 1996. The EA is a Non-Departmental Public Body concerned with protecting and improving the land, air and water environment of England and Wales. It has a board and the board members are appointed by the Secretaries of State for the Environment and Wales and the Minister of Agriculture Fisheries and Food. The Scottish Environment Protection Agency has a similar role and function in Scotland.

The principal aim of the Agency is to protect and enhance the environment and to make a contribution towards "attaining the objective of achieving sustainable development". Objectives towards this aim include the adoption of an integrated approach to environmental protection and enhancement which considers impacts of substances on all environmental media and on natural resources.

Insurance companies

Insurance companies have become increasingly aware that they may have under valued the risks related to some companies they are insuring. This has caused them to look again at the risks and the factors that lead to claims. In conjunction with this they influence organisations to minimise the risks in order to control their level of premium. The new approach includes a focus on the status of management of health and safety in the organisation insured, which has been found to be a useful predictor of future loss.

POWERS OF INSPECTORS UNDER THE HEALTH AND SAFETY AT WORK ACT 1974

Enforcing authority inspectors (enforcing officers) are provided for in the HASAWA 1974. Their role is to protect, enforce and advise on all matters related to health and safety management and standards. Here, the term inspector applies to either:

- Health and Safety Executive - e.g. Health and Safety Inspector, Agricultural Inspector.
- Office of Rail Regulation (ORR) - ORR Inspector [appointed by virtue of The Health and Safety (Enforcing Authority for Railways and Other Guided Transport systems) Regulations 2006 (EARR)].
- Local Authorities - Environmental Health Officer.

Although they are perhaps best known for their enforcement role, equal importance is placed on their role as advisors and for the dissemination of information on best practice.

Summary of powers of inspectors under the HASAWA 1974

- To enter any premises at any reasonable time.
- Take a constable or some other authorised person if there is an obstruction in the execution of his duty.
- To examine and investigate.
- Direct that a premises or part of premises remain undisturbed.
- Take photographs, measurements.
- Sample or retain unsafe articles and substances.
- To order the testing, dismantling and examination.
- Take possession of items.
- To require answers to questions with a signed statement, if necessary.
- To inspect and copy statutory records and documents or any other relevant documents.
- To provide assistance.
- Any other power.
- To serve:
  - Improvement notice.
  - Prohibition notice (may be suspended).
- Conduct own cases in England and Wales.

Enforcement notices

General points

The criteria for use of enforcement notices are set out in sections 20-22 of the Health and Safety at Work etc Act (HASAWA) 1974. Enforcement notices are one of a number of options open to enforcing officers in order to regulate health and safety in the workplace. Before issuing a notice an officer will have considered the value of providing comment on compliance level and actions in oral and written form that is not a formal notice. There are two types of enforcement notice, an improvement notice and a prohibition notice. It should be remembered that both notices are a confirmation of non-compliance with legislation. When choosing to use a notice the enforcing officer has chosen not to prosecute for the offence at that point in time. When enforcing officers serve a notice they have a duty to inform a relevant employee health and safety representative of the circumstances, in addition to the person the notice is served on.

Improvement notices

Enforcing officers can serve an ***improvement notice*** if they are of the opinion that there:

- Is a contravention of one or more of the relevant statutory provisions.

■ Has been a contravention of one or more of those provisions in circumstances which make it likely that the contravention will continue to be repeated.

The effect of the notice is to require a specified improvement to take place in order to bring the situation back into legal compliance.

In the improvement notice the enforcing officer must:

■ State that the enforcing officer is of the opinion that there is or has been a contravention.
■ Specify the provisions, in their opinion, which are contravened.
■ Give particulars of the reasons for their opinion.
■ Specify a period of time within which the person is required to remedy the contravention.

Examples of where an improvement notice may be used:

■ Incomplete or no health and safety policy.
■ Incomplete or no general risk assessment.
■ Inadequate or no general training of managers.
■ Restricted walkways or trailing cables in offices.
■ Storage of oils causing risk of slipping.

The improvement specified must be complied with within the stated time. The responsibility to confirm compliance remains with the employer, the enforcing officer may or may not return to determine compliance with the notice. Notices are not 'lifted' by the enforcing officer but the act of being in compliance satisfies the notice. The notice must provide sufficient time for the employer to appeal; therefore the time to improve must be in excess of the 21 days allowed to appeal. The time to make the improvement should reflect the scale and complexity of what is required. If the employer felt it did not, this may be grounds for appeal.

Prohibition notices

If enforcing officers are of the opinion that a workplace activity involves, or will involve, the ***risk of serious personal injury***, they can serve on the person responsible for the activity a ***prohibition notice***. The notice will usually take immediate effect and require the activity to cease. In circumstances where the enforcing officer considers the immediate stopping of the activity to be inappropriate (it may present its own risk) the notice can come into effect at a fixed date. A notice can relate to a system of work, equipment, workplace or a person.

A prohibition notice must:

■ State that the enforcing officer is of the opinion that there is a risk of serious personal injury.
■ Specify the matters which create the risks.
■ Direct that the activities must not be carried out, unless the matters are remedied.

Examples of where a prohibition notice may be used:

■ Unguarded machinery.
■ Incomplete scaffold.
■ Untrained personnel using high risk equipment e.g. rough terrain fork lift truck or a person hoist.
■ Inadequate procedures for entry into a confined space e.g. sewers.

Appeals against notices

Right of appeal

A person on whom either type of notice is served can appeal to an Employment Tribunal (ET) within 21 days from the date of service of the notice. The tribunal can extend this period on written application that it was not reasonably practicable for the appeal to be brought within 21 days.

Effect of appeal

a) When an appeal is lodged against an improvement notice it ***is*** suspended.
b) When an appeal is lodged against a prohibition notice it ***is not*** suspended until the tribunal hears the appeal and makes a decision.

When the appeal is heard the Employment Tribunal will consider the facts of the appeal and may make a number of responses in view of their findings. The options are to uphold the notice as originally defined, amend the notice (for example, the time to comply with an improvement notice) or quash it.

Penalties for failure to comply

An advantage of formalising an enforcing officer's comment in the form of an enforcement notice is that failure to comply with the notice is an offence in itself, which carries a possible penalty of up to 2 years prison sentence. In addition, the enforcement officer retains the right to prosecute for the original identified non-compliance with legislation.

Formal cautions and warnings

A formal caution is widely used by non-health and safety enforcement bodies and has been adopted for health and safety by local authorities. The HSE in England and Wales use it as an additional procedure for dealing with certain offenders in limited circumstances where a prosecution might otherwise be taken. A formal caution recognises that a breach of law exists that could lead to a successful prosecution of an individual or corporate body but that it may not be in the public interest to proceed to prosecution.

This might be where a court appearance may have a serious adverse effect on a victim's health or the accused is elderly or very ill.

A formal caution is unlikely to be used in the more serious offences and should not be seen as letting the accused off. Evidence is gathered in the same way and to the same extent as when a prosecution is to be taken. The offender must admit the offence and agree to be cautioned.

> *"A formal caution is a statement by an Inspector that is accepted in writing by the duty holder, that the duty holder has committed an offence for which there is a realistic prospect of conviction. A formal caution may only be used where a prosecution could be properly brought. 'Formal cautions' are entirely distinct from a caution given under the Police and Criminal Evidence Act by an Inspector prior to asking questions of a suspect concerning an alleged offence. Enforcing authorities should take account of current Home Office guidelines when considering whether to offer a formal caution".*

Figure 1-1-5: Formal cautions.   *Source: HSE Enforcement Policy Statement HSE41.*

An enforcing authority warning is where an inspector has advised a duty holder that they believe they are not complying with the law and that they need to take action. This can be verbally or in writing. Failure to comply with a warning does not, on its own, automatically lead to a prosecution, but should be taken into account when considering future enforcement action.

Prosecution

Summary offences (minor)

Summary offences are those offences that the law recognises to arise from less serious breaches of law. It should be remembered that the HASAWA 1974 contains general duties that relate to all workplaces, all situations and all risks. It is logical that a prosecution may be deemed necessary in some situations that are straightforward and where relatively minor offences have occurred.

The same point may be made with Regulations, for example, a straightforward failure to report an accident, required under RIDDOR 1995 might fit into this category. These offences are normally heard in the Magistrates Court in England and Wales.

Indictable offences (serious offences)

Indictable offences are more serious or repeated offences, and are tried in the Crown Court in England and Wales, for example, a failure to comply with a notice issued by an enforcement officer.

Initiation and prosecution of an offence

In England and Wales the parties that may initiate or prosecute a health and safety offence include the Health and Safety Executive (HSE), Office of Rail Regulation (ORR), a local authority, police or the Crown Prosecution Service (CPS).

The HSE are empowered to take a case in person in the Magistrates court but refer indictable offences to the CPS. The other enforcing authorities refer their cases to the CPS. In the case of fatal incidents in the workplace the police would gather evidence, with the assistance of the other relevant enforcing authority, and place it before the CPS. The CPS decides whether prosecutions for manslaughter or corporate manslaughter should be brought, prepares the case and takes it to court.

Procurators Fiscal are qualified lawyers who are responsible for prosecuting crime in Scotland. They also investigate sudden and suspicious deaths, including homicide and corporate homicide, and conduct fatal accident enquiries. District procurators fiscal and their deputies prosecute cases in all courts except the High Court of Judiciary. They work closely with Crown Counsel or Advocates Depute. In Scotland the enforcing authority gathers evidence and refers the case to the Procurators Fiscal.

ROLE OF THE COURTS

The role of the lower courts is to hear cases presented to them and decide if there is a case to answer, if there is, whether they have the appropriate powers to decide the case and provide suitable punishment relative to the circumstances of the case. If they do not have appropriate powers they may elect that the case be heard on indictment in a higher court. At the hearing the court will decide on the case and the penalty necessary, they may also award a compensatory order.

Penalties

Health and safety penalties for the HASAWA 1974 and associated regulations are controlled by Section 33 of HASAWA 1974. It sets out the following levels of penalty for different offences; essentially they are stated to be either summary offences or indictable offences. Some offences may be said to be triable either way, i.e. as summary or indictable depending on the seriousness of the circumstances of the breach.

Health and Safety (Offences) Act 2008

The Health and Safety Offences Act (HSOA) 2008 amended Section 33 of the HASAWA 1974, raised the maximum penalties available to the lower courts in respect of certain health and safety offences and raised the maximum penalties that can be imposed for breaching regulations in the lower courts from £5,000 to £20,000.

See figure ref 1-1-6 which gives details of the penalty structure.

Offence	Penalty on summary conviction	Penalty on conviction on indictment
Failure to comply with sections 2-6 and 8 of the Health and Safety at Work Act 1974.	Imprisonment for a term not exceeding 6 months, or a fine not exceeding £20,000, or both.	Imprisonment for a term not exceeding two years, or an unlimited fine or both.
Failure to comply with section 7 of the Health and Safety at Work Act 1974.	Imprisonment for a term not exceeding 6 months, or a fine not exceeding £5,000, or both.	Imprisonment for a term not exceeding two years, or an unlimited fine, or both.
Failure to comply with section 9 of the Health and Safety at Work Act 1974.	A fine not exceeding £20,000.	An unlimited fine.
Failure to comply with any Regulations made under the Health and Safety at Work Act 1974.	Imprisonment for a term not exceeding 6 months or a fine not exceeding £20,000, or both.	Imprisonment for a term not exceeding two years, or an unlimited fine, or both.
Breach of the terms of an enforcement notice.	Imprisonment for a term not exceeding 6 months or a fine not exceeding £20,000, or both.	Imprisonment for a term not exceeding two years, or an unlimited fine, or both.
Any other offence under existing statutory provisions, for example a breach of a licence; such as for those who are 'Licensed Removers of Asbestos'.	Imprisonment for a term not exceeding 6 months or a fine not exceeding £20,000, or both.	Imprisonment for a term not exceeding two years, or an unlimited fine, or both.

Figure 1-1-6: Health and Safety (Offences) Act 2008. *Source: RMS.*

Compensatory awards

On hearing a case a court can impose a compensation order as well as a penalty. This may be particularly useful where the loss is relatively small and easily quantifiable or the injured party is in need of immediate financial help arising from the offence. The victim may prefer a compensation award from the criminal proceedings instead of taking separate civil action. Where the loss is not easily quantifiable or disputed the court can require additional evidence, like a medical report, or may decide not to make a compensatory order.

DEFENCES

In order to provide a defence an individual must prove that they took all reasonable care and an employer must prove they took all reasonable foreseeable precautions and that both exercised all due diligence in doing so.

The accused employer must prove that it was not practicable or reasonably practicable (as the case may be) to do more than what was done or that there was no better practicable way than was in fact used.

Meaning of civil law

Civil law exists in order to regulate *disputes between individuals* over the rights and obligations people have when dealing with each other.

The *burden of proof* in most civil cases is that the case must be proved on the "balance of probability". Here the *claimant sues the defendant* for the *purpose of claiming compensation,* no presumption of favour is held with either party involved in the case and it is necessary for both sides to argue their case sufficiently. It is generally accepted that the "balance of probability" is less onerous on either party to prove than that of "beyond reasonable doubt", which is used in criminal cases.

Under civil law it is possible for a civil case to become *statute barred* due to the passage of time. Essentially, this means that if a person was injured and then, many years later, decided to bring a claim against the party that caused them harm, they may automatically lose in court because they took too long to bring the action. In the UK the Limitations Act 1980 provides that the claimant has 3 years from the date of discovering (or ought to have discovered) the loss to commence a lawsuit. If a civil action is brought after the 3 year period, the defendant can bring a motion for summary judgment on the basis that the claim is statute barred under the Act.

Structure of civil courts

See figure ref 1-1-3: The courts and tribunal system (England and Wales).

SMALL CLAIMS COURT

The small claims courts underpin the county court structure. A registrar typically hears cases. Personal injury claims of up to £5000 may be made to this court. Appeal is to the County Court.

COUNTY COURT

County courts have civil jurisdiction only, but deal with almost every kind of civil case arising within the local area for which the court is established. County courts can hear cases in contract up to £25,000 and tort claims of up to £50,000 in the case of actions for damages relating to personal injury. They may exceed the limit with consent of both parties. In practice they deal with the majority of the country's civil litigation. The case is heard by a judge, on his/her own, and appeal is to the Court of Appeal.

HIGH COURT

The High Court deals with claims over £50,000 - it has no upper limit. The case is heard by a judge, on his/her own, and appeal is to the Court of Appeal.

COURT OF APPEAL

The Court of Appeal hears cases referred from both the County Court and the High Court and the Employment Appeal Tribunal. Typically three judges will hear cases. It does not conduct a complete rehearing of the case but reviews the record of the evidence in the lower court and the legal arguments put before it. It may uphold or reverse the earlier decision or order a new trial. A majority decision is given and dissenting judgements are stated. Appeal from this court is to the Supreme Court.

SUPREME COURT

Apart from the limited jurisdiction of the European Court of Justice (of the EC), the Supreme Court is the highest court of appeal in the United Kingdom and replaced the role of the House of Lords in October 2009. It is an independent institution and is presided over by twelve independently appointed judges; known as Justices of the Supreme Court. A majority decision is given and dissenting judgments are stated. The Court hears appeals from both the civil and the criminal divisions of the Court of Appeal (and in certain circumstances directly from the High Court).

Civil law liabilities

CIVIL WRONG (TORT/DELICT)

There are many branches of civil law including contract law and the law of tort (England and Wales)/delict (Scotland). Contract law deals with the legally binding relationships which individuals enter into, whereas tort/delict law is aimed at redressing the wrongs committed by one person against another. Examples of torts include negligence and breach of statutory duty.

A tort/delict is a civil wrong committed by one party against another. Negligence together with action for breach of statutory duty is the most common cause of action for harm caused at work.

TORT/DELICT OF NEGLIGENCE

Negligence is a tort/delict. It is based on the provision of the common law duty of care to a reasonable standard (principle of liability for loss caused by failure in the duty of care, in Scotland). Negligence is generally defined as conduct that falls below what a reasonable person would do to protect another individual from foreseeable risk of harm. It is actionable in a civil court for compensation.

DUTY OF CARE (NEIGHBOUR PRINCIPLE)

"You must take reasonable care to avoid acts or omissions when you can reasonably foresee would be likely to injure your neighbour".

Figure 1-1-7: Duty of care.   *Source: Donoghue v Stevenson (1932).*

(The NEBOSH National General Certificate examination does not require you to be able to quote case names).

The above case established a principle of duty of care to your 'neighbour'. In general life neighbours are the people around us that foreseeably might be affected by what we do. The duty applies to an employer just as it does an individual. If the employer fails to meet this duty, they may be considered negligent.

The duty that the employer has (through the neighbour principle) extends to employees and to others (e.g. visitors) who might foreseeably be affected. It follows that employees have the right to work in a workplace in a manner that provides reasonable protection from harm. This should not be interpreted to mean absolute safety.

TESTS AND DEFENCES FOR TORT/DELICT OF NEGLIGENCE

Tests for tort/delict of negligence

In order to prove a case of negligence and obtain damages (usually in the form of financial compensation) the injured party must show that:

- They were owed a duty of care.
- There was a failure to fulfil the duty to a reasonable standard (breach of duty).
- Damage, loss or injury directly resulted from the breach.

Duty owed

For example, a duty of reasonable care is owed by the employer to employees or someone that may foreseeably be affected by the employer's acts or omissions. This is part of what is sometimes called 'the neighbour principle'. Duties to employees are clear, whereas duties to other people depend on the circumstance. An example of where a duty might exist is where an employer occupies premises as an occupier then he would have a duty to lawful visitors.

Breach of duty

A breach of the duty of care is required when proving negligence. This depends on the standards of care that may be expected by the "reasonable man". In the case of an employer breaching a duty to employees this might include such things as failing to provide a safe place of work.

Loss resulted

The injury (loss) was a result of the breach. Generally, the injury must be "reasonably foreseeable". There are exceptions to this rule; for example, it is no defence to show that an injured person was unforeseeably weak (the thin skull rule). The loss must not be too remote from the breach and a direct causal link established by the facts of the case (on the balance of probability).

Defences for tort/delict of negligence

The main defences available are similar to the tests of proof.

Denial of duty to take care

The first defence is one of a denial of a duty to take care of the person. It is difficult to show an employer has no duty to an employee as the neighbour principle establishes an employee as someone who could be foreseeably affected by the employer. It is however sometimes possible to show someone else had a duty, not you, e.g. a contractor instead of employer or a client instead of contractor.

Reasonable care was taken (no breach of duty)

Everything that could reasonably have been done was done and despite exercising reasonable care the accident still happened.

No actionable injury or damage

This can include the defence that no actual injury or damage was sustained or some of the following.

Breach did not lead to damage

There may have been a failure to fulfil the common law duty of care, but that was not what led to the loss. The employer may have failed to provide training on manual handling, but the claimant hurt his back reaching over to pick up his pen.

Foreseeability

In some cases, the injury or damage may not be foreseeable. This may particularly be the case with the introduction of new substances to the workplace.

Volenti non fit injuria

"Volenti non fit injuria - translated from Latin this means 'to one who is willing no harm is done'".

Figure 1-1-8: Definition of volenti non fit injuria.   *Source: Murray v Harringay Arena (1951).*

(The NEBOSH National General Certificate in Health and Safety does not require you to be able to quote case names).

This is a complete defence to negligence by the defendant, and is used where the claimant agreed to run the risk of accidental harm. This true consent must be freely given and has been used in connection with spectators injured in the course of hazardous events, for example, motor racing.

An employee, however, does not consent to any abnormal or unnecessary risks merely by accepting the job or continuing to do it. This defence is unlikely to succeed when defending claims made by rescuers who volunteered for the risk in order to safeguard others, whether or not the rescuers are members of the public or public service employees.

Statute of limitations

In general, legal proceedings in respect of personal injuries must be started within three years of the accident; after that time they are "statute barred". This time may be extended in special cases. For long-term health related cases the time is taken from the time the person had knowledge of the condition.

TORT OF BREACH OF STATUTORY DUTY

When a statutory duty is broken there is liability for penalty stipulated in the statute. However, a person suffering damage as a result of the breach may also bring a civil action in tort (the tort of breach of statutory duty) to obtain compensation. It should be noted that the injured person might sue for both negligence and breach of statutory duty (known as a 'double-barrelled action').

TESTS AND DEFENCES FOR BREACH OF STATUTORY DUTY

Tests for breach of statutory duty

In order to establish a claim for breach of statutory duty, the claimant must establish the following:

- The defendant was in breach of the statute.
- This breach caused the injury.
- The claimant was of a class of person the statute was intended to protect.
- The type of injury was one the statute was intended to prevent.

Defences for breach of statutory duty

Statute barred

The first defence to a claim of breach of statutory duty could be that the statute was barred. In other words, the chosen statute is one that is not allowed to be used in a civil claim. The Health and Safety at Work etc. Act (HASAWA) 1974, s.47 states that civil liability is excluded for sections 2-7 or any contravention of section 8, which in effect means that the Act has only criminal liability.

Generally, the Construction (Design and Management) Regulations (CDM) 2007 excludes action under civil law. There are though some exceptions. For example Regulation 9(1)(b) the duty placed on the client to ensure that adequate welfare facilities are provided. Regulation 13(6) the duty placed on contractors to ensure that reasonable steps have been taken to prevent access by unauthorised persons to that site and Regulation 22(1)(l) the duty placed on the principal contractor is to take reasonable steps to prevent access by unauthorised persons to the construction site.

No breach of statutory duty

There was no breach of duty under the statute. Everything that must be done was done or was done so far as is practicable or reasonably practicable, or was suitable and sufficient in whatever the statute required.

Breach did not cause the loss

There may have been a breach of statutory duty but the defence could be that this did not cause the loss. For example a hand rail might be missing on a stair but the person injured was carrying a large sheet of glass in both hands when they fell. The defence could be that the absence of the hand rail did not cause the loss as the person carrying the glass could not have made use of the rail.

Injured party not within the class of persons protected by the statute

The claimant was not a class of persons that the statute was there to protect. For example, if a visitor was the claimant and the duties under the statute were to an employee then the visitor's claim would fail.

Injury not of the type that the statute was designed to prevent

If the injury done to the claimant was not the type the statute was there to prevent, the claim would fail. For example, if someone suddenly sneezed and hit their head on the side of a machine the resultant injury would not be one the Provision and Use of Work Equipment Regulations (PUWER) 1998 was designed to prevent.

ROLE OF THE COURTS

The role of the civil courts is to hear disputes between individuals over the rights and obligations people have when dealing with each other.

Cases are heard at the level of court that relates to the claim being made. The lower courts hear cases where the claim for compensation is small and the higher courts where claims are higher. The court has no favour with either party involved in the case and it is the responsibility of both sides to argue their position on the case. This will mean the judge will decide who has proved their case sufficiently. The **burden of proof** in most civil cases is that the case must be proved on the "balance of probability". If someone does not agree with the decision of the judge they may appeal, in the first instance to the court of appeal. The judge will award the compensation that they consider appropriate.

ROLE OF EMPLOYMENT TRIBUNALS

An employment tribunal usually consists of a legally-qualified chairperson appointed by the Lord Chancellor and two lay members - one representing management interests and the other employees. These are selected from panels kept by the Department of Employment after nominations from employers' organisations and trades unions.

Employment tribunals deal with the following issues:

- Victimisation.
- Dismissal, actual or constructive, following a breach of health and safety law, regulation and/or term of an employment contract.
- Appeals against improvement and prohibition notices.
- Safety representatives and safety committees (time off, payment functions and training of representatives under the Safety Representatives and Safety Committees (SRSC) Regulations 1977).

- Representatives of employee safety (pay and time off under the Health and Safety (Consultation with Employees) Regulations (HSCER) 1996).
- Suspension from work for medical reasons (Employment Protection (Consolidation) Act 1978).
- Suspension from work on maternity grounds.

Appeals from employment tribunals lie to the Employment Appeal Tribunal (EAT), except in the case of health and safety notices, where appeal lies in the High Court. Appeal, in either case, is made on a point of law (not a point of fact).

COMPENSATION

The claimant, as part of the claim, will identify what loss they have sustained. In view of this they will seek damages from the other party. The damages may be seen as compensation, intended to put the claimant in the original position before the injury. This is a contentious area as the harm done to the claimant is often difficult to quantify in financial terms. General damages include a figure for pain, suffering and loss of amenity. Special damages are awarded for the financial burden imposed on the claimant e.g. loss of earnings, medical costs and special care.

CONTRIBUTORY NEGLIGENCE

Where an injury is partly the fault of the injured person, and if that person may be said to have contributed to the injury, then any damages they may recover will be reduced in proportion to their blameworthiness.

VICARIOUS LIABILITY

Vicarious liability (i.e. liability for the acts of a third party) is the principle that the employer is liable for the torts of their employees provided that they are committed during the course of the employees' employment. Thus if an employee causes damage or injury by not fulfilling a common law duty of care then the employer will be liable. This liability exists even if the employer has not been negligent.

This liability must be insured against under the Employer's Liability (Compulsory Insurance) Act 1969.

EMPLOYER'S CIVIL COMMON LAW DUTY

In common law the employer must take reasonable care to protect employees. Wilson's and Clyde Coal Co. Ltd v. English (1938) is a notable precedent used to identify an employer's common law duties as the provision and maintenance of:

- A safe place of work.
- Safe appliances and equipment.
- A safe system of work.
- Competent and safety conscious personnel.

DOUBLE BARRELLED ACTION

When someone takes civil action to gain compensation for personal injury they may be able use two types of tort to bring the claim. These are the tort of negligence and the tort of breach of statutory duty. Depending on the case, there may be specific legislation that creates a duty to prevent the personal injury suffered, and this may be used to establish a breach of statutory duty.

This can sometimes be the most straightforward way to establish a claim for compensation, particularly if there has already been a successful criminal prosecution of the defendant related to the breach. The option to claim negligence can then be taken if the claim of breach of statutory duty fails. When these two torts are used together this is commonly referred to as a "double-barrelled" action.

The meaning of common law

PRECEDENTS AND CASE LAW

Principles derived from judgments are written down and are known as *case law.* They establish a standard made in earlier cases which creates a binding precedent on subsequent similar cases. Precedents and case law are made in both civil and criminal proceedings. This process is particularly important to the establishing of common law.

Binding *precedents* are decisions made in a higher court that are binding on all lower courts. Thus, a decision made by the Supreme Court is binding on all lower courts. Since 1966 the Supreme Court (formerly known as the House of Lords) is no longer bound to follow its own decisions, but it would be rare for the Supreme Court to overrule a previous precedent. The Court of Appeal binds all lower, criminal and civil courts (i.e. High Court, County Court, Employment Appeals Tribunals and Tribunals, Crown and Magistrates Courts). Decisions made by courts of equal status create persuasive precedent only. The process of precedence does allow some deviation from an established precedent, but the decision has to be justified,

THE IMPORTANCE OF COMMON LAW

Common law, rather than being laid down by Parliament, has grown up over the centuries being created and amended by the decisions (precedents) from cases that are heard in court. Cases heard have established common law rights, duties and principles that affect many aspects of life. Though not written down as a formal code, as statutory legislation is, common law is expressed in writing in the form of the decisions of cases, in case law.

Unlike criminal law which requires statutes to be amended or repealed from time to time to meet changing societal expectations, there is scope in common law for the courts to interpret new circumstances and set common law precedents to meet changing circumstances.

For example, the compensation amount to be paid for an injury today might be increased to reflect the change in cost of living compared with compensation made in similar cases several years earlier.

RELEVANCE TO CRIMINAL AND CIVIL LAW

Common law is a *source* to both criminal and civil law. Common law is relevant to civil law in that it establishes a duty of care which if not met can lead to an injured person suing for negligence. The employer's duty of care in common law has been established for some time and obliges the employer to take *'reasonable care of those that might foreseeably be affected by its acts or omissions'*. In common law the employer must take reasonable care to protect employees; this involves the provision and maintenance of:

- A safe place of work.
- Safe appliances and equipment.
- A safe system of work.
- Competent and safety conscious personnel.

These duties are similarly reflected in criminal law in the statutory duties of HASAWA 1974 Section 2, which emphasises the fact that plant (and equipment) must be provided and maintained such that it is safe and healthy. The duties under the HASAWA 1974 extend the need to provide a safe place of work to include means of access and egress to that place of work. The HASAWA 1974 requires systems of work, as well as plant, to be provided and maintained such that work is safe and healthy. The HASAWA 1974 does not specify that employees must be competent, but expresses a requirement to provide information, instruction, and training. Though it is only implied, the purpose of this provision would be to ensure competence. These provisions are supported by a requirement for supervision, as necessary. If people were not competent a good deal of supervision would be required. The duties are qualified by terms such as 'so far as reasonably practicable' rather than the civil common law duty to take 'reasonable care'.

This has established a level of consistency between criminal and civil law and means that if harm is done an employer may be prosecuted and sued for compensation.

There is a well established criminal common law duty of care which if breached to a gross extent and leads to someone's death is called manslaughter (homicide in Scotland). Such a breach is prosecutable in a criminal court. The common law crimes of manslaughter and homicide have been clarified by a criminal law statute in the form of the Corporate Manslaughter and Corporate Homicide Act (CMCHA) 2007.

Meaning of statute law

STATUTE LAW

Statute law is a *source* of both criminal and civil law. Statute law consists of primary legislation (Acts of Parliament) and delegated legislation such as regulations (e.g. the Management of Health and Safety at Work Regulations (MHSWR) 1999, as amended in 2002 and Orders. Some statutes, such as the HASAWA 1974 are entirely criminal law. Similarly, some statutes are actionable only under civil law (e.g. the Occupiers' Liability Act 1957, which extends the occupiers duty, not to cause harm to employees, to visitors and others). It must be understood, however, that many health and safety related statutes may be used both as a basis for prosecution and as a platform for civil actions relating to personal injury suffered in the workplace.

ACTS OF PARLIAMENT

Acts of parliament begin their life in draft form and are known as a Bill, this is presented to both houses of parliament to allow debate. After several stages of debate and amendment the Bill will be voted on and if passed will go to the Queen for 'Royal Assent', after which it is entered on the statute books and remains until amended or repealed. Acts of parliament are used to set out framework legislation on a given topic and may be legislating on criminal or civil matters.

HEALTH AND SAFETY AT WORK ETC ACT 1974

The Health and Safety at Work etc. Act (HASAWA) 1974 sets out general responsibilities in a legal framework. It places responsibilities on people, covering all the main parties that contribute to health and safety in the workplace e.g. employers, employees, designers and suppliers.

The duties are designed to be general rather than specific in order to make them widely applicable to all workplaces and all work activities. The HASAWA 1974 established means of regulation of behaviour in the form of enforcement notices and penalties, designed to match the circumstances that enforcing officers find.

The general basis of the HASAWA 1974 is that measures taken should, as a minimum, reflect the level of risk for the issue being considered. This is because the HASAWA 1974 sets out general duties, its structure allowed for the creation of more specific legislation, in the form of regulations, to be made in order to set out specific requirements and to control specific risks. In turn, the HASAWA 1974 made provision for the creation of approved codes of practice (ACOPs) to support its general provisions and the regulations made under the HASAWA 1974.

HEALTH AND SAFETY REGULATIONS

These contain specific details. They give substance to the requirements of acts. The Secretary of State may make regulations, but is required to consult the Health and Safety Commission (HSC) and other interested parties.

When the Regulations have been made, they are laid on the table of the Houses of Parliament to enable observation. It is usual for the Regulations to come into force after forty days, unless either House passes a negative resolution. It should be noted that acts and regulations both carry the full force of the law. Failure to comply with either can be both a criminal offence and a basis for civil action. ACOPs and/or guidance notes supplement acts and regulations.

APPROVED CODES OF PRACTICE

ACOPs are approved by the Health and Safety Executive (formally by the Health and Safety Commission) with the consent of the Secretary of State and provide a recognised interpretation of how an employer may comply with the associated legislation. The approved code of practice is not a piece of legislation and it does not have binding force. Therefore, it is not automatically a criminal offence to break it, nor will a breach of it automatically give rise to civil liability. However, it can be cited in evidence and a person who breaks it is much more likely to be held to be in breach of criminal law and negligent in civil law. Employers must either meet the standards contained in an ACOP or show that they have complied with an equal or better standard.

Examples of ACOPs are: "Managing Health and Safety in Construction - Construction (Design and Management) Regs", "Safe Use of Work Equipment" (which supplements the Provision and Use of Work Equipment Regulations (PUWER) 1998), "Workplace Health, Safety and Welfare" (supplementing the Workplace (Health, Safety and Welfare) Regulations (WHSWR) 1992) and "Rider Operated Lift Trucks - Operator Training".

OFFICIAL GUIDANCE

The Health and Safety Executive sometimes issue guidance notes that are purely advisory and have no standing in law. The advice is generally more practical than that contained in an ACOP, and may be referred to in criminal and civil cases as persuasive argument of what may have been done to prevent a breach or injury.

Examples of Guidance Notes are those that accompany the Personal Protective Equipment Regulations (PPER) 1992 and the Manual Handling Operations Regulations (MHOR) 1992.

ABSOLUTE AND QUALIFIED DUTIES

Statute law, because it is prescribed in a written form, provides an opportunity for the level of duty it expects to be specified. The level of duty specified will often relate to the level of risk of the issue being controlled and/or the knowledge we have that the specified action can be completed in the way that it would require. There are three distinct levels of statutory duty giving rise to criminal liability:

1) *Absolute.*
2) *Practicable.*
3) *Reasonably practicable.*

Absolute statutory requirements

Where the risk of injury is inevitable if health and safety precautions are not taken, a statutory duty may well be absolute. Absolute duties are worded as "shall" such as in the Provision and Use of Work Equipment Regulations (PUWER) 1998, Regulation 9, which requires that:

> *"Every employer shall ensure that all persons who use work equipment have received adequate training for the purposes of health and safety...........".*

Figure 1-1-9: Regulation 9 of PUWER 1998.   *Source: Provision and Use of Work Equipment Regulations (PUWER) 1998.*

This duty does not allow choice and takes no allowance of how much an employer can afford.

Practicable requirements

This means they must be carried out and are only limited by the current state of knowledge and invention, even though implementation may be difficult, inconvenient and/or costly. For example, the PUWER 1998, Regulation 11, requires:

> *"The provision of fixed guards enclosing every dangerous part or rotating stock-bar where and to the extent that it is practicable to do so".*

Figure 1-1-10: Regulation 11 of PUWER 1998.   *Source: Provision and Use of Work Equipment Regulations (PUWER) 1998.*

Reasonably practicable requirements

A statutory duty which has to be carried out as far as is reasonably practicable is one where there is a risk/benefit trade off. An employer is entitled to balance costs of remedy against benefits in reduction of risk and if the benefit is minimal compared to the cost, he/she need not carry out the duty.

"Reasonably practicable" is a narrower term than "physically possible" and implies that a computation must be made, in which the quantum of risk is placed on one scale and the sacrifices involved in the measures necessary for averting the risk (whether in money, time or trouble) is placed on the other, and that if it can be shown that there is a gross disproportion between them, the defendants discharge the onus on them to take that measure. It should be remembered that this would not mean no action at all is taken to control the risk, just that a less costly and less effective measure would be used instead.

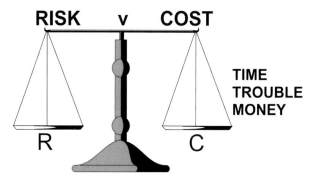

Figure 1-1-11: Reasonably practicable. *Source: RMS/Corel Clipart.*

COMPARISON OF TWO SOURCES OF LAW

Common law	Statute law
Judge - made law through decisions of cases, builds up over time as cases are heard and sets principles.	Established by Parliament.
Not written down.	Written down and codified in Acts and Regulations.
Duty of reasonable care.	A range of levels of care used e.g. reasonably practicable.
In the area of health and safety, forms the basis of most civil cases.	Failure to comply normally (but not always) constitutes a criminal offence, although it can also be used in civil actions unless specifically disallowed.
Establishes the common law criminal offence of personal manslaughter - gross negligence.	Sets out some civil liabilities, for example occupier's liability.

Figure 1-1-12: Comparison between common and statute law.   *Source: RMS.*

1.4 - Health and Safety at Work etc. Act (HASAWA) 1974

SCOPE

The HASAWA 1974 sets out its intent in section 1:

(a) Securing the health, safety and welfare of persons at work.

(b) Protecting persons other than persons at work against risks to health or safety arising out of or in connection with the activities of persons at work.

(c) Controlling the keeping and use of explosive or highly flammable or otherwise dangerous substances, and generally preventing the unlawful acquisition, possession and use of such substances.

The Health and Safety at Work etc. Act (HASAWA) 1974 covers all employment activities, apart from private domestic workers.

HASAWA 1974 applies to employers, self-employed persons, subcontractors and visitors to places of employment, members of the public affected by the employer's activities, designers, suppliers, importers, employees, directors and managers. It also provides the enforcing authorities, e.g. the Health and Safety Executive inspectors and the Local Authorities' Environmental Health Officers, with various enforcement powers. Sections 2 - 6 and 9 are the duties on the employers and others, Section 7 is the duty on the employee and Section 8 is the duty on the person. Section 2 (1) Is the general duty on the employer to his employees and Section 2, subsections (2), (3) (4-7) are the more specific duties. The duties are expressed in general terms so that they apply to all workplaces and work activities. The absolute duties placed on the employer are qualified by *"so far as is reasonably practicable"* and the duty on the employee is to take *reasonable care*.

Section 2 - duties of employers to employees

Section 2(1)

To ensure, so far as reasonably practicable, the health, safety and welfare at work of employees. This is a general duty which is expanded on by the following sections.

Section 2(2)

Ensuring, so far as **reasonably practicable**, the health, safety and welfare at work of employees through:

(a) Safe plant and systems of work e.g. provision of guards on machines and the safe use of the machine.

(b) Safe use, handling, storage and transport of goods and materials e.g. good manual handling of boxes, mechanical handling of trusses, storage of flammable gases or movement of goods by road.

(c) Provision of information, instruction, training and supervision e.g. provision of induction training, instruction on action in the case of fire and information on chemicals that are handled. Supervision must be provided as necessary; inexperienced employees will require more supervision as will higher risk tasks.

(d) Safe place of work including means of access and egress e.g. aisles kept clear, safe ladders to a scaffold platform or emergency exit from a building. The requirements cover not only buildings but, for example, open air sites, boats, exhibition sites; the duty extends to the structure of any item.

(e) Safe and healthy working environment and welfare arrangements e.g. good lighting, appropriate temperature, washing facilities, seating and first aid.

Figure 1-1-13 Storage of gas cylinders.   *Source: RMS.*

Figure 1-1-14: Office workplace.   *Source: RMS.*

Section 2 (3) safety policies

An employer must prepare, and revise when necessary, a written statement of policy with respect to health and safety at work and, in particular, outline the organisation and arrangements which have been implemented to ensure that the policy is being carried out. Such a statement should be drawn to the attention of the employees. Under separate regulations, employers with fewer than five employees are exempt from having a written policy statement.

Section 2 (4) appointment of safety representatives

Allows the Secretary of State to make regulations dealing with consultations between employers and recognised trade unions and their method of representation. (This led to the Safety Representatives and Safety Committee Regulations (SRSC) Regulations 1977). Those representatives shall represent the employees in consultations with the employer.

Section 2 (6) consultation

Duty of employer to consult recognised trade union representatives (under SRSC Regulations 1977).

Section 2 (7) safety committee

Duty of employers to establish a safety committee if requested to do so by recognised trade union representatives (in accordance with SRSC Regulations 1977).

Section 3 - duties of employers and self-employed to persons other than employees

The employer shall so far as **reasonably practicable:**

(a) Not expose them to risk to their heath and safety e.g. an area used by a contractor on a busy site should be separated from hazards by barriers.

(b) Give information about risks which may affect them e.g. providing an induction for contractors.

Visitors

Some of the practical steps that an organisation might take in order to satisfy its responsibility to ensure the health and safety of visitors to its premises are:

■ Identify visitors by signing in and the provision of badges.

■ Provide information regarding the risks present and the site rules and procedures to be followed, particularly in emergencies.

■ Provide escorts to supervise visitors throughout the site and restrict access to areas where higher risk activities take place.

Many organisations issue badges to visitors. The main purpose of this is to ensure that visitors are clearly identified, but the issuing of badges may be combined with recording visitors and providing information on emergency procedures that can be included on the badge. In addition, badges may be used to identify regular contractors or people who may only have access to certain parts of the business, e.g. by differently coloured badges.

It is important that badges are numbered and that at the end of the working day (or whenever) a note is made of outstanding badges to ensure that all are accounted for. Action should be taken to determine what has happened to the badge-holders. In organisations where it is common practice to issue badges to employees it is important that visitors' badges are noticeably different (e.g. in style or colour). Badges for employees and regular contractors should have a photograph of the holder in order to aid identification.

Contractors

Contractors are often used to perform a wide variety of tasks on behalf of employers. Whilst the contractor may have duties of their own, the employer carries responsibility for the work done by contractors as part of the employer's undertaking. These responsibilities are both organisational and legal. In the organisational sense the employer commissions contractors to perform tasks on its behalf, and in doing this appropriately it is essential for good management that health and safety be included, along with provision of the service on time and with quality. In addition, the employer will need to take reasonable care to control the work of contractors to discharge their duties at common law and reasonably practicable steps to discharge its duty under the HASAWA 1974. These responsibilities work in harmony with the employer's responsibility to look after the contractor while the contractor is working in a workplace that the employer controls.

It is important to conduct risk assessments with contractors in mind and clearly define the task of the contractor in a way that includes health and safety issues. In this way the risks to a contractor can be identified and controlled. For example, if an employer needs a contractor to work at a height above the entrance to an office building using a scaffold, it is necessary for the employer to control this work such that it is conducted safely for the protection of contractors working on the scaffold and anyone passing near the scaffold. The provision of toe boards, guard rails, and lighting and the siting of the scaffold are factors that affect contractors and others.

The public

Employers need to be aware of the ways in which their work can affect the public and their responsibilities for control of these risks. The public may be visitors to the workplace by specific invitation or by straying into the workplace. The employer may invite and encourage the public into the workplace to enable them to purchase goods or services.

It is important that the employer controls the exposure of the public to risks, such as slippery floors in shops, an unprotected excavation by the side of a pathway, operation of vehicle maintenance equipment in a garage, and a release of cement dust or dust from a demolition site to neighbouring houses.

Section 3 (2) self-employed

Similarly, self-employed persons should conduct their undertakings so that neither themselves, nor others, are affected by their activities and exposed to health and safety hazards. The above are qualified by "reasonably practicable".

Section 4 - duties of those in control of premises

Anyone in control of premises or plant used by persons not in their employment must:

- Ensure safe access and egress to premises and plant.
- Ensure that plant or substances in the premises, or provided for their use, are safe and without risk to health.

Both are tempered by the reasonable practicability of this exercise.

Section 4 (3) tenancies

The obligations under Section 4 are transferred to the tenant, or person under contract, if the terms of the agreement are related to maintenance and repair of premises, access or egress from there, safety of plant or substances and any health risks arising from these.

Section 6 - duties of those who manufacture etc

This section places specific duties to ensure that articles and substances for use at work are as safe and without risks as is reasonably practicable. The responsibility relates to both new and second hand articles as well as all substances (including micro-organisms) supplied to workplaces. The section covers:

- Safe design, installation and testing of articles (including fairground equipment).
- Substances that are safe and without risks to health.
- Carry out or arrange for tests or examinations to ensure safe design and construction of articles and to ensure substances will be safe and without risk to health.
- Provision of information on use and conditions essential to health and safety, and information about new and serious risks which come to light is to be provided to those supplied.
- Carry out research to minimise risks.
- Erectors and installers of articles for use at work must ensure they do not make the article unsafe or a risk to health.

Importers and suppliers carry the same duties as designers and manufacturers. It would usually be enough for them to rely on the tests and examinations conducted by the manufacturer/designer. Importers would be expected to prove that the article had the same standard of health and safety as a United Kingdom (UK) supplier; conformity with European harmonised standards would usually be sufficient.

Section 7 - duties of employees

These sections place general obligations upon all employees.

Briefly, the general duties require that employees should:

- Take reasonable care of their own health and safety and that of others who may be affected by their acts or omissions.
- Co-operate with the employer so as to ensure that the employer can comply with his statutory obligations.

Some examples of what this means in practice are: employees should obey reasonable instructions such as wearing personal protective equipment (PPE) when requested; not leave hazardous situations that could harm fellow workers such as trailing cables, maintenance staff replacing guards on machines that have been removed during maintenance work before returning the equipment back into service and employees in supervisory roles, not expecting or putting unrealistic work demands on people causing them to work unsafely.

Middle managers and supervisors are employees and carry a general duty to take reasonable care for those that might be affected by their acts or omissions. This would include responsibility for the health and safety of subordinates who might be affected by the way in which the manager or supervisor did their job. Failing to supervise effectively could be an omission, while directing someone to conduct a task without taking reasonable care to consider the risks could be seen as an act.

Section 8 - duties of all persons

No person shall intentionally or recklessly misuse or interfere with anything provided under the HASAWA 1974 and other legislation in the interests of health, safety or welfare.

Section 9 - duty of employer not to charge

The employer shall *not charge employees* for anything done or provided to comply with a specific legal obligation, e.g. provision of personal protective equipment, health surveillance, welfare facilities etc. This does not extend to anything that an employer may choose to do to provide health, safety and welfare standards beyond legal requirements. For example, a particular style of safety footwear that might be preferred by employees might cost more than a standard pair. In this case it would be usual to charge employees for the difference between the style they prefer and a standard pair. The same may be said for eye-sight correction spectacles for display screen equipment.

Section 36 - offences due to the fault of another person

Where the commission by any person of the breach of legislation is due to the act or default of some other person, that other person shall be guilty of the offence and may be charged with and convicted of the offence whether or not proceedings are taken against the first mentioned person. Case law indicates that 'other person' refers to persons lower down the corporate tree than mentioned in HASAWA 1974 section 37, e.g. middle managers, safety practitioners, training officers, and may extend to people working on contract e.g. architects, consultants, CDM co-ordinator and insurance engineers.

Section 37 - offences by the body corporate

Where there has been a breach of legislation on the part of a body corporate (limited company or local authority) and the offence can *"be proved:*

- *To have been committed with the consent or connivance of.*
- *To be attributable to any neglect on the part of any director, manager, secretary or similar officer of the body corporate, he, as well as the body corporate, can be found guilty and punished accordingly".*

1.5 - Management of Health and Safety at Work Regulations (MHSWR) 1999

SCOPE

The Management of Health and Safety at Work Regulations (MHSWR) 1999 set out some broad general duties which apply to almost all kinds of work. They are aimed mainly at improving health and safety management. You may already be familiar with broad health and safety law of this kind - as it is the form taken by the Health and Safety at Work Act (HASAWA) 1974. The Regulations work in a similar way and in fact they can be seen as a way of expanding on what is already in the HASAWA 1974. The 1999 Regulations replace the Management of Health and Safety at Work Regulations 1992, the Management of Health and Safety at Work (Amendment) Regulations 1994, the Health and Safety (Young Persons) Regulations 1997 and Part III of the Fire Precautions (Workplace) Regulations 1997. The Principal Regulations are discussed below.

RISK ASSESSMENT (REGULATION 3)

The regulations require employers (and the self-employed) to assess the risk to the health and safety of their employees and to anyone else who may be affected by their work activity. This is necessary to ensure that the preventive and protective steps can be identified to control hazards in the workplace. Where an employer is employing or about to employ young persons (under 18 years of age) he must carry out a risk assessment which takes particular account of:

- The inexperience, lack of awareness of risks and immaturity of young persons.
- The layout of the workplace and workstations.

- Exposure to physical, biological and chemical agents.
- Work equipment and the way in which it is handled.
- The extent of health and safety training to be provided.
- Risks from agents, processes and work listed in the Annex to Council Directive 94/33/EC on the protection of young people at work.

Where 5 or more employees are employed, the significant findings of risk assessments must be recorded in writing (the same threshold that is used in respect of having a written safety policy). This record must include details of any employees being identified as being especially at risk.

See also NGC1 - Element 4.2 - Principles and practice of risk assessment.

PRINCIPLES OF PREVENTION TO BE APPLIED (REGULATION 4)

Regulation 4 requires an employer to implement preventive and protective measures on the basis of general principles of prevention specified in Schedule 1 to the Regulations. These are:

- Avoiding risks.
- Evaluating the risks which cannot be avoided.
- Combating the risks at source.
- Adapting the work to the individual, especially as regards the design of workplaces, the choice of work equipment and the choice of working and production methods, with a view, in particular, to alleviating monotonous work and work at a predetermined work rate and to reducing their effect on health.
- Adapting to technical progress.
- Replacing the dangerous by the non-dangerous or the less dangerous.
- Developing a coherent overall prevention policy which covers technology, organisation of work, working conditions, social relationships and the influence of factors relating to the working environment.
- Giving collective protective measures priority over individual protective measures.
- Giving appropriate instructions to employees.

HEALTH AND SAFETY ARRANGEMENTS (REGULATION 5)

Appropriate arrangements must be made for the effective planning, organisation, control, monitoring and review of preventative and protective measures (in other words, for the management of health and safety). Again, employers with five or more employees must have their arrangements in writing.

HEALTH SURVEILLANCE (REGULATION 6)

In addition to the requirements of specific regulations such as Control of Substances Hazardous to Health (COSHH) 2002 and asbestos regulations, consideration must be given to carry out health surveillance of employees where there is a disease or adverse health condition identified in risk assessments.

HEALTH AND SAFETY ASSISTANCE (REGULATION 7)

The employer must appoint one or more competent persons to assist him in complying with the legal obligations imposed on the undertaking. The number of persons appointed should reflect the number of employees and the type of hazards in the workplace.

If more than one competent person is appointed, then arrangements must be made for ensuring adequate co-operation between them. The competent person(s) must be given the necessary time and resources to fulfil their functions. This will depend on the size of the undertaking, the risks to which employees are exposed and the distribution of those risks throughout the undertaking.

The employer must ensure that competent person(s) who are not employees are informed of the factors known (or suspected) to affect the health and safety of anyone affected by business activities.

Competent people are defined as those who have sufficient training and experience or knowledge and other qualities to enable them to perform their functions.

Persons may be selected from among existing employees or from outside. Where there is a suitable person in the employer's employment, that person shall be appointed as the 'competent person' in preference to a non-employee.

PROCEDURES FOR SERIOUS AND IMMINENT DANGER AND FOR DANGER AREAS (REGULATION 8)

Employers are required to set up emergency procedures and appoint **competent persons** to ensure compliance with identified arrangements, to devise control strategies as appropriate and to limit access to areas of risk to ensure that only those persons with adequate health and safety knowledge and instruction are admitted. The factors to be considered when preparing a procedure to deal with workplace emergencies such as fire, explosion, bomb scare, chemical leakage or other dangerous occurrence should include:

- The identification and training requirements of persons with specific responsibilities.
- The layout of the premises in relation to escape routes etc.
- The number of persons affected.

- Assessment of special needs (disabled persons, children etc).
- Warning systems.
- Emergency lighting.
- Location of shut-off valves, isolation switches, hydrants etc.
- Equipment required dealing with the emergency.
- Location of assembly points.
- Communication with emergency services.
- Training and/or information to be given to employees, visitors, local residents and anyone else who might be affected.

CONTACTS WITH EXTERNAL SERVICES (REGULATION 9)

Employers must ensure that, where necessary, contacts are made with external services. This particularly applies with regard to first-aid, emergency medical care and rescue work.

INFORMATION FOR EMPLOYEES (REGULATION 10)

Employees must be provided with relevant information about hazards to their health and safety arising from risks identified by the assessments. Clear instruction must be provided concerning any preventative or protective control measures including those relating to serious and imminent danger and fire assessments. Details of any competent persons nominated to discharge specific duties in accordance with the regulations must also be communicated as should risks arising from contact with other employer's activities (see Regulation 11).

Before employing a child (a person who is not over compulsory school age) the employer must provide those with parental responsibility for the child with information on the risks that have been identified and preventative and protective measures to be taken.

CO-OPERATION AND CO-ORDINATION (REGULATION 11)

Employers who work together in a common workplace have a duty to co-operate to discharge their duties under relevant statutory provisions. They must also take all reasonable steps to inform their respective employees of risks to their health or safety which may arise out of their work.

PERSONS WORKING IN HOST EMPLOYERS' OR SELF EMPLOYED PERSONS' UNDERTAKINGS (REGULATION 12)

This regulation extends the requirements of regulation 11 to include employees working as sole occupiers of a workplace under the control of another employer. Such employees would include those working under a service of contract and employees in temporary employment businesses under the control of the first employer.

CAPABILITIES AND TRAINING (REGULATION 13)

Employers need to take into account the capabilities of their employees before entrusting tasks. This is necessary to ensure that they have adequate health and safety training and are capable enough at their jobs to avoid risk. To this end consideration must be given to recruitment including job orientation when transferring between jobs and work departments. Training must also be provided when other factors such as the introduction of new technology and new systems of work or work equipment arise. Training must:

- Be repeated periodically where appropriate.
- Be adapted to take account of any new or changed risks to the health and safety of the employees concerned.
- Take place during working hours.

EMPLOYEES' DUTIES (REGULATION 14)

Employees are required to use machinery, equipment, substances, transport means of production and safety devices in accordance with the instructions and training that they have received.

They must also inform their employer (or an employee with health and safety responsibility) of any situation representing a serious and immediate danger or shortcoming in the health and safety arrangements, where they affect their health and safety or arise out of their work.

TEMPORARY WORKERS (REGULATION 15)

Consideration is given to the special needs of temporary workers on fixed term contracts or employed through an employment business. In particular, the employer must provide health and safety information on qualifications required to perform the task safely and requirements for health surveillance.

RISKS ASSESSMENT IN RESPECT OF NEW OR EXPECTANT MOTHERS (REGULATION 16

Where the work is of a kind which would involve risk to a new or expectant mother or her baby, then the risk assessment required by regulation 3 should take this into account.

If the risk cannot be avoided, then the employer should take reasonable steps to:

- Adjust the hours worked.

- Offer alternative work.
- Give paid leave for as long as is necessary.

CERTIFICATE FROM A REGISTERED MEDICAL PRACTITIONER IN RESPECT OF NEW OR EXPECTANT MOTHERS (REGULATION 17)

Where the woman is a night shift worker and has a medical certificate identifying night shift work as a risk then the employer must put her on day shift or give paid leave for as long as is necessary.

NOTIFICATION BY NEW OR EXPECTANT MOTHERS (REGULATION 18)

The employer need take no action until notified in writing by the woman that she is pregnant, has given birth in the last six months, or is breastfeeding.

PROTECTION OF YOUNG PERSONS (REGULATION 19)

Employers of young persons shall ensure that they are not exposed to risk as a consequence of their lack of experience, lack of awareness or lack of maturity.

No employer shall employ young people for work which:

- Is beyond their physical or psychological capacity.
- Involves exposure to agents which are toxic or carcinogenic, cause heritable genetic damage to the unborn child or that chronically affect human health in some other way.
- Involves harmful exposure to radiation.
- Involves a risk to health from extremes of temperature, noise or vibration.
- Involves risks which could not be reasonably foreseen by young persons.

This regulation does not prevent the employment of a young person who is no longer a child for work:

- Where it is necessary for their training.
- Where the young person will be supervised by a competent person.
- Where any risk will be reduced to the lowest level that is reasonably practicable.

1.6 - Responsibilities of clients and contractors

Relationship between client and contractor

CLIENTS

Clients, as employers, are obliged both by criminal and civil law to protect their workforce and others from health risks and personal injury and to conduct all undertakings in such a way as to ensure that members of the public around or entering their premises are likewise protected. The main statutory provisions relating to health and safety with regard to managing contractors are embodied in the HASAWA 1974, MHSWR 1999, and the Construction (Design and Management) Regulations (CDM) 2007.

Clients contract operations for a wide range of situations, from activities such as window cleaning, catering or security to large-scale construction works. Construction works could include the building of an extension to premises or new premises on land not previously used, often referred to as a "green field" site. Consultation with contractors prior to a contract being signed, commencement of work and during the course of the work is of the utmost significance if a safe and healthy site is to be maintained.

CONTRACTORS

In the context of health and safety at work, the term contractor is commonly applied to those who visit the premises of others to conduct work. This is usually in connection with the repair, maintenance, refurbishment or installation of plant and equipment, or building alterations, and in this sense will be either an employer or self-employed person.

Contractors carrying out maintenance works are a significant cause of accidents in the workplace. In general, visiting contractors are less familiar with the workplace and associated risks than the indigenous workforce, yet often carry out more hazardous operations. In order to minimise the risk potential of such activities and to ensure that all concerned are made aware of their health and safety responsibilities, a detailed knowledge of relevant legislation/health and safety standards is essential, risks must be identified and effective control methods introduced.

Duties to each other and to the other's employees

SHARED CONTROL OF PREMISES

The occupier of premises has civil duties under the Occupiers' Liability Acts 1957 and 1984 regarding the state and condition of the premises. *(The occupier's liability acts are not examined as specific items in the NEBOSH National General Certificate - only the concept of civil liability of the occupier is necessary).* When contractors are working on a premise it could be argued that they are joint occupiers with an employer under these Acts. Therefore, both employer and the contractor have joint liabilities in 'common areas'. The occupier is not normally liable for dangers associated with the contractors' work activities, provided that in selecting the contractor they took care to ensure competency and they are satisfied that the work is being carried out properly.

Figure 1-1-15: Joint occupancy, trip hazards in common area.
Source: RMS.

Figure 1-1-16: Occupier's liability - to public, safety barriers in place.
Source: RMS.

In a similar way, considering criminal law, if more than one employer was in control of premises at the time that contracted work was being undertaken, these being the client and contractor; they may each be prosecuted for failing to meet responsibilities under section 4 of HASAWA 1974. In addition to the aspect of control of the premises, each party has civil and criminal duties to each other for the health and safety risks arising from their work, notably sections 2 and 3 of HASAWA 1974.

GENERAL POINTS

The principal duties to each other and to the other's employees are expressed in Sections 2-4 of HASAWA 1974. Sections 3 and 4 of HASAWA 1974 show that a client has duties towards a contractor and their employees as visitors to their workplace.

When a contractor performs work on behalf of a client, they must do so with regard for those that may be affected. Section 3 of HASAWA 1974 sets out a duty for contractors to protect people not in their employment from risks to their health and safety. This will include the client and their employees, as well as other contractors' employees and the public. When the contractor takes control of part of a client's premises they become responsible for that part under Section 4 of HASAWA 1974.

In addition, when a client commissions a contractor to conduct work relating to the client's undertaking the client retains responsibility to see that it is conducted in a safe and healthy manner. Section 2 of HASAWA 1974 sets out the duty on the client to ensure the work does not cause harm to employees and section 3 of HASAWA 1974 the duty to prevent harm to others, such as members of the public.

A contractor that agrees to a contract for service must provide appropriate health and safety standards when conducting the work - this will benefit all those that might be affected. It is the responsibility of both parties to build health and safety into the contract and work methods. To this end, it is essential that they co-operate with each other, seeking to plan and co-ordinate activities.

MHSWR 1999 - Regulation 12 - Persons working in host employers' or self employed persons' undertakings

Host employers and self-employed people must ensure that people carrying out work on their premises receive relevant information. If reliance is placed on the employer of the visiting employees providing information, a check should be made to ensure information has been passed on. The information should be enough to allow the employer of the visiting employee to comply with their responsibilities at law and would address the risks arising from the host employer's undertaking.

In addition, information should identify people nominated by the host employer to help with emergency evacuation. Such employees would include those working under a contract of service and employees provided by temporary employment businesses under the control of a host employer.

Effective planning and co-ordination of contracted work

It is essential that all contracted work be planned and co-ordinated. Contracted work carries particular risks in that workers may be unfamiliar with the workplace and work may be organised such that activities conflict with each other putting contractors or employees at risk. It is essential that a risk assessment of work activities be made foreseeing how they interact with each other. The MHSWR 1999 require that employers make arrangements to plan, organise, control, monitor and review activities that it controls. This would, naturally, extend to contract work commissioned by the employer. In addition, the CDM 2007 Regulations set out specific requirements for all construction projects and additional duties for those that are notifiable to the Health and Safety Executive.

CO-OPERATION AND CO-ORDINATION

MHSWR 1999 - Regulation 11 - Co-operation and co-ordination

Employers who work together in a common workplace, such as where contracted work is carried out in the workplace of a client, have a duty to co-operate in order to discharge their duties under relevant statutory provisions. This will include consideration of each other when conducting risk assessments and provision of procedures for serious or imminent danger. For example, when establishing fire evacuation arrangements on a site occupied by the client and contractors, whole of the work activities should be considered. Each party should co-operate with a co-ordinated response.

It is necessary for all employers and self employed involved in situations where they have a common workplace to satisfy themselves that the arrangements are adequate. Employers should ensure that all relevant employees, and in particular competent people appointed under the MHSWR 1999, are aware and fully take part. They must also take all reasonable steps to inform other employers concerned of risks to their employees' health or safety that may arise out of their work.

Management controls for significant construction projects

The management controls for significant construction projects are set out in the CDM 2007 Regulations. The Regulations contain specific duties for those who have particular roles in the health and safety of projects.

DUTIES AND RESPONSIBILITIES

Client duties

For **all** projects, ensure that:

- Work can be carried out safely.
- Adequate welfare facilities are provided.
- Any workplace complies with the Workplace (Health, Safety and Welfare) Regulations (WHSWR) 1992.
- Make relevant pre-construction health and safety information available.

Where a project is notifiable, the client shall:

- As soon as practicable appoint a competent CDM co-ordinator.
- Then appoint a competent principal contractor.
- Promptly provide the CDM co-ordinator and principal contractor with pre-construction information.
- Not allow work to start until the construction phase plan and adequate welfare facilities are in place.
- Provide the CDM co-ordinator with information for inclusion in the health and safety file.
- Keep health and safety file available for inspection and revised as necessary.

Designer duties

For **all** projects, ensure that:

- The client is aware of their duties.
- Take account of other design considerations.
- Design to avoid foreseeable risk during construction, use and maintenance of the building.
- Give priority to collective measures over individual measures.
- Ensure where it is not possible to avoid risks that they are minimised.
- Provide adequate information about materials used in the design that could affect the health and safety of persons carrying out construction work.

Where a project is notifiable:

- Shall not commence until a CDM co-ordinator has been appointed.
- Provide the CDM co-ordinator with information for inclusion in the health and safety file.

CDM Co-ordinator's duties

CDM Co-ordinators should:

- Be in a position to give advice to clients.
- Ensure co-operation between persons involved in the project.
- Ensure that designers include among the design considerations the principles of prevention.
- Liaise with principal contractor regarding information for the health and safety plan and health and safety file.
- Identify and collect pre-construction information.
- Ensure that designers comply with their duties.
- Ensure co-operation between designers and principal contractor in relation to any design change.
- Prepare a health and safety file.
- Ensure that a health and safety file is delivered to the client.
- Notify the Health and Safety Executive (HSE).

Principal contractor's duties

The principal contractor should:

- Plan, manage and monitor the construction phase to ensure that it is carried out without risk.
- Liaise with the CDM co-ordinator.
- Ensure adequate welfare facilities are provided.
- Draw up site rules.
- Display the notification details.
- Prevent unauthorised access to the site.

Ensure that every contractor is:

- Informed of the minimum amount of time allocated for planning and preparation.
- If necessary, consulted about the health and safety plan.
- Given access to the health and safety plan.
- Given any relevant information.
- Informed about the information that may be required for inclusion in the health and safety file.

Ensure that every worker is provided with:

- Site induction.
- Information that has to be provided by a contractor (see below).
- Any further information that might be necessary.

Contractors duties

For *all* projects, ensure that:

- They do not start work unless they are aware of their duties.
- Plan, manage and monitor work to ensue that it is carried out without risk.
- Every contractor that the contractor appoints is provided with relevant information.
- Every worker under the contractors control is given information and training which should include:
  - Site induction (if not provided by the principal contractor).
  - Results of risk assessments and control measures.
  - Site rules.
  - Emergency procedures and the persons involved in implementing the procedures.
- They do not commence work until unauthorised access to the site has been prevented.
- Ensure that adequate welfare facilities are provided.

Where a project is notifiable the contractor shall:

- Not start work unless the contractor knows the names of the CDM co-ordinator and principal contractor, has been given access to the health and safety plan and the project has been notified to the HSE.
- Provide relevant information to the principal contractor on the health and safety risks created by their works and how they will be controlled.
- Identify any contractors they have appointed to the principal contractor.
- Comply with directions given by the principal contractor and any rules in the health and safety plan.
- Provide the principal contractor with any Reporting of Injuries, Diseases and Dangerous Occurrences Regulations (RIDDOR) 1995 reports.

HSE NOTIFICATION OF PROJECTS

CDM 2007 applies to all construction projects. However, construction projects with a construction phase longer than 30 days or involving more than 500 person days of construction work are notifiable to the HSE. Notification by the CDM Co-ordinator must be in writing and can be made using the form F10 (rev).

HEALTH AND SAFETY PLAN

Pre-construction information

Pre-construction information is essentially a collection of information about the significant health and safety risks of the construction project which the principal contractor will have to manage during the construction phase. The pre-construction information will mainly come from:

- *The client* - who has to provide information relevant to health and safety to the CDM co-ordinator. This could include existing drawings, surveys of the site or premises, information on the location of services, etc.
- *Designers* - who have to provide information about the risks which cannot be avoided and will have to be controlled by the principal contractor and other contractors. Typically, this information may be provided on drawings, in written specifications or in outline method statements.

The pre-construction information serves three main purposes:

- During its development the plan can provide a focus at which the health and safety considerations of design are brought together under the control of the CDM co-ordinator.

■ Secondly, the plan plays a vital role in the tender documentation. It enables prospective principal contractors to be fully aware of the project's health, safety and welfare requirements. This will allow prospective principal contractors to have a level playing field as far as health and safety is concerned on which to provide tender submissions.

■ Thirdly, the plan provides a template against which different tender submissions can be measured. This helps the CDM co-ordinator to advise the client on the provision of resources for health and safety and to assess the competence of prospective principal contractors.

The CDM co-ordinator is responsible for ensuring that the pre-construction information is prepared. This does not mean that the CDM co-ordinator must produce the plan directly, but the CDM co-ordinator must ensure that it is prepared.

Content of the pre-construction information pack

The contents of the pre-construction information will depend on the nature of the project itself. However, the following areas should be considered:

■ Project description and programme details.
■ Details of client, designers, CDM co-ordinator and other consultants.
■ Extent and location of existing records and plans.
■ Client's considerations and management requirements.
■ Structure and organisation.
■ Safety goals for the project and arrangements for monitoring and review.
■ Permits and authorisation requirements.
■ Emergency procedures.
■ Site rules and other restrictions on contractors, suppliers and others e.g. access arrangements to those parts of the site which continue to be used by the client.
■ Activities on or adjacent to the site during the works.
■ Arrangements for liaison between parties.
■ Security arrangements.
■ Environmental restrictions and existing on-site risks.
■ Hazards.
a) Safety hazards, including:
   • Boundaries and access, including temporary access.
   • Adjacent land uses.
   • Existing storage of hazardous materials.
   • Location of existing services - water, electricity, gas, etc.
   • Ground conditions.
   • Existing structures - stability, or fragile materials.
b) Health hazards, including:
   • Asbestos, including results of any surveys.
   • Existing storage of hazardous materials.
   • Contaminated land, including results of surveys.
   • Existing structure's hazardous materials.
   • Health risks arising from client's activities.
   • Significant design and construction hazards.
   • Design assumptions and control measures.
   • Arrangements for co-ordination of on-going design work and handling design changes.
   • Information on significant risks identified during design (health and safety risks).
   • Materials requiring particular precautions.

Format of the pre-construction information pack

If the pre-construction information is to be effective in helping to select a principal contractor, the CDM co-ordinator and any other professional advisers who put together the tender documentation will need to determine what the most suitable format for the plan is. Clearly the way the pre-construction information is included in the tender documentation and is structured is essential if responses on health and safety are to be made by prospective principal contractors.

The pre-construction information does not have to be a separate document. If the project is a large and complex one, a separate document which ensures that the key information is highlighted, may be appropriate. However, on small projects, some of the information outlined will already be in existing tender documentation. In this case, the key information can be highlighted in a covering letter or by use of an index pointing to which information should be considered.

Source: HSE Construction Information Sheet No. 42.

The construction phase health and safety plan

The purpose of the construction heath and safety plan, developed by the principal contractor, is to establish the foundation on which the health and safety management of the construction work is based. The contents of the construction phase health and safety plan will depend on the nature of the project itself.

However, the health and safety plan can usefully open with:

- A description of the project. This will include details of key dates, details of other parties and the extent and location of existing records and plans.
- The management structure and responsibilities of the various members of the project team, whether based at site or elsewhere.
- The health and safety standards to which the project will be carried out. These may be set in terms of statutory requirements or high standards that the client may require in particular circumstances.
- Means for informing contractors about risks to their health and safety arising from the environment in which the project is to be carried out and the construction work itself.
- All contractors, the self employed and designers to be appointed by the principal contractor are properly selected (i.e. they are competent and will make adequate provision for health and safety).
- Means for communicating and passing information between the project team (including the client and any client's representatives) the designers, the CDM co-ordinator, the principal contractor, other contractors, workers on site and others whose health and safety may be affected.
- Arrangements for the identification and effective management of activities with risks to health and safety, by carrying out risk assessments, incorporating those prepared by other contractors, and also safety method statements which result. These activities may be specific to a particular trade or to site-wide issues.
- Emergency arrangements for dealing with and minimising the effects of injuries, fire and other dangerous occurrences.
- Arrangements for passing information to the principal contractor about accidents, ill health and dangerous occurrences that require to be notified to the health and safety executive (HSE) under RIDDOR 1995.
- Arrangements for the provision and maintenance of welfare facilities.
- Arrangements to ensure the principal contractor checks that people on site have been provided with health and safety information and safety training.
- Arrangements that have been made for consulting and co-ordinating the views of workers or their representatives.
- Arrangements for making site rules and for bringing them to the attention of those affected.
- Arrangements for passing on information to the CDM co-ordinator for the preparation of the health and safety file.
- Arrangements should be set out for the monitoring systems to achieve compliance with legal requirements and the health and safety rules developed by the principal contractor.

PROVISION OF INFORMATION

To ensure the health and safety of persons affected by the project and to assist the persons to whom information is provided under this regulation in order to perform their duties under these Regulations, every client shall ensure that:

- Every person designing the structure who may be bidding for the work (or who intend to engage), is conversant with the project-specific health and safety information needed to identify hazards and risks associated with the design and construction work.
- Every contractor who has been or may be appointed by the client is promptly provided with pre-construction information in accordance with the CDM 2007 Regulations.

The pre-construction information shall consist of all the information in the client's possession (or which is reasonably obtainable), including:

- Any information about or affecting the site or the construction work.
- Any information concerning the proposed use of the structure as a workplace.
- The minimum amount of time before the construction phase which will be allowed to the contractors appointed by the client for planning and preparation for construction work.
- Any information in any existing health and safety file.

PREPARATION OF THE HEALTH AND SAFETY FILE

The purpose of the health and safety file is to provide information needed to allow future construction work, including cleaning, maintenance, alterations, refurbishment and demolition. The CDM co-ordinator is responsible for ensuring the health and safety file is prepared. Putting together the health and safety file is a task which should ideally be a continual process throughout the project and not left until the construction work is completed. Early on in the construction project the CDM co-ordinator may find it useful to discuss the health and safety file with the client. This will help determine what information the client requires and how the client wishes the information to be stored and recorded.

When the client's requirements are known, procedures may need to be drawn up by the CDM co-ordinator so that all those who will be contributing to the health and safety file (e.g. designers and contractors) are aware of:

- The information which needs to be collected.
- How the information is to be collected, presented and stored.

The CDM co-ordinator may find it useful to detail in the pre-tender stage health and safety plan requirements on how and when the information for the health and safety file is to be prepared and passed on. The principal contractor may also find it useful to include similar procedures in the health and safety plan for the construction phase. Throughout the project those who carry out design work (including contractors) will need to ensure so far as is reasonably practicable that information about any feature of the structure which will involve significant risks to health and safety during the structure's lifetime are passed to either the CDM co-ordinator or to the principal contractor.

Providing this information on drawings will allow for amendments if any variations arise during construction. It will also allow health and safety information to be stored on one document, therefore reducing the paperwork. The principal contractor may need to obtain details of services, plant and equipment which are part of the structure from specialist suppliers and installers, e.g. mechanical and electrical contractors and pass this information on.

Contractors have a specific duty in the CDM 2007 Regulations to pass information for the health and safety file to the principal contractor, who in turn has to pass it to the CDM co-ordinator. This information could include:

- Brief description of the work.
- Hazardous materials used.
- 'As built' and 'as installed' drawings.
- Information on the removal or dismantling of plant.
- Operation and maintenance manuals, e.g. for equipment provided for cleaning or maintaining the structure.
- Nature, location and markings of significant services, e.g. underground cables; gas supply equipment, fire fighting services.
- Key structural principles and safe working loads for floors and roofs, particularly where these may preclude placing scaffolding or heavy machinery there.
- Any residual hazards which remain and how they have been dealt with.

At the end of the project the CDM co-ordinator has to hand over the health and safety file to the client. In some cases it might not be possible for a fully developed file to be handed over on completion of the project. This may happen because the construction work was finished rapidly to meet a tight deadline and completion of the health and safety file was not possible. Clearly a common sense approach is needed so that the health and safety file is handed over as soon as practicable after a completion certificate or similar document has been issued.

Assessment, selection and control of contractors

The main elements to a strategy for the effective control of contractors are:

Assessment
- Assessment of potential contractors.

Selection
- Checking of the health and safety aspects of bids and selection of contractor.
- Contractor agrees to be subject to client's rules.

Control
- Control of the contractor on site.
- Checking after completion of contract.

The extent to which each element is relevant will depend upon the degree of risk and nature of work to be contracted.

ASSESSMENT

Acquiring the services of a competent contractor with relevant professional qualifications and a proven safety record is fundamental to any risk control programme. This should be a proactive exercise. As far as is possible the types of works and activities that are likely to involve contractors working in the premises should be identified, e.g. electrical, mechanical, gas, maintenance, etc. It will be possible from this to draw up a list of professionally suitably qualified contractors and carry out an investigation into their safety policies and their safety performance at previous locations.

Employers should additionally check out their qualification to do the required works. For example, for work involving gas appliances, the contractor should be registered with the Gas Safe Register. The employer should produce a pre-qualification questionnaire which should be completed by each contractor to assist in the vetting process. This could include the following:

- A copy of contractor's health and safety policy document.
- Details of any previous works carried out by the contractor.
- Details of any risk assessments which have been carried out and the risk control measures that have been introduced (e.g. MHSWR 1999, hazardous substances, noise, electricity, manual handling, PPE).

- References from previous employers of the contractor.
- Details of any accidents or incidents that occurred in any other works contracts (check with the relevant HSE area office if these are reportable under the Reporting of Injuries, Diseases and Dangerous Occurrences Regulations 1995 (RIDDOR)).
- Details of the contractor's emergency procedures for their employees, e.g. fire, accident, injury and first aid.
- The effect of contractor's works on the employer's staff and premises.
- The appointment of 'competent persons' to assist in health and safety matters (liaison).
- Details of health and safety training provided.
- Brief details of safe systems of work (e.g. permit-to-work).
- Brief details of how the contractor controls their sub-contractors.

Following the above exercise, a 'short-list' of competent contractors can be produced. This procedure could prove to be invaluable, as often the services of contractors are needed in emergency situations when sufficient time is not available to carry out these vetting procedures.

A checklist should be followed in order to define a specification for the contract; this will give a pointer to most if not all the common health and safety problems which may arise during the work. These should be communicated to the contractor in the specification before the bid is made, and the received bid checked against them to ensure that proper provision is being made for the control of risk and that the contractor has identified the hazards. Suitable headings for the checklist could include:

- Special hazards and applicable national or local Regulations and Codes of practice (asbestos, noise, permits to work).
- Safe access/egress to, from, on the site, and to places of work within the site.
- Buried and overhead services.
- Confined space entry.
- First-aid/emergency rescue.
- Welfare amenities.

SELECTION

When the bids are returned, it should be possible to distinguish the potentially competent at this stage. An 'approved list' of contractors, scrutinised at intervals, can save the need for carrying out a complete selection process as described on every occasion.

Before any contract work is commenced, a responsible person representing the main contractor must discuss with the occupier the health and safety precautions necessary as far as his own workforce is concerned and any other parties on site.

A basic principle of control is that as much as possible should be set down in detail in the contract. An important condition should be that the contractor agrees to abide by all the provisions of the client's safety policy, which may affect his employees or the work, including compliance with site health and safety rules.

Areas of concern, which should be covered by general site rules and within the client's safety policy, should be communicated to the contractor in the form of site rules.

They include:

- Materials storage, handling, disposal.
- Use of equipment which could cause fires.
- Noise and vibration.
- Scaffolding and ladders, access.
- Cartridge-powered fixing tools.
- Welding equipment - and use of client's electricity supply etc.

CONTROL

- Appointment/nomination of a person or team to co-ordinate all aspects of the contract, including health and safety matters.
- A pre-contract commencement meeting held with the contractor to review all safety aspects of the work.
- Control access to contractor work area.
- Arrangement of regular progress meetings between all parties, where health and safety is the first agenda item.
- Regular (at least weekly) inspections of the contractor's operations by the client.
- Participation in safety committees on site by contractors should be a condition of the contract.
- Provision by the contractor of risk assessments and/or written method statements in advance of undertaking particular work, as agreed.
- The formal reporting to the client by the contractor of all lost-time accidents and dangerous occurrences, including those to sub-contractors.
- The contractor should leave the work site clean and tidy, removing all waste, materials, tools and equipment. This should be checked.

1.7 - The court and tribunal structure for Scotland

INTRODUCTION

As in England and Wales there are also two legal systems in Scotland, one for criminal and one for civil cases. The court structure differs from those in England, Wales and Northern Ireland (Northern Ireland is similar to that of England and Wales).

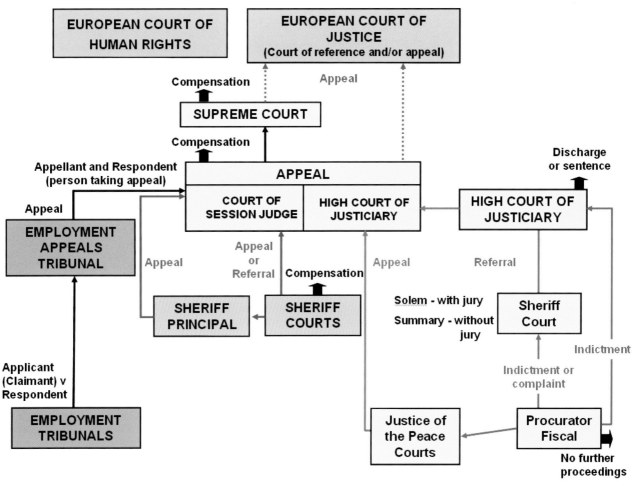

Figure 1-1-17: Court and tribunal structure - Scotland.   Source: RMS.

It is essential to differentiate between criminal and civil liability.

Criminal liability occurs where a breach of criminal legislation occurs and may result in a prosecution in a criminal court where the purpose will be to punish by fine, or imprisonment - or by other means if found guilty.

Civil liability occurs only if the alleged wrongdoer has committed a civil wrong recognised by law, e.g. "the general law of delict"; "breach of some specific statutory duties" etc. In addition, the person affected can only sue if they have a cause of action, i.e. has been injured as a result of the wrongdoer's negligence.

CRIMINAL LAW

Prosecution of crime in the Scottish Courts is taken by the Lord Advocate or his local representative, the regional Procurator Fiscal in each Sheriff Court district. The Lord Advocate is the head of the Crown Office, which is the administrative headquarters of the Procurator Fiscal service. There are two types of criminal procedure in Scotland.

In **summary** procedure in Sheriff and District Courts, the judge sits without jury and decides both questions of facts and law.

In **solemn** procedure in both High Court of Judiciary and Sheriff Court, trial is before a judge and jury of 15 lay people.

■ Judge decides questions of law.   ■ Jury decides questions of fact.

PENALTIES

Please refer to the 'Legal system (England and Wales)' section.

CIVIL LAW

Civil liability occurs only if the alleged wrongdoer has committed a civil wrong recognised by law, for example "the general law of delict" or "breach of some specific statutory duties". Generally a master (employer) is liable for his own delict, i.e. "personal liability" and for the delict committed by his own employees, in the course of their employment, i.e. vicarious liability. In general the employer is not responsible for the delict of independent contractors employed by him.

Source	Principles established in previous cases.
Civil Courts	Sheriff Court, Summary Cause. Up to £1500.
	Sheriff Court, Ordinary Cause. Over £1500.
Appeal Courts	Sheriff Principal, Court of Session, House of Lords.

UNIT NGC1
MANAGEMENT OF HEALTH AND SAFETY

Health and safety management systems 1 - policy

Learning outcomes

On completion of this element, candidates should be able to demonstrate understanding of the content through the application of knowledge to familiar and unfamiliar situations. In particular they should be able to:

2.1   Outline the key elements of a health and safety management system.

2.2   Explain the purpose and importance of setting policy for health and safety.

2.3   Describe the key features and appropriate content of an effective health and safety policy.

Content

Sources of reference

The Management of Health and Safety at Work (ACOP) (L21), HSE Books ISBN 0-7176-2488-9

Successful Health and Safety Management (HSG65), HSE Books ISBN 0-7176-1276-7

An Introduction to Health and Safety (INDG259 Rev 1) HSE Books ISBN 0-7176-2685-7

Relevant statutory provisions

The Health and Safety at Work etc. Act (HASAWA) 1974

Employers' Health and Safety Policy Statements (Exception) Regulations (EHSPS) 1975

The Management of Health and Safety at Work Regulations (MHSWR) 1999 (as amended)

2.1 - The key elements of a health and safety management system

HSG65 - Successful health and safety management

HSG65 - the HSE Accident Prevention Unit first prepared Successful Health and Safety Management in 1991 and a second edition was published in 1997. Having a management system in place that allows health and safety to be managed professionally brings many economic benefits. Among these are: *[handwritten: ← arguments for NGC report (exam 3)]*

- Increased productivity.
- Improved morale.
- Reduction in down time.
- Lower absence rates.

- Enhanced corporate image.
- Lower insurance costs.
- Less chance of legal actions.
- Lower staff turnover.

The key elements of successful health and safety management are set out below and the relationship between them is outlined in the diagram taken from HSG65.

POLICY

Organisations that are successful in achieving high standards of health and safety have health and safety policies which contribute to their business performance, while meeting their responsibilities to people and the environment in a way which fulfils both the spirit and the letter of the law.

In this way they satisfy the expectations of shareholders, employees, customers and society at large. Their policies are cost effective and aimed at achieving the preservation and development of physical and human resources and reductions in financial losses and liabilities. Their health and safety policies influence all their activities and decisions, including those to do with the selection of resources and information, the design and operation of working systems, the design and delivery of products and services, and the control and disposal of waste.

ORGANISING

Organisations that achieve high health and safety standards are structured and operated so as to put their health and safety policies into effective practice. This is helped by the creation of a positive culture that secures involvement and participation at all levels. It is sustained by effective communications and the promotion of competence that enables all workers to make a responsible and informed contribution to the health and safety effort.

The visible and active leadership of senior managers is necessary to develop and maintain a culture supportive of health and safety management. Their aim is not simply to avoid accidents, but to motivate and empower people to work safely. The vision, values and beliefs of leaders become the shared 'common knowledge' of all.

PLANNING

These successful organisations adopt a planned and systematic approach to policy implementation. Their aim is to minimise the risks created by work activities, products and services. They use risk assessment methods to decide priorities and set objectives for hazard elimination and risk reduction. Performance standards are established and performance is measured against them. Specific actions needed to promote a positive health and safety culture and to eliminate and control risks are identified. Wherever possible, risks are eliminated by the careful selection and design of facilities, equipment and processes or minimised by the use of physical control measures. Where this is not possible, provision of a safe system of work and personal protective equipment are used to control risks.

MEASURING PERFORMANCE

Health and safety performance in organisations that manage health and safety successfully is measured against pre-determined standards. These reveal when and where action is needed to improve performance. The success of action taken to control risks is assessed through active self-monitoring involving a range of techniques. This includes an examination of both hardware (premises, plant and substances) and software (people, procedures and systems), including individual behaviour.

Failures of control are assessed through reactive monitoring which requires the thorough investigation of any accidents, ill health or incidents with the potential to cause harm or loss. In both active and reactive monitoring, the objectives are not only to determine the immediate causes of sub-standard performance but, more importantly, to identify the underlying causes and the implications for the design and operation of the health and safety management system.

AUDITING AND REVIEWING PERFORMANCE

Learning from all relevant experience and applying the lessons learned are important elements in effective health and safety management. This needs to be done systematically through regular reviews of performance based on data both from monitoring activities and from independent audits of the whole health and safety management system. These form the basis for self-regulation and for securing compliance with sections 2 to 6 of the HASAWA 1974.

Commitment to continuous improvement involves the constant development of policies, approaches to implementation and techniques of risk control. Organisations which achieve high standards of health and safety assess their health and safety performance by internal reference to key performance indicators and by external comparison with the performance of business competitors. They often also record and account for their performance in their annual reports.

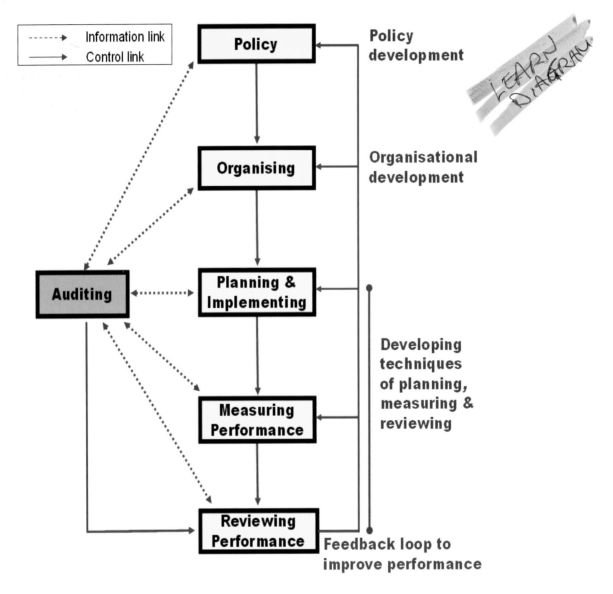

Figure 1-2-1: Key elements of successful health and safety management.   *Source: HSG65, HSE books.*

2.2 - Purpose and importance of setting policy for health and safety

Role of the health and safety policy

Without active management involvement in health and safety any attempt at organised accident prevention will be restricted and predominantly reactive. The overall role of a policy is to provide direction for an organisation, establishing a remit that will both guide the organisation to satisfy the goals set by it and to bind it so that it does not stray from the standards that it sets. This will influence the decisions made by an organisation, in that they will need to fall within the intent of the policy.

Organisations differ greatly in their goals, risks, structure and what they feel capable of committing themselves to. In the same way a policy is therefore a 'personal' thing setting out a particular organisation's position at that point in time. The policy enables the organisation to communicate its commitment, expectations from people and approach to health and safety.

The legal requirements and guidance

The Health and Safety at Work etc Act (HASAWA) 1974 set out an obligation to manage the risks that organisations create, and a cornerstone of this was seen to be the establishment of an active health and safety policy. This has been consistently misunderstood and underestimated by many over the years since the HASAWA 1974 came into force. With the introduction of the Management of Health and Safety at Work Regulations (MHSWR) 1999 this has received a fresh focus.

Section 2 (3) of the Health and Safety at Work etc Act (HASAWA) 1974 requires all employers, except for the smaller organisations (currently those with fewer than five employees) to:

- Create a written health and safety policy statement.
- Bring the policy to the attention of employees.
- State the organisation/arrangement to bring the statement into effect.
- Revise the policy as necessary.

The Management of Health and Safety at Work Regulations (MHSWR) 1999 - Regulation 5 - Health and Safety Arrangements

Appropriate arrangements must be made for the effective *planning, organisation, control, monitoring and review* of preventative and protective measures (in other words, for the management of health and safety). Again, employers with five or more employees must have their arrangements in writing. The Health and Safety Executive have set out guidance on managing health and safety in a document called "Successful Health and Safety Management" (HSG 65). It seeks to emphasise the importance of setting out policy on health and safety, supporting this with good organisation, establishing controls (arrangements), measurement of performance, review and audit.

2.3 - Features and content of an effective health and safety policy

Aims, objectives and key elements of a health and safety policy

OVERALL AIMS

The aim of the policy of an organisation is to create a structure to its approach to health and safety.

OBJECTIVES

The objectives are to ensure clear definition of the organisation's goals, set out responsibilities for health and safety matters and describe the arrangements in place to ensure health and safety is achieved.

KEY ELEMENTS

A health and safety policy contains:

- A general statement of management commitment *(What)* - states the overall aims of the organisation in terms of health and safety performance.
- Details of the organisation *(Who)* - defining structure, role, relationships and responsibilities of individuals.
- Arrangements to control the risks *(How)* - expected to set the direction, scope and actions of an organisation to manage health and safety. This part of the policy document specifies the arrangements for achieving general and specific aims for health and safety.

To be effective the policy should be:

- In a number of formats.
- Effectively communicated.
- Revised as appropriate.
- Monitored through audits.

The effective communication of the policy is important; all affected by it must understand it. In order to achieve this, a good deal has to be done. Merely posting it or distributing a copy to employees is not enough. Training and briefings will be necessary, as a minimum, to ensure effective communication. For new employees this is often done as part of the induction process. The format, complexity and language used should be considered. Experience shows that no one form of document is adequate to meet everyone's needs; therefore the document is usually produced in at least a summary and a detailed format. If it is likely to be revised frequently, a loose-leaf scheme will be advisable for the detailed version. This is especially true when the names and contact telephone numbers of people are included.

General statement of intent

A particularly effective way of demonstrating management commitment to health and safety is by communicating a policy *statement of intent*. It sets quantifiable organisational objectives for health and safety. In order to accentuate this commitment the statement should be *signed* and dated by the most senior member of the management team. Lack of firm management commitment of this kind leads to the perception that health and safety is not equal to other business objectives. The addition of a date to the statement will indicate the last time the statement was reviewed.

Organisations should translate their overall aims that are set out in the statement into *objectives* for the organisation, key parts of the organisation and key individuals. In line with other business objectives, health and safety objectives should be set out as *quantifiable targets*. An easily quantifiable item is the number of accidents occurring in an organisation. This is probably why people are attracted to targets for accident reduction; however it is important to look at the effect of such targets on accident reporting. Objectives should, ideally, be proactive; though it is not uncommon to have reactive objectives related to reduction in accidents as part of a group of objectives. Proactive objectives related to such things as manager training completed or risk assessments conducted are important to maintain progress on health and safety. Many organisations seek to compare their performance against other organisations, sometimes called *'benchmarking'*.

This is easiest done with performance indicators that are measurable, the most obvious of which are accident statistics. Though they are often unreliable for comparison in this way they are still used and limitations accepted. In more recent times organisations have compared other proactive factors such as the percentage of managers that hold a NEBOSH National General Certificate in Health and Safety.

Though not required by the Health and Safety at Work etc Act (HASAWA) 1974, good practice would suggest that the statement is signed by the senior person in the organisation. This shows that the senior person has accepted their authority, gives authority to the policy and demonstrates senior management commitment to the health and safety cause. By signing the policy, the personal commitment shown should mean that managers are more likely to implement the policy and workers more likely to believe in it and follow it.

Defining health and safety roles and responsibilities

It is usual to express the organisation by showing an organisational chart, allowing reporting/communication structures of line and function staff to be depicted. Clear **allocation of responsibilities** for all levels of management, and duties of employees are necessary, as are the role and functions of health and safety professional staff. Part of organising for health and safety is to establish a clear perspective of the role and function of employee representatives and committees, including clarification of the **communication lines** and **feedback loops**.

The active involvement of managers in achieving health and safety is important for its success; this includes the **role of the line manager** in ensuring compliance with the policy. It is necessary for managers to ensure resource is in place and work is being carried out in a safe and healthy way. It is essential therefore that they **monitor the effectiveness** of the policy and the practices used to achieve it.

It is important that employees understand their role and responsibilities. This section of the policy gives employers the opportunity to clearly identify issues such as:

- Ensuring their own health and safety and that of other employees.
- Co-operating with the employer.
- Refraining from interfering with or misusing anything provided in the interests of health and safety.
- Following health and safety instructions.
- Wearing personal protective equipment where this is provided.
- Reporting accidents, ill-health and other incidents.
- Reporting hazards and defects in risk control measures that have been provided.

Health and safety arrangements

This section of the policy details the practical arrangements for planning, organising, and controlling hazards, as well as monitoring compliance with and **assessing the effectiveness** of the arrangements. The main headings of arrangements that could be detailed in the health and safety policy might include:

General arrangements:

- Allocation of finance for health and safety.
- Planning.
- Organising.
- Control of hazards - general e.g. risk assessments.
- Consultation.
- Communication.
- Competence.
- Accident, ill-health and other incident reporting.
- Hazard reporting.
- Monitoring compliance.

Specific arrangements for hazards, such as those relating to:

- Contractors.
- Electricity.
- Fire.
- Maintenance.
- Manual handling.
- Stress.
- Substances.
- Transport.
- Work at a height.
- Work equipment.

The scope of the arrangements needs to reflect that of the organisation. Though there will be some common elements, a policy for a construction company should be different to one for a charity that looks after dogs, as the risks they manage are different.

To ensure arrangements are understood and followed, it is essential to have good consultation and communication with those who will be affected throughout the design and implementation phase of the arrangements. In addition, arrangements that are made can quickly become outdated by changes in the way that things are done in the organisation; this can undermine their effectiveness. It is essential that systems be in place to monitor and assess this. Ongoing monitoring will ensure that the best practices are being used and that they remain effective.

Because it is useful to plan for arrangements to change it is worth producing policy documents in such a way that it is easy to identify changes. This can involve highlighting the different changes on the document, explaining the reasons for change, having a controlled number of copies of the document issued and recording that the changes have been issued to those that hold copies.

Reviewing the policy

A number of circumstances may lead to a need to review the policy, for example, the passage of time, technological, organisational or legal changes and the results of monitoring. Reviewing the policy will assist in ensuring it remains **current** and **effective**.

As **time** passes the arrangements for control of health and safety are influenced by people finding different ways of doing the same thing. Arrangements as practised can therefore differ greatly from the original way it was set out in the policy.

Technological change is happening in the workplace all the time, and this can mean that arrangements may be set out against circumstances that do not exist anymore because equipment or substances have been altered. It might also be that the organisation has been able to take advantage of technological advances in something, for example in materials handling, yet the policy refers to the earlier way of working.

Changes in **organisation** have a specific bearing on the arrangements. For example, if reporting of accidents is set out in the policy and in relation to a certain post, this may be influenced by a reorganisation that removes the post. Similarly, changes in work patterns e.g. shift working could influence arrangements that have been made.

Legislation changes periodically and usually reflects a strengthening of society's expectations. This may mean that specific arrangements set out in the policy may no longer conform with the law, in that it may be incomplete or not be to a satisfactory standard. For example, the change to the Workplace (Health, Safety and Welfare) Regulations (WHSWR) 1992 that requires rest rooms to have "adequate number of tables and adequate seating with backs".

If **monitoring** methods are in place and are working they could identify a gap in a specific arrangement or that something is unclear or contradictory. This might be from enforcement action, professional advice such as an audit or following accident investigation.

This page is intentionally blank

UNIT NGC1
MANAGEMENT OF HEALTH AND SAFETY

Health and safety management systems 2 - organising

Learning outcomes

On completion of this element, candidates should be able to demonstrate understanding of the content through the application of knowledge to familiar and unfamiliar situations. In particular they should be able to:

3.1 Outline the organisational health and safety roles and responsibilities of employers, directors and managers.

3.2 Explain the concept of health and safety culture and its significance in the management of health and safety in an organisation.

3.3 Outline the human factors which influence behaviour at work in a way that can affect health and safety.

3.4 Explain how health and safety behaviour at work can be improved.

3.5 Outline the need for emergency procedures and the arrangements for contacting emergency services.

3.6 Outline the requirements for, and effective provision of, first aid in the workplace.

Content

Sources of reference

The Management of Health and Safety at Work (ACOP) (L21), HSE Books ISBN 0-7176-2488-9

Successful Health and Safety Management (HSG65), HSE Books ISBN 0-7176-1276-7

Health & Safety Executive 'Ready Reckoner' website at www.hse.gov.uk/costs

Reducing Error and Influencing Behaviour (HSG48), HSE Books ISBN 0-7176-2452-8

First Aid at Work, The Health and Safety (First-Aid) Regulations 1981 (L74)

HSE Books ISBN 0-7176-1050-0

HSE Books ISBN 0-7176-1405-0

Leading health and safety at work (INDG417) HSE Books, ISBN 978 0 7176 6267 8

Relevant statutory provisions

The Health and Safety at Work etc. Act (HASAWA) 1974

The Management of Health and Safety at Work Regulations (MHSWR) 1999 (as amended)

The Safety Representatives and Safety Committees Regulations (SRSC) 1977

The Health and Safety Information for Employees Regulations (IER) 1989

The Health and Safety (Consultation with Employees) Regulations (HSCER) 1996

Corporate Manslaughter and Corporate Homicide Act (CMCHA) 2007

3.1 - Organisational health and safety roles and responsibilities

Organisational roles of directors/managers

DIRECTORS AND SENIOR MANAGERS

Directors and senior managers implement the employer's responsibilities and are accountable for ensuring health and safety is established. In practice this will include ensuring that an appropriate health and safety policy is in place and that it is worked to. Failure to do so may render the director or senior manager personally accountable under the Health and Safety at Work etc Act (HASAWA) 1974.

HASAWA 1974 - Section 37 - Breaches by the body corporate

Where there has been a breach of legislation on the part of a body corporate (limited company or local authority) and the offence can be proved to have been committed with the consent or connivance of any director, manager, secretary or similar officer of the body corporate or to be attributable to any neglect on the part of any director, manager, secretary or similar officer of the body corporate, they, as well as the body corporate, can be found guilty and punished accordingly.

MIDDLE MANAGERS AND SUPERVISORS

In a similar way to senior managers, managers at all levels in an organisation are expected to ensure health and safety is effectively established in their area of control. If they fail to do this they could be held accountable for their failings. This may be seen as a separate accountability to that of senior managers or the employer. All could be prosecuted for the part they played in the situation. The HASAWA 1974 may be used to prosecute managers and supervisors.

Section 36 of the HASAWA 1974 would be appropriate for the prosecution of middle managers, e.g. a store manager of a supermarket, and section 7 would be appropriate for prosecution of a supervisor. The supervisor plays a particularly important role on behalf of the employer in that they provide the supervisory control that ensures immediate causes of accidents (hazards) are identified and controlled. If they fail to take reasonable care in their provision of supervision they could be held accountable.

HASAWA 1974 - Section 36 - Another person

Where the commission by any person of the breach of legislation is due to the act or default of some other person, that other person shall be guilty of the offence and may be charged with and convicted of the offence whether or not proceedings are taken against the first mentioned person. Case law indicates that 'other person' refers to persons lower down the corporate tree than mentioned in HASAWA 1974 section 37, e.g. middle managers, safety advisors, training officers, and may extend to people working on contract e.g. architects, consultants, CDM co-ordinator.

Middle managers and supervisors carry a general duty to take reasonable care for those that might be affected by their acts or omissions. This would include responsibility for the health and safety of subordinates who might be affected by the way in which the manager or supervisor did their job. Failing to supervise effectively could be an omission, while directing someone to conduct a task without taking reasonable care to consider the risks could be seen as an act.

See also - Employees' responsibilities - later in this element.

THE HEALTH AND SAFETY PRACTITIONER

The health and safety practitioner is appointed by the employer to provide advice and assistance to the employer in meeting the employer's responsibilities. The appointment of a practitioner does not remove line management responsibilities for health and safety, but it provides support to line mangers in fulfilling these responsibilities. The health and safety practitioner provides a specific role by assisting with the review of health and safety performance.

The health and safety practitioner is an employee and has responsibilities to take reasonable care for their acts and omissions when conducting their work, for example, failure to provide advice or agreed service such as an inspection or inadequate advice or service. This would apply equally to an occupational health nurse or fire specialist.

The Management of Health and Safety at Work Regulations (MHSWR) 1999 place a legal duty on the employer to appoint competent persons to provide health and safety assistance.

Senior management demonstrating commitment

RESOURCES FOR A HEALTH AND SAFETY MANAGEMENT SYSTEM

There are a number of approaches available to enable managers to develop a health and safety management system. Guidance note HSG65, "Successful health and safety management", sets out the perspective of the HSE with its model of Policy, Organising, Planning and Implementing, Measuring Performance, Reviewing performance and Audit. Some organisations favour the use of the British Standard OHSAS 18001, with the added benefit of regular third party checks if the accreditation process is adopted.

When determining resources to establish, implement and maintain a health and safety management system the organisation should consider:

- The amount of support from senior management needed.
- Financial.
- Time.
- People.
- Technical.
- Organisational.
- The need for information, expertise, knowledge and training.

Resource commitment for the introduction of an effective health and safety management system should not be underestimated. If we consider a simple analogy in manufacturing terms it is the equivalent commitment an organisation might make following the identification of the need to install a new piece of equipment, for example, a bottle filling line extension to a milk packaging company. The design of the project will have to be considered, the allocation of funds to purchase and install the equipment will need to be reserved, the installation planned, proofing and quality checks will need to be organised and the training of staff in its use will need to be implemented. Perhaps more importantly the equipment will need to be maintained for the whole of its life cycle with an on-going review of quality and efficiency of the process.

There will need to be provision in the budget for the unexpected; any review will need to include taking into account any changes in legislation that may occur over the period of its use, for example, a reduction in statutory noise action levels.

ROLES AND RESPONSIBILITIES

Whatever approach is used, it is essential to define the roles and responsibilities of workers and managers clearly and concisely to achieve and maintain a good level of health and safety performance. Particular commitment should be made by senior management to establish roles and responsibilities for those that play a specific role in health and safety. This will include the most senior manager (top manager), members of the senior management team and anyone in the senior management team taking a lead role in health and safety. Others that should be defined specifically include:

- Health and safety practitioners.
- Those that conduct governance audits, if they include health and safety.
- Human resources and training managers.
- Purchasing managers.
- Worker health and safety representatives.

Managers' role and responsibilities should be clear and enabling; it is not sufficient to only write "the manager will be responsible for all health and safety in their area", as this would not adequately convey specific expectations. Responsibilities should at least include:

- Planning for health and safety - e.g. meetings. risk assessments.
- Implementation - communication, information, training, keep workplace safe and healthy.
- Monitor - carry out inspections and investigations into incidents.

It is important to recognise that workers and managers can only achieve success within their current knowledge and experience. Therefore, a training needs analysis should be carried out to identify any gaps relating to their responsibilities within the management system. This is not a one-off exercise; a similar competency assessment will need to be carried out before there are any changes in the operation or function of the individuals are made, for example, promotion of an employee to a supervisor. A employee's normal role would not automatically provide the competency to carry out all the roles of the new post. A competency assessment would need to be carried out before the individual was authorised to carry out high risk duties, for example, the issue of a permit to work authorising the use of welding equipment in an area where there is a need to remove or protect flammable materials before work can commence.

SENIOR MANAGEMENT APPOINTEE

An important part of management commitment is that the senior management team embrace their responsibilities for health and safety. Though the senior manager has overall responsibility for health and safety, the team share this responsibility. Some organisations demonstrate their commitment to health and safety by selecting someone from the team to provide the team with extra focus and act as a 'conscience' to ensure that health and safety is an integral part of the senior management team activities. This appointment ensures that sufficient time and effort is committed at senior management level. It provides a focus for the receipt of communications and reports and can add senior management commitment to activities.

The management appointee usually has responsibility for presentation of data on health and safety performance and reports to the senior management team. They would also be involved in organising the periodic review of health and safety performance.

The appointee can be anyone from the team. Some organisations may feel it is a role of the senior manager, others may feel that the attributes of another better suit the role. It may be decided that the role will rotate each year round the management team. Whatever the option chosen, the increased demonstration of commitment can have a strong effect on the health and safety culture of the organisation.

APPOINTING COMPETENT PERSONS

Regulation 7 of the Management of Health and Safety at Work Regulations (MHSWR) 1999 places an absolute duty on the employer to take the following actions:

- Appoint one or more competent persons to assist with compliance with health and safety legislation.
- Make arrangements for the persons to co-operate.
- Ensure the number of people appointed, time available and means at their disposal are adequate. Consider the size of the organisation, its risks and distribution of the risks.
- Persons appointed that are not employees are provided with information.
- Persons appointed are informed of any person working under a fixed-term contract or employed in an employment business.

The regulations state that competence means having sufficient training and experience or knowledge and other qualities. The approved code of practice (ACOP) says employers should consider:

- Knowledge and understanding of work involved.
- Principles of risk assessment and prevention.
- Current health and safety applications.
- Capacity to apply to tasks required.
- Identifying problems.
- Assessing the need for action.
- Designing and developing strategies and plans.
- Implementing these strategies and plans.
- Evaluating their effectiveness.
- Promoting and communicating health, safety and welfare advances and practices.
- Understanding of relevant current best practice.
- Awareness of own limitations.
- Membership of a professional body or similar.
- Willingness and ability to supplement existing experience and knowledge.
- Holding competence based qualification (NVQ/SVQ).

The regulations do not require the self employed, who are themselves competent, to appoint anyone. The regulations do not require individuals in business partnership to appoint a person if one of them is competent.

The appointment of competent persons must be clearly identified with an expression of management commitment in order to maximise its effect. It is important that managers and workers understand that the competent persons are appointed to assist the organisation and senior management in matters of health and safety. Reporting lines to the senior management should be clear and enable managers and workers to see that competent persons for health and safety, and health and safety itself, are taken seriously.

ROLE IN REVIEWING

Reviews of the management of the organisation's health and safety performance should be carried out by the senior management team on a periodic basis, for example, annually. Management system reviews should focus on the functioning of the management system and consider whether it is effective in meeting the policy and objectives of the organisation. This is best conducted with the senior management team's involvement, as it is more likely that it is going to be seen as a system they own. This level of periodic commitment is important for all levels of management and workers motivationally, but is also important practically as the senior management team will decide resources for the continuing success of the organisation's health and safety performance.

For further information on 'reviewing' see NGC1 - Element 5 - Health and safety management systems 4 - Measuring, audit and review.

3.2 - Concept of health and safety culture

Meaning and extent of the term 'health and safety culture'

"The safety culture of an organisation is the product of individual and group values, attitudes, perceptions, competencies, and patterns of behaviour that determine the commitment to, and the style and proficiency of, an organisation's health and safety management".

Figure 1-3-1: Safety culture. *Source: ACSNI.*

Any organisation develops beliefs, attitudes and common ways of behaving, this may be consciously or unconsciously. The cumulative parts of how an organisation sees things and does things are called its culture. This may be a positive shared position or negative, in the way it affects health and safety. Organisations may have expectations that focus on the short term and problem solving or they may have interest in and value the longer term and a more controlled, preventive approach. The culture of the organisation will lead to shared expectations about the perception of risk and standards to be adopted.

In organisations with a positive health and safety culture each decision taken is influenced by the culture, the priorities and importance of health and safety which are naturally embodied in those decisions.

Relationship between culture and health and safety performance

The correlation between health and safety culture and health and safety performance can be illustrated by research that has been conducted.

For example, after the introduction of a safety programme in the range of forestry and logging organisations in Columbia, it was found by Painter and Smith (1986) that there were dramatic improvements in performance. The accident frequency rate was reduced by 75% and the workers' compensation costs were reduced by 62%. In further research, Lauriski and Guyman (1989) found that after a safety management programme had been introduced at the Utah Power & Light Company, lost time injury rates were reduced by 60% over a period of five years. From 1980 to 1988, the accident frequency rate was reduced from 40 to 8 per annum, while production more than doubled.

Research has shown that improvements in health and safety management are influential in achieving a positive health and safety culture. This leads to reduced accident rates, which is seen as a positive step forward and a further influence on the health and safety culture.

Indicators to assess an organisation's health and safety culture

Developing and promoting a positive health and safety culture is an important aspect of health and safety management. A health and safety culture is an intangible thing, which has tangible manifestations. These manifestations can be measured.

EFFECTIVE COMMUNICATION

Effective communication is a factor in achieving a positive health and safety culture; therefore effectiveness of communication can be used as a measurement. Considering a practical example - an organisation's health and safety policy must be communicated to the employees - therefore asking them about it will give an indication as to how well it has been communicated.

LEADERSHIP AND COMMITMENT

Evidence of commitment by personnel at all levels of the organisation can be measured. The evidence can be shown by *the clear identification and acceptance of responsibility* for health and safety from the top. Du Pont have been quoted as saying: "The chairman takes the role of Chief Safety Officer". Indicators that can be considered include management membership of the health and safety committee, and their participation in the committee. Another indicator is where there is evidence of managers' responsibilities being accepted and taken seriously, for example the following of health and safety rules like wearing personal protective equipment where necessary. Measurement of what the organisation is achieving compared to the standards that have been set in their health and safety policy can be done by conducting an *audit.* Another indicator of a positive health and safety culture is where non-compliance situations are dealt with promptly.

EQUAL PRIORITY

This includes evidence that health and safety is treated as an equal partner alongside other important business issues such as quality, finance, production, etc. The health and safety policy should be integrated with other corporate policies e.g. purchasing, training, etc.

ACCIDENT INVESTIGATION

Findings of accident investigations can be used as a measurement of a health and safety culture. Root cause accident investigation can show where things are going wrong, for example, by considering:

- Technical, procedural and behavioural aspects and controls.
- Validity of management controls.
- Level of commitment to working safely.

The procedure for dealing with the findings of the accident investigation, that is, the recommendations for improvement and prevention, is another way to measure the health and safety culture. For example:

- People responsible for action should be named.
- Completion dates for each action.
- Follow up for actions not completed.
- Findings not communicated to the workers.

CONSULTATION

Proactive involvement of employees and/or their representatives in decision making, for example, when selecting access equipment for work at height. Discussion with employees about work methods and conditions of work will result in fewer or no complaints.

SPECIFIC TANGIBLE OUTPUTS INDICATORS

- Accidents.
- Absenteeism.
- Level of compliance with health and safety rules and procedures.
- Staff turnover.
- Sickness rates.
- Complaints about working conditions.

Measurement of these specific indicators may be easily done with 'direct labour' employees, but this can present a greater challenge where workers are mainly contractors.

INFLUENCE OF PEERS

Peer pressure will often promote good health and safety within a work team. If the team members believe that working safely is the only way to do the job, each member of the team will watch over the activities of the other and the group as a whole will ensure any new member follows their example to ensure a safe output.

FACTORS PROMOTING A NEGATIVE HEALTH AND SAFETY CULTURE

Just as a positive health and safety culture starts with commitment from the most senior manager, a negative health and safety culture will develop from lack of it. There are, however, other factors involved which may lead to a negative health and safety culture.

When a company is *reorganising*, it is a time of upheaval, personal as well as corporate. Individuals and groups tend to be resistant to change, especially when they are unsure of the need for it. Lack of proper communication can lead to rumours of closure, redundancy or changes in the company's structure. The resulting decrease in morale may lead to a lack of belief in the company's commitment. Reorganisation can also lead to people changing their position in the company structure with more, fewer or different responsibilities than previously. Without proper communication and necessary training this can lead to *uncertainty* and a mistrust of the company and its aims and objectives.

The company may state the aims and objectives, but the achievability may be in doubt. The aims and objectives may state a commitment to health and safety, yet the changes in work patterns do not allow for safe working. This could be from the point of view that production is seen as all-important and safety must be secondary or an 'add on' done only if time allows for it.

A practical example would be if a company decided on a speed limit of five miles an hour for fork lift trucks as a control to prevent accidents, but then increased the amount of material a driver had to move in a work period. This would be seen as mixed signals. On the one hand, the company is showing commitment to health and safety by restricting the speed of the vehicles, but on the other, no one seems to care that the increased workload means that the drivers must break the speed limit to get their job done. The management and employees then have different aims and objectives and energy is exerted by each fighting the other. These *management decisions* prejudice mutual trust and lead to mixed signals regarding commitment to health and safety. This promotes a negative health and safety culture.

Organisations have a responsibility to set standards for health and safety performance when selecting potential contractors or suppliers. Any contracts entered into may represent or impose the equivalent requirements of a contract of service for employees. The system of awarding contracts, of itself, does not have a positive or negative influence on health and safety. Influence rather depends on the standards expected by the person who establishes the contract and those delivered by the contractor, and finally by the level of monitoring / enforcement of the contract.

3.3 - Human factors which influence behaviour at work

Organisational factors

As stated previously, organisations need to produce a *culture* that promotes staff commitment to health and safety and emphasises that deviation from corporate safety goals, at whatever level, is not acceptable.

Producing such a culture requires clear, visible, management commitment to safety from the most senior level in the organisation. The commitment should be not just a formal statement but be evident in the day-to-day activities of the company. This commitment must be known and understood by the employee. Individuals may be reluctant to err on the side of caution in matters that have health and safety implications if their decisions to do so are likely to be subject to unwarranted criticism from their superiors or their peers.

The attitude of a strong personality at a senior level within the organisation may have either a beneficial or an adverse effect on health and safety behaviour. Inevitably, junior employees will be influenced by that person's *leadership* through following their example.

Health and safety procedures soon fall into disuse if there is no system of ensuring that they are followed. Too often procedures lapse because of management neglect, or operators are discouraged from working to them by peer groups or other pressures, such as production targets. Where managers become aware of deficiencies in health and safety procedures but do not act to remedy them, the workforce readily perceive that such actions are condoned.

Individuals may not understand the relevance of procedures or appreciate their significance in controlling risk. Sometimes procedures are faulty, irrelevant, or lacking in credibility. When accidents happen managers cannot blame individuals for taking short cuts which seemed safe and were allowed to become routine if they have not explained the importance of, or monitored, procedures they originally laid down.

To promote a proper working culture, it is essential to have an effective system for monitoring health and safety that identifies, investigates and corrects deviations.

The introduction and operation of such systems requires considerable effort by managers and only by allocating adequate *resources* can they be confident that failures will be prevented or controlled.

In short, the organisation needs to provide:

- Clear and evident commitment, from the most senior management downwards, which promotes a *culture* for health and safety in which management's objectives and the need for appropriate standards are *communicated* and in which constructive exchange of information at all levels is positively encouraged. To be effective this will require the *resource* of both time and money to ensure the best systems and work practices are established to minimise risk.
- An analytical and imaginative approach identifying possible routes to human factor failure. This may well require access to specialist advice. Consideration of *work patterns* and shift rotas to ensure fatigue and boredom are minimised.
- Procedures and standards for all aspects of critical work and mechanisms for reviewing them.
- Effective monitoring systems to check the implementation of the procedures and standards.
- Incident investigation and the effective use of information drawn from such investigations.
- Adequate and effective supervision with the power to remedy deficiencies when found.

Job/task factors

Tasks should be designed in accordance with ergonomic principles to take into account limitations in human performance and physical ability. Matching the job to the person will ensure that they are not overloaded and that they will make the most effective contributions to the company. Physical match includes not only the design of the equipment associated with the task but the whole workplace and working environment. Mental match involves the individual's information and decision-making requirements, as well as their perception of the tasks. Mismatch between job requirements and workers' capabilities provide potential for human error.

The major considerations in the design of the job include the following:

a) Identification and comprehensive analysis of the critical (high risk) *tasks* expected of individuals and appraisal of likely errors.

b) Evaluation of required operator decision making and the optimum balance between the human and automatic contributions to safety actions.

c) Application of ergonomic principles to the design of person-machine interfaces, including *displays* of plant and process information, and suitable positioning, labelling of *control* devices and panel layouts.

d) Design and consistency of presentation of procedures and operating instructions.

e) Organisation and control of working *environment*, including the workspace, access for maintenance, lighting, noise and thermal conditions.

f) Provision of correct tools and equipment.

g) Scheduling of work patterns, including shift organisation and *workload*, control of stressors such as noise or heat to reduce fatigue.

h) Arrangements to cover for absence and *procedures* for emergencies such as a fire.

i) Efficient and suitable communications, both immediate and over periods of time.

Individual factors

INDIVIDUAL DIFFERENCES

All individuals are different. These differences will influence patterns of work behaviour and may limit the effectiveness with which an individual carries out a job. They will also influence how safely the work tasks are carried out.

These individual differences arise from an interaction between the 'inherited characteristics' (passed on from the parents) and the various 'life experiences' through which the individual passes from the moment of conception.

- Experiences in the womb.
- Birth trauma.
- Family influences.
- Geographical location.
- Pre-school influences.

- Education - opportunities, quality, support.
- Occupational factors - training and retraining.
- Hobbies and interests.
- Own family influences - marriage, children.
- Ageing.

Any, many or all of the above will help to create a unique person different from all other individuals. The ways in which people differ are many and various and it is important to bear this in mind from the point of view of work effectiveness and safety.

It is vital to know what a particular job entails (the job description) and to specify the characteristics required to enable a person to perform that job effectively (the person specification). Physical differences will need to be considered carefully when establishing controls for work activities; some differences may limit or prohibit individuals from certain tasks.

Summary of individual differences

Physical	Mental
Gender - e.g. females not exposed to lead.	Attitude - e.g. all PPE is uncomfortable.
Build - e.g. may restrict movement in a confined space.	Motivation - e.g. risks v reward.
Health - e.g. colour blindness.	Perception - e.g. risk perception, do not respond to alarms.
Capability/strength - e.g. manual handling.	Capability - e.g. ability to follow safety instructions.

Figure 1-3-2: Summary of individual differences.

Source: RMS.

The significance of individual factors

Employees bring to their job personal habits, attitudes, skills, *personality* and so on, which in relation to task demands may be strengths or weaknesses. Individual characteristics influence behaviour in complex and significant ways. Some characteristics, such as *personality*, are fixed and largely incapable of modification. Others such as skills and attitudes are amenable to modification or enhancement. The job should be matched to the person.

Important considerations within the personal factor category include the following.

a) *Thorough task analysis* (especially for critical jobs) which should enable a detailed job description to be generated. From this, a specification can be drawn up to include such factors as age, physique, skill, qualifications and experience, aptitude, knowledge, intelligence and personality. Personnel selection policies and procedures should ensure the specifications are matched by the individuals.

b) *Training* will produce a *competent* employee, capable of working without close supervision with confidence to take on responsibility and perform effectively, providing that initial selection is done properly. Training should be carried out from induction and throughout the career of the individual to reflect not only changes in work, but to maintain, through refresher training, standards of performance. Training may be necessary for experienced employees who are in a later stage of their career if the following circumstances arise: the introduction of new processes, equipment and methods of work; a job change which involves a wider range of responsibilities, for example, promotion to a management role; the introduction of new legislation; after an accident or incident; where risk assessments indicate existing competence is not adequate; refresher training such as first aiders; to counteract the possibility of employees becoming complacent and lax in following established procedures for health and safety.

Self confidence and job satisfaction grow significantly when people are trained to work correctly under both routine and emergency conditions. Human reliability improves because employees become more aware of the process and task, their perception of danger increases and there should be an improvement in the employee's motivation and attitude.

This will not only benefit individuals themselves and their colleagues but greatly improve the achievement of organisational objectives. Training should aim to give all individuals the *skills* to allow them to understand the workings of plant and processes. It is not a once-and-for-all activity but in so far as procedures and processes change and complex skills (particularly when under used) deteriorate, is a regular contribution to individual performance.

c) *Monitoring of personal performance* in relation to health and safety. An old maxim states: "That which gets measured, gets done". All work practices should be monitored through direct supervision. The degree of supervision or frequency will be risk based and will be influenced by many factors such as the experience or skill of the worker or the supervisor.

Monitoring should not be at the task level only, but carried out by all of the management team, from the most senior down. This will ensure delegated tasks are performed correctly and ensure statutory requirements for health and safety are met.

d) *Fitness for work and health surveillance.* For certain jobs there may be specified medical standards for which pre-employment and/or periodic health surveillance is necessary. These may relate to the functional requirements of the job or the impact of specified conditions on the ability to perform it adequately and safely. An example is the medical examination of divers.

There may also be a need for routine surveillance of the effects of exposure to workplace hazards, both physical, such as the effects of acute heat stress: or chemical, for example, absorption of organic phosphorous insecticides which may impair ability to control a tractor or aircraft. Medical surveillance is not a substitute for proper control of the hazardous agent.

e) *Review of health on return to work from sickness absence.* The recognition of the purpose of counselling and provision of advice during periods of individual need, such as dealing with anxiety or stress related to failure to achieve work objectives, in this context alcohol or drug abuse and the possible adverse side effects of prescribed drugs may be relevant stressors. Access to specialist assistance may be appropriate with the possible need for temporary or permanent re-deployment.

Attitude, aptitude and motivation

ATTITUDE

"The tendency to respond in a particular way to a certain situation"

Attitudes are another set of factors that constitute ways in which individuals differ one from another. Attitudes are not directly observable and can only be assessed by observing behavioural expression (physical or verbal behaviour).

Clearly, a person's attitudes will govern the way in which an object or situation is viewed and it will dictate the resultant response or pattern of behaviour. This is obviously very important when considering an individual's working patterns and any safety aspects associated with them. Attitudes, like other aspects of individual differences, are formed (not necessarily consciously) because of a lifetime of experiences and as such are not easily changed. A person's attitudes are not simply an aid to coping with their environment, but may determine how they wish to change what is there. Any attempts to change such a fundamental part of an individual's personality will be resisted. The individual will feel their very being is under threat. This is worth remembering in the context of safety propaganda campaigns.

> *"People's attitudes and opinions that have been formed over decades of life cannot be changed by holding a few meetings or giving a few lectures".*

Figure 1-3-3: Observation made by Chairman Mao Tse Tung.   *Source: "Little Red Book".*

Examples of attitudes affecting safe working:

1) It will never happen to me.
2) We have never had an accident.
3) Its only the price of a plaster.
4) I know my limits.

Everyone at work should attempt to change their own and their colleague's attitudes to health and safety from: work safely because:

I have to. ➔   I should. ➔   I want to. ➔   It is automatic.

Remedial action
- Train, and retrain when need for reinforcement is evident.
- Change by experience (involvement), e.g. selection of personal protective equipment (PPE).

Organisational factors that may cause a person to work unsafely even though they are competent include:

- Management or peer group pressure.
- A poor safety culture in the organisation.
- A lack of resources or equipment.
- A lack of clarity in roles and responsibilities.
- Inadequate supervision.
- Poor working conditions.

APTITUDE

"A tendency to be good at certain things"

Aptitude is closely linked to personality. Some people are particularly good at certain things, for example, an individual may be good at working with his hands, while another may say they "could not change a light bulb".

Aptitude can be developed over time as a skill, but it is more likely to be part of that person's characteristics. This can be a factor when placing people in particular jobs. A person with no aptitude for precision work, but superb at felling trees is 'an accident waiting to happen' if given the job of soldering electronic components.

MOTIVATION

"The driving force behind the way a person acts in order to achieve a goal"

In the context of the working situation there have been many attempts to identify why people work. The earliest approach (by F. W. Taylor) was that people worked for money and fear of losing their livelihood. Financial reward was seen as the prime motivator. The more they were paid the harder they worked. This led to a new management philosophy:

- Payment by results.
- Incentive schemes.
- Piece work.
- Danger money.

From a health and safety management viewpoint, this theory is unsound since most bonus schemes encourage people to work **unsafely** by cutting corners, rushing to get the job done etc. with safe working practices being ignored or compromised.

Money **is** important but other factors are more important, e.g. social belonging, acceptance by one's peers. With this in mind, motivating people to adopt safe working practices should include:

- Establishment of a positive health and safety culture where risk taking is frowned upon by all employees but especially supervisors and managers.
- Setting realistic objectives with regard to accident rates.
- Involvement in health and safety policy setting.
- Clarification of responsibilities.
- Developing a positive reward structure.
- Monitoring health and safety performance.

■ Improving employees' knowledge of the consequences of not working safely (through information and training).
■ Showing the commitment of the organisation to safety (by providing resources and a safe working environment).
■ Involving employees in health and safety decisions (by consultation, team meetings etc).
■ Recognising and rewarding achievement.

Positive motivation (i.e. employees working safely because that is how they want to work) tends to be more effective than negative motivation (i.e. employees working safely for fear of disciplinary action), although both have a place.

Remedial action ■ Establish positive health and safety culture. ■ Set clear objectives e.g. accident statistics.
■ Positive reward structure.

Figure 1-3-4: Maslow's hierarchy of needs. *Source: Maslow.*

(The NEBOSH National General Certificate does not require detailed knowledge of Maslow's Hierarchy).

Perception of risk

PERCEPTION

"The way that a person views a situation"

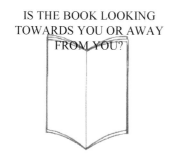

IS THE BOOK LOOKING TOWARDS YOU OR AWAY FROM YOU?

Figure 1-3-5: Examples of perception images. *Source: Ambiguous.*

Factors that influence the effectiveness are:

■ A boring, repetitive job may result in 'day dreaming' which may result in a lowering of the impact of a stimulus.
■ Warnings (or threats) may not be strong enough to get through the perceptual set.
■ Patterns of behaviour and habits can be carried from one situation to another where they are no longer appropriate or safe (e.g. we tend to drive too quickly after leaving a motorway).
■ Individuals can get 'used to' a stimulus and, if it is not reinforced, it ceases to command the attention and is ignored.
■ Intense concentration on one task may make paying attention to another stimulus difficult or impossible.
■ Some hazards may not be obvious or they are hidden such as electricity or certain gases like carbon monoxide.
■ The presence of hazards may be masked by environmental issues such as poor lighting or ambient noise. Similarly, the use of PPE may interfere with the user's senses.

Remember: ***We do not see what is there!***

                        We see what we expect to be there!

                        We do not see what we do not expect to be there!

                        We do not see what we do not want to be there!

Remedial Action

- Information.
- Training.

- Instruction.
- Drills.

Process of perception

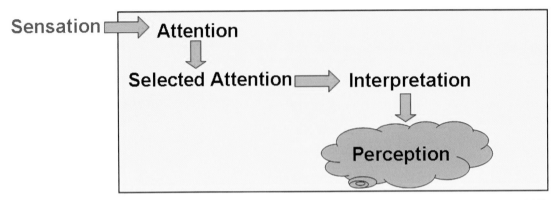

Figure 1-3-6: Model of perception.   *Source: RMS.*

Within each individual, these processes of attention and interpretation are closely interlinked. The factors that influence these processes and the way in which they operate are often referred to as the "perceptual set" of the individual.

Errors and violations

HUMAN ERROR AS A CAUSE OF ACCIDENTS

It is estimated that over 80% of accidents can be attributed, at least in part, to the actions or omissions of people. Many accidents are blamed on the actions or omissions of an individual who was directly involved in operational or maintenance work. This typical but short-sighted response ignores the fundamental failures that led to the accident. These are usually rooted deeper in the organisation's management and decision-making functions. Our history teaches us much more about the origins of human failure. Attributing accidents to "human error" has often been seen as sufficient explanation in itself and something that is beyond the control of managers. Organisations must recognise that they need to consider human factors as a distinct element which needs to be assessed and managed effectively.

The table that follows illustrates the influence of human factors in some recent major incidents:

Accident	Consequences	Human contribution
Three Mile Island 1979.	Serious damage to core of nuclear reactor.	Operators failed to recognise a valve that was stuck open due to poor design of the control panel. Maintenance failures had happened before but no steps had been taken to prevent a recurrence.
Space Shuttle 'Challenger' 1986.	Explosion killed all 7 astronauts on board.	Inadequate response to internal warnings about the faulty design of a seal. Decision taken to go ahead with launch in very cold temperature despite faulty seal. Decision making result of conflicting scheduling/safety goals, mindset and effects of fatigue.
Herald of Free Enterprise 1987.	Ferry sank killing 189 passengers and crew.	No system for checking that bow doors were shut. Inquiry reported that the company was "infected with the disease of sloppiness". Priority was to turn the ship around in record time.
Kings Cross fire 1987.	Major fire killed 31 people.	Organisational changes had led to poor escalator cleaning. The fire took hold because of inadequate fire fighting equipment and poor staff training. There was a culture that viewed fires as inevitable.
Piper Alpha 1988.	Major explosion on North Sea oil platform killed 167 workers.	Maintenance error that eventually led to the leak was the result of inexperience, poor procedures and poor learning. There was a breakdown in communications and the permit-to-work system at shift changeover and safety procedures were not properly practised.

Figure 1-3-7: Influence of human factors in recent major incidents.   *Source: HSE.*

         © **RMS**

CAUSES OF HUMAN FAILURE

There are two different types of human failure - errors and violations.

A *human error* is an action or decision that was not intended, which involved a deviation from an accepted standard, and which led to an undesirable outcome.

A *violation* is a deliberate deviation from a rule or procedure.

ERRORS

Errors fall into three categories:

1) *Slips.*

2) *Lapses.*

3) *Mistakes.*

Figure 1-3-8: Human failures flow chart.   *Source: HSG48.*

Slips and lapses

Once we have learned a skill, there is little need for much conscious thought about what we are doing. We can carry out a task without having to think too much about the next step. We learn to ride a bike or drive a car in this way. We need to pay attention to the road and the traffic, but we manipulate the pedals and change gear without thinking about it. If our attention is diverted, we may fail to carry out the next action of the task, or we could forget the next action or lose our place resulting in an error.

Mistakes

Mistakes are a little more complex than slips and lapses. We may do the wrong thing believing it to be right. We have a tendency to use familiar rules or procedures, often when they don't apply. The wrong application of a rule to a situation can result in an error, for example, use of a water based extinguisher on an electrical equipment on fire.

In unfamiliar situations, we may have to apply knowledge-based reasoning. If this is miscalculated or the situation is misdiagnosed, then a mistake may occur.

These errors typically occur with trained, experienced people, but also occur with untrained and inexperienced people. The untrained and inexperienced may base their decisions on misunderstandings and a lack of perception of risk.

VIOLATIONS

These violations are rarely acts of vandalism or sabotage, but are often carried out in order to get the job done, for example, using a convenient ladder of insufficient length. Many accidents, injuries and cases of ill-health come about because of violations.

Routine violations

Routine violations are where breaking the rules or procedure has become the normal way of working, for example, not removing work clothes when taking refreshment breaks in a canteen facility. New workers come in and learn the incorrect ways, not realising they are wrong. The incorrect method may have come about because it is a quicker way to work or because the rules are seen as too restrictive. In one company, it was felt that the work could not be finished on time if all of the rules were followed.

Situational violations

Situational violations may occur with pressures from the job: time pressure, extreme weather conditions, wrong equipment, etc. Roof work may continue without edge protection, because the correct equipment has not been provided.

Exceptional violations

Exceptional violations occur when something has gone wrong. A decision has to be made to solve the problem and that might involve breaking a rule and taking a risk, for example, temporary repair to equipment hydraulic lines that become permanent. It is erroneously believed that the benefits outweigh the risk.

The influence of peers

Nearly all human beings need the company and social acceptance of their fellows. When we are in a group situation, it is very difficult to behave differently to others. The group will have established a norm for behaviour. The norm behaviour is what keeps the group together. There are two main groups, social and work.

The social group is formed out of individuals with common beliefs, interests, expectations, etc. Individuals in the social group will be under its influence most of their time. Within the workplace we have groups of individuals working together often with common skills, but not always common beliefs.

The work group is different to the social group; individual behaviour may be strongly influenced by their peers (others in the group) and personal choice may be changed by the peer pressure. This group behaviour is what sets the standard of performance and the method of achieving the particular work goal or situation. The observance of health and safety rules may strongly be influenced within a group. If the norm is to follow the rules, for example, a pre flight equipment check on an aircraft before take off, then the rules will be obeyed. Conversely, if the norm is to flout the rules, e.g. failure to wear eye protection for a grinding operation, then the rules may well be disobeyed by an individual who may know the risks.

Link between individual, job and organisational factors

HUMAN FAILURES:

Errors		*Violations*	
	■ Slips.		■ Routine.
	■ Lapses.		■ Situational.
	■ Mistakes.		■ Exceptional.

The reasons why human failures take place can be traced to the three main human factors: individual, job and organisational. When errors and violations occur, they are greatly influenced by all three factors, each one to a greater or lesser extent.

Examination of human failures has shown that what appears to be a simple individual failing has often been shaped by the circumstances the persons find themselves in (job factors) and the organisational factors that lead these job factors to exist. Each factor is linked to each other and in order to prevent accidents and ill-health they must all be in place and working effectively.

CONTROL MEASURES:

Individual factors:

- Increase skill and competence levels.
- Select staff according to their capabilities.
- Provide health surveillance wherever necessary.
- Job rotation to prevent boredom.

Job factors:

- Correct ergonomic design of tools and equipment.
- Prevent disturbances and interruptions.
- Provide clear instructions.
- Maintain equipment to a suitable standard.
- Minimise exposure to unpleasant working conditions such as noise, heat, adverse weather etc.

Organisational factors:

- Good work planning to avoid high work pressure.
- Adequate safety systems and barriers.
- Respond quickly to previous incidents.
- Consultation rather than information.
- Clear identification of responsibilities.
- Thorough management training.
- Create positive health and safety culture.

3.4 - How health and safety behaviour at work can be improved

Securing commitment of management

Securing the commitment of management is an important factor in improving health and safety behaviour at work. This means not only senior management but line management as well.

Management are responsible for the creation of good health and safety behaviour at work and must accept their responsibility by making a commitment to this. If health and safety is not part of the values of management then other values will be seen by workers and other managers as more important and these may take precedence over good health and safety behaviour.

Management should commit to things that will improve the health and safety culture of the organisation as this will lead to good health and safety behaviour at work.

THE "FOUR C'S"

The main activities necessary to promote a positive health and safety culture are split into:

- Methods of *control*.
- Means of securing *co-operation*.
- Methods of *communication*.
- *Competence* of individuals.

Control

Control is achieved by:

- Getting the commitment of workers to clear health and safety objectives.
- Managers taking full responsibility for controlling the factors that could lead to loss.
- Nominating a senior figure to monitor the policy implementation.
- Allocating responsibilities to line managers and health and safety specialists.
- Encouraging worker health and safety representatives to make a contribution.
- Setting performance standards.

The emphasis is on a collective effort to develop and maintain systems of control before the event - not on blaming individuals for failures afterwards.

Co-operation

Pooling knowledge and experience through participation, commitment and involvement means that safety becomes everybody's business.

- Consultation with workers and their representatives is essential.
- Involve them in planning and reviewing performances, writing procedures and solving problems.
- Information on loss and experience should be shared with contractors.

Competence

- Assess the skills needed to carry out tasks safely.
- Provide the means to ensure that all workers, including temporary workers, are adequately instructed and trained.
- Ensure that employees on especially dangerous work have the necessary training and experience to carry out the work safely.
- Arrange and encourage access to sound advice and help.

It should not be assumed that those that manage the provision of services and quality issues are skilled in managing health and safety. Their competence should be confirmed through formal training in health and safety management.

Communication

- Provide information about hazards, risks and any preventative measures.
- Discuss health and safety regularly.

Implementing the above "Four C's" will greatly assist in ensuring a positive health and safety culture within an organisation.

Promoting health and safety standards by leadership and example

Management actions at all levels should send clear signals to workers and others within the workplace of the importance of observing the health and safety standards which have been set. Leadership through example will include such issues as correct use of personal protective equipment, observance of rules, which might require special skills or training and commitment by seniors to attending health and safety training identified for development of subordinate managers.

Organisations should identify key performance indicator (KPI) standards for heath and safety. The standards should be achievable and designed not to compete with other organisational performance standards such as those set for production/service or quality. The standards must be agreed at the highest level within the organisation in order to show management commitment to them.

Management controls must be established to ensure the standards are met and to show leadership and commitment to health and safety. The management controls must be designed to send a clear signal, that health and safety is an equal partner to the other organisational objectives. Management controls take many forms and all should show this continuing management commitment. They offer an opportunity for managers to show leadership through making health and safety important by reinforcing the agreed standards. This could involve managers showing leadership by making system checks to see that standards are being applied, such as random examination of completed permits to work, observations of high risk work activities or periodic health and safety tours.

Competent personnel

If people, management and workers, are to be effective in contributing to the right health and safety behaviour at work it is essential that they are competent. This means more than just providing them with training and will include ensuring that the relevant knowledge, skill and work experience is established, before a worker is put to work. Factors such as individual aptitude, dexterity and physical ability/endurance may also be important, e.g. not everyone will be comfortable or able to work at height or in confined spaces.

High-risk tasks may utilise simulation equipment to allow skill to be developed, at no risk to the individual or others, for example, the use of aircraft flight simulators.

Similarly, it may be necessary for the trainee to be under close supervision (an instructor flies with a new pilot of an aircraft) until their skill can be demonstrated as appropriate through their displayed actions and ability. This will apply to managers as much as workers; it is important that new managers develop their experience under controlled conditions. Managers should be assessed for their range of competencies prior to appointment and should be coached to develop the right experience that will help establish and maintain appropriate health and safety behaviour. Workers need sufficient knowledge, skill and experience to enable them to have the right behaviour and should be supervised to the level necessary, relating to their current competence.

Effective communication within the organisation

COMMUNICATION METHODS

It is the job of the middle manager and first line manager (supervisor) to translate decisions from senior managers into actions and, at the same time, be aware of the needs, desires, capabilities and expectations of workers in order to communicate them to senior managers. Because of the higher levels of education amongst workers, the job of the middle manager has become harder. The days of imposing fines on and using discipline against workers are now seen as inapplicable to the modern organisation. The ideal is increasingly seen to be that of giving information and explanation. The emphasis must be on good communication at all levels to enable good decisions.

One factor which prevents workers from communicating with their supervisors is a lack of trust. For some time it has been known that honest and open communication, the essentials of participation, correlate highly with workers' trust in management. A related issue, which grows out of trust, is the amount of influence workers feel they have in an organisation, if workers do not feel that their communication of health and safety matters will make a difference they will tend not to bother. For this reason, it is important to provide managers and workers with feedback on what they communicate, particularly where it has had a positive influence on health and safety.

Barriers to effective verbal communication

It is imperative that verbal communication is clear, concise and easily understood. However, this is not always the case and the reasons listed in the lowing sections. These are some of the barriers to effective verbal communication:

- Noise and distractions.
- Complexity of information.
- Language and/or dialect of the speaker.
- Sensory impairment (perhaps deafness).
- Ambiguity.

- Use of technical jargon.
- Mental difficulty.
- Inexperience on the part of the recipient.
- Lengthy communication chains.
- Inattention.

Some barriers to communication that may lead to workers failing to comply with health and safety instructions or procedures:

- Unrealistic or ill-considered procedures.
- Inadequate training.
- Lack of involvement in consultation.
- Peer group pressure.
- Risks not perceived.
- Poor safety culture in the organisation.

- Mental and/or physical capabilities not taken into account.
- Complacency or lack of motivation.
- Other priorities and pressures.
- Fatigue and stress.

General principles of communication

Communication is a skill that we take for granted. Like any other skill, some people are better at it than others. Communication is a two-way process where the needs of the receiver are equally as important as the needs of the speaker. Because it is a two-way process, both participants must be sure they are using the same language. The speaker should not assume that the receiver has understood what has been said. To ensure the success of the communication the speaker should:

- Communicate in a form capable of being understood by the recipient.
- Use open ended questions to investigate understanding.
- Use closed questions, which yield yes/no answers, to confirm.

- Use clear and unambiguous terms.
- Be assertive but not aggressive.
- Keep content concise.
- Check to ensure understanding.
- Budget time to encourage feedback.
- Direct themselves towards the intended recipient.

All communication has two aspects:

Content   The receiver can be influenced by the facts, opinions, suggestions put forward and influenced by the additional content.

Relationship   The receiver will also be influenced by the 'way' the content is presented and the relationship it suggests between themselves and the speaker.

Take, for example, the responses:

"We are unable to accept your findings as they do not take into account the rate of inflation," and,

"This is abysmal, we can't accept this!"

Both have approximately the same content but define very different relationships. This relationship aspect, which is part of all communication, establishes the way in which the content is to be received. When communication is assertive, the relationship is established as honest, direct and fair. Thus more detailed attention can be directed toward the content. Where it is aggressive, passive or devious, the relationship itself limits the content and the information that can be discussed.

Written communication

The primary purpose of written information is to communicate. The writer should, therefore, always have the reader in mind when producing the text. The use of plain English must be encouraged - this is particularly important for health and safety related material. One useful method of written communication of information is the *report.* A simple structure is as follows:

- Introduction and background.
- Summary.
- Main body of the report.

- Recommendations.
- Conclusions.

For more information on effective report writing see Element 5.1 Active and reactive monitoring.

Graphic communication

Graphical communications may be used instead of or in support of other forms of communication. Verbal presentations and written reports will often include graphs to illustrate or clarify complex relationships such as changes in accident incidence frequency rates over a period of time.

Graphical communication is used to good effect with health and safety signs, where the colour and pictorial representation of hazards is used. This avoids problems where workers may have limited English language abilities and would struggle to read words. Graphical communication is also used in posters and moving image communications, for example an electronic induction package.

USE AND EFFECTIVENESS OF VARIOUS COMMUNICATION MEASURES

Notice boards

A traditional communication technique is to post safety information on notice boards. The advantage of this method is that the communication is available to everyone in a particular work area. Notice boards should only be used to make general statements or to keep workers aware of current information or proposed developments. Notice boards should not be used where the currency or completeness of the information impacts on safety critical issues. The information must be kept up to date and maintained in a legible condition if it is to be effective. Notice board information relies on a person's ability to read, understand and apply the information correctly. Care needs to be taken to ensure appropriate language(s) are used.

Health and safety media

There are many forms of health and safety 'media' which aim to sell the health and safety message. Their effectiveness in modifying human behaviour and attitudes has been the subject of much debate. Many health and safety practitioners view some to be of little value - however there is a marked reluctance to abandon them.

Films, videos, DVD's

Films, videos and DVD's are often used to renew attention during periods of training. The visual impact is a strong stimulus on the delegate; the video enables the training to expand experience outside the training room or the experience of the trainees. Shock videos are sometimes used to illustrate what might happen if procedures are not followed. It has been found that their effect does not change attitude in the longer term. A common use for videos is at site induction, for both new employees and contractor.

Poster campaigns

Posters displaying information are sometimes seen as an inexpensive and visible way of showing commitment to safety. This attitude can be self-defeating if management place too much reliance on them. For example, the workforce can perceive this as an excuse for a proper safety policy. To be effective messages must be:

Positive - posters exhorting people to 'be safe' or threatening dire consequences if a particular action is not taken are rarely effective. People are not necessarily rational or logical - particularly in giving priority to safety over even a small cut in take home pay or comfort. Messages should emphasise positive safety benefits by letting people know 'what's in it for them'.

Aimed at the correct audience - posters quickly blend into the background. This is compounded when messages are seen as irrelevant. Campaigns must be carefully targeted and posters positioned in order to have a captive audience. For example, a poster warning of the dangers of loose clothing being entangled in machinery should be sited close to the relevant machine.

Believable - messages should be relevant, credible and realistic.

Care must be taken to avoid offending or distracting your audience away from the message. Sexual images can often offend both men and women. Similarly, pictures of horrific accidents can lead to a rejection of the message on the basis that it could not happen to them. Posters should be changed regularly to avoid them becoming wallpaper.

Summary:

Advantages:

- Relatively low cost.
- Flexibility (allowing them to be displayed in the most apposite positions).
- Brevity (allowing messages to be easily understood).
- Use in reinforcing verbal instructions or information and in providing a constant reminder of important health and safety issues.
- The potential to allow employees to become involved in their selection.

Disadvantages:

- Need to change posters on a regular basis if they are to be noticed.
- They may become soiled, defaced and out-of-date.
- The possibility that they might be seen to trivialise serious matters.
- They might alienate people if inappropriate stereotypes (e.g. of the 'stupid worker') are used.
- No direct way of assessing whether the message has been understood.
- They may be perceived by unscrupulous employers as an easy, if not particularly effective, way of discharging their responsibility to provide health and safety information, and even of shifting the responsibility onto the workforce for any accidents that may occur.

Toolbox talks

Toolbox talks are often used in organisations that operate work on a continuous shift basis. The technique is very good for fast communication on specific subjects. It relies on the cascade of information from supervisors or team leaders to their work group. Issues are normally kept to a minimum and two-way communication is very effective with individuals within the work group. Issues raised may be current, such as warning of some concerns over equipment reliability, or recent good or poor safety trends i.e. accidents. Other, future issues may be raised, such as proposed changes in personal protective equipment or work practice(s).

Memos/e-mails

Memos are often used to communicate on short-term issues. The memo is an easier and faster vehicle to use than the more formal document change procedure. Safety related issues may be concerned with person, job or hours worked or work patterns. Written communication is effective in that it states what is to change and from when, but again relies on individual interpretation and understanding. It is often one way, as proof of issue is not always proof of receipt. As with memos, e-mails have similar limitations. Software is available to check whether the recipient has opened the correspondence, but not that it has been read, understood or actioned.

Employee handbooks

Employee handbooks are often issued to new employees at induction. They are useful in communicating site rules and information such as accident and injury reporting mechanisms. Similarly, they will often contain information on site emergency arrangements such as fire and first aid. To be effective a mechanism needs to be established to recall and reissue the handbooks when changes occur. Some organisations operate a loose-leaf folder design. Consideration needs to be given to where each employee keeps the information provided.

Health and Safety Information for Employees Regulations 1989

The Regulations require that information relating to health and safety at work be furnished to all employees by means of posters and leaflets in a form approved by the Health and Safety Executive (HSE).

The HSE has published a new, simplified version of the **Health and Safety Law Poster.** It tells workers what they and their employers need to do in simple terms, using numbered lists of basic points. The employer is required by law to either display the HSE-approved poster or to provide each of their workers with the equivalent 'leaflet'. The law has been changed - for the new poster; it is no longer required for the employer to add the contact details of the enforcing authority and the HSE's Employment Medical Advisory Service. Details may be added of any employee safety representatives or other health and safety contacts, but this is not compulsory.

The existing **"Health and Safety Law - what you should know"** poster can continue to be displayed until 5 April 2014, so long as they are readable and contain up-to-date contact details. Workers can be given copies of the equivalent 1999 leaflet until 5 April 2014. After this date, the 2009 approved poster must be displayed or workers must be provided with personal copies of the 2009 equivalent

The approved poster should be placed in a prominent position. The HSE may approve a particular form of poster or leaflet for use in relation to a particular employment and where any such form has been approved, the Executive shall publish it. If a poster is used, the information must be legible and up to date and the poster must be prominently located in an area to which all employees have access. If a leaflet is used, new leaflets must be issued to employees when any similar changes occur.

MHSWR 1999 Regulation 10 - Information for employees

Employees must be provided with relevant information about hazards to their health and safety arising from risks identified by the assessments.

Clear instruction must be provided concerning any preventative or protective control measures including those relating to serious and imminent danger and fire assessments.

Details of any competent persons nominated to discharge specific duties in accordance with the regulations must also be communicated as should risks arising from contact with other employer's activities.

Before employing a child (a person who is not over compulsory school age) the employer must provide those with parental responsibility for the child with information on the risks that have been identified and preventative and protective measures to be taken.

CO-OPERATION AND CONSULTATION WITH THE WORKFORCE

Roles and benefits of employee participation

Managers should involve the workers in any proposed changes in work practices, or methods before they are implemented. Involvement will draw on the worker's experience and knowledge of unwritten methods of working. This can often improve the effectiveness of health and safety measures and the acceptance of any new methods of working.

Figure 1-3-9: Health and safety law poster. *Source: HSE Books.*

Role and benefits of health and safety committees and employee feedback

Health and safety committees are a useful forum to bring worker representatives and managers together to promote health and safety and to resolve any health and safety work related issues such as accidents or near misses. However, effective communication by committee representatives back to the general workforce is often poor or fragmented.

Consideration should be given to making copies of the minutes readily available to all workers, by posting sufficient copies in rest areas used by workers and by making an electronic copy available on the company intranet as appropriate.

Managers may introduce health and safety measures, after consultation, and not know how well they work or how effective they have been. Employee feedback can provide insight into this and enable difficulties in working with the control measures to be identified. If the measures work well, in part because of good consultation, it is important to communicate this to employees to encourage their participation in the future.

Duties to consult

The primary responsibility to consult employees is set out in the Health and Safety at Work etc Act (HASAWA) 1974. This is further specified in regulations that express how this is done with regard to Trade Union Safety Representatives (Safety Representatives and Safety Committee Regulations (SRSC) 1977) and other, non-union employees (The Health and Safety [Consultation with Employees] Regulations (HSCER) 1996).

HASAWA 1974 - SECTION 2(4)

Recognised Trade Unions have the right to appoint safety representatives to represent their member employees in consultations with the employer about health and safety matters.

HASAWA 1974 - SECTION 2(6)

Employers must consult with any safety representatives appointed by recognised Trade Unions.

HASAWA 1974 - SECTION 2(7)

Employers must establish a safety committee if requested to do so by two or more safety representatives.

A version of HSG263 'Involving your workforce in health and safety' is available from www.hse.gov.uk/pubns/hsg263.pdf.

Figure 1-3-10: Involving your workforce in health and safety. *Source: HSE Books.*

The guide is mainly aimed at medium to large employers. It is designed to help them in their duty to consult and involve their employees on health and safety matters. The guide provides practical help, supported by case studies.

APPOINTMENT, FUNCTIONS AND RIGHTS OF EMPLOYEE REPRESENTATIVES

Trade union appointed - Safety Representatives (SR)

Safety Representatives and Safety Committees Regulations (SRSC) 1977

The HASAWA 1974 made provision for the appointment of Safety Representatives by recognised trade unions and the formation of Safety Committees. The SRSC 1977 establish their appointment, functions, and rights.

Appointment

A trade union safety representative must be elected by the workers they represent and appointed by a recognised trade union in writing to the employer. This should set out the group of employees they represent. The safety representative should have experience in the workplace in question or a similar one for a period of 2 years and would cease to be a representative on leaving the union, the employer's workplace or on removal notified to the employer in writing by the trade union.

Functions

The SRSC Regulations grant safety representatives the opportunity to carry out certain functions as outlined in the following lists.

- To carry out investigations into potential hazards and dangerous occurrences.
- Examine the causes of accidents in the workplace.
- To carry out investigations into complaints by any employee they represent relating to health, safety or welfare.
- To represent the employees they were appointed to represent in consultations with the employer.
- To carry out inspections of the workplace:
  - Provided it has not been inspected in the last 3 months.
  - When reasonable notice is provided in writing to the employer.
  - At more frequent intervals if the employer agrees.
  - Or when a substantial change has occurred.
  - Or when new information is provided by Health and Safety Executive (HSE)/Health and Safety Commission (HSC).
  - Or following an accident, occurrence or disease.
  - Inspect / copy documents relevant to those they represent.
  - The employer is to provide facilities to assist.
- To bring to the employer's notice, any unsafe or unhealthy conditions, or unsafe working practices, which come to their attention whether during an inspection/investigation or day to day observation.
- To represent the employees they were appointed to represent in consultations with the Enforcing Authority inspectors.
- To receive information from an Enforcing Authority inspector on behalf of employees they represent.
- To attend meetings of safety committees related to matters affecting employees they represent.
- In order to fulfil the functions the safety representative should:
  - Take all reasonably practical steps to keep themselves informed.
  - Encourage co-operation between their employer and his employees.
  - Bring to the employer's notice, normally in writing, any conditions that come to their attention.

Rights

The SRSC 1977 set out duties on employers towards Safety Representatives - these in effect provide rights to the Safety Representative that make the provision of their function easier.

Information

The SRSC 1977 require employers to make any information within their knowledge available to safety representatives that are necessary to enable them to fulfil their functions.

This should include:

- Information about the plans and performances and any changes that may affect the health and safety at work of their employees, e.g. the plan to re-organise the layout of a manufacturing site.
- Information of a technical nature about hazards to health and safety and precautions deemed necessary to eliminate or minimise them, e.g. about substances that workers are exposed to.
- Information which the employer keeps relating to the occurrence of any accidents, dangerous occurrences or notifiable industrial disease and any statistical records relating to such accidents, dangerous occurrences or cases of notifiable industrial disease, e.g. a copy of a report of an accident to an enforcing authority.
- Any other information relating to matters affecting the representative's employees, including any measurements to check the effectiveness of health and safety arrangements.
- Information on articles or substances which the employer issues to home workers.

However, an employer is not obliged to disclose the following information:

- Personal medical or other information to an employee representative without the consent of the individual concerned.

- Information that would be against the interests of national security.
- Information not relating to health and safety.
- Where the information was obtained by the employer in connection with legal proceedings.
- Where it would damage the employer's business interests.

Consultation

The SRSC 1977 were modified by MHSWR 1999 which place a duty on the employer to consult, provide facilities and assistance with regard to:

- Introduction of any measures which might substantially affect health and safety, e.g. the introduction of a new substance or a longer shift period.
- Arrangements for appointing persons to provide the employer with health and safety assistance e.g. a nominated person/organisation to provide health and safety advice.
- The appropriateness of information to be provided to employees as required to meet legislation requirements, e.g. related to substances workers are exposed to or the provision of an employee handbook/rule book on health and safety.
- The planning and organisation of any health and safety training required under particular health and safety laws; e.g. induction training or how to operate equipment safely.
- The health and safety consequences for employees of the introduction of new technologies into the workplace e.g. the computerisation of office processes or introduction of mechanical handling equipment to assist with manual handling.

Time off work to carry out functions and to attend training

The union appointing the safety representative may wish them to be trained on a Trades Union Congress (TUC) approved course. However, there is much to be gained by employers approaching the trades unions active in their workplace with the objective of holding joint courses. This has a particular advantage in that management may also be involved and enable the training to focus on the specific issues affecting the employer's organisation. In any event it is prudent for the employer to carry out company/industry orientated training to supplement the broad-based TUC course. The functions and training of the safety representatives may be carried out during normal working hours.

The representative must receive normal earnings whilst carrying out their functions or training and this must take account of any bonuses that would have been earned if carrying out their normal work activities.

Appeals/complaint

A safety representative may make a complaint to an Employment Tribunal if:

- The employer has failed to permit the safety representative to take reasonable time off to perform their functions.
- The employer has failed to allow the safety representative to attend reasonable training.
- The employer has failed to pay him for the time taken to perform these functions or attend training.

The complaint to the Employment Tribunal must be presented within three months of the date when the failure occurred.

Elected - Representatives of Employee Safety (RES)

The Health and Safety (Consultation with Employees) Regulations (HSCER) 1996

The HSCER 1996 extend the rights of consultation on matters relating to health and safety to all workers regardless of trade union status. Employers can consult either directly with employees or, in respect of any group of employees, one or more elected representatives of that group. These are referred to as "representatives of employee safety" (RES). If the latter option is chosen, then employers must tell the employees the name of the representative and the group he/she represents. An employer that has been consulting a representative may choose to consult the whole workforce. However, the employer must inform the employees and the representatives of that fact.

Functions

Representatives of employee safety (RES) have the following functions:

- To make representations to the employer on potential hazards and dangerous occurrences at the workplace which affect, or could affect the represented employees.
- Make representations to the employer on general matters of health and safety.
- To represent the employees in workplace consultations with enforcing authority inspectors.

Rights

Information

If the employer consults employees directly then it must make available such information, within the employers' knowledge, as is necessary to enable them to participate fully and effectively in the consultation. If a representative is consulted, then the employer must make available all necessary information to enable them to carry out their functions. In addition, the employer must make available any record made under the RIDDOR

1995 which relates to the represented group of employees. This does not provide a right to inspect or copy any document which is not related to health and safety.

Consultation

Where there are employees not represented by the SRSC 1977, the employer shall consult those employees in good time on matters relating to their health & safety at work. Essentially the matters on which the employees must be consulted are the same as those for safety representatives. In particular they must be consulted on:

- Introduction of any measures which might substantially affect health and safety, e.g. the introduction of a new substance or a longer shift period.
- Arrangements for appointing persons to provide the employer with health and safety assistance e.g. a nominated person/organisation to provide health and safety advice.
- The appropriateness of information to be provided to employees as required to meet legislation requirements, e.g. related to substances workers are exposed to or the provision of an employee handbook/rule book on health and safety.
- The planning and organisation of any health and safety training required under particular health and safety laws; e.g. induction training or how to operate equipment safely.
- The health and safety consequences for employees of the introduction of new technologies into the workplace e.g. the computerisation of office processes or introduction of mechanical handling equipment to assist with manual handling issues.

Time off work to carry out their function or for training

Representatives of employee safety must be given reasonable training in order to carry out their functions. Employers must meet the costs of the training and any travel and subsistence. They must also permit the representatives to take time off with pay during working hours in order for them to carry out their functions. Time off shall also be given, with pay, where this is required for any person standing as a candidate for election as a representative. Employers must also provide suitable facilities for the representatives to carry out their functions.

Appointment

It is the employer's decision as to the manner of consultation; if it is deemed that appointment of RES's is appropriate it is necessary to put this to employees to decide who they would like to appoint. This would be done by election, and it need not be a complicated or overly formal approach. Time off and suitable facilities are to be given where any person is standing as a candidate for election as a representative. It would be reasonable that RES's be appointed for local workplace issues and some of those be appointed for consultation on company wide issues. When electing RES's, factors to be considered are: the size of the workplace and the number of employees, the nature of the work being done with the focus on the types of risk, any areas not represented by Trade Unions and shift patterns. ***See also - Relevant statutory provisions section.***

Facilities

An employer must provide reasonable facilities to enable a safety representative to carry out his/her functions. Depending on the particular circumstances, such facilities might include a private room, telephone, fax machine, photocopier and relevant reference material.

SAFETY COMMITTEES

Legal requirement

If two or more trade union appointed safety representatives request in writing the formation of a safety committee, the employer must implement this request within three months. Consultation must take place with the representatives making the request and recognised trade unions the members of which work in the workplace that the committee relates to.

Constitution

The employer must post a notice stating the composition of the committee and the workplace it represents, where it may be easily read.

Objectives

- The promotion of co-operation on safety, health and welfare matters.
- Provision of a forum for discussion, ideas and recommendations to the employer.
- To promote and support normal employee/employer systems for the reporting and control of workplace problems.

Functions

- To review the measures taken to ensure health and safety, e.g. purchasing and maintenance programmes.
- To review accident and occupational health trends.
- The examination of safety audit reports.
- To consider enforcing authority reports and information releases.
- To consider reports which safety representatives may wish to submit.
- To assist in the development of safety rules and systems of work and procedures.

- To consider the effectiveness of the health and safety content of employee training.
- To consider the adequacy of communication and publicity in the workplace.
- To consider new developments and proposed changes, e.g. legislation and new technology.
- The provision of a link with enforcing authority.

Composition

The membership and structure of the safety committee should be settled in consultation between management and the trade union representatives concerned. This should be aimed at keeping the total size as compact as possible.

- Chairperson.
- Secretary.
- Management representatives.
- Employee representatives.
- Health and safety practitioner.
- Other management, e.g. project engineers, planning engineers, electrical engineers.
- Operational supervision.

Requirements for effectiveness

A basic requirement for a successful safety committee is the desire of both employee and management to show honest commitment and a positive approach to a programme of accident prevention and the establishment of a safe and healthy environment and systems of work. For any committee to operate effectively, it is necessary to determine clear objectives and functions. It is important to establish a committee that is balanced in representation of employees and management.

Frequency of meetings

This would depend on the nature of the organisation's business, the risks involved, how active the health and safety programme is, items on the agenda and other local considerations (such as a hierarchy of committees representing departments/locations/sites). Usually, meetings are held at a frequency varying between once a month and every three months.

Minutes and agenda

The minutes must be circulated as soon as possible after the meeting. A suggested agenda is:

- Apologies for absence.
- Minutes of the previous meeting.
- Matters arising.
- Reports of health and safety practitioner.
- Other reports e.g. fire officer, nurse, and occupational hygienist.
- New items (and emergency items).
- Date of next meeting.

Reasons why safety committees are effective

- A clear management commitment.
- Clear objectives and functions.
- An even balance between management and employee representatives.
- Agenda agreed, distributed in advance and adhered to in meeting.
- Minutes or notes of the meetings being produced promptly and distributed in good time for actions to be taken before the next meeting.
- Personal copy of minutes provided to each member, each representative covered by the committee and the senior manager of the organisation.
- Effective publicity given to discussions and recommendations, including posting/displaying copies.
- Effective chairing of meeting enabling points to be raised but within the agenda; controlling points taken as any other business.
- Full participation by members.
- Access to the organisation's decision-making processes through the chairperson so that the committee's views are taken into account.
- Speedy decisions by management on recommendation promptly translated into action and effectively publicised.
- Regular meetings at a frequency that reflects the matters to be discussed.
- Meetings not cancelled or postponed except in very exceptional circumstances.
- Dates of meetings arranged well in advance and published to members, e.g. for a one year period.
- Appropriate topics.
- Access to health and safety expertise.
- Sub-committees established where there is a need to focus in detail on specifics and report back.

Training

THE EFFECT OF TRAINING ON HUMAN RELIABILITY

General points

There is a legal requirement under section 2 of the HASAWA 1974, namely, the employer must provide such information, instruction, training and supervision, so far as is reasonably practicable, to ensure the health and safety at work of all employees. Regulation 13, Capabilities and Training, of the MHSWR 1999, makes this requirement, which is essential to underpin health and safety standards, more specific.

Training is an important part of competency, but is not sufficient on its own; experience in applying what has been learnt during training is important as well. Training should take account of foreseeable work conditions relate to the risks and controls for dealing with the risks. It should not only consider routine aspects of work but also work that takes place infrequently such as maintenance and emergencies.

Employers need to consider the capabilities of their employees before entrusting tasks to them. This is necessary to ensure that they have adequate health and safety training and are capable enough at their jobs to avoid risk. To this end, consideration must be given at recruitment and when transferring between jobs and work departments. Training must also be provided when other factors, such as the introduction of new technology and new systems of work or work equipment, arise.

Training must be repeated periodically, where appropriate, to ensure employees retain knowledge, skill and the right experience. Particular attention should be paid to infrequent, complex or safety critical tasks. Training should be adapted to take account of any new or changed risks to the health and safety of the employees concerned and should take place during working hours. A health and safety training programme should be implemented for all employees from general workers to director level. This should include:

- Specialist training.
- Internal and external courses.

- Formal and informal training.

All the training should be recorded and the employer needs to recognise the importance of further training at each stage of a person's career.

Effects and benefits of training

Benefits to employee

- Better understanding and involvement raises staff morale/job satisfaction.
- Understanding of relevance of systems of work and controls reduces risk.
- Understanding of welfare arrangements aids health, safety and hygiene.
- Allows employee to reach experienced worker standard more quickly.
- Increases flexibility of staff.

Benefits to employer

- Reduces accident frequency and severity.
- Reduces injury related absenteeism.
- Reduces claims and insurance premiums.
- Reduces the chance of prosecution.
- Increases profits/benefit.

OPPORTUNITIES AND NEED FOR TRAINING PROVISION

Induction training for new employees

Induction training is generally defined as the information, instruction and training given when a person starts a new job, task or process. Its purpose is to orientate the individual to his or her environment in order to maximise both productivity and safety. Thus, a workforce that is aware of the risks is familiar with procedures and systems of work, knows how to recognise and report unsafe conditions. This ensures that the employee shares a common commitment to health and safety and it contributes strongly to a safer workforce.

Key health and safety topics to be covered

Induction training for new employees should include:

- Review and discussion of the safety policy.
- Specific training requirements.
- Fire and emergency procedures.
- Welfare facilities.

- First aid procedures and facilities.
- Personal protective equipment (PPE) provisions - limitations, use and maintenance etc.

Refresher training

As time passes a worker's approach to health and safety can drift away from that intended by the employer. This may simply be because they have forgotten, sometimes because of infrequent use, or because they prefer to have a different understanding or way of working. It is important that regular refresher training be used to reinforce the employer's desired approach. A common refresher period, used for first aiders and lift truck operators is three years. This may be an acceptable interval for some tasks but the period may need to be shorter for others. Refresher training needs to be provided to managers as well as workers that use health and safety skills.

Job change/process change

Required at appropriate intervals to update techniques and ensure awareness of correct methods. Training will include information and skills relevant to:

- Introduction of new substances/processes.
- Changes in working procedure.

- Changes in work patterns.
- Review of risk assessments.

This assesses the behaviour of the workforce and their attitude. In addition, further safety training may be required following an increase in accidents/incidents.

Introduction of new legislation

Employers have a duty to bring to the attention of employees specific changes in legislation which may have an effect on their safety or the safety of others. Changes that may affect personal health and safety include revisions to HSE Guidance EH40, where a reduction in occupational exposure limits may cause employees to adopt more stringent exposure controls.

Introduction of new technology

The introduction of new technology will often require the adoption of new work practices, for example improvements in manual handling by using mechanical aids. Such training will include developing skills to interpret equipment control layouts and data display.

Specific health and safety training

Specific training for certain workers will include:

- Safe systems of work e.g. permit to work procedure.
- Equipment training e.g. dumper truck-driving skills.
- Personal protective equipment (PPE) training.
- Fire training.
- Health and safety inspections.
- First aid training.

Supervisor and general management training

To ensure responsibilities are known and the organisation's policy is carried out. Main points that should be covered:

- The health and safety policy.
- Legal framework and the duties of the organisation.
- Health and safety inspection techniques.
- Cause and consequences of accidents.
- Risk assessment.
- Accident prevention techniques.
- Disciplinary procedures.
- The use of reactive and active monitoring techniques.

Preparing for a training session

Training is a crucial area in health and safety and careful preparation prior to delivering a training session is vital to its success. One of the first considerations is to identify the particular aspect of health and safety that is to be addressed so that the objectives and the content (breadth and depth) of the training session can be established. Other factors to be considered are:

- The training style and methods to be used e.g. lecture, video, role play, group work, use of equipment, site visit etc.
- The target audience e.g. existing knowledge and skills, relevance, motivation, etc.
- The number of trainees.
- The time available.
- The skills required of the trainer.
- Audio-visual and other training aids required. (Make sure that they work and that you know how to use them!).
- The suitability of the training facilities e.g. location, room layout, size, lighting, etc.
- Provision of refreshments if necessary.
- How the effectiveness of the training is going to be evaluated, both at the time (e.g. course evaluation forms) and afterwards (e.g. greater compliance with procedures, reduction in accidents, etc).

Provision of short training sessions

Should include:

- Setting objectives.
- Preparation of the programme.
- Briefing of trainee(s).
- Follow up.
- Review of the contents of the session.
- Presentation of the training session (using visual aids if possible).

Preparing for training

When we train, it is important to prepare:

The trainer	The requirement for lesson notes. The amount of time available.	*Equipment/materials*	Availability and condition. The amount required for the trainee to practice.
Training area	Are we free from interruptions? Is it safe and healthy?	*Trainees*	Done in agreed working hours, consideration has been given to covering their routine work whilst on the course.

Figure 1-3-11: Training preparation.

Source: RMS.

	Trainer	*Group*
Aids to learning	Visual aids. Questions. Praise. Commitment. Mnemonics.	Physical comfort. Interest. Confidence.
Barriers to learning	Lack of preparation. Information overload. Tutor disinterest. Time of day.	Lack of motivation. Distractions. Noise. Concerns regarding routine work load not being covered whilst on course.

Figure 1-3-12: Aids and barriers to learning.   *Source: RMS.*

3.5 - Emergency procedures and contacting emergency services

The importance of developing emergency procedures

Adequate emergency procedures should be in place, or developed, to control likely incidents, e.g. fire, spillage, poisoning exposure to pathogens etc. Procedures should be in writing and regularly tested through drills and exercises. The results of such exercises should be recorded and the procedures amended as necessary. For identified high-risk activities arrangements should be formalised with local Accident and Emergency services (A&E), for example, where there may be a need to have available special anti toxins or isolation facilities.

Emergency procedures should be subject to regular review to determine if any new factors are affecting them and their effectiveness. Fire is a specific risk which will need regular review throughout a major build or modification project. The exit routes may need to be redefined and signed and those affected trained and drilled. Similarly, assembly points may change. Local arrangements should consider the provision of fire suppression equipment, such as extinguishers, whenever contractors use equipment which may present a source of ignition.

Arrangements for contacting emergency and rescue services

The employer must consider the risks arising from their undertaking and the related emergencies that could result. MHSWR 1999 require that written procedures be in place to deal with significant emergencies. In addition, there is a requirement to ensure that where necessary contacts are made with external emergency and rescue services. This can include alerting them to the timing of special, high hazard tasks such as work in a confined space or where there is a significant risk that people may need to be rescued. In some cases it will mean contacting services and agreeing the boundary of what support can be expected from external services and what must be arranged by the employer.

The employer must identify and assess the nature of any injury likely to occur and consider the distance to emergency hospital facilities. It may be necessary to provide a first aid room and to train staff in specific emergency techniques, for example, resuscitation or to engage more capable staff with medical qualifications.

Part of the arrangements must ensure the means to contact the appropriate services at the time of the emergency - by telephone, radio or suitable other means.

3.6 - First-aid in the workplace

First-aid requirements

THE HEALTH AND SAFETY (FIRST-AID) REGULATIONS (FAR) 1981 - MAIN REQUIREMENTS

Reg 2   Regulation 2 defines first aid as: '...treatment for the purpose of preserving life and minimising the consequences of injury or illness until medical (doctor or nurse) help can be obtained. Also, it provides treatment of minor injuries which would otherwise receive no treatment, or which do not need the help of a medical practitioner or nurse'.

Reg 3   Requires that every employer must provide equipment and facilities which are adequate and appropriate in the circumstances for administering first-aid to his employees.

Reg 4   An employer must inform his employees about the first-aid arrangements, including the location of equipment, facilities and identification of trained personnel.

Reg 5   Self-employed people must ensure that adequate and suitable provision is made for administering first-aid while at work.

PROVISION OF FIRST AID FACILITIES

To ensure compliance with Regulation 3, an employer must make an assessment to determine the needs.

Consideration of the following is required:

- Different work activities - some, such as offices, have relatively few hazards and low levels of risk; others have more or more specific hazards (construction or chemical sites). Requirements will depend on the type of work being done.
- Difficult access to treatment - an equipped first-aid room may be required if ambulance access is difficult or likely to be delayed.
- Employees working away from employer's premises - the nature of the work and its risk will need to be considered.
- Employees of more than one employer working together - agreement can be made to share adequate facilities, with one employer responsible for their provision.
- Provisions for non-employees - under FAR employers do not have to make first-aid provision for any person other than their employees. Liability issues and interpretation placed on employers by the HASAWA 1974 may alter the situation, as, for example, in the case of a shop or other place where the public enter.
- Having made this assessment, the employer will then be able to work out the number and size of first-aid boxes required. The Approved Code of Practice outlines minimum standards for their contents and facilities - at least one will always be required. Additional facilities such as a stretcher or first-aid room may also be appropriate.

Role, training and number of first-aiders and appointed persons

ROLE OF FIRST AIDERS

The role of first aiders is to:

- Give immediate assistance to casualties with workplace injuries or illness.
- To summon an ambulance or other professional help.

TRAINING OF FIRST AIDERS

FAR Regulation 3(2) states that in order to provide first aid to injured or ill employees:

"A person shall not be suitable unless he has undergone:

- *Such training and has such qualifications as the Health and Safety Executive may approve for the time being in respect of that case or class of case.*
- *Such additional training, if any, as may be appropriate in the circumstances of that case".*

A first-aider is someone who has undertaken training and has a qualification that the HSE approves. This means that they must hold a valid certificate of competence in either:

- First aid at work (FAW), issued by a training organisation approved by HSE (minimum of 18 hours training over 3 days).
- Emergency first aid at work (EFAW), issued by a training organisation approved by HSE or a recognised Awarding Body of Ofqual/Scottish Qualifications Authority (minimum of 6 hours training over one day).

Lists of suitable training providers and Awarding Bodies are available from HSE's infoline. The employer must carry out a first-aid needs assessment to decide whether first-aiders should be trained in FAW or EFAW. EFAW training enables a first-aider to give emergency first aid to someone who is injured or becomes ill while at work. FAW training includes EFAW and also equips the first-aider to apply first aid to a range of specific injuries and illness. Providing they have current skills in first aid, the training and experience of the following qualify them to administer first aid in the workplace without the need to have an FAW or EFAW certificate:

- Doctors registered with the General Medical Council.
- Nurses registered with the Nursing and Midwifery Council.
- Paramedics registered with the Health Professional Council.

First aid at work training courses must offer the range of competencies listed in Appendix 4 and 5 of the Health and Safety (First Aid at Work) Regulations (FAR) 1981:

"On completion of training, successful candidates should be able to:

(a) Provide emergency first aid at work as set out in the following lists.

(b) Administer first aid to a casualty with:

- *Injuries to bones, muscles and joints, including suspected spinal injuries.*
- *Chest injuries.*
- *Burns and scalds.*
- *Eye injuries.*
- *Sudden poisoning.*
- *Anaphylactic shock.*

(c) Recognise the presence of major illness and provide appropriate first aid".

The Approved Code of Practice to the FAR 1981 specifies the following training requirements for emergency first aid at work:

"On completion of training, successful candidates should be able to:

(a) Understand the role of the first-aider including reference to:

- *The importance of preventing cross-infection.*

- *The need for recording incidents and actions.*
- *Use of available equipment.*

(b) Assess the situation and circumstances in order to act safely, promptly and effectively in an emergency.

(c) Administer first aid to a casualty who is unconscious (including seizure).

(d) Administer cardiopulmonary resuscitation.

(e) Administer first aid to a casualty who is choking.

(f) Administer first aid to a casualty who is wounded and bleeding.

(g) Administer first aid to a casualty who is suffering from shock.

(h) Provide appropriate first aid for minor injuries".

The training must be provided by a training provider whose training and qualifications are approved by the Health and Safety Executive. Certificates of qualification are valid for three years. A refresher course, followed by examination, is required before re-certification.

To help keep their basic skills up to date, it is strongly recommended by the HSE that first aiders undertake annual refresher training.

The Approved Code of Practice to the FAR 1981 specifies the following annual refresher training requirements:

Candidates should demonstrate their competence to:

(a) Assess the situation in an emergency.

(b) Administer first aid to a casualty who is unconscious (including seizure).

(c) Administer cardiopulmonary resuscitation.

(d) Administer first aid to a casualty who is wounded and bleeding.

(e) Administer first aid to a casualty who is suffering from shock.

Appointed person

In appropriate often low risk circumstances, an employer can provide an "appointed person" instead of a first-aider. Typically, low hazard activities with less than 25 people or higher hazard activities with less than 5 people. The "appointed person" is someone appointed by the employer to take charge of the situation (for example, to call an ambulance) if a serious injury occurs in the absence of a first-aider.

Number of first aiders

The employer must ensure that adequate numbers of "suitable persons" are provided to administer first-aid. "Suitable persons" are those who have received training and acquired qualifications approved by the HSE. All relevant factors have to be taken into account when deciding how many "suitable persons" will be needed.

These include:

- Workplace hazards and risks.
- Situations where access to treatment is difficult.
- The size of the organisation.
- The organisation's history of accidents.
- Employees working on shared or multi-occupied sites.
- Employees regularly working away from the employer's premises.
- The numbers of the employees, including fluctuations caused by shift patterns. The more employees there are, the higher the probability of injury.
- Absences of first-aiders through illness or annual leave.
- Work patterns including shift work.
- Special needs e.g. young people or employees with disabilities.

A complex build or modification project will require regular review of the number of first aiders or first aid equipment and location required. This will involve liaison with contractors and the self employed to ensure adequate cover for all periods of working.

Low hazard e.g. offices, shops, libraries	Less than 25	At least one appointed person
	25-50	At least one first-aider trained in EFAW
	More than 50	At least one first-aider trained in FAW for every 100 employed (or part thereof)
Higher hazard e.g. light engineering and assembly work, food processing, warehousing, extensive work with dangerous machinery or sharp instruments, construction, chemical manufacture	Less than 5	At least one appointed person
	5-50	At least one first-aider trained in EFAW or FAW depending on the type of injuries that might occur
	More than 50	At least one first-aider trained in FAW for every 50 employed (or part thereof)

Figure 1-3-13: Suggested numbers of first-aid personnel to be available at all times people are at work.　　　　　*Source: HSE.*

Selection of first aiders

The selection of first aiders depends on a number of factors, including an individual's:

- Reliability.
- Disposition.
- Communication skills.
- Aptitude and ability to learn.
- Ability to cope with stressful situations.
- Availability at short notice.

Requirements for first-aid boxes

The employer must ensure that an adequate quantity of suitable first aid equipment is provided, taking account of how many first aiders will be using them. In addition, there is the extra consideration that some people may need equipment to administer their own first aid.

There is no standard list of items to put in a first-aid box. It depends on what you assess the needs are.

However, as a guide, and where there is no special risk in the workplace, a minimum stock of first-aid items would be:

- A leaflet giving general guidance on first aid e.g. HSE leaflet "Basic advice on first aid at work".
- 20 individually wrapped sterile adhesive dressings (assorted sizes), appropriate to the type of work.
- Two sterile eye pads.
- Four individually wrapped triangular bandages (preferably sterile).
- Six safety pins.
- Six medium sized (approximately 12 cm x 12 cm) individually wrapped sterile unmedicated wound dressings.

Figure 1-3-14: First-aid box.   Source: RMS.

- Two large (approximately 18 cm x 18 cm) sterile individually wrapped un-medicated wound dressings.
- One pair of disposable gloves.

You should not keep tablets or medicines in the first-aid box.

The above is a suggested contents list only - based on the guidance to the regulations - equivalent but different items would be considered acceptable.

Where an employer decides to provide a defibrillator in the workplace those who may use it should be trained, the HSE does not specify content or have approval system for the training.

Any first-aid room provided must be easily accessible to stretchers and to any other equipment needed to convey patients to and from the room and the room must be sign-posted by using a sign complying with the Health and Safety (Safety Signs and Signals) Regulations 1996.

Coverage in relation to shift work and geographical location

Additional staff will be necessary to cover for out of hours, shift working or overtime. In particular where there is a specific legal duty to provide such coverage - e.g. first aid provisions. The person with overall control of the site must ensure that coverage remains in place throughout the period work is going on.

Particular care must be paid to high risk work being conducted outside normal working hours. It may be possible to maintain good emergency cover for these times by ensuring, where there is permanent security staff, that these are appropriately trained.

If the area of work is geographically large, for example, gas, electrical or telecommunication field work, all staff may need to be trained and equipped with first aid equipment in order that they may self administer first aid. This may be by means of a full first aid kit in a vehicle or a personal provision in a pouch. Particular attention should be given to the likelihood and type of injuries when equipping people in this way.

SHARED FACILITIES AND ARRANGEMENTS

Where a site has multiple occupancy or groups of contracting employers exist within a site, arrangements need to be in place to identify and inform people of where first aid equipment is and who might be responsible for performing first aid duties. It is possible for an agreement to be made such that each occupier or employer does not have to make separate arrangements. This can be particularly useful in providing cover for each other's first aiders and will avoid the need for small contractors to provide their own first aid if they can obtain it from a main contractor's facilities.

Where small works are going on in a host's premises the contractor may find an acceptable agreement may be made with the host to provide first aid and other facilities. It is important that such agreements be made formally, preferably with a written agreement that will substantiate the existence of such an arrangement if it is challenged or people change their mind as the work unfolds.

This page is intentionally blank

UNIT NGC1
MANAGEMENT OF HEALTH AND SAFETY

Health and safety management systems 3 - planning

On completion of this element, candidates should be able to demonstrate understanding of the content through the application of knowledge to familiar and unfamiliar situations. In particular they should be able to:

4.1   Explain the importance of planning in the context of health and safety management systems.

4.2   Explain the principles and practice of risk assessment.

4.3   Explain the general principles of control and a basic hierarchy of risk reduction measures.

4.4   Identify the key sources of health and safety information.

4.5   Explain what factors should be considered when developing and implementing a safe system of work for general activities.

4.6   Explain the role and function of a permit-to-work system.

Content

Sources of reference

Successful Health and Safety Management (HSG65), HSE Books ISBN 0-7176-1276-7

The Management of Health and Safety at Work (ACOP) (L21), HSE Books ISBN 0-7176-2488-9

Five Steps to Risk Assessment - Case Studies (HSG183), HSE Books ISBN 0-7176-1580-4

Five Steps to Risk Assessment (INDG163), HSE Books ISBN 0 7176 6189 X

The right start: Work experience for young people (INDG364), HSE Books ISBN 0-7176-2547-8

http://www.hse.gov.uk/risk/casestudies/index.htm

New and Expectant Mothers at Work - A guide for employers HSG122 ISBN 0 7176 2583 4

Safe work in confined spaces, Confined Spaces Regulations 1997 (L101)

Guidance on permit-to-work systems, a guide for the petroleum, chemical and allied industries (HSG250) HSE Books ISBN 0717629430

Bird F E, 1974, Management guide to Loss Control, Institute Press, Atlanta, Georgia, USA

Relevant statutory provisions

N/A

4.1 - Importance of planning

System to establish, implement and maintain requirements

HSG65 - SUCCESSFUL HEALTH AND SAFETY MANAGEMENT

Planning is part of one of the main elements of successful health and safety management, as set out in HSG65 Successful Health and Safety Management, and part of the overall health and safety management system of an organisation.

Successful organisations adopt a planned and systematic approach to policy implementation. Their aim is to minimise the risks created by work activities, products and services. They use hazard identification and risk assessment methods to decide priorities and set objectives for hazard elimination and risk reduction.

Specific actions needed to promote a positive health and safety culture and to eliminate and control risks are identified and plans made to fulfil them.

Wherever possible, it is planned that risks are eliminated by the careful selection and design of facilities, equipment and processes or minimised by the use of physical control measures. Where this is not possible, plans for the provision of a safe system of work and personal protective equipment are made to control risks.

The planning process includes the identification of legal requirements and other requirements that can influence the level of health performance that the organisation has to establish.

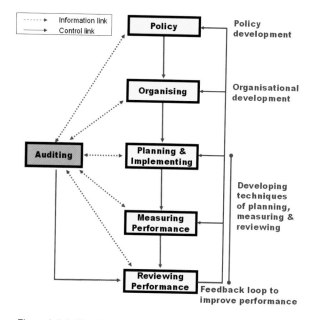

Figure 1-4-1: Planning as part of a system. *Source: HSG65.*

This, in conjunction with the risk assessment process, is used to establish a planned programme for health and safety implementation that includes the setting of health and safety objectives.

Setting health and safety objectives

Setting objectives is an integral part of the planning process. Setting objectives is essential because they provide:

- A target to aim for, therefore actions and efforts can be focused on attaining the objectives instead of being diverted inefficiently.
- Participants with a sense of direction.
- Motivation, through structured progress and successful achievement in meeting them.

A health and safety objective is a mutually understood agreement about a specific health and safety outcome that a person is expected to achieve during a defined objective cycle. It is not a list of all the health and safety activities or responsibilities that relate to the function or level of the organisation, but the role will include fulfilment of the objectives.

Organisations should set objectives to meet their commitments established in their health and safety policy. Objectives must be reviewed on a periodic basis in order that they remain relevant. After the review objectives are set for the following period; this may contain some objectives from the prior period that are current or revised objectives that are more relevant or new objectives introduced to ensure continual improvement.

Objectives must be set for the organisation as a whole, *each function and level*. This means that objectives will be established and for different functions, for example, the primary part of the organisation that deals with delivery of a service, those that maintain the fabric and facilities of the organisation and those that administer the organisation. Each level in the organisation should have objectives set that are relevant to them, this will reflect organisational objectives and local objectives to ensure health and safety performance remains relevant to workers.

The objectives that relate to the whole organisation should be *set by the top management team*. The team should consult widely on what the objectives should be, as they relate to everyone in the organisation. This will involve the managers that will be responsible for the fulfilment of the objectives. In addition, the objective setting process will need to consider those who have an interest in the outcome of the objectives, such as workers, worker health and safety representatives and health and safety practitioners. This process of consultation and setting can be replicated to set objectives for the different functions and levels.

It is important that objectives set for the whole organisation, functions and levels are *documented*. They must be seen as an obligation that must be fulfilled and effort must be made to meet them.

Managers responsible for meeting them should keep them in focus and monitor progress on completion. Objectives should be communicated to those whose support will be needed for their fulfilment and to other relevant parties, such as workers, contractors and other stakeholders.

Legal and organisational commitments should be stated in the health and safety policy and translated into organisation-wide, functional and level based objectives. As objectives are set at the various levels in the organisation they can be made more relevant and specific to ensure that the detail of legislative requirements are met.

There should be a direct link between the work workers perform and the organisation's objectives. Commonly, objectives revolve around the idea of minimising accidents through the control of hazards and the management of risk. When objectives are set it is important that they are not limited to objectives that only set an expectation to reduce the number of accidents. The objectives should also express the actions required that will lead to the reduction in accidents, for example, the provision of training, the re-organisation of internal transport routes and the introduction of manual handling aids. In this way, they will more readily reflect the **hazards and risks** of the organisation.

Objectives should also include consideration of **technological options** and take account of any technical advances that may have become available since the last review. Good objectives will also reflect the organisation's **financial, operational and business** requirements and take into account the **views of interest parties**, such as pressure groups, who may voice concern regarding the work the organisation is currently involved in or proposing to do, contractors and neighbours.

It is important that objectives are clear to those that they are assigned to; in order to achieve these many organisations adopt the 'smart' objectives approach. This ensures that they are specific, measurable, achievable, relevant and timely; and help managers responsible for fulfilling them to identify what is being done, by whom, with what outcome and by when.

SMART objectives:

S pecific	A specific objective has a much greater chance of being accomplished than a general goal. To set a specific objective it is necessary to determine: ■ **Who**: is involved. ■ **What**: is to be accomplished. ■ **Where**: identify the location. ■ **When**: a time frame should be established. ■ **Which**: identify requirements and any constraints. ■ **Why**: specific reasons, purpose or benefits of accomplishing the goal.
M easurable	Establish a reliable system to measure progress towards the achievement of the objective. Avoid using words like "understand" as an objective since understanding can be very difficult to measure.
A chievable	Many objectives are realistic. However, the time it takes to achieve them may be unrealistic. For example, it is realistic for a person to want to lose ten pounds in weight. However, it is unrealistic to want to lose ten pounds in one week. Any barriers to the success of the objective should be identified. Each barrier identified can then be analysed to determine how it may be overcome and within what time frame.
R elevant	Availability of resources will determine how realistically an objective can be achieved within a particular time frame.
T imely	For short term or project related objectives to be effective a defined time frame for completion should be set. For requirements where work is ongoing, support objectives to achieve the level of performance may be necessary, such as with food processing, where the objective (ongoing) may be the periodic checking that the food is within a specified temperature range, or the level of staff hygiene is appropriate for associated workers.

Source: RMS.

Figure 1-4-2: SMART objectives.

Objectives such as "prevent accidents" and "reduce emissions" are not good examples. A 'smart' example of an objective would be the requirement for all team leaders to carry out a workplace inspection each week and to present their written report to the health and safety committee ahead of the meeting on the first Thursday of every month.

Identifying and keeping up to date with legal requirements

The organisation should have made a commitment to compliance with legislation in the health and safety policy statement. Legislation states the minimum standards that must be achieved by employers and employees alike. Legislative requirements are taken into account when risks are assessed and systems of work are established.

Organisations should put systems into place that ensure they have identified legal requirements that affect them and are kept up to date with changes. In the last few years new standards have been introduced through regulations such as the Control of Noise at Work Regulations (CNWR) 2005, the Work at Height Regulations (WHR) 2005, the Health and Safety (Offences) Act (HSO) 2008 and Control of Artificial Optical Radiation at Work Regulations (CAORWR) 2010. Being able to identify these changes in advance of their introduction allows organisations to plan their activities and phase in any extra controls that might be necessary.

See also - Section 4.4 - Sources of health and safety information for options on how to identify and obtain information on legal and other requirements. Legal requirements should be evaluated for their applicability, provision should be made for those that need access to them and the requirements should be communicated to them.

4.2 - Principles and practice of risk assessment

Legal requirements

MANAGEMENT OF HEALTH AND SAFETY AT WORK REGULATIONS (MHSWR) 1999

Regulation 3 of MHSWR 1999 requires employers (and the self-employed) to assess the risk to the health and safety of their employees and to anyone else who may be affected by their work activity. This is necessary to ensure that the preventive and protective steps can be identified to control hazards in the workplace.

The duty under Regulation 3 of MHSWR 1999 is a general duty, as it relates to risk assessments for all risks. Other legislation sets out legal requirements for risk assessment for specific risks.

Where five or more employees are employed, the significant findings of risk assessments must be recorded in writing (the same threshold that is used in respect of having a written safety policy). This record must include details of any employees being identified as being especially at risk.

OTHER LEGISLATION

Specific risk assessment requirements exist for specified risks, this includes:

- Substances harmful to health, including biological substances - Control of Substances Hazardous to Health Regulations (COSHH) 2002.
- Manual handling - Manual Handling Operations Regulations (MHOR) 1992.
- Display screen equipment - Health and Safety (Display Screen Equipment) Regulations (DSE) 1992.
- Fire - Regulatory Reform (Fire Safety) Order (RRFSO) 2005.
- Noise - Control of Noise at Work Regulations (CNWR) 2005.
- Vibration - Control of Vibration at Work Regulations (CVWR) 2005.
- Ultraviolet, visible light, and infrared radiation - Control of Artificial Optical Radiation at Work Regulations (CAORWR) 2010.

The general duties set out in the MHSWR 1999 exist in conjunction with these more specific ones; however, that will not mean that risk assessments have to be done twice.

For example, if you have done a risk assessment to comply with the Control of Substances Hazardous to Health Regulations (COSHH) 2002 you will not have to do it again for the same hazardous substances to comply with the MHSWR 1999. As a rule, a specific duty will take the place of a general one that duplicates it. ***See also NGC1 - Element 1 - Foundations in health and safety.***

Meaning of hazard and risk and risk assessment

HAZARD

"Something that has the potential to cause harm (loss)"

"The potential to cause harm, including ill-health and injury, damage to property, plant, products or the environment, production losses or increased liabilities".

Figure 1-4-3: Definition of hazard.   Source: Successful Health and Safety Management, HSG65, HSE.

Hazards can include:

- Articles, for example, tools such as chisels.
- Substances and chemicals such as pesticides or cement.
- Plant or machines, for example, mobile cranes or a fixed grinder for sharpening tools.
- Methods of work, for example, production line workers or workers at height.
- The working environment, for example, cold environments such as a frozen food storage warehouse or hot and humid ones such as an industrial laundry.
- Other aspects of work organisation such as shift or lone working.

A practical example would be that of a substance, such as cement, which has a particular inherent hazard i.e. chemical (alkaline) burn, which may occur if the cement or concrete comes into contact with the skin or eyes of a worker.

RISK

"The likelihood of potential harm from a hazard being realised"

"The likelihood that a specified undesired event will occur due to the realisation of a hazard by, or during, work activities or by the products and services created by work activities".   *.*

Figure 1-4-4: Definition of risk.   *Source: Successful Health and Safety Management, HSG65, HSE.*

For example, the risk from a substance is the likelihood that it will harm a person in the actual circumstances of use. This will depend upon:

- The hazard presented by the substance.
- How it is controlled.
- Who is exposed, to how much and for how long, and what they are doing.

In the example of cement this may cause temporary injury, dermatitis or sensitise the skin resulting in a permanent effect where the skin is sensitised whenever the person comes into contact with cement in the future.

RISK ASSESSMENT

"To evaluate the risk(s) arising from the hazard(s), identifying preventive and protective measures, taking into account the adequacy of any existing controls, and deciding whether or not the risk is acceptable"

Risk assessment is therefore an analytical process that identifies hazards, which may be harmed and in what way they may be harmed, and it also takes into account factors that make the risk more likely and those that make it less likely.

Objectives of risk assessment; prevention of workplace accidents

The objective of risk assessment is the prevention of workplace accidents. This is achieved through the:

- Identification of all the factors which may cause harm to workers and others (the *hazards*).
- The considerations of the chance of that harm actually befalling anyone in the circumstances of a particular case, and the possible consequences that could come from it (the *risks*).
- Introduction and monitoring of preventive measures to ensure that the risks are adequately controlled at all times.

Risk assessment involves:

1) The identification of hazards.
2) Identification of the population at risk, who might be harmed and how.
3) The evaluation of the risks from the hazards (likelihood, frequency and severity (consequence)) and the deciding on precautions (adequacy of current controls and need for additional controls).
4) Recording significant findings and the implementation of them.
5) Reviewing the risk assessment and updating it if necessary (periodically or when there is a significant change e.g. process or legislative change).

Most people undertake risk assessment as a normal part of their everyday lives. Routine activities, such as crossing the road and driving to work, call for a complex analysis of the hazards and risks involved in order to avoid damage and injury. Therefore, most people are able to recognise hazards as they develop and take corrective action. People do, however, have widely different perceptions regarding risk and may find it difficult to apply their experience to the formal workplace risk assessments required by law. The assessment must be *suitable and sufficient* and should cover the whole undertaking; it should also be broad enough so that it remains valid for a reasonable period. Risks arising from the routine activities, associated with life in general, can usually be ignored *unless* the work activity compounds these risks.

Distinction between different types of incident

ILL-HEALTH

The health and well-being of individuals may be affected by a number of work-related factors. Ill-health may develop over a long period of time; these are commonly called chronic diseases. Typical examples of work-related ill-health are asbestosis, pneumoconiosis and silicosis, where the ill-heath effects may take several years to develop. More recently, ill-health effects have been related to work load and stress.

INJURY ACCIDENT

Some injury effects will be acute in nature and recognised immediately, such as strains or sprains of muscles or ligaments caused by inappropriate lifting of heavy items. Other common injuries include cuts, burns, and bruises.

DANGEROUS OCCURRENCE

The schedule to the Reporting of Injuries, Disease and Dangerous Occurrences (RIDDOR) 1995 lists incidents that must be formally reported to the relevant enforcement agency.

They are significant events, such as the collapse of, the overturning of, or the failure of any load-bearing part of any lift or hoist; mobile powered access platform; access cradle or window-cleaning cradle; excavator; pile-driving frame or rig having an overall height, when operating, of more than 7 metres; or fork lift truck; the collapse of a scaffold of more than five metres high.

NEAR-MISS

A near-miss is an incident with the potential to cause harm, but where there is no measurable loss. A near-miss is classified as one type of event under the term incident:

"An unplanned, uncontrolled event which led to, or could have led to loss"

It is important to analyse near-miss events to assess the potential of the event, had circumstances been different. This will enable corrective action to be put in place to prevent a reoccurrence of the incident.

DAMAGE-ONLY

Substantial damage occurs to property and materials at work annually. Often the most significant losses are associated with workplace fires, when the workplace may be destroyed. The study of the incidence of damage-only losses may be a useful predictive tool to identify situations that might result in injury to people. For example, a series of collisions into a scaffold, requiring minor repair by replacement of a scaffold tube, may be predictive of a later collision involving total scaffold collapse, leading to major personal injury. Such considerations enable the employer to take corrective action before any human loss occurs.

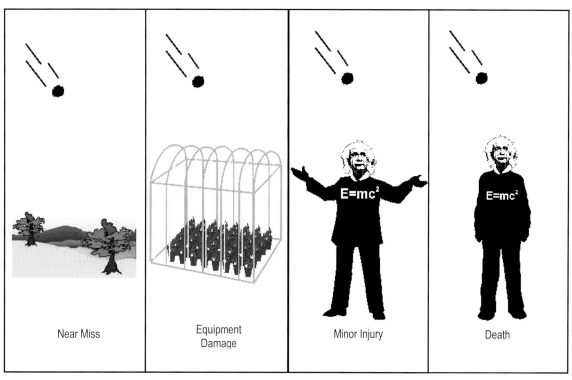

Figure 1-4-5: Results of an incident.   *Source: RMS.*

The distinction between different incidents in summary

An incident is an event that brings about a result. We must not think of injuries etc. as incidents, but rather as the results of incidents. In short, incidents result in losses of one kind or another. The following incident model is offered to illustrate the above statement. In a situation where a spanner falls from height the following could result:

- Falls into a pile of sand and there is no damage or injury, *a near miss.*
- Hits an item of equipment, resulting in *damage,* but no injury.
- Hits a person causing cut and bruises to hand. *This is an injury accident.*
- If the person was working directly under the spanner when it fell there could have been a fatality, *or injury accident.*

This definition, therefore, includes "near-misses", i.e. where no injury or damage etc. occurs. The difference between a near-miss and a fatal accident in terms of time and distance can be very small. It is therefore clear that the damage to persons or property is not the incident, but part of the effects of the incident, the result or consequences of the incident.

Apart from being unpleasant and perhaps very costly, every incident constitutes an opportunity to correct some problem. For this purpose, a near-miss is just as valuable as a serious injury/damage, in fact even more valuable in its role of providing preventative analysis.

RATIOS OF INCIDENT OUTCOMES

Some years ago, a study of 1,750,000 accidents in 21 industries, led by Frank Bird, Management guide to loss control, showed that there is a fixed ratio between losses of different severity and accidents where no loss occurred, i.e. near misses. This is illustrated in the pyramid model of incident outcomes - Frank Bird's accident ratio study.

Pyramid model of incident outcomes

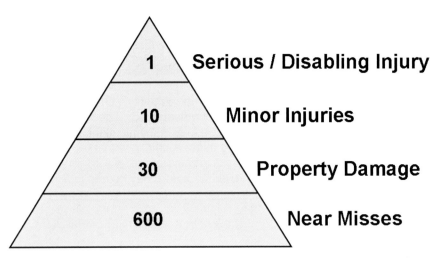

Figure 1-4-6: Accident ratio study.   Source: Frank Bird.

As can be seen by the incident ratio model, in a typical organisation there is likely to be a larger number of near misses than incidents resulting in injury.

UTILITY AND LIMITATIONS OF INCIDENT RATIOS IN ACCIDENT PREVENTION

The incident ratio study described by Frank Bird illustrates that the organisation, site or department that has most incidents may, over time, be likely to have the most serious injuries/losses. This can usefully convey to managers and workers the importance of reporting incidents that do not involve injury to people, as they are more likely to occur and they represent an opportunity to establish their causes and the possibility that this will prevent later injury to people.

It follows that if we thoroughly address the causes of minor loss incidents we will automatically reduce the serious loss incident causes as well.

The incident ratio pyramid therefore has wide application. However, it is important that managers and workers do not misunderstand the incident ratio pyramid. The numbers shown in figure ref 1-4-5 only represent an average of the organisations evaluated by Frank Bird; some higher risk organisations may have a much narrower pyramid, illustrating that when incidents do happen they have a higher likelihood of injury. In lower risk organisations the pyramid may be wider, as injury is less likely.

It is important that managers and workers do not see the pyramid as giving them a quota of near misses that they can have before they have an injury accident; the first incident that happens may have circumstances that cause injury. The principle that the incident ratio pyramid helps with is not to waste the learning opportunities presented by non-injury based incidents.

Risk assessors

COMPOSITION OF A RISK ASSESSMENT TEAM

Risk assessment is generally more thorough and effective when performed by a team. The size of a risk assessment team varies according to the following:

- The risk assessment approach selected.
- The complexity of the task.
- The environment within which the task is being carried out.

The team should bring together knowledge on different disciplines and a variety of experience and expertise. However, a team that is too large can lead to difficulty in remaining focused or reaching consensus. The composition of the team can vary during the risk assessment process according to the expertise required for a specific problem. A team leader, dedicated for the period of the risk assessment process, should be clearly identified, as the success of the risk assessment depends on the team leader's skills.

The team leader should be fully responsible for ensuring that all the tasks involved in planning, performing and documenting the risk assessment are carried out and that the results/recommendations are reported to the appropriate person(s).

Team members should be selected according to the skills and expertise required for the risk assessment.

The team should include those people who:

■ Can answer technical questions about the design and functions of the equipment or process.
■ Have actual experience of how the equipment or process is operated, set-up, maintained, serviced, etc.
■ Have knowledge of the accident history of this type of equipment or process.
■ Have a good understanding of the relevant regulations, standards and any specific safety issues associated with the task; understand human factors, for example, why workers may make mistakes to not follow procedures.

A typical risk assessment team would include:

■ Team leader - often the manager responsible for ensuring the risk assessments take place.
■ First line manager - someone with knowledge of the situation being assessed.
■ Worker representative - someone who can provide a perspective on how tasks and work activities take place.

Depending on the health and safety competence of those involved and the complexity of what is being assessed, the team may benefit from the input of a health and safety practitioner.

It is not always necessary to set up a team for risk assessment, particularly where the situation is not complex, the hazards are well understood and the risk is not high.

COMPETENCE

Risk assessments must be carried out by a competent person or persons. The number of competent persons required to conduct risk assessments in an organisation will depend on the size of the organisation and its geographical spread. The competent assessor must be able to demonstrate health and safety knowledge and experience which is relevant to the organisation and have the ability to apply these qualities to practical situations. The assessor(s) must have the ability to interpret technical information and standards, be systematic in their approach and be capable of communicating the findings in a comprehensible and relevant manner.

The content of a training course to assist with competence of people who are to carrying out risk assessments should include:

■ Legal requirements with respect to risk assessment.
■ Process of identifying hazards and evaluating risks.
■ Identification and selection of appropriate control measures.
■ Awareness of the individual's own limitations and the occasions when specialist assistance might be required.
■ Accessing sources of information, such as ACOPs and in-house information including accident records.
■ Report-writing skills.
■ Interpretation of regulations and standards.
■ Means available for disseminating the outcomes of the assessment.

Criteria for a 'suitable and sufficient' risk assessment

MANAGEMENT OF HEALTH AND SAFETY AT WORK REGULATIONS 1999

The Approved Code of Practice to regulation 3 of the Management of Health and Safety at Work Regulations (MHSWR) 1999 states that in order to be suitable and sufficient a risk assessment must identify the risks arising from or in connection with work.

■ For small businesses presenting few or simple hazards, a simple approach based on informed judgement and reference to appropriate guidance will be enough.
■ In many intermediate cases the risk assessment will need to be more sophisticated. Some areas of the risk assessment may require specialist advice, for example, relating to complex processes or where specialist analytical techniques are required to measure worker exposure to the hazard and to assess its impact.
■ Large and hazardous sites will require the most developed and sophisticated risk assessments, particularly where there are complex or novel processes.
■ Risk assessments must consider all those who might be affected, for example, contractors and members of the public.
■ Employers and the self-employed are expected to take reasonable steps to help themselves identify risks, for example, by looking at appropriate sources of information or seeking advice from competent sources.
■ The risk assessment should be appropriate to the nature of the work and should identify the period of time for which it is likely to remain valid.

Identifying hazards

SOURCES AND FORM OF HARM

The first step in the risk assessment process is to identify the hazards.

Sources of hazard may be related to:

■ People - they may carry infections or be violent.
■ Equipment - which may have mechanical or electrical hazards associated with it.

- Materials - which may be sharp, heavy or toxic.
- Environment - which could have characteristics like of height or slipperiness.
- Systems/situations - the way work is carried out may put undue pressure on a worker.

Examples of the *form* a hazard takes include:

- Slippery surfaces.
- Height.
- Sharp edges.
- Unstable items.
- Heavy items.
- Poor ergonomic layout.

- Asphyxiant materials.
- Electricity.
- Toxic substances.
- Moving vehicles.
- Noise.
- Work pressure.

The identification of hazards can be done in many ways. For complex activities it may be necessary to break the activity down into its component parts by, for example, *job safety analysis or task analysis*.

For a large machine, this could mean looking at:

- Installation.
- Normal operation.
- Breakdown.

- Cleaning.
- Adjustment.
- Dismantling.

The hazards associated with each part of the job or task could then be identified more easily and thoroughly.

It is necessary to identify contingent hazards, which can arise from failures of a system, component, or checking and maintenance; as well as continuing hazards, i.e. those that are present continuously. Examples may include:

- Mechanical hazards.
- Electrical hazards.
- Thermal hazards.
- Noise and vibration.

- Radiation.
- Toxic materials.
- Ergonomic design.

Once the area/activity has been selected, the method(s) of hazard identification can be chosen. If a hazard is defined as being something with the potential to cause harm, then hazard identification can be carried out by observing the activity and noting the hazards as they occur in the actual work setting. This has advantages over carrying out hazard identification as a desktop exercise using the health and safety manual, the manual may not reflect how work is actually done and workers may have developed their own method of working, contrary to instructions and training.

Legislation can identify hazards that may exist in the workplace, for example, regulations and supporting documents set limits for noise, vibration and substances. Exposure above these limits would be a hazard. Changes to legislation, such as the reduction in noise action values under the Control of Noise at Work Regulations (CNWR) 2005, could indicate an increased hazard. Manufacturer's information, such as user manuals for equipment and safety data sheets for substances could indicate hazards that should be assessed.

Hazards may be identified during active monitoring activities like inspections and tours. They may also be identified during incident investigation, especially if the incident was not foreseen. An incident will not be wasted if it highlights previously unforeseen hazards. *Incident statistics*, from internal and external sources, can also be used for hazard information.

In more complex organisations it may be appropriate to use other, more advanced, hazard identification techniques:

- Hazard and operability studies (HAZOP), which are much used by the chemical industry at the design stage of processes and equipment.
- Reliability analysis and failure mode and effect analysis (FMEA), which are inductive techniques.
- Fault tree analysis (FTA) and Event tree analysis (ETA), which are deductive techniques.

Identifying population at risk

In the risk assessment process it is necessary to identify the population at risk. In practice this may mean noting groups or types of people at risk, for example, all nursing staff in the operating theatre or members of the public or patients. It is not necessary to list all workers in a category as this would be too much detail for most risk assessments.

A suitable and sufficient risk assessment will identify all groups of people at risk. When considering the people who might be affected it is important to remember certain groups of workers who may work unusual hours, for example, security staff and cleaners. Similarly, maintenance staff needs to be considered and, where relevant, the fact that they may be contracted workers identified. Members of the public, visitors, students, and work experience people and even trespassers should be considered in the risk assessment process. In addition, special risk groups include those with disabilities, young people, pregnant women or nursing mothers.

GENERAL GROUPS AT RISK

This category includes vulnerable people that might be at risk from a particular hazard. For example, women of childbearing age (or more particularly any unborn foetus they may be carrying) may be deemed to be at risk from exposure to the hazards presented by lead. Other at risk groups could be the public (because of their lack of knowledge of the hazard/risk), young persons, people with health conditions, workers that have come from other countries where language or work practices may be different to the UK. The 'at risk group' depends on the hazard and the circumstances.

SPECIFIC GROUPS AT RISK

Operators

Typically, operators are individuals engaged in production type activities where they have little control over their environment or work routine. Issues include repetitive strain, slips, trips and falls, together with a variety of equipment hazards. Consideration of the task and issues of fatigue and loss of concentration are usually significant.

Maintenance staff

Maintenance issues, which may result in injury, are usually associated with poor access and egress. Some maintenance work is carried out infrequently and it can cause a lack of familiarity which can lead to serious mistakes. The fact that a maintenance worker is working alone may make the risk of harm and possible injuries worse.

Cleaners

Cleaners may be at risk from the materials that they use or that which they clean. Often the turnover of cleaners is high and their competency, in terms of such issues as the correct use and health effects of the materials they use or remove, is low.

Contractors

Contractors may be involved in work that has a particularly high risk due to its unusual nature or complexity. They are a particular group to identify as they may not be as familiar with the workplace as other workers. They may not understand the hazards of the workplace and may not be as equipped as other workers to deal with the hazards.

Visitors/public

Visitors and the public are particular groups of people that need to be identified because they may not perceive or understand hazards and may behave in a different way to workers. They are seen as a vulnerable group because of their lack of awareness and ability to protect themselves from hazards.

Evaluating risk and adequacy of current controls

LIKELIHOOD OF HARM AND PROBABLE SEVERITY (CONSEQUENCE)

After the hazards have been identified it is necessary to evaluate the risk. The risk assessment process requires a judgment for each hazard to decide, realistically, what is the most likely outcome and how likely is this to occur. It may be a matter of simple subjective judgement or it may require a more complex technique depending on the complexity of the situation. In order to do this, at least two factors must be considered - the likelihood and the severity (consequence) of harm.

1) *Likelihood* - when conducting a risk assessment we take account of the circumstances in which the hazard may be encountered and the current controls in place as these can greatly influence the likelihood of a person being harmed by a hazard. The circumstances may relate to environmental factors that can mask or make a hazard more obvious, for example, poor or good lighting; where the hazard in placed, away from normal workers or in a busy walkway. The person encountering the hazard is another factor affecting likelihood. Someone that does not perceive the hazard because of lack of knowledge or reduce visual ability makes it more likely that they will contact the hazard. Hazard controls in use may have only a limited effect, may fail, be defeated or become inactive at various times and these factors also influence the likelihood. Reliance on a control like personal protective equipment would normally increase the likelihood compared to a control that put the hazard behind a protective barrier.

   Other factors that might be considered include:

   - Competence of workers.
   - Levels and quality of supervision.
   - Attitudes of workers and supervisors.
   - Environmental conditions e.g. adverse weather.
   - Frequency and duration of exposure.
   - Work pressures.

2) *Severity (consequence)* - this considers the probable outcome of contact with the hazard, which may include death, major injury, minor injury, damage to plant/equipment/product, or damage to the environment. It is important that this is the most probable outcome, not possible outcome, as it may be possible to think of some extreme circumstances that all hazards may have the outcome of death. Again, it is important to take into account the nature of the hazard and the circumstances in which the hazard is encountered. The severity of contact with electricity is greatly reduced if the nature of the hazard is that it is operating at low voltage. Also, the circumstances may be that electricity is encountered in wet conditions which could increase the probable severity due to the increased conductivity. Similarly, the person coming

into contact with the hazard may have an influence on severity; if it was a large healthy adult the severity may be different to an unhealthy child.

RISK RATING AND PRIORITISATION

Risk rating

In order to manage risks it is important to understand the scale of them: are they significant or not? One way to evaluate this is to describe the two components of risk, likelihood and severity (consequence), in terms of how large they are as a factor of the risk. Everyone has their own perception of risk because of their personal experiences and background. A method is therefore required in order to have a common approach and attempt to overcome individual differences. A guided approach to assigning a value to likelihood and severity (consequence) is used. Words commonly associated with the scale of likelihood and severity (consequence) are provided to guide the decision process. These words have a numeric value attached to them. The risk rating is a combination of the likelihood and severity (consequence) value.

Risk rating = likelihood x severity (consequence)

Where the:
Likelihood	Is how likely a loss will occur as a result of contact with the hazard.
Severity	Is the degree or amount of the resultant loss from contact with the hazard.
Risk rating	Is the level of the remaining risk after current controls have been taken into account.

Likelihood categories

5.	Almost Certain	Absence of any management controls. If conditions remain unchanged there is almost a 100% certainty that an accident will happen (e.g. broken rung on a ladder, live exposed electrical conductor, and untrained personnel).
4.	High	Serious failures in management controls. The effects of human behaviour or other factors could cause an accident but is unlikely without this additional factor (e.g. ladder not secured properly, oil spilled on floor, poorly trained personnel).
3.	Medium	Insufficient or substandard controls in place. Loss is unlikely during normal operation, however it may occur in emergencies or non-routine conditions (e.g. keys left in forklift trucks; obstructed gangways; refresher training required).
2.	Low	The situation is generally well managed, however occasional lapses could occur. This also applies to situations where people are required to behave safely in order to protect themselves but are well trained.
1.	Improbable	Loss, accident or illness could only occur under exceptional conditions. The situation is well managed and all reasonable precautions have been taken.

Severity (Consequence) categories

The severity (consequence) can be assessed on a scale of 1 to 5.

5.	Major	Causing death to one or more people. Loss or damage is such that it could cause serious business disruption (e.g. major fire, explosion or structural damage). Loss/damage in excess of (£_____).
4.	High	Causing permanent disability (e.g. loss of limb, sight or hearing). Loss/damage in excess of (£_____).
3.	Medium	Causing temporary disability (e.g. fractures). Loss/damage in excess of (£_____).
2.	Low	Causing significant injuries (e.g. sprains, bruises, and lacerations). Loss/damage in excess of (£_____) e.g. damage to fixtures and fittings.
1.	Minor	Causing minor injuries (e.g. cuts, scratches). No lost time likely other than for first aid treatment. Loss/damage in excess of (£_____) e.g. superficial damage to interior decorations.

The loss amounts in each of the above categories will depend on the size and type of organisation. Senior management should decide these figures in each case. Using the formula stated above, Risk Rating = Likelihood x Severity (consequence), the risk rating can be calculated. It will fall into the range of 1 - 25.

Risk prioritisation

In managing risks it is necessary to identify those risks that are most significant, the higher risks should be considered for action first. This risk rating is used to help prioritise the evaluated risks. The risk rating will be a number between 1 and 25, and in order to discern priorities at a glance these are often grouped into risk rating classifications as follows:

- Risk Rating 1 - 9   Low.
- Risk Rating 10 - 15   Medium.
- Risk Rating 16 - 25   High.

RESIDUAL RISK

This is the risk which remains when controls have been decided. For example, whilst a slip which could result in a fall from height may be prevented by a guard rail, the potential to slip on the level would remain, and this would be the residual risk after the guard rail was provided. Similarly, if local exhaust ventilation equipment removes a substance from a workplace it will only work to a degree of efficiency. It may reduce the level of substance to just below the workplace exposure limit (WEL), but the amount of substance remaining in the atmosphere will have a residual risk.

Acceptable/tolerable risk levels

After controls have been applied the residual risk has to be considered to determine if it is at an acceptable level. This will be influenced by what society considers being acceptable or tolerable. This may be influenced by how much knowledge there is on a given hazard or the level of risk people expect to be exposed to. Societal standards change and risk acceptability reduces each year within Europe. The noise action levels have been reduced in recent times, illustrating this change in acceptability.

Legislation places a general duty to reduce the level of risk so far as is reasonably practicable. The standard "practicable" requires employers to use any new improvements in technology.

GUIDANCE

When making a judgement about risks and whether controls are adequate care has to be taken to consider relevant guidance. This can be in the form of guidance to legislation - HSE guidance documents, industry standard guidance and relevant British Standards. If this is not done then the risk assessment may be determined to be not suitable and sufficient.

Legislation applying controls to specified hazards

Duties to apply specific controls are found in the schedules to the Control of Substances Hazardous to Health Regulations (COSHH) 2002, including exposure standards for substances in EH40. Similar requirements are provided in the Control of Lead at Work Regulations (CLAW) 2002 and Control of Asbestos Regulations (CAR) 2006. The guidance to the Manual Handling Operations Regulations (MHOR) 1992 provides comprehensive information on the evaluation of risk and the application of controls to manual handling operations.

GENERAL HIERARCHY OF CONTROL

We use the hierarchy to determine the highest level of control to remove or reduce the risk to the lowest level. The principle is to address each risk in the order of priority expressed in a general control hierarchy, for example:

E liminate - the substance or work practice.
R educe - the use or frequency or substitute - for a lesser hazard or change the physical form (dust to pellets).
I solation - glove box for handling hazardous biological agents.
C ontrol - at source, i.e. fume dust extraction, totally enclose.
P PE - a physical barrier between you and the risk.
D iscipline - follow the rules, obey signs and instructions.

Often a combination of measures is used to control a risk adequately.

The **application of the hierarchy based on prioritisation** of risk encourages the use of the highest level of control for those risks with the highest rating. Only when we have found that it is not possible to use this control should we move to the next highest control.

APPLYING CONTROLS TO SPECIFIED HAZARDS

Many workplace hazards are supported by guidance and codes of practice, such as COSHH, HSE guidance notes such as permit to work (HSG250) and work sector standards or British standards, such as BS EN ISO 12100-1 on machinery health and safety. These will aid in the application of controls to specific hazards.

DISTINCTION BETWEEN PRIORITIES AND TIME SCALES

There may be a high priority to reduce a high risk. However the action needed may take a very long time to carry out. It is therefore not always helpful to class all high risks as requiring a solution within an immediate timescale. It is important not to ignore the risk and often it is possible to carry out some aspects of lesser control on an interim basis, while the longer-term solution is being established.

Recording significant findings

FORMAT

Employers with five or more employees are required to record the **significant findings** of their risk assessments. This may be in writing or electronically, so long as it may be retrieved.

It should be noted that there are many forms and systems designed for recording assessments and while these may differ in design, the methodology broadly remains the same.

Information to be recorded

The task/plant/process/activity together with the hazards involved, their associated risks and persons affected by them together with existing control measures, should be recorded. The necessary actions required to further reduce the risk are then dealt with and are usually recorded separately.

Some items, particularly those with a high-risk rating, may require a more detailed explanation or there may be a series of alternative actions. Information on risk assessments and any controls must be brought to the attention of those assigned the task of work. Risk assessment information should be included in lesson plans to ensure items are not missed when staff are trained or retrained.

No.	Hazard Identification	Associated Risks	No. At Risk	Existing Controls	Consequence	Likelihood	Current Risk Rating	Comments

Figure 1-4-7: Risk assessment form.   Source: RMS.

Reasons for review

The risk assessment should be periodically reviewed and updated, and in addition, a review of risk assessments should be carried out following any significant changes to a workplace.

Examples of circumstances that would require the review of the validity of a risk assessment are:

■ When the results of monitoring (accidents, ill-health effects, environmental) are adverse and not as expected.
■ A change in process, work methods (introduction of shifts) or materials.
■ Changes in personnel.
■ Changes in legislation.
■ The introduction of new plant or technology.
■ New information becoming available.
■ As time passes - the risk assessment should be periodically reviewed and updated. A common approach would be no longer than 5 years.

The validity of risk assessment should be monitored through a combination of monitoring techniques such as:

■ Preventive maintenance inspections.
■ Safety representative/committee inspections.
■ Statutory and maintenance scheme inspections, tests and examinations.
■ Safety tours and inspections.
■ Occupational health surveys.
■ Air monitoring.
■ Safety audits.

Routine analysis of accident and ill-health reports, damage accident reports, and 'near-miss' reports can also provide a trigger to an earlier than planned review of risk assessments.

Special case applications of risk assessment

YOUNG PERSONS

Another specific group of people who must be considered in risk assessments are young people (under 18 years of age) and children (under compulsory school leaving age). Regulation 19 of the MHSWR 1999 requires the employer to carry out the risk assessment before young workers start work. These risk assessments must pay particular attention to the following risks:

■ Work which is beyond their physical or psychological capacity.
■ Work involving harmful exposure to agents which are toxic, carcinogenic or cause heritable genetic damage, harm to the unborn child or other chronic health affect.
■ Work involving harmful exposure to radiation.
■ Work involving risk of accidents, which it may reasonably be assumed cannot be recognised or avoided by young persons owing to their insufficient attention to safety or lack of experience or training.
■ Work in which there is a risk to health from extreme cold or heat, noise or vibration.

Where children are involved, regulation 10 requires that the significance of assessments must be communicated to the people who have parental responsibility.

Factors such as lack of knowledge, experience or training, the tendency of young persons to take risks because of over-enthusiasm and to respond more readily to peer pressure should also be taken into account when carrying out risk assessments.

EXPECTANT AND NURSING MOTHERS

Regulation 16 of MHSWR 1999 requires specific attention to women of childbearing age and the new or expectant mother. There are many factors that may increase risks to pregnant employees in the workplace. These include: exposure to chemicals such as pesticides, lead and those causing intracellular changes (mutagens) or affecting the embryo (teratogenic); biological exposures (e.g. hepatitis); exposure to physical agents such as ionising radiation and extremes of temperature; manual handling; ergonomic issues relating to prolonged standing or the adoption of awkward body movements; stress; and issues associated with the use and wearing of personal protective equipment.

DISABLED WORKERS

When a general risk assessment is conducted it is common for the assessor to principally have in mind the majority of the working population being considered. For most situations this will be people that are not disabled or otherwise vulnerable. It is essential that if this is the case and disabled workers are, or are going to be, involved in the work being considered that the risk assessment take full account of them. This may mean conducting a separate risk assessment for the disabled workers. As disabilities vary greatly it may be necessary to conduct separate risk assessments related to the specific disabilities that the workers have. In this way they are more likely to be both suitable and sufficient. Care should be taken to consider the particular disabilities in relation to the job when it is functioning normally, when problems arise from it and where emergencies may exist.

LONE WORKERS

Risk assessments that relate to people working alone are a special case in that special risks can arise from this work that are not present in other work. It should be remembered that work that is risk assessed on the basis of it normally being conducted whilst other people are around, in the main part of the day, can quickly become lone working when people work late, come in early or work weekends. Essentially the hazards from the work are often the same as those if the person was working with others but the additional risk control of having others at hand to provide routine assistance, for example to move something or hold something, are not available. Furthermore, lone working leads to the removal of another risk control - the ability of a co-worker to observe if another worker is suffering harm from the risks they are exposed to and the ability for the co-worker to respond or obtain assistance. When assessing the risks it is therefore essential to identify how the risks are controlled to take account of the lone working and whether this is adequate.

In summary, the Health and Safety Executive's approach to risk assessment is detailed in their publication INDG 163: Five Steps to Risk Assessment.

The recommended steps are:

- Identify the hazards.
- Decide who might be harmed and how.
- Evaluate the risk and decide on precautions.

- Record your findings and implement them.
- Review your assessment and update if necessary.

4.3 - General principles of control and risk reduction measures

General principles of prevention

In order to control the risks identified by risk assessments, employers and the self-employed need to introduce a risk control strategy of preventive and protective measures. To be effective a risk control strategy needs to encompass technical, behavioural and procedural controls. Regulation 4 of the Management of Health and Safety at Work Regulations (MHSWR) 1999 requires that:

"Where an employer implements any preventive and protective measures he shall do so on the basis of the principles specified in Schedule 1 to these Regulations".

Figure 1-4-8: Regulation 4 of MHSWR 1999.   *Source: Management of Health and Safety at Work Regulations (MHSWR) 1999.*

These are outlined below.

AVOIDING RISKS

If risks are avoided completely then they do not have to be either controlled or monitored. For example, not using pesticides or not working at height.

EVALUATING UNAVOIDABLE RISKS

Carry out a suitable and sufficient assessment of risks.

CONTROLLING (COMBATING) HAZARDS AT SOURCE

Repairing a hole in the floor is safer than displaying a warning sign. Other examples are the use of local exhaust ventilation to remove a substance at source, the design of equipment so that mechanical movement is enclosed and does not create a hazard and the replacement of a defective bearing to control the hazard of noise at source.

ADAPTING WORK TO THE INDIVIDUAL

This emphasises the importance of human factors in modern control methods.

If the well-being of the person is dealt with, there is less chance of the job causing ill-health and less chance of the person making mistakes which lead to accidents. Consideration should be given to the design of any equipment used, frequently used controls should be close to the operator, start buttons should be positioned to avoid inadvertent use, stop buttons should be close to the operator and easy to operate in an emergency. All equipment should be clearly labelled. Consideration should be given to minimisation of fatigue. Alleviating monotonous work by breaks or task rotation can help the individual to remain alert and pay attention to the task.

ADAPTING TO TECHNICAL PROGRESS

This can lead to improved, safer and healthier working conditions, for example, the provision of new non-slip floor surfaces or the bringing into use of less hazardous equipment such as new sound proofed equipment to replace old noisy equipment. In recent years this has included the use of waste chutes for removal of materials from scaffolds and the use of equipment, which produces levels of vibration.

REPLACING THE DANGEROUS BY THE NON/LESS-DANGEROUS

For example, using a battery operated drill rather than a mains powered tool, providing compressed air at a lower pressure or providing water based chemicals instead of solvent based chemicals.

DEVELOPING AN OVERALL COHERENT PREVENTION POLICY

Taking a holistic stance to the control of risk, this involves consideration of the organisation through the establishing of risk/control identification systems, consideration of the job, the use of task analysis and selection of the people, which includes consideration of human factors that affect an individual such as mental and physical requirements.

GIVING PRIORITY TO COLLECTIVE PROTECTIVE MEASURES OVER INDIVIDUAL PROTECTIVE MEASURES

Organisations with a less developed approach to health and safety may mistakenly see the solution to risks is to provide individuals with protective measures such as warning people of hazards and provision of personal protective equipment - using the 'safe person' (and healthy person) strategy. A more developed and effective approach is to give priority, where possible, to collective measures that provide protection to all workers such as provisions of barriers around street works or cleaning up a slippery substance spill rather than putting signs to warn workers - using the 'safe place' (and healthy place) strategy. These two strategies are supported by a third strategy sometime called the 'safe system' (and healthy system) strategy. This strategy establishes the correct way to do things in the form of rules and procedures, for example, the rule that says 'clean up after you do work' in order that the place is left in a safe and healthy condition.

Reliance on only a safe/healthy person strategy is the weakest of controls. The preferred strategy is the safe/healthy place and priority must be given to using it where possible. By ensuring a safe/healthy place all people that find themselves in it will gain protection. This approach is reflected in the hierarchy used for safeguarding dangerous parts of equipment - our first priority is to provide guards around the dangerous parts (making it a safe place) and for the remainder that cannot be enclosed in this way we provide information, instruction and training to those that use the equipment (making the safe person).

In practice, the most successful organisations use a combination of the three strategies, with the emphasis on making the place safe/healthy, supporting this with systems of work (procedures) and paying attention to the person element so that they support rather than undermine the other strategies. Many organisations that feel they have invested effort in getting the place and procedures right are taking a fresh look at the actions necessary to ensure the person is right also. Studies have shown that this too is a critical aspect of effective management of health and safety.

PROVIDING APPROPRIATE INFORMATION AND INSTRUCTIONS TO EMPLOYEES

It is essential to distinguish between: information, instruction, training and supervision. This will ensure clarity of purpose for each and suggest the best way to communicate each effectively.

Information

Purpose	To improve awareness about health and safety generally and in relation to specific hazards, their controls and management performance to bring about these controls. In itself passive, it relies on the recipient to interpret.		
Subjects	Legislation. Company policy statements.	Accident statistics. General hazards and controls.	Names of appointed first aiders.
Means of communication	Bulletins and news sheets. Notice boards, propaganda, films.	Team briefing. Written material for visitors.	Site signs and labels.

Instruction

Purpose	To control employees, contractors and visitors behaviour with regard to general and specific health and safety arrangements. Typically one way, often no real check or understanding.		
Subjects	Health and safety rules. Policy, arrangements and plans.	Use of PPE. Specific hazards e.g. smoking.	Emergency procedures. Reporting accidents.
Means of communicating	Formally using verbal, written and visual material, notice boards, induction and job training, direct issue of document, 'tool-box talks'.		

Training

Purpose	To develop people, their attitudes, perception and motivation with regard to health and safety to ensure acceptable actions. Training should use two-way communication - information/instruction given and understanding checked. This may be by observation of a person's practical skill, for example, by driving a fork lift truck or using a simulator, and/or by written or verbal assessment.		
Subjects	Accident investigation. Conducting risk assessments. Conducting inspections/audits. How to comply with instructions.	How to set up your display screen workstation. How to use work equipment e.g. rough terrain fork lift truck.	Use of personal protective equipment. Manual handling techniques. Emergency procedures.
Means of communicating	On/off the job. Internal/external trainers.	Explanation, demonstration, discussion and practice.	One-to-one or group. Written, oral and visual material.

Arrangements for induction

It is essential that systematic arrangements are in place to ensure a consistent standard of induction for health and safety. It is an important integral part of the prevention process, setting out standards of behaviour and workplace conditions for the organisation. It illustrates hazards that workers may create and helps to make them aware of what they may encounter on site. It must focus on the controls that should be used as well as the hazards that may be encountered.

This creates an expectation of health and safety to be achieved and to be expected from each other. It provides confidence to the workforce that health and safety is an important part of doing work in the right way. It provides clarity of reporting chains for supervision and explains who workers can go to if they identify a conflict of interest with what is being expected and getting the work done.

Some organisations use a health and safety passport system to confirm that people coming to site have received basic training in general health and safety, and whilst this is an excellent approach it does not substitute for all of the site induction arrangements. It is still necessary for workers to know the relevant hazards and controls for each location that they are working in.

For example, this will mean knowing areas they can and cannot go to, the use of walkways, where rest facilities are, who the first aiders are and who they report hazards/accidents to. For induction training to be meaningful, it has to be relevant to the trainee.

For example, the information given to a driver who makes both internal and external deliveries could include:

- Information on internal traffic routes.
- Speed limits.
- Parking/loading areas.
- Any hazardous substances on site.
- The need to carry out regular inspections of the vehicle and how to report defects.
- Company rules regarding the carrying of passengers, mobile phones, etc.
- How to report accidents and incidents.

Supervision

Supervision consists of the provision/reinforcement of performance standards of employees to ensure health and safety. It includes monitoring that agreed work practices are followed and the use of motivation techniques such as involvement of the workforce in task design to help ensure compliance with the required actions.

The success of information instruction and training activities needs to be measured to enable updating to take place to cater for changes in the workplace.

The supervisor has a crucial part to play in this monitoring process. It is important to balance the amount and timing of supervision against the work being done. It is generally appropriate that the level of supervision necessary increases with the level of risk related to the work. It can be said that when considering supervision of individuals it is important to take account of the competence of the person.

In cases where a person has qualifications but has no experience and is therefore low in competence (e.g. a young person straight from college) then supervision must increase accordingly.

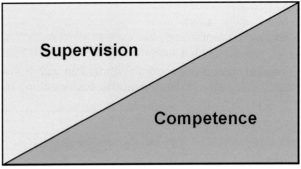

Figure 1-4-9: Competence v supervision.　　　Source: RMS.

General hierarchy of control

ELIMINATION/AVOIDING RISKS

Avoiding risk at source is the best option for controlling risk. It means that everyone is protected and there is no residual risk to manage. In many cases this may be a difficult option to achieve; however, it is something that must be considered by designers at the conception stage of a project. For example, in order to avoid the risk of falling it is important, where possible, to design out the need to work at height.

Removal of the hazard in total from the working environment should be aimed for, but this is not always practical.

REDUCING/SUBSTITUTION

Reducing the hazard to an acceptable level by substituting something less hazardous/or reducing the strength of the hazardous material/or reducing the quantity in use/etc.

Reduction of exposure may be achieved by keeping the numbers at risk to a minimum by timing certain work so that other tasks are not taking place nearby. Rotating work schedules, to minimise the exposure to any one person, for example, by reducing the frequency and duration of exposure to radiation, noise or vibration is another possibility.

ENGINEERING CONTROL

A common engineering control involves the *isolation* of the hazard from people. For example, enclosing the hazard so there is a controlled barrier between people and the hazard, for example, fitting fixed guards around dangerous parts of a machine, provision of guard rails on scaffolds or barriers round street works.

Other engineering controls limit the chance or amount of exposure to hazards. For example, provision of an overload or over run device on a crane or hoist, control of dust/fumes released into the atmosphere by local exhaust ventilation, or to limit the noise level emitted by use of sound insulation.

SIGNAGE, WARNINGS AND ADMINISTRATIVE CONTOLS

Administrative controls

A safe system of work is an example of an administrative control; it is a formal procedure which results from systematic examination of a task in order to identify all the hazards and the controls necessary for health and safety. It defines safe methods of working, to ensure that hazards are eliminated or risks minimised. In some cases the system of work is controlled by the use of structured checklists that ensure steps in the system of work are carried out. This is often called a permit to work. For administrative controls to be effective there will need to be good information, instruction, training and supervision, signs and warnings may accompany administrative controls to help to ensure people are aware of the hazards and respond as intended.

Signs and warnings

Role of safety signs and signals

The role is to provide warning of hazards in the workplace, instruction on health and safety controls needed and information on safe conditions provide in the workplace.

In order to avoid possible confusion due to language ability and reading skills, the shape, colour and symbols used on safety signs are governed by the Health and Safety (Safety Signs and Signals) Regulations (SSSR) 1996. The regulations ensure that employers provide and maintain standard signs and signals in the workplace, where significant risks have not been avoided by other means, to enable more consistent use, clearer communication and better understanding of information.

Requirements of Health and Safety (Safety Signs and Signals) Regulations (SSSR) 1996

The regulations require employers to provide specific safety signs whenever there is a significant risk which has not been avoided or controlled by other means, e.g. by engineering controls and safe systems of work. Where a safety sign would not help to reduce that risk there is no need to provide a sign.

They require employers to:

■ Maintain the safety signs which are provided by them.
■ Explain unfamiliar signs to their employees and tell them what they need to do when they see a safety sign.
■ They require, where necessary, the use of road traffic signs within workplaces to regulate road traffic.

The regulations do not apply in connection with transport or labelling of substances, other signs are to be used instead. They also do not cover the colour coding of pipe work containing hazardous substances, a system of marking is contained in BS 1710.

Categories and features

Signs are defined as those combining shape, colour and a pictorial symbol to provide specific health and safety information and instruction.

The regulations require that safety signs comply with BS 5378 and fire safety signs comply with BS 5499. The Regulations cover 4 main categories of signs:

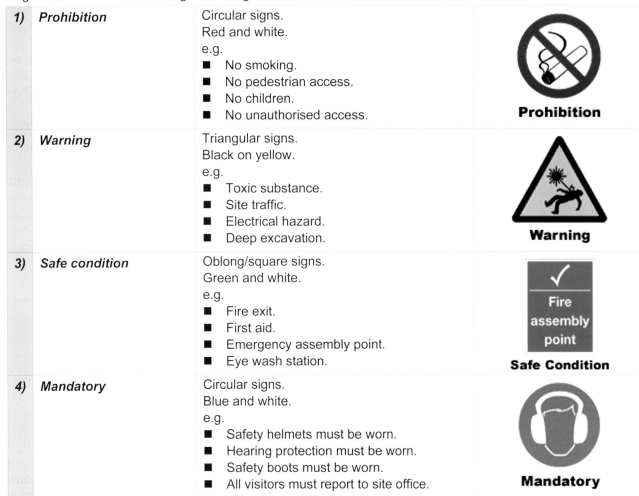

1)	*Prohibition*	Circular signs. Red and white. e.g. ■ No smoking. ■ No pedestrian access. ■ No children. ■ No unauthorised access.	**Prohibition**
2)	*Warning*	Triangular signs. Black on yellow. e.g. ■ Toxic substance. ■ Site traffic. ■ Electrical hazard. ■ Deep excavation.	**Warning**
3)	*Safe condition*	Oblong/square signs. Green and white. e.g. ■ Fire exit. ■ First aid. ■ Emergency assembly point. ■ Eye wash station.	**Safe Condition**
4)	*Mandatory*	Circular signs. Blue and white. e.g. ■ Safety helmets must be worn. ■ Hearing protection must be worn. ■ Safety boots must be worn. ■ All visitors must report to site office.	**Mandatory**

Figure 1-4-10: Categories of safety signs. *Source: RMS.*

Supplementary signs provide additional information. For example where a noise hazard is identified by a warning sign - 'hearing protection available on request' may be added as supplementary information.

Figure 1-4-11: Prohibition signs. *Source: RMS.*

Figure 1-4-12: Warning and mandatory sign. *Source: RMS.*

Figure 1-4-13: Mandatory sign.   *Source: RMS.*

Figure 1-4-14: Safe condition sign.   *Source: RMS.*

Supplementary safety signs can be used to mark obstacles e.g. the edge of a raised platform and dangerous locations e.g. an area where objects may fall or an area where work is going on that the public should not access. These may be yellow and black or red and white - in each case they consist of alternate colour stripes set at 45° angles. These supplementary signs must not be used as a substitute for other signs as defined above.

Figure 1-4-15: Hazard identification - obstruction. *Source: RMS.*

Figure 1-4-16: Hazard identification - restricted width. *Source: RMS.*

Signals

The regulations establish principles for acoustic, verbal and hand signals. Acoustic signals have to be able to be heard and would usually be set at a level of 10dB above the level of ambient noise and at an appropriate frequency. Verbal signals can be used to direct hazardous operations and may be made by either human, for example when directing lifting operations or artificial voices such as those used to indicate that a vehicle is reversing. Spoken messages must be clear, concise and understood by the listener. People involved need a good knowledge of the language used. Where English is not the first language of most staff the codes used do not have to be in English.

Code word	Meaning
Start	Start an operation
Stop	Interrupt or end an operation
End	Stop an operation
Raise	Raise a load
Lower	Lower a load
Forwards	Move forward
Backwards	Move backwards
Right	Move to signaller's right
Left	Move to signaller's left
Danger	Emergency stop
Quickly	Speed up a movement

Figure 1-4-17: Codes for verbal signals.   *Source: Health and Safety (Safety Signs and Safety Signals) Regulations 1996.*

Hand signals may be used to direct hazardous operations such as cranes or vehicle manoeuvres. It is essential that they be precise, simple, and easy to make and to understand.

A standard set of signalling codes as proposed by the SSSR 1996 are set as follows.

Hand signals must be precise, simple, easy to make and to understand, and clearly distinct from other such signals.

Meaning	Description	Illustration
General signals:		
START Attention Start of Command	Both arms are extended horizontally with the palms facing forwards	
STOP Interruption End of movement	The right arm points upwards with the palm facing forwards	
END of the operation	Both hands are clasped at chest height	
Vertical movements:		
RAISE	The right arm points upwards with the palm facing forward and slowly makes a circle	
LOWER	The right arm points downwards with the palm facing inwards and slowly makes a circle	
VERTICAL DISTANCE	The hands indicate the relevant distance	
Horizontal movements:		
MOVE FORWARDS	Both arms are bent with the palms facing upwards, and the forearms make slow movements towards the body	
MOVE BACKWARDS	Both arms are bent with the palms facing downwards, and the forearms make slow movements away from the body	
RIGHT to the signalman's	The right arm is extended more or less horizontally with the palm facing downwards and slowly makes small movements to the right	

Meaning	Description	Illustration
Horizontal movements - cont'd:		
LEFT to the signalman's	The left arm is extended more or less horizontally with the palm facing downwards and slowly makes small movements to the left	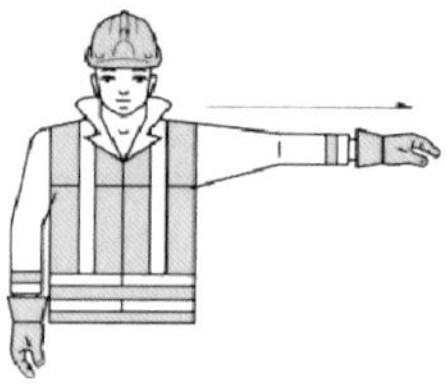
HORIZONTAL DISTANCE	The hands indicate the relevant distance	
Danger:		
DANGER Emergency stop	Both arms points upwards with the palms facing forwards	
QUICK	All movements faster	
SLOW	All movements slower	

Figure 1-4-18: Hand signals.   Source: Health and Safety (Safety Signs and Safety Signals) Regulations 1996.

PERSONAL PROTECTIVE EQUIPMENT

Requirements

Personal protective equipment (PPE) is a low level control. It is often in the form of a simple barrier between the user and the risk, for example gloves and acid, and as such its effectiveness is subject to correct fit or adjustment. PPE is best used for low risk protection or as additional protection to safeguard against engineering control limitations or failure, for example, breathing apparatus to protect against fume extraction limitations or failure when dealing with volatile toxic substances. It is important to determine the limitations of particular PPE before use.

The main benefits include low cost and portability when considered against engineering strategies.

The Personal Protective Equipment at Work Regulations (PPER) 1992 state:

- Ensure PPE is suitable for hazard and person.
- No PPE should be issued without adequate training/instruction.
- Issue, obtain signature and record.
- Set-up monitoring systems.
- Organise routine exchange systems.
- Implement cleaning/sterilisation.
- Issue written/verbal instructions, define when and where to use.
- Provide suitable storage.

Training and instruction in the use of personal protective equipment will include both:

- **Theoretical -** provision of a clear understanding of the reasons for wearing the PPE, factors which may affect the performance, the cleaning, maintenance and identification of defects.
- **Practical -** practising the wearing, adjusting, removing, cleaning, maintenance and testing of PPE.

Benefits and limitations

"Whatever PPE is chosen, it should be remembered that, although some types of equipment do provide very high levels of protection, none provides 100%".

Figure 1-4-19: PPE quote.   Source: Guidance on the Personal Protection Equipment Regulations 1992.

PPE includes the following when worn for health and safety reasons at work:

- Aprons.
- Adverse weather gear.
- High visibility clothing.
- Gloves.
- Safety footwear.
- Safety helmets.
- Eye protection.
- Life-jackets.
- Respirators.
- Safety harness.
- Underwater breathing gear.

There are numerous reasons why personal protective equipment (PPE) should be considered only after other possibilities have been exhausted:

- It is a legal requirement (e.g. within the COSHH 2002 and MHSWR 1999) that other means of control are considered first.
- PPE may not provide adequate protection because of such factors as poor selection, poor fit, incompatibility with other types of PPE, contamination, and misuse or non-use by employees.
- PPE is likely to be uncomfortable and relies for its effectiveness on a conscious action by the user.
- In certain circumstances, its use can actually create additional risks (for instance, warning sounds masked by hearing protection).
- PPE only protects the wearer and not others who may be in the area and also at risk.
- The introduction of PPE may bring another hazard such as impaired vision, impaired movement or fatigue.
- PPE may only be capable of minimising injury rather than preventing it.

Protection will depend upon how well the personal protective equipment fits in many cases, e.g. with respirators, breathing apparatus, noise protection devices.

Factors that can influence fit are whether adequate training and instruction have been given and certain other individual conditions such as:

- Long hair.
- Wearing of spectacles.
- Male facial hair growth, during a shift, may necessitate the progressive adjustment of respiratory protection worn during the work period.

PPE will not be suitable unless:

- It is appropriate to the risk involved and the prevailing conditions of the workplace.
- It is ergonomic (user-friendly) in design and takes account of the state of health of the user.
- It fits the wearer correctly, perhaps after adjustment.
- It is effective in preventing or controlling the risk(s) [without increasing the overall risk], so far as is practicable.
- It must comply with EU directives or other specific standards.
- It must be compatible with other equipment where there is more than one risk to guard against.

The use of PPE should only be used for low risk activities or to provide additional protection in case primary control measures fail. In general PPE should only be used as a last resort after all other options have been explored. The order of control of hazards should follow a hierarchy. One such hierarchy that places PPE at the bottom is:

> *E* liminate.
> *R* educe/substitute.
> *I* solate.
> *C* ontrols - other engineering and administrative.
> *P* PE.

4.4 - Sources of health and safety information

Internal to the organisation

ACCIDENT/ILL-HEALTH AND ABSENCE DATA

Used properly, accident/ill-health and absence data allow comparisons to be made between different organisations and business sections by monitoring year on year performance. Analysis can be made to identify areas of possible concern and the overall effectiveness of any new control measures that may have been introduced. Data can be collected internally using accident books and report forms (e.g. RIDDOR 1995) and can be related to data gathered by other organisations such as:

- The World Health Organisation (WHO).
- The International Labour Organisation (ILO).
- The Department of the Environment (Labour Force Survey).
- The HSE (including Statistical Services Unit and HSC Annual Report Statistical Supplement).
- Industry associations.

There are several methods of presenting data for analysis and some of the more common ones are given below. Methods should not be mixed and figures should only be used to compare like with like.

Accident/injury frequency rates

Some parts of industry prefer to calculate injury frequency rates, usually per million hours worked. Considering the hours worked rather than the number of employees avoids the problem of part-time workers and overtime causing a distortion as it does in the incidence rate calculation. It should be noted that the International Labour Office and HSE use 1,000,000 for the frequency rate, USA use 200,000.

Workplace organisations tend to use a smaller multiplier, for example, 100,000.

$$\frac{\text{Number of accident/injuries in the period} \times 1,000,000}{\text{Total hours worked during the period}}$$

Accident/injury incidence rates

The HSE's formula for calculating an annual injury incidence rate is:

$$\frac{\text{Number of reportable injuries in financial year} \times 100,000}{\text{Average number employed during year}}$$

This is the rate per 100,000 employees. It does not allow for part-time workers or overtime and should only be used for a comparison of an annual calculation. There must be an adjustment made if shorter periods are to be considered. The HSE calculate national incidence rates. When workplace organisations calculate their own incident rate the number employed and injuries will be far less and it is common practice to use a smaller multiplier, for example 1,000.

Accident/injury severity rates

$$\frac{\text{Total number of days lost} \times 1,000}{\text{Total hours worked}}$$

The injury severity rate does not necessarily correlate well with the seriousness of the injury. The data may be affected by the propensity of people in different parts of the country to take time off after a particular injury, e.g. food industry for poisoning.

Mean duration rate

$$\frac{\text{Total number of days lost}}{\text{Total number of accidents}}$$

Duration rate

$$\frac{\text{Number of hours worked}}{\text{Total number of accidents}}$$

Absence data

Analysing absence data is important for two reasons:

- The process enables an organisation to determine whether it has a work related absence problem.
- It can help the organisation to understand the causal effects of absenteeism.

Assessing the magnitude of absenteeism

Days lost per employee and percentage lost time are the two measures used to gain an overall understanding of the magnitude of the problem.

$$\text{Days lost per employee} = \frac{\text{Total days lost}}{\text{Number of employees}}$$

$$\text{Percentage lost time} = \frac{\text{Number of days lost through absence} \times 100}{(\text{Number of employees}) \times (\text{Number working days})}$$

Technically, percentage lost time is the better overall measure of absenteeism. Days lost per employee, however, has an advantage in terms of simplicity of calculation. For this reason, it is the measure most commonly used by organisations to assess absenteeism.

RESULTS OF AUDITS/INSPECTIONS

The aim of audits and inspections is to give management a detailed picture regarding the standards of health and safety management within the organisation. Thus audits and inspection are, essentially, confirmatory exercises which demonstrate that the health and safety management system is effective. The level and detail of audits/inspections carried out will depend on the type of organisation and its confidence in the existing management system.

Information from audits and inspections enables both symptoms as well as the cause to be identified and appropriate action taken. It is important to ensure that risk control measures provided by the organisation, including equipment and systems of work, are appropriate and that action is taken to establish and maintain good standards. Auditors will normally obtain information from three sources:

1) Interviewing individuals both about the operation of the health and safety management system and practices and their knowledge, understanding and perceptions of it.
2) Examining documentation for completeness, accuracy and reliability.
3) Visual observation of physical conditions and working practices to ensure conformity to legal and organisational standards.

Inspections generally rely on examination and observation of physical conditions in the workplace. Inspections can provide a perspective of the level of control of workplace hazards.

INVESTIGATION REPORTS

Any accident may result in a claim. It is essential that organisations anticipate this and at the earliest opportunity, assemble data necessary to consider whether a claim may be defended.

Investigating accidents and copying relevant data to a document controlled file is normally part of the accident investigation process. Immediate and root causes of accidents should be analysed and appropriate preventative measures identified and implemented.

MAINTENANCE RECORDS

If a system of planned maintenance is implemented then, by definition, any breakdown is likely to be accidental. Therefore, all breakdowns must be reported and investigated. Trends and patterns of failures can be analysed and the necessary preventative action taken. Equipment often fails due to an unsafe condition, for example, the brakes on a car. Being able to predict, and therefore prevent these situations is an essential safety management tool.

External to the organisation

MANUFACTURERS' DATA

The HASAWA 1974 section 6 requires manufacturers to make adequate information available to those they supply with articles or substances. The information should be sufficient to enable the person to use the article or substance safely and should cover reasonably foreseeable risks including those arising from disposal and dismantling. If, as a result of testing or research, new hazards come to light, reasonably practicable steps must be taken to pass on information to those supplied.

LEGISLATION (E.G. ACTS AND REGULATIONS)

These are available from the Her Majesty's Stationary Office (HMSO) (which is now part of the Office of Public Sector Information) and are prime sources which give the precise legal requirement. They can, however, be difficult to read without some legal understanding. It is also easy to miss changes and amendments unless an updating service is used.

The aim of the Office of Public Sector Information is to publish all UK Statutory Instruments on the Internet simultaneously with, or within 24 hours of, their publication in printed form. However, any document which is especially complex in terms of its size or its typography may take longer to prepare. New statutory instruments may be accessed from the internet via http://www.opsi.gov.uk.

EUROPEAN

The European Safety Agency was set up by the European Union (EU) to bring together the vast reservoir of knowledge and information on OSH-related issues and preventive measures.

HSE PUBLICATIONS

HSE Books publishes both approved codes of practice (ACOPs) and guidance notes. While failure to follow an ACOP is not in itself an offence, a defendant would have to show that the steps they took were equally effective thus transferring the burden of proof onto the defendant. Guidance notes, and other advisory literature, are persuasive in a law court; however they can set standards higher than the basic legal minimum. Electronic versions of HSE publications are available free via their website, http://www.hse.gov.uk. Lists of both priced (hard copy) and free publications are also available from HSE Books via http://www.hsebooks.com.

TRADE ASSOCIATIONS

Trade associations such as the Confederation of British Industry (CBI) and Engineering Employers Federation (EEF) often produce guidance and codes of practice for companies as do industrial training boards such as the Construction Industry Training Board (CITB) and the Paint Makers Association.

Manufacturers and suppliers of articles and substances have a legal duty to provide information under s.6 of the HASAWA 1974 and the Chemicals (Hazard Information and Packaging for Supply) Regulations (CHIP).

BRITISH, EUROPEAN AND INTERNATIONAL STANDARDS

The British Standards Institute (BSI) provides some high quality advice which is usually above the legal minimum standard. There is a distinct trend towards linking British Standards with legislation, for example, with the Safety Signs Regulations and BS 5378 as described in the communications module.

Of particular interest to health and safety is the BSI Occupational Health and Safety Assessment Series standard BS OHSAS18001:2007 "Occupational health and safety management systems - requirements". BS 18001 is intended to help organisations develop a framework for managing occupational health and safety so employees and others who may be affected by the organisation's activities are adequately protected.

There is also progressive harmonisation to European Standards (CEN) and the use of CE Marking. Some British and European standards are being used as a basis for international standards and are being adopted as ISO standards, such as that for machinery health and safety BS EN ISO 12100-1.

ILO AND OTHER AUTHORATIVE SOURCES

The International Labour Organisation (ILO) deals with labour standards, fundamental principles and rights at work. They have a website and a database listing all types of work-related information. The ILO produces an Encyclopaedia of Occupational Health and Safety, it is a widely respected comprehensive publication which is now available free of charge on the ILO website.

The World Health Organisation is the United Nation's specialised agency for health and was established in 1948. It has information on health, where good health is defined as "a state of complete physical, mental and social well-being and not merely the absence of disease or infirmity".

There are several occupational health and safety oriented books available from bodies such as ROSPA, IOSH, RMS Publishing and the British Safety Council. They are very useful, providing a range of features including detailed reference, updates on new legislation, information on new publications and 'in depth' explanatory articles. The product and equipment advertising may also be a useful source of information.

PROFESSIONAL BODIES

There are a number of safety related professional bodies such as the Institution of Occupational Safety and Health (IOSH). These provide local newsletters, regular meetings and a subscription to their magazine as part of the membership package. People who are interested in health and safety can join as affiliate members with no formal qualifications.

IT SOURCES

There is an increasing amount of information available on-line using a computer and an internet service provider. The World Wide Web provides a consistent interface with which to access many safety organisations, including the HSE (http://www.hse.gov.uk). Care should be taken to verify information from an unknown web source by an alternative source; also, some material found may be out of date, applicable to another territory or incorrect. There is also a range of electronic subscription services available that aim to keep the subscriber informed of relevant health and safety issues, provide access to information and an updating service.

4.5 - Developing and implementing a safe system of work

Employer's duty to provide safe system of work

In criminal law the **Health and Safety at Work etc. Act (HASAWA) 1974** clearly requires the provision and maintenance of plant and systems of work that are, so far as is reasonably practicable, safe and without risks to health. The employer should also provide safe systems of work in order to fulfil his common law duty of care established in principles of negligence.

Definition of safe system of work (SSW):

"The integration of   *P eople*
                         E quipment and
                         M aterials in the correct
                         E nvironment to ensure health and safety"

This means that all work must be conducted in a healthy and safe way, but does not require that all work has to be prescribed in a written form. It is perfectly acceptable that a safe system of work be established and communicated orally at the time of the need to conduct the work e.g. work for using a ladder to inspect a pipe joint.

In contrast, it does not mean that all systems of work can be specified orally. The higher the risks the more appropriate it is to specify safe systems of work in writing. This is reflected in the more formal approach to specifying a safe system of work for entry into a confined space, where the safe system of work is accompanied by a permit to work to provide higher assurance that it is followed correctly.

COMPONENTS OF THE SYSTEM (PEME)

People

Safe behaviour - sound knowledge, skills (both mental and physical), risk and control aware, willingness to conform with the system (motivation), resistance to pressures to behave unsafely, adequately trained, with job experience and supervised, working in harmony with each other.

Equipment

Good design and safety specification of plant, machinery and equipment - taking into account the work that it is to do, the environment and ergonomic factors, inspection and maintenance requirements.

Materials

Consideration should be given to safety and health issues in both the raw material state and as the finished product - appropriate purchasing and quality standards; to include consideration of use, handling, storage, transport and safe disposal of waste, should be established.

Environment

Establishing critical elements in the workplace that surround the people - effective control of heating, lighting and ventilation; safe levels of noise and vibration; effective control of dust, fumes, radiation, chemicals and biological hazards; effective means of access and egress and a good standards of welfare amenity provision (sanitation, hand washing, showers, clothing storage, catering, drinking water, and first aid).

The role of competent persons

It is important that those involved in the development process gain a perspective on the acceptability of the standards of proposed systems of work. This will mean consideration of the proposed safe system of work by people competent to provide a perspective. In a general sense this could be a health and safety practitioner who would be able to provide a general review of the proposed system of work against legal and practical requirements.

In addition, depending on the technical complexity and the risks associated with the task, it may be necessary to get a perspective from someone that is competent in the technical health and safety issues involved, for example, an electrical specialist. Care should be taken not to presume the health and safety competence of specialist engineers or similar, and this should be confirmed before involvement in the development process. The onus is on the employer to determine the competence of people who may be involved in for example development of safe systems of work, carrying out risk assessments, inspections, or issuing permits to work. Broadly, a competent person should have knowledge (practical and theoretical) and skill, as well as experience.

Importance of employee involvement

Employee involvement in the development of safe systems is essential to ensure their safe behaviour when working to the system. The employee knows all the practical difficulties in working to theoretical systems of work, such as the absence of equipment specified or requirements that mean more people to do the task than are available. They have frequently encountered circumstances that make the work difficult and how they get round them, such as poor access/egress. By discussing proposed systems of work with employees it is possible to learn these practicalities and ensure the system of work takes account of them. Involvement in this way often ensures that the agreed system of work is followed.

Importance and relevance of written procedures

Where the safe system of work is complex or the risks of not working to it are high it is important to define what must be done in written procedures. This does not mean that written procedures have to be complicated or wordy; some of the most effective are those that are clear, simple and easily understood. The importance of creating written procedures is that they serve as a clear setting of standards of work, including how the risks of the work are to be combated. This is particularly relevant when communicating to a client how a contractor is going to conduct work safely. This will contribute to tender documents used to win work, to a construction stage plan to satisfy the Construction (Design and Management) Regulations (CDM) 2007. It will also enable supervisors and others that monitor health and safety to do so against clear standards of performance.

Written procedures may relate to specific work to be done, such as carrying out a cutting operation or to general health and safety matters such as reporting accidents. The construction industry makes particular use of written procedures in the form of method statements. As the name suggests they are documents that express how work is to be conducted, the order of events, the health and safety considerations and the measures that will make it safe and healthy for those that might be affected.

It is important that procedures express how the work is done, not just how it should be done in theory. If there is a poor match between the procedure and what can be done in practice it will devalue that and other procedures and cause confusion. If a good match is achieved, in a manner that is clear to workers and supervisors, there is a higher chance that it will be complied with and the supervisor is more able to enforce it. Job/task analysis is not only necessary to identify the hazards and controls, but is essential for preparing written procedures. These can then be translated into comprehensive training plans to ensure the correct skill and knowledge content for the work to be carried out safely.

Technical, procedural and behavioural controls

In the workplace we use a variety of controls. In order to give emphasis to them and to help identify how complete our approach is to health and safety we group controls into a number of categories. The categories tend to reflect the main strategies used to improve health and safety. The categories reflect the general principles of prevention referred to earlier in section 4.3, but use slightly different words. It is important to note that in order to deal effectively with a hazard we will need to use all three forms of control, to a greater or lesser degree, for example with the use of a hard hat for the control of a hazard of falling materials. A hard hat is a technical control that will afford a quantity of protection - the technical aspects of this come into play when we consider how long a hard hat lasts and what type is suitable for what work/person. Purchasing hard hats will not be effective if procedures are not in place to enable issue and replacement.

These controls will be immediately undermined if we do not provide education and training to those that wear and enforce the wearing of hard hats in order to ensure the right behaviour of the wearer.

Risk control measures:

Technical	(place)	(job)
Procedural	(system)	(organisation)
Behavioural	(person)	(person)

Technical controls include:

- Equipment - design (e.g. guarding) and maintenance.
- Access/egress - provision of wide aisles, access kept clear of storage items.
- Materials (substances and articles) - choice of packaging to make handling easier.
- Environment (temperature, light, dust, noise) - local exhaust ventilation (LEV).
- Issue of the correct PPE for the task.

Procedural controls include:

- Policy and standards.
- Rules.
- Procedures.
- Permit to work.
- Authorisation and co-ordination of actions.
- Purchasing controls.
- Accident investigation and analysis.
- Emergency preparedness.
- Procedures in the issue, use and maintenance of PPE.

Behavioural controls include:

- Awareness, knowledge, skill, competence.
- Attitude, perception, motivation, communication.
- Supervision.
- Health surveillance.
- Training in the issue of PPE.

In practice, the most successful organisations use a combination of the three strategies, with the emphasis on making the place safe/healthy (providing technical controls) and supporting this with procedures and paying attention to the person. Many organisations that feel they have done all that is necessary to get the place and procedures correct are taking a fresh look at the actions necessary to ensure the person's behaviour is correct also. Studies have shown that this too is a critical aspect of effective management of health and safety.

Development of a safe system of work

ANALYSING THE TASK

Assessment of the task must consider not only the job to be done, but the environment where it is to be done, to allow a full consideration of the hazards to be made. This may involve a detailed review known as Job or Task Analysis. Job/task safety analysis consists of a formal step by step review of the work to be carried out. All aspects of the task should be considered and recorded in writing to ensure that nothing is overlooked. Typical considerations would be:

- The task to be done.
- Where the task is done.
- That which is used.
- The current controls.
- Adequacy of controls.
- Correct use by the operators of the controls.
- Behavioural factors operators/supervisors (error considerations).

The objective is to establish the hazards and controls at each stage of the procedure to ensure a safe result. How the progress of work, in particular safety arrangements, will be monitored should be considered. Any special requirements for monitoring should be specified during the planning stage, e.g. gas testing, temperature or pressure levels, measurement of emissions.

Job/task analysis

Job/task analysis is the identification of all the accident prevention measures appropriate to a particular job or area of work activity, and the behavioural factors which most significantly influence whether or not these measures are taken. The approach is diagnostic as well as descriptive. Analysis can be:

1) Job based: operators of plant, fork lift truck drivers.
2) Task based: manual handling activities, housekeeping.

The results can be used to correct existing analyses and to improve such things as emergency procedures, reporting of information and the layout of work areas. The process of job analysis needs to be carried out methodically through a series of steps and the whole analysis should be documented.

Intrinsic hazards

1) Hand contact with moving filler and capping press, and when changing cap supply.
2) Cuts to hand from removal of broken bottles from filler.
3) In-running nip to conveyor.
4) Flying glass splinters due to occasional bottle explosions.
5) Broken glass on floor.
6) Noise - occupational deafness.
7) Slips and falls on wet floor.

Information used and obtained in the job/task analysis

EXAMPLE JOB ANALYSIS SHEET

Job Title: Filling machine operator

Department: Finishing

Purpose: Filling beer bottles using automatic filler and capper

Machinery and Equipment

Vickers Dawson rotary filler incorporating capping press

Empty bottle conveyor, marshalling table and filled bottle conveyor

Hand Tools - spanners, steel lever

Materials

Empty bottles

Protection

1) Clothing, one-piece overall and apron
2) Safety shoes/Wellingtons as necessary
3) Eye protection against bottle breakages
4) Hair enclosed in combined drill cap and snood
5) Heavy duty gloves
6) Ear defenders.

Guards

Total enclosure of rotary filler and capping press; conveyor end adjacent to filler.

Figure 1-4-20: Example of a job analysis sheet. *Source: RMS.*

Incidence of accidents

Four machines of this type are in regular use in the same department. The operator with least experience has been doing this job for 8 months; others have up to 20 years' experience. No recent accidents can be recalled although the risk of flying and broken glass is always present.

Work organisation

A bonus system is operated and the work is mainly repetitive. After setting-up, a large order could run for two or three days. On the other hand, a series of small orders are done occasionally which requires re-setting the machine after every 4 minute cycle when much more time would be spent setting than running the machine.

Operator and assistant are inter-changeable but the operator always does the adjustment to the flow control device to ensure even and smooth running. Little engineering work is required on the machine, which is very reliable. Typical repairs are replacing a driving belt and adjusting the brake which are straightforward operations occupying a short period.

Tasks

1) Setting up machine.
2) Regulating flow control device.
3) Controlling input of bottles to machine.
4) Removing broken bottles and caps, together with any broken glass present.

Example - Job/task analysis

	Task	Hazards	Good skills	Influences on behaviour	Learning method
1	Sharpening a knife using a 'steel'.	Cuts to hand, arms.	Co-ordination of knife and steel movement.	Sharpness of knife. Condition of knife. Space limitations. Other people present. Condition of floor.	Demonstration of technique. Repetitive practice until speed increases.
2	Dispensing strong chemical compounds from 200 litre container.	Burns to eyes, face and body. Inhalation of fumes.	Correct position of drum cradle, drip tray and container, use of tap. Correct protective clothing, fitting and limitations.	Strength of chemicals. Type of fume. Corrosive effects. Illumination. Ventilation.	Demonstration of techniques. Practice using PPE. Hazards of spillage, splashing and fumes.

Figure 1-4-21: Example of a job/task analysis. *Source: RMS.*

HAZARD IDENTIFICATION AND RISK ASSESSMENT

The identification of hazards and the assessment of risks are key factors arising from the task analysis step of developing safe systems of work. From this, appropriate controls can be built in to the system of work and workers can be warned of the risks and how to minimise them. MHSWR 1999, Regulation 3, requires a suitable and sufficient risk assessment to be made of all risks to which employees and others who may be affected by them are exposed. Where a significant risk is identified through the general risk assessments a more formal detailed analysis is often required to develop a safe system of work e.g. work to inspect the lifting equipment of an office passenger lift. Considerations should be given to who does what, when and how.

See also - Section 4.2 - Principles and practice of risk assessment - for further information on hazard identification and risk assessment.

INTRODUCING CONTROLS AND FORMULATING PROCEDURES

Define the safe and healthy methods

1) Where possible, hazards should be eliminated at source. Residual hazards should be evaluated and controlled.
2) Specific responsibilities at various stages and the person in control of work should be clearly identified.
3) The need for protective or special equipment should also be identified, as should the need for the provision of temporary protection, guards or barriers.
4) Adequate emergency procedures should be in place, or developed, to control likely incidents e.g. fire, spillage.
5) If there is a possibility that injury could result during the task, rescue methods should be identified.
6) The system should be checked against three main criteria:
    - It should adequately control hazards associated with the task.
    - It should comply with company standards.
    - It should comply with relevant legal standards.

Implementation

Once the system has been developed and agreed, preparation for implementation can proceed. Provision for the communication of relevant information to all involved or affected should be an essential requirement to any system of work. It is important that care be taken to ensure that controls referred to when the system of work was being developed are available to the workers when the procedure is implemented. If they are not they will devalue the procedure and cause the workers to have to work outside the arrangement, possibly in an unsafe way.

The process of implementation will involve:

1) The person in charge of work must ensure that elements outlined in the planning and organisation stages are clearly understood and implemented.
2) If problems arise which necessitate modification to the system, formal approval and documentation should be made.
3) Any permanent record of any monitoring must be kept and regularly checked by a member of the management team.

INSTRUCTION AND TRAINING IN THE OPERATION OF THE SYSTEM

Many organisations may be tempted to issue procedures without instruction and training. This can lead to a great deal of misunderstanding about what the system of work is and will often lead to people not being motivated to work to the system. This is particularly the case when the system is a change from the usual way that workers may have worked. Workers, and supervisors, can have a naturally high resistance to change.

Simply providing information will not usually be sufficient to change behaviour. A more assured way to introduce the system would be to utilise such things as 'tool box' talks (where team leaders brief their work group at the start of shift regarding any relevant day to day issues or the introduction of new technology or equipment), which provide practical opportunity to develop the workers' understanding of the operation of the system and if these are done as part of a cascade training method the supervisor or similar person will have received training from someone committed to the new system and will be better placed to get over the resistance of workers to change.

When the system of work relates to work equipment it is essential to ensure that training takes place. The Provision and Use of Work Equipment Regulations (PUWER) 1998 require that supervisors be adequately trained to enable them to identify the hazards and control strategies associated with work equipment under their control.

Job/task analysis is not only useful to identify the hazards and controls, but is essential for preparing written procedures and specifying the skill and knowledge content of the work to be carried out. The analysis will not only identify the sequence of work but often the work rate expected - sometimes timeliness is an important consideration, particularly in relation to certain chemical manufacturing processes. The analysis is then incorporated into job training programmes.

- For certain high risk tasks this will often involve a training course to develop knowledge and understanding. This is then followed by practical application either utilising a work simulator (e.g. train driver/aircraft pilot) or close one to one supervision while on the job (e.g. forklift truck driver).
- Where training requirements have been identified, a record of those affected should be made. The required training should be conducted, confirmed as successful and recorded.

MONITORING THE SYSTEM

All safe systems should be formally monitored and records kept of compliance and effectiveness. This can be done by direct observation or by discussion at team meetings or safety committee meetings. SSW should not be simply imposed upon the people responsible for their operation. A system of monitoring and feedback should be implemented to ensure it is effective. Audits and accidents that occur can provide a valuable insight into whether systems of work are effective.

Confined spaces

A failure to appreciate the dangers associated with confined spaces has led not only to the deaths of many workers, but also to the demise of some of those who have attempted to rescue them. A confined space is not only a space which is small and difficult to enter, exit or work in; it can also be a large space, but with limited/restricted access. It can also be a space that is badly ventilated e.g. a tank or a large tunnel.

Figure 1-4-22: Confined space - chamber.   *Source: RMS.*

Figure 1-4-23: Confined space - sewer.   *Source: RMS.*

Figure 1-4-24: Confined space - tank.   *Source: RMS.*

Figure 1-4-25: Confined space - open tank.   *Source: RMS.*

The Confined Spaces Regulations (CSR) 1997 define a confined space as any place, including any:

Chamber   Caisson, cofferdam, or interception chamber for water.

Tank   Storage tanks for solid or liquid chemicals.

Vat   Process vessel which may be open, but by its depth confines a person.

Silo   May be an above the ground structure for storing cereal, crops.

Pit   Below ground, such as a chamber for a pump.

Pipe   Concrete, plastic steel etc, fabrication used to carry liquids or gases.

Sewer   Brick or concrete structure for the carrying of liquid waste.

Flue   Exhaust chimney for disposal of waste gases.

Well   Deep source of water.

Or other similar space, in which, by virtue of its enclosed nature, there is a foreseeable risk of a 'specified occurrence'.

A "SPECIFIED OCCURRENCE"

Is defined as:

a) Fire or explosion.
b) Loss of consciousness or asphyxiation of any person at work arising from gas, fumes, vapour or lack of oxygen.
c) Drowning of any person at work.
d) Asphyxiation of any person at work arising from a free flowing solid.
e) Loss of consciousness of any person arising from a high ambient temperature.

WORK IN CONFINED SPACES

- No person shall work in a confined space where it is reasonably practicable for that work to be carried out without entering the space.
- No person at work shall enter, leave or carry out work in a confined space other than in accordance with a safe system of work.
- Before work in a confined space can be carried out it must be shown that it cannot be considered "reasonably practicable" to carry out the work without entering the confined space. The employer (or self-employed) must then carry out a risk assessment to identify the precautions necessary to ensure a safe system of work.

The risk assessment will in particular help to identify the need for a formal permit to work system which will typically involve procedures for:

- Testing the atmosphere.
- Respiratory protective equipment and other personal protective equipment for those risks which cannot be controlled by other means.
- Equipment for safe access and exit.
- Suitable and sufficient emergency rescue arrangements.

TESTING THE ATMOSPHERE

- Testing of the atmosphere may be needed where the atmosphere might be contaminated or abnormal.
- The appropriate choice of testing equipment will depend on particular circumstances. For example, when testing for toxic atmospheres, chemical detector tubes or portable atmospheric monitoring equipment is appropriate. However there may be cases requiring monitoring equipment specifically designed to measure for flammable atmospheres.
- Only persons experienced and competent in the practice should carry out testing and records should be kept. Personal gas detectors should be worn whenever appropriate to mitigate the hazard of local pockets of contaminant.

SAFE ACCESS TO AND EGRESS FROM CONFINED SPACES

- Openings need to be sufficiently large and free from obstruction to allow the passage of persons wearing the necessary protective clothing and equipment and to allow access for rescue purposes.
- Practice drills will help to check that the size of openings and entry procedures are satisfactory.
- Where entry to a confined space is necessary, employers will need to ensure that the necessary safety features are followed. For example, alongside openings which allow for safe access these might include a safety sign warning against unauthorised entry and platforms to enable safe working within the confined space.

RESPIRATORY PROTECTIVE EQUIPMENT (RPE)

Where RPE is provided or used in connection with confined space entry (including emergency rescue), it must be suitable. Other equipment - ropes, harnesses, lifelines, resuscitating apparatus, first aid equipment, protective clothing and other special equipment will usually need to be provided.

Figure 1-4-26: Entrance to a confined space.   *Source: RMS.*

Here a worker wearing full breathing apparatus is also wearing a harness with a lanyard connected to a winch so that he can be hauled to the surface in an emergency without others having to enter the manhole to rescue him.

Figure 1-4-27: Access to a confined space. *Source: HSG150, HSE.*

EMERGENCY ARRANGEMENTS

The Regulations prohibit any person to enter or carry out work in a confined space unless there are suitable and sufficient rescue arrangements in place. Emergency arrangements shall be suitable and sufficient provided they:

- Require the provision and maintenance of resuscitation equipment.
- Require the provision and maintenance of such equipment as is necessary to enable the emergency rescue to be carried out effectively.
- Restrict, so far as is reasonably practicable, the risks to health and safety of any rescuer.
- Shall immediately be put into operation when circumstances arise requiring a rescue.

The arrangements for emergency rescue will depend on the nature of the confined space, the risks identified and consequently the likely nature of an emergency rescue. The arrangements might need to cover:

1) Rescue and resuscitation equipment.
2) Special arrangements with local hospitals (e.g. for foreseeable poisoning).
3) Raising the alarm and rescue.
4) Safeguarding the rescuers.
5) Safeguarding the third parties.
6) Fire fighting.
7) Control of plant.
8) First aid.
9) Public emergency services.

SUMMARY OF MAIN POINTS FOR CONFINED SPACES

Identify the hazards, for example:

- Flammable substances.
- Oxygen deficiency or enrichment.
- Toxic gas, fume or vapour.
- Ingress or presence of liquids.
- Solid materials which can flow e.g. flour, grain, sugar.
- Excessive heat.

Prevent the need for entry by:

- Use of viewing panels for inspection.
- Clean from outside using water jets, long handled tools.
- Use vibrators to clear blockages.

Develop safe working practice:

- To control residual risks.
- Based on a permit to work.

Develop emergency procedures, to include:

- Means of raising the alarm.
- Safeguarding the rescuers.
- Fire safety.
- Notifying public emergency services.

Provide training, to include:

- Awareness of CSR 1997.
- Need to avoid entry.
- Hazards and precautions.
- How emergencies arise.
- Emergency arrangements.

Lone working

Lone workers are those who work by themselves without close or direct supervision. They are found in a wide range of situations and some examples are given below.

People in fixed establishments where:

- Only one person works on the premises e.g. petrol stations, kiosks, shops and also home workers.
- People work separately from others e.g. in factories, warehouses, leisure centres or fairgrounds.
- People work outside normal hours e.g. cleaners, security, facilities management staff or contractors conducting special tasks better done at this time.

Mobile workers working away from their fixed base:

- On construction, plant installation, maintenance and cleaning work, electrical repairs, painting and decorating.
- Agricultural and forestry workers.
- Service workers e.g. rent collectors, postal staff, home helps, drivers, district nurses.

Although there is no general legal prohibition on working alone, the broad duties of the HASAWA 1974 and MHSWR 1999 still apply. These require identifying hazards of the work, assessing the risks involved, and putting measures in place to avoid or control the risks.

Control measures may include instruction, training, supervision, protective equipment etc. When the risk assessment shows that it is not possible for the work to be done safely by a lone worker, arrangements for providing help or back-up should be put in place. Where a lone worker is working at another employer's workplace, that employer should inform the lone worker's employer of any risks and the control measures that should be taken. This helps the lone worker's employer to assess the risks.

Risk assessment should help decide the right level of supervision. There are some high-risk activities where at least one other person may need to be present. Examples include some high-risk confined space working where a supervisor may need to be present, as well as someone dedicated to the rescue role, and electrical work at or near exposed live conductors where at least two people are sometimes required.

Employers need to be aware of any specific law on lone working applying in their industry; examples include supervision in diving operations, vehicles carrying explosives, fumigation work.

Establishing safe working for lone workers is no different from organising the safety of other employees. Employers need to know the law and standards which apply to their work activities and then assess whether the requirements can be met by people working alone.

CONSIDER

- Any special risk associated with the workplace.
- Safe access and egress for one person.
- Ease of handling of temporary access equipment, such as portable ladders or trestles.
- All plant, substances and goods involved in the work can be safely handled within the capacity of one person.
- Requirements for one person to operate essential controls for the safe running of equipment.
- A risk of violence.
- Female special risks.
- Young workers special risks.

IMPORTANCE OF TRAINING

- Where there is limited supervision.
- Experienced enough to understand the risks and precautions of lone working fully and to avoid panic reactions in unusual situations.
- Competent to deal with circumstances which are new, unusual or beyond the scope of training e.g. when to stop work and seek advice from a supervisor and how to handle aggression.
- Able to respond correctly to emergencies, also given information on established emergency procedures and danger areas.
- Able to administer first aid.

SUPERVISION

- To ensure that employees understand the risks associated with their work and that the necessary safety precautions are carried out.
- Can provide guidance in situations of uncertainty.
- Supervision can be carried out when checking the progress and quality of the work. May take the form of periodic site visits combined with discussions in which health and safety issues are raised.
- Important when an employee is new to a job, undergoing training, doing a job which presents special risks, or dealing with new situations and may need to be accompanied at first.
- Level of supervision required should be based on the findings of a risk assessment and competency of the worker.

PROCEDURES FOR MONITORING PURPOSES

- Supervisor's periodically visiting and observing people working alone.
- Regular contact using either a telephone or radio.
- Automatic warning devices which operate if specific signals are not received periodically from the lone worker e.g. systems for security staff.
- Other devices designed to raise the alarm in the event of an emergency and which are operated manually or automatically by the absence of activity.
- Check returned to their base or home on completion of a task.

MEDICAL CONSIDERATIONS

- Check that lone workers have no medical conditions making them unsuitable for working alone.
- Consider both routine work and foreseeable emergencies which may impose additional physical and mental burdens on the individual.
- Ensure they have access to first-aid facilities and mobile workers should carry a first-aid kit suitable for treating minor injuries.

4.6 - Role and function of a permit to work system

What is a permit to work system

In July 1988 167 men died as the result of an explosion and fire on the Piper Alpha oil rig located in the North Sea off the east coast of Scotland. In the public inquiry that followed, Lord Cullen concluded that one of the primary causes of the disaster was the failure of the permit to work (PTW) system employed by Occidental.

A permit to work system is a formal written system used to control certain types of jobs that have high hazard potential.

A permit to work system is not just permission to carry out a dangerous job and should not be applied to every task as this may detract from their importance and lead to them being treated as nothing more than a bureaucratic, form completion exercise.

The term 'permit-to-work' refers to the paper or electronic 'permit' document that is used as part of the overall system of work, which has been devised to identify and control the risks involved in the work.

Role and function in controlling a safe system of work

The role of a permit to work system is to ensure that full and proper consideration is given to the risks of the particular work that it relates to and to control the way of working in order to ensure a safe system of work is followed.

The function of a permit to work system is to:

- Ensure the proper authorisation of specified work.
- Confirm the identity, nature, timing, extent and limitations of the work.
- Establish criteria to be considered when identifying hazards and what they are.
- Confirm that hazards have been removed, where possible.
- Confirm that control measures are in place to deal with residual hazards.
- Confirm work is started, suspended, conducted, and finished safely.
- Control and confirm who has control of the location and equipment relating to the work when it passes between parties.
- Controlling change and considering other work activities that might interact with specified work.
- Providing a record of the steps in the process.

Operation and application

REQUIREMENTS OF THE SYSTEM

- Must be formal and documented.
- Simple to operate.
- Have commitment of those who operate and are affected by it.
- Provide concise and accurate information.
- Liaison with controllers of other plant or work areas whose activities may be affected by the permit to work.
- Boundary or limits of work area must be clearly marked or defined.
- Contractors undertaking specific tasks must be included in the permit to work system, including any briefing prior to commencement.
- Training in the system for all working under it and affected by it.

PERMIT TO WORK DOCUMENT

- A description of the task to be performed.
- An indication of the duration of the validity of the permit.
- Details and signature of the person authorising the work.
- Identifies the hazards affecting the work and the precautions to be taken.
- The isolations that have been made and the additional precautions required.
- Is a clear record that:
  - All foreseeable hazards have been considered.
  - All precautions are defined and taken in the correct sequence.
- Acceptor assumes responsibility for safe conduct of work.
- Establishes a safe system of work.
- An acknowledgement of acceptance by the workers carrying out the task, who would then need to indicate on the permit that the work had been completed and the area made safe in order for the permit to be cancelled.
- Overrides any other instructions until cancelled.
- Excludes work not described within the permit.
- In the event of a change to the programme of work, it must be amended or cancelled and a new permit issued.
- Only the originator may amend or cancel.

Circumstances in which they may be appropriate

A permit to work system is a formal safety control system designed to prevent accidental injury to personnel, damage to plant, premises and product, particularly when work with a foreseeable high hazard content is undertaken and the precautions required are numerous and complex.

The Health and Safety Executive suggest in their document HSG 250, guidance on permit to work systems that permit to work systems are normally considered most appropriate to:

- Non-production work (e.g. maintenance, repair, inspection, testing, alteration, construction, dismantling, adaptation, modification, cleaning etc).
- Non-routine operations.
- Jobs where two or more individuals or groups need to co-ordinate activities to complete the job safely.
- Jobs where there is a transfer of work and responsibilities from one group to another.

HOT WORK

Typically involving welding operations, such as pipe work where the risk of sparks may ignite nearby flammable materials. Elimination or protection of such combustible items will need to be considered. The provision of fire fighting equipment and trained personnel to deal with inadvertent ignition is also important.

The Dangerous Substances and Explosive Atmospheres Regulations (DSEAR) 2002 specify the application of permits to work, to be used in hazardous places or involving hazardous activities.

HOT WORK PERMIT - APPLIES ONLY TO AREA SPECIFIED BELOW
Part 1
Site:.. Floor:..
Nature of the job (including exact location) ....
....
The above location has been examined and the precautions listed on the reverse side have been taken.
Date:..
Time of issue:.. Time of expiry:..
NB. This permit is only valid on the day of issue.
Signature of person issuing permit: ....
Part 2
Signature of person receiving permit:..
Time work started:...
Time work finished and cleared up:...
Part 3   FINAL CHECK UP
Work areas and all adjacent areas to which sparks and heat might spread (such as floors above and below and opposite side of walls) were inspected one hour after the work finished and were found fire safe.
Signature of person carrying out final check: ....
After signing return permit to person who issued it.

Figure 1-4-28: Hot work permit - front of form.   *Source: Lincsafe.*

HOT WORK PERMIT - PRECAUTIONS
Hot Work Area
☐   Loose combustible material cleared.
☐   Non moveable combustible material covered.
☐   Suitable extinguishers to hand.
☐   Gas cylinders fitted with a regulator and flashback arrester.
☐   Other personnel who may be affected by the work removed from the area.
Work on walls, ceilings or partitions
☐   Opposite side checked and combustibles moved away.
Welding, cutting or grinding work
☐   Work area screened to contain sparks.
Bitumen boilers, lead heaters etc.
☐   Gas cylinders at least 3m from burner.
☐   If sited on roof, heat insulating base provided.

Figure 1-4-29: Hot work permit - reverse of form.   *Source: Lincsafe.*

WORK ON ELECTRICAL SYSTEMS

Work on electrical equipment, such as a transformer, will require safe isolation, access and egress, work at a height and heavy lifting to be considered.

MACHINERY/PLANT MAINTENANCE

Machinery/plant maintenance sometimes requires workers with different disciplines to work on large complex plant at the same time. This is aggravated by the fact that the plant may be spread over a number of floors in a building, such as power generation plant, flour mills or lift systems in an office block. This sort of work can involve many risks - related to a variety of services and energy sources, dangerous parts of the equipment, problems with access, risk of falling or being trapped inside the plant. These risks are best controlled by a well established system of work, supported by a permit to work.

CONFINED SPACES

The definition of "Confined Space" is more concerned with the level of risk to someone who is working there than its location or physical dimensions. A confined space, therefore, is one in which there is a reasonably foreseeable risk to someone by virtue of working there, or to quote the definition from the Confined Space Regulations (CSR) 1997:

"Confined Space means any place, including any chamber, tank, vat, silo, pit, trench, pipe, sewer, flue, well or other similar space in which, by virtue of its enclosed nature, there arises a reasonably foreseeable specified risk".

Figure 1-4-30: Definition of confined space.   *Source: Confined Space Regulations (CSR) 1997.*

It is worth noting that although this definition refers to an "enclosed space", this does not mean that the space must be totally enclosed. Such examples as a "pit", a "trench" and a "well" are included, all of which might be open to the sky. Nevertheless, the high risks associated with confined spaces are well documented and must be controlled by a permit to work system.

See also - Section 4.5 - Developing and implementing a safe system of work - for more information on confined spaces.

EXAMPLE				ENTRY INTO CONFINED SPACES		
Possible Lay-Out For A Permit-To-Work Certificate						
Permit-To-Work Certificate						
PLANT DETAILS (Location, identifying number, etc)				ACCEPTANCE OF CERTIFICATE Accepts all conditions of certificate		
WORK TO BE DONE						
				Signed	Date	Time
WITHDRAWAL FROM SERVICE				COMPLETION OF WORK All work completed - equipment returned for use		
	Signed	Date	Time			
ISOLATION Dangerous fumes Electrical supply Sources of heat				Signed	Date	Time
	Signed	Date	Time			
CLEANING AND PURGING Of all dangerous materials	Signed	Date	Time	EXTENSION		
TESTING For contamination	Contaminations tested		Results	Signed	Date	Time
	Signed	Date	Time			
I CERTIFY THAT I HAVE PERSONALLY EXAMINED THE PLANT DETAILED ABOVE AND SATISFIED MYSELF THAT THE ABOVE PARTICULARS ARE CORRECT (1) THE PLANT IS SAFE FOR ENTRY WITHOUT BREATHING APPARATUS (2) BREATHING APPARATUS MUST BE WORN Other precautions necessary:				THIS PERMIT TO WORK IS NOW CANCELLED. A NEW PERMIT WILL BE REQUIRED IF WORK IS TO CONTINUE		
Time of expiry of certificate:	Signed			Signed	Date	Time
Delete (1) or (2)	Date	Time		RETURN TO SERVICE	I accept the above plant back into service	
					Signed Date Time	

Figure 1-4-31: Example of a permit to work for entry into confined spaces.   *Source: HSE Guidance note on permits to work.*

WORK AT HEIGHT

Work above 2 metres used to be considered the height from which persons should be protected from falling. However, statistics show that many major injuries result from falls from heights of less than 2 metres.

Thus, a permit to work should be issued when a person could fall a distance liable to cause injury - no minimum height is specified. A height is classified as anything above floor level.

Working at height includes:

- Using ladders.
- Stepladders.
- MEWP (mobile elevated working platforms).
- Roof working.

This page is intentionally blank

Health and safety management systems 4 - measuring, audit and review

Learning outcomes

On completion of this element, candidates should be able to demonstrate understanding of the content through the application of knowledge to familiar and unfamiliar situations. In particular they should be able to:

5.1   Outline the principles, purpose and role of active and reactive monitoring.

5.2   Explain the purpose of, and procedures, for health and safety auditing.

5.3   Explain the purpose of, and procedures for, investigating incidents (accidents, cases of work-related ill-health and other occurrences).

5.4   Describe the legal and organisational requirements for recording and reporting incidents.

5.5   Explain the purpose of, and procedures for, regular reviews of health and safety performance.

Content

Sources of reference

Successful Health and Safety Management (HSG65), HSE Books ISBN 0-7176-1276-7

Guide to the Reporting of Injuries, Diseases and Dangerous Occurrences Regulations 1995 (L73) HSE Books ISBN 0-7176-6290-6

Investigating Incidents and Accidents at Work (HSG245) HSE Books ISBN 0-7176-2827-2

RIDDOR Explained (HSE 31 Rev 1) HSE Books ISBN 0-7176-2441-2

OHSAS 18001 Occupational health and safety management systems - Requirements

Relevant statutory provisions

The Management of Health and Safety at Work Regulations (MHSWR) 1999

The Reporting of Injuries, Diseases and Dangerous Occurrences Regulations (RIDDOR) 1995

5.1 - Active and reactive monitoring

Introduction

Organisations need to monitor their health and safety performance to assess how effective they are, in the same way that they would measure finance, production or sales objectives. Monitoring is an essential component of good management. An old maxim is "what gets measured tends to get done".

In modern, active and changing organisations it is essential to identify and confirm what is working and why in order to prevent these successful management actions being 'lost' at a time when resources are being reviewed.

Monitoring provides the opportunity and information to enable:

- The assessment of the effectiveness and appropriateness of health and safety objectives and arrangements, including control measures.
- The making of recommendations for review of the current management systems.

It is essential for organisations to learn from their experiences and take the opportunity to decide how to improve performance. Audits by an organisation's own staff or people external to the organisation complement other monitoring activities by looking to see if the policy, organisation and arrangements (systems) are actually achieving the right results.

The Management of Health and Safety at Work Regulations (MHSWR) 1999 (Reg. 5) require employers with five or more employees to record their arrangements for the effective monitoring of preventive and protective measures.

MONITORING SYSTEMS

There is a need for a range of both active and reactive measures to determine whether objectives have been met. A balanced approach to monitoring seeks to learn from all available sources. Hence two forms of monitoring are required:

- *Active monitoring*, before the event, involves identification through regular, planned observations of workplace conditions, systems and the actions of people, to ensure that performance standards are being implemented and management controls are working e.g. workplace and plant inspections.
- *Reactive monitoring*, after the event, involves learning from mistakes, whether they result in injuries, illness, and property damage or near misses e.g. accident investigation.

Organisations need to ensure that information from both active and reactive monitoring is used to identify situations that create risks, and to do something about them. Priority should be given where risks are greatest. Both monitoring methods require an understanding of the immediate and the underlying causes of events.

Active monitoring procedures

OBJECTIVES OF ACTIVE MONITORING

The primary objectives of active monitoring are to:

- Check that health and safety objectives and plans have been implemented.
- Monitor the extent of compliance with the organisation's systems/procedures, and with its legislative/technical standards.

Active monitoring will tell the organisation about the reliability and effectiveness of its systems, before their limitations are made obvious through accidents. This provides a good basis from which decisions and recommendations for maintenance and improvement may be made.

Active monitoring provides an opportunity for management to confirm commitment to health and safety objectives. It also reinforces a positive health and safety culture by recognising success and positive actions, instead of 'punishing' failure after an undesired event.

Organisations must see active monitoring as an integral and normal part of the management function. As such it must take place at all levels and at all opportunities in the organisation's operation.

Managers should be given responsibility for the monitoring of objectives and compliance with performance standards for which they and their subordinates are responsible. The actual method of monitoring will depend on the situation and the position held by the person monitoring.

METHODS OF ACTIVE MONITORING

The Health and Safety Executive (HSE) guidance document "Successful health and safety management" - HSG65 sets out the various methods and levels of active monitoring as:

- Routine procedures to monitor specific objectives, e.g. quarterly or monthly reports or returns.
- Periodic examination of documents to check that systems relating to the promotion of the health and safety culture are complied with, e.g. the way objectives for managers are established or appraised, assessment of records of training needs and delivery of training.

- Systematic inspection of premises, plant, and equipment by supervisors, maintenance staff, management, health and safety representatives and other employees to ensure continued effective operation of workplace precautions.
- Environmental monitoring and health surveillance to check on the effectiveness of health control measures and to detect early signs of harm to health.
- Systematic direct observation of work and behaviour by first-line supervisors to assess compliance with risk control systems (RCSs) and associated procedures and rules.
- The operation of audit systems.
- Consideration of regular reports on health and safety performance by the board of directors.

Active monitoring effort should be applied on a risk basis. Monitoring of workplace precautions would typically be more detailed and frequent than management system activities that carry a low risk if misapplied.

MONITORING PERFORMANCE STANDARDS

Health and safety performance in organisations that manage health and safety effectively is measured against established standards. This enables confirmation of compliance with standards and where improvement is required. By establishing standards of expectation it enables deficiencies to be quickly translated into improvement actions.

The success of action to manage risks is assessed through active monitoring involving a range of techniques. This includes techniques which examine technical measures (equipment, premises and substances), procedural measures (systems of work, method statements, safety cases, and permits to work), and behavioural measures (motivation, attitudes, and competencies).

Deficiencies in control measures are assessed through reactive monitoring which requires the thorough investigation of accidents, ill health or events with the potential to cause harm or loss.

In both active and reactive monitoring, the objectives are not only to determine the immediate causes of sub-standard (at risk) performance but, more importantly, to identify the underlying causes and the implications for the structure and operation of the health and safety management system.

SYSTEMATIC INSPECTION OF PLANT AND PREMISES

The systematic inspection of plant and premises can identify health and safety conditions, providing an indication of the effectiveness of controls used to prevent sub-standard conditions, for example, planned maintenance or cleaning operations.

If inspections are done on a timely basis it is possible to limit the harmful effects that can arise from sub-standard conditions. Periodic inspection provides a monitoring method that gives early indication of standards (declining or improving) by comparison with the previous results of inspections over time.

Role of inspections, sampling, surveys and tours in monitoring

INSPECTIONS

The role of health and safety inspections is to identify the health and safety status of what is being inspected and what improvements are needed. They are particularly well suited to identifying workplace hazards and determining if they are under satisfactory control or not.

Conducting workplace inspections may also affect the organisational health and safety culture, particularly where workers' views are sought as part of the inspection. In this way, the employer's commitment to health and safety can be demonstrated, ownership of health and safety can be shared and worker morale can be increased by simple improvements being implemented at the time of the inspection.

In addition to general workplace inspections, inspections are used to confirm the safe condition of work equipment. Regulation 6 of Provision and Use of Work Equipment Regulations (PUWER) 1998 lays down requirements for inspecting work equipment to ensure that health and safety conditions are maintained and that any deterioration can be detected and remedied in good time.

PUWER Regulation 6 - inspection

"Every employer shall ensure that work equipment exposed to conditions causing deterioration which is liable to result in dangerous situations is inspected:

- *At suitable intervals.*
- *Each time that exceptional circumstances which are liable to jeopardise the safety of the work equipment have occurred, to ensure that health and safety conditions are maintained and that any deterioration can be detected and remedied in good time.*

Every employer shall ensure that the result of an inspection made under this regulation is recorded and kept until the next inspection under this regulation is recorded."

Other legislation requires the regular and timely inspection of such things as excavations, scaffolds and local exhaust ventilation systems.

SAMPLING

The role of sampling is to select a representative, partial amount of a group of items, people or area; which is examined to establish facts about it and used to indicate the standard of compliance of the whole group.

When a representative sample is taken this is considered to reasonably represent the situation for the whole group.

A very small sample, such as the examination of three pieces of lifting tackle, may only give a rough, but acceptable, indication of the situation relating to lifting tackle as a whole.

Sampling is conducted relating to the following:

- Specific hazards - such as noise or dust - typically conducted by those trained in appropriate hygiene techniques.
- Good practice - such as the wearing of personal protective equipment - typically conducted by first-line managers.
- General workplace hazards - such as those identified during a defined walk through a work area - typically conducted by first-line managers, worker health and safety representatives and workers.

OBSERVATIONS OF PHYSICAL CONDITIONS

Category	Number Checked (C)	Number Standard (S)	% Meeting Standard $\frac{S \times 100}{C}$	Comments
EQUIPMENT *For Guidance Notes consider Audit 123 Level 1 - Sections 4 and 7*				
Guarding				
Hand tools				
Power tools				
Electrics (visual)				
Electrics (technical inspection)				
Pressure systems				
Ladders and mobile towers				
Personal protective equipment				
Total Score				Total % Compliance $\frac{\text{Total S} \times 100}{\text{Total C}}$

Figure 1-5-1: Sampling - extract from Audit 123 Level 3 Section 1 Workbook [ISBN 978-1-900420-50-1].   *Source: RMS.*

SURVEYS

The role of a survey is to examine a narrow field of the health and safety programme on an exploratory basis, with no fixed expectation of findings. The term 'survey' is usually applied to an exercise that involves a limited number of critical aspects, for example:

- Noise survey - usually with the aid of noise measuring equipment.
- Lighting survey - usually with the aid of a light meter.
- Temperature survey (to measure both high and low temperature levels) - usually with the aid of a thermometer.
- Personal protective equipment needs survey - usually involving a review of standards and workplace conditions/activities.

The term 'survey' is also used to define an exercise in which managers and workers are interviewed in order to identify knowledge, understanding, and details of specific needs within the working environment.

Examples of these might be:

- Training needs - usually involving written questionnaires to managers and workers.
- Attitudes to health and safety - usually involving written questionnaires to managers and workers.
- The need for specific health and safety rules for specific tasks - usually involving the review of standards and workplace conditions/activities.

Should these exercises seek to identify details from only a small number of people within a subject group or small geographical area, it would cease to be a survey and would become a sample.

TOURS

The role of tours is to provide an opportunity for management to explore the effectiveness of risk control measures through planned visits to the workplace to observe and discuss the controls in use by the workers carrying out the tasks.

It is important, when developing a positive health and safety culture, that management commitment is visible. The conducting of planned tours to workplaces to meet work groups is one effective way of achieving this. As such it is a monitoring method that senior and middle managers would find useful. It has the advantage of enabling direct contact and communication between workers and senior management. This gives an accurate picture of work conditions and the understanding of workers.

It can indicate deficiencies or success in managers carrying the organisation's objectives through to action. It also provides a forum for gaining the viewpoint of workers directly, without the translation that takes place through formal management channels.

In order to be planned there must be an intended outcome e.g. to communicate or review a topic, even if this includes some free time for other comment. Details of the tour and outcomes, including improvement actions, must be recorded to be effective.

Approach to inspections

When establishing an approach to inspections some of the factors to consider during the planning stage are:

- What needs inspecting?
- Who is to conduct the inspections and are they competent?
- When should inspections be conducted: changing circumstances or regular frequency?
- What standards are to be used?
- Is a checklist required?
- What equipment is to be used and does it need to be calibrated?
- Is any personal protective equipment (PPE) required?
- Where are findings recorded?
- Who will prepare the inspection report and develop the action plan?
- Who will be responsible for ensuring that any remedial action is carried out?

FREQUENCY AND TYPE OF INSPECTION

There are different types of inspections for different purposes, they include:

- General workplace inspections - carried out by local first-line managers and worker health and safety representatives.
- Statutory thorough examination of equipment, e.g. boilers, lifting equipment - carried out by specialist competent persons.
- Statutory inspections of equipment, e.g. excavations and equipment used in work at height - carried out by a competent person.
- Preventive maintenance inspections of specific (critical) items - carried out by maintenance staff.
- Pre-use 'checks' of equipment, e.g. vehicles, fork lift trucks, access equipment - carried out by the user.

The frequency of inspections should be planned to take place at regular intervals. The time between most inspections is often at the employer's discretion.

Factors that will influence the timescales are the changing nature of the workplace, manufacturer's recommendations, type and frequency of use, environmental conditions, severity of failure and previous history of failure. Principally this establishes a frequency on the basis of risk. Occasionally, minimum intervals are set by legislation such as that referring to local exhaust ventilation, lifting equipment, scaffolds and excavations.

General workplace inspections may be carried out in lower risk organisations that are not affected by change on a frequency so that every workplace is inspected once in a three month period; this may suit an office environment. In organisations that have higher risks, such as manufacturing, this may be increased to once in a month. Where risks are higher and changes to the workplace are more likely, such as in maintenance or construction operations, this may be increased to weekly or daily.

Equipment inspections are usually made on a periodic basis and after changes are made to the equipment. So, for example, minimum inspection requirements for work equipment specified for use for work at height are set out in Regulation 12 of the Work at Height Regulations (WAH) 2005.

Requirements are:

- Where safety depends on how it is installed or assembled in any position - before used in that position.
- Where exposed to conditions causing deterioration which is liable to result in dangerous situations, to ensure that health and safety conditions are maintained and that any deterioration can be detected and remedied in good time - at suitable intervals and each time that exceptional circumstances which are liable to jeopardise the safety of the work equipment have occurred.
- Work platforms used for construction work in which a person could fall 2 metres or more - inspected in position, or if a mobile work platform is inspected on the site, within the previous 7 days.

COMPETENCE OF INSPECTOR

Inspections normally involve physical examination of the workplace or equipment with a view to identifying hazards and determining if they are effectively controlled. They are usually carried out by a manager, worker health and safety representative, equipment user or technical specialist.

It is important that the inspector be competent to inspect what it is that they are inspecting. This will include techniques of conducting the inspection, recognising conditions that are of a good standard, recognising conditions that are or will become substandard and the acceptable response to what they find.

One of the most important competencies an inspector must have is the ability to know their own limitations of competency and what action they should take when they identify something that falls within their limitations.

USE OF CHECKLISTS

In many cases inspections are based on checklists. If this is the case, then managers relying on inspections must be mindful that the system of using a checklist has advantages and disadvantages.

Advantages	*Disadvantages*
■ Enables prior preparation and planning.	■ Does not encourage the inspector to think beyond the scope of the checklist.
■ Quick and easy to arrange.	
■ Brings a consistent approach.	■ Items not on checklist are not inspected.
■ Clearly identifies standards.	■ May tempt people who are not authorised / competent to carry out the inspection.
■ Thorough.	
■ Provides ready made basis for inspection report.	■ Can be out of date if standards change.
■ Provides evidence for audits.	■ Inspectors might be tempted to fill in the checklist without checking the work area/equipment.

An inspection checklist is typically a list of "the way things should be". When a work area or item of equipment fails this test it is considered substandard and represents a hazard. Each substandard condition should be assessed and corrective action identified and details recorded.

Checklists relating to work equipment tend to reflect the specific, critical health and safety conditions of the equipment. Factors to be considered when creating a checklist for a general workplace inspection should include: substances or materials being used, condition of traffic routes and means of access and egress, work equipment, work practices (manual handling, etc.), work environment, electricity, fire precautions, welfare provision including first aid arrangements and workstation ergonomics.

ALLOCATION OF RESPONSIBILITIES AND PRIORITIES FOR ACTION

Inspections will not improve health and safety performance unless, where a deficiency is identified, corrective and preventive actions are identified, responsibilities are allocated and they are fully implemented. Standards will continue to deteriorate where workers/managers find their inspection efforts, which identify improvement needs, are not followed through and actions are not implemented. They may quickly regard their efforts as "a waste of time". It is, however, equally important to avoid putting in a substandard or inadequate solution as this is bound to result in a waste of the organisation's resources (time, equipment, money etc.). To get the right solution implemented will usually take a quantity of management time and effort, and if the risk is significant clearly this is warranted. Whenever a substandard (at risk) situation is identified two important steps must be taken:

- Each situation must be evaluated as to its risk potential.
- The underlying cause(s) of the situation must be identified.

The first step ensures that resources are prioritised and allocated on a worst first basis, and the second step ensures that the appropriate corrective action will reduce the risk and prevent its return to the same level.

When situations that require most urgent attention are identified and corrective actions have been determined, the maximum time period by which the action is to be completed, tied to the risk potential, can be agreed. A simple approach to risk potential levels and allocation of time for actions may follow the method shown in the following section:

- High risk (likely to cause a major loss) - complete within 24 hours.
- Moderate risk (likely to cause a serious loss) - complete within 7 days (1 month if preferred).
- Low risk (will possibly cause a minor loss) - complete within 30 days (3 months if preferred).

A structured approach is necessary to ensure that the actions needed are initiated and followed up (monitored) in such a way that they are not simply forgotten. Responsibilities for action should be clearly allocated to those that have responsibility to ensure the action takes place.

When compiling an action plan following an inspection, the following issues have to be taken into consideration:

- The clear identification of any problem or defect.
- Prioritisation of actions.
- Details of corrective and preventive actions.
- The identification of who is responsible for carrying out the corrective and preventive action.
- The setting of realistic timescales for completion and dates for reviewing progress.
- The allocation of resources.
- Communicating details of the inspection to interested parties.

Effective report writing

The primary purpose of written information is to communicate. One useful means of communicating information is the report. It is important to produce a report which has the right *style* for the purpose it is being used. The writer should, therefore, always bear the reader in mind when producing the text.

The use of plain English must be encouraged; this is particularly important for health and safety related material. The style of report writing tends to be written formally, factually, in the past tense and from the perspective of the third person.

One simple **structure** is as follows:

- Introduction and background.
- Summary.
- Main body of the report.
- Recommendations.
- Conclusions.

INTRODUCTION AND BACKGROUND

This section includes the title page which should clearly identify the writer and the document. It should contain a brief explanation of the subject described in the document title and the reason for the document. Consider the aim of the report and inform the reader of the problems it intends to address.

SUMMARY

Most reports benefit from a summary which seeks to provide the reader with an overview of the strengths and weaknesses of the subject being reported on. It should be sufficient to motivate the reader to read the rest of the report with an idea of what it is going to cover.

MAIN BODY OF THE REPORT

The content of this section deals with details of observations made, facts and findings. The style should be kept simple and to the point, avoiding the use of jargon or embellishment. It is important to **emphasise** what was observed that was of a good standard, what was substandard and why things might need to be changed. A **persuasive** argument will establish the significance of the findings by identifying any breaches of the law, discussing the effects on workers and the potential financial impact if the observations are not accepted and acted on. Inaccuracy, inadequate and poor presentation can distract the reader and lessen the impact.

RECOMMENDATIONS

These should flow logically from the main body of the report. Recommendations should consist of a plain statement of action without repeating the arguments of the preceding section. In simple reports the recommendation may follow each of the findings and therefore appear in the main body of the report. In other reports the recommendations are drawn up into an action plan or recommendations table and come at the end of the report.

CONCLUSIONS

This section should contain a summary of the main findings and inferences. The conclusions should leave the reader with a persuasive argument in favour of the significance of the findings and the recommended actions. Ideally, the writer should end on a positive note.

Reactive monitoring measures

OBJECTIVES OF REACTIVE MONITORING

The objective of reactive monitoring is to measure the negative outcomes from the organisation's efforts to ensure health and safety in order to identify the significance of these outcomes and opportunities for improvement.

In order to carry out reactive monitoring effectively systems must be in place to identify the event, record it and report it. Without this nothing may be learnt. Indeed, what little data that is communicated might serve to reinforce that there is no need to put in a great deal of health and safety effort. If reporting etc. is planned and encouraged it is not uncommon to find a large increase in recorded events. This does not necessarily mean an increase in events, merely an increase in reporting.

Events contribute to the 'corporate memory', helping to prevent a repeat in another part of the organisation or at a later time. Though it should be remembered that the 'corporate memory' is said to be short, in the average organisation (one undergoing some change) it is said to be 4 years. Data may be gained from other organisations to reinforce or extend experience of events and the hazards involved.

METHODS OF REACTIVE MONITORING

These methods are deemed to be after the event and are therefore reactive monitoring measures:

- Identification.
- Reporting.
- Investigation.
- Collation of data and statistics, on the events.

The events monitored include those resulting in:

- Accidents, e.g. resulting in lost time, physical injury.
- Dangerous occurrences, e.g. significant damage to plant, equipment or facilities.
- Near misses, e.g. accidents with no measurable loss.
- Ill-health, e.g. resulting from exposure to substances or repetitive actions.
- Complaints by workforce, e.g. headaches, acne, blanched fingers.
- Enforcement action, e.g. issue of verbal instructions or written notices by an enforcer.
- Other downgrading events.

It is important to identify, in each case, why performance was substandard. Trends and common features may be identified, such as when, where and how these events occur. This provides an opportunity to learn and put into place improvements to the overall management system and to specific risk controls.

ACCIDENT STATISTICS

Many organisations spend considerable time developing data on their health and safety performance based on the accidents, dangerous occurrences, near misses, ill-health, complaints by workforce and enforcement actions they have.

Whilst there is value in doing so it has the limitation of being after the event. Accidents must occur to get the data, thus tending to reflect what is done to prevent a recurrence rather than what was being done prior to the event.

A more complete approach to monitoring will tend to include 'before the event' (active) actions such as audits and inspections to indicate what is currently being done to prevent accidents.

A low injury accident rate is not a guarantee that risks are being effectively controlled. In some cases this might be a matter of good fortune, or the fact that incidents are not being reported, rather than effective management.

Figure 1-5-2: Accident statistics.   Source: RMS.

If organisations wait until an event occurs to determine where health and safety effort is required then some sort of loss must have occurred. In order to gain sufficient management attention this could be an event resulting in personal injury to someone. Clearly this is an undesirable way of learning, particularly as, with an amount of effort, planning and thought, the event could have been foreseen and prevented. The more mature organisation seeks to learn most from activities (e.g. risk assessment) before the event or, at the very least, learn from those events that result in no personal injury, e.g. near misses.

The obvious use of accident data is to identify specific problem areas by recording instances where control measures have failed. However, analysis of the data allows general trends to be shown in order perhaps to identify common root causes, as well as comparisons to be made with others in order to learn from successes elsewhere. Accident data can also help to raise awareness in the minds of both managers and employees of health and safety in general, and of specific problems in particular. In addition, collection of data allows costs to be calculated, which can increase the likelihood of resources being allocated.

Examples of statistical analysis in common usage by workplace organisations are:

Frequency rate = $\dfrac{\text{Number of accidents in the period}}{\text{Total hours worked during the period}}$ x 100,000

Incidence rate = $\dfrac{\text{Number of accidents in the period}}{\text{Average number employed during the period}}$ x 1,000

For further examples of accident, ill-health and absence data see element 4.4 Sources of health and safety information.

For statistics to be of value their limitations have to be understood. Variables in work methods, hours of work, hazard controls and management systems make it difficult to make comparisons outside the organisation deriving the data. Indices such as these are best suited to comparison of performance of the same organisation over similar periods of time, for example, yearly. In this way trends may be observed and conclusions drawn. If comparisons are to be made outside the organisation, it should be remembered that other organisations might have a different understanding of the following:

- Definition of an accident (lost time or reportable).
- Hours worked may not be actual (contracted minimum hours may be used as it is easier to work out).
- Who is included (are contractors included or excluded)?
- What multiplier is used (International Labour Office and HSE use 1,000,000 for the frequency rate, USA use 200,000)?

5.2 - Health and safety auditing

Meaning of the term audit

An audit is an exercise which determines the level of compliance of something to a set of agreed standards. In the field of health and safety, minimum standards may be derived from relevant legislation. Therefore, an audit may determine the extent to which an organisation is compliant with legislation.

A health and safety management system audit is that part of the management system that subjects the other components to a rigorous, systematic examination.

> *An audit is a systematic, critical examination of an organisation's systems to determine the extent of compliance with a set of agreed standards.*

Figure 1-5-3: Definition of term audit. Source: RMS.

> *Systematic, independent and documented process for obtaining "audit evidence" and evaluating it objectively to determine the extent to which "audit criteria" are fulfilled.*

Figure 1-5-4: Definition of term audit. Source: ISO 9000:2005.

Scope and purpose of auditing

The main purpose of an audit is to assess how well health and safety is being managed compared with expectations (standards). The audit process will identify strengths, weaknesses and areas of vulnerability. The outcome from the audit is a report to management and an action plan which will allow health and safety to be managed successfully.

The entire scope of the health and safety management system of an organisation should be subjected to a comprehensive audit from time to time. Individual aspects of the health and safety system and procedures can, of course, be subjected to individual audits, for example:

- Reporting and management of incident data.
- Occupational stress.
- Work at height.
- Fire prevention and control.
- Review of health and safety as part of the management system.

Distinction between audits and inspections

Health and safety audits assess the health and safety system, or parts of it, to determine if the system is ensuring health and safety. One of the parts of the system that may be examined by an audit is active monitoring methods like inspections. In this way the audit would identify if the right people were conducting them, using the right methods, at the right frequency and how effective they were. Inspections usually involve the examination of the workplace, work equipment or work activities; with the purpose of identification of hazards, or conditions that can lead to hazards, and to put in controls to mitigate the hazards. It can therefore be said that inspections are concerned with hazard identification in the workplace, whereas auditing relates to the systems that manage the prevention and control of hazards.

Pre-audit preparations

INFORMATION GATHERING

The audit must be structured and co-ordinated in its assessment of the systems. This is best achieved by utilising audit checklists developed or obtained before the audit.

5/02	*Chains Ropes and Lifting Tackle*	*Consider:*
	Does the organisation ensure that statutory inspections are carried out?	■ Examined by a competent person
		■ Examined every period of six months
	Notes:	■ Register of examination
		■ Certificate of test and examination
		■ Distinguishing number or mark
		■ Safe working load (SWL) - displayed
		■ Fault procedure
		■ Monitoring

Figure 1-5-5: Extract from Audit 123 Level 2 Vol 1 of 2 Auditor's Guidance [ISBN 978-1-900420-96-9]. Source: RMS.

The audit involves interviewing people, observations in the workplace and assessment of documents such as:

- Health and safety policy.
- Health surveillance records.
- Records of statutory inspections such as lifting equipment and portable appliances.
- Procedures for method statements / permits to work.
- Maintenance procedures.
- Risk assessments.
- Insurance documents.
- Training records, etc.
- Accident/incident reports

Whilst some of this information may be assessed in the workplace, it is useful to gather information through analysis of documents that set out the expectation of the organisation before conducting the audit.

Information should be obtained on the results of prior audits, the organisational structure, policy and objectives of the organisation and other important information that will enable the audit to be effective, such as shift patterns, where work is taking place off site and critical activities that may be of interest to the audit.

NOTIFICATIONS AND INTERVIEWS

In order to prepare for an audit it is necessary to decide who needs to be interviewed and organise a timetable in order to meet them on a planned and organised basis. It is important that people involved in the audit are notified of arrangements for interview and informed of what type of documents they need to make available. In this way there is a better chance that they will be provided at the time of audit.

Interviews should be structured to provide the interviewee with opportunity to express what they are doing to meet the requirements being audited.

SELECTION OF STAFF

If audits are to be carried out internally, organisations should be mindful of the fact that, very often, the result of the audit may appear to be critical of the organisation's and/or individual performance. This can lead to feelings of resentment or even violence towards the auditor. When selecting the people to carry out the audit employers should be sure that the auditor is sufficiently strong of mind to deal with these situations. It is important when carrying out internal audits that the auditor is impartial; this will usually mean that the auditor does not audit a function of the organisation that they have responsibility for.

COMPETENCE OF AUDITORS

The auditor must be familiar with audit techniques, familiar with work practices, have the ability to interpret standards and be in a position to be able to keep up to date with new information and standards. Consideration should be given to the auditor receiving formal, generic audit skills training to enable them to conduct audits efficiently and effectively.

TIME AND RESOURCES

Audits are an in-depth analysis of compliance with standards and must not be treated lightly. The planning of the audit alone can be very time consuming. Evidence gathering and verification can also take a long time, depending on the scope of the audit. Employers should not apply pressure on the auditor to get the job done in less time than is appropriate and must be prepared to allocate sufficient time to the task.

Similarly, the auditor might need other resources than time, such as access to documentation, measuring equipment, electronic storage facilities, and research facilities (internet, library, etc) in order to do a thorough job.

Responsibility for audits

The responsibility to ensure audits take place rests within the organisation. Conducting audits will assist the organisation in complying with the Management of Health and Safety at Work (MHSWR) Regulations 1999 requirement to have in place arrangements to monitor. In addition it will help confirm the level of compliance with general duties under the Health and Safety at Work Act (HASAWA) 1974 and specific regulations.

Audits should be conducted by people that are both independent and competent. Health and safety practitioners that have received specific training in health and safety auditing techniques would usually be able to carry out this function.

Audits can be carried out by the management of the organisation, provided that the managers do not audit their own efforts directly (bias must be eliminated) and that the managers concerned have been trained in audit techniques.

Often a small team will be commissioned to conduct a full management systems audit, in order to widen the experience base and establish some degree of independence. A team may comprise three essential groups of people:

- A manager.
- A representative from the workforce.
- A health and safety practitioner.

Extra individuals with specific skills may join the team when specific topics are under assessment. A more independent approach would be to conduct an audit using auditors from outside the organisation or location. It should be remembered that the auditors are responsible for reporting on their findings and line management are responsible for the implementation of any corrective or improvement actions arising from the audit.

Advantages and disadvantages of external and internal audits

	Advantages	Disadvantages
Internal audits	■ Internal audits ensure local acceptance to implement recommendations and actions. ■ The auditor often has intimate knowledge of the hazards and existing work practices. ■ An awareness of what might be appropriate for the industry. ■ Familiarity with the workforce including their strengths and weaknesses. ■ Relatively low cost and easier to arrange.	■ May not possess auditing skills. ■ May not be up to date with current legislation and best practice. ■ The auditor may also be responsible for implementation of any proposed changes and this might inhibit recommendations because of the effect on workload. ■ May be subject to pressure from management and time constraints.

External audits	■ External audits are usually impartial; auditors will have a range of experience of different types of work practices. ■ May be able to offer solutions to what might be considered unsolvable problems within. ■ Not inhibited by criticism. ■ Will assess the organisation's performance without prior bias.	■ Need to plan well to identify nature and scope of the organisation. ■ Individuals may not be forthcoming, be nervous or resistant to discussing their workplace with an outsider. ■ May seek unrealistic targets.

Source: RMS.

Figure 1-5-6: Advantages and disadvantages of external and internal audits.

Actions taken following audit

The outcome from an audit should be a detailed report of findings and recommendations to improve or maintain the health and safety management system. A structure and approach to the report should be agreed at the pre-audit stage.

The final report should give a clear assessment of the overall performance of the organisation. It should identify deficiencies and make recommendations for improvement. It should also identify the observed strengths and suggest how they can be built upon. All audit reports need to be accurately and clearly communicated. In addition to the provision of a detailed written report a verbal presentation of the report may be provided soon after the close of the audit, in order to give an early opportunity for management to learn and take action.

RECOMMENDATIONS

Recommendations should flow logically from the main body of the report. They should be clearly connected to the results of the rest of the report, it may be necessary to make those connections explicit at this point - the reader should be clear in their understanding of what has been written. Recommendations should consist of a plain statement of action without repeating the arguments of the preceding findings section of the report. Include justification for the recommendation by referring to information summarised.

A recommendation's justification is usually based on a reference to material already provided in the summary.

CORRECTING NON-CONFORMITIES

Responsibility for carrying out actions for correcting non-conformities should be assigned to those in line management responsible for them, together with target completion dates. It is essential that management take ownership of both the audit and the subsequent action plans. Progress on correcting non-conformities should be monitored; this can be through reports or feedback at meetings.

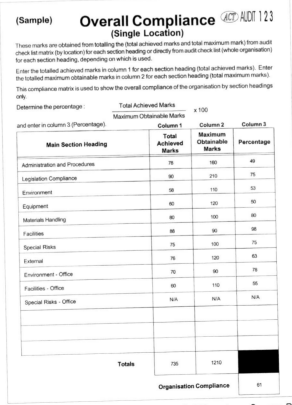

Figure 1-5-7: Sample page from the RMS Audit 123 system. *Source: RMS.*

5.3 - Investigating incidents

Incident investigation as a reactive monitoring measure

WHY INVESTIGATE?

The reasons for investigating accidents are the same as for accident prevention, that is:

- Humane.
- Economic.
- Legal - including need to report under the Reporting of Injuries, Diseases, and Dangerous Occurrences Regulations (RIDDOR) 1995.

The findings should be applied to prevent recurrence by improving workplace standards, procedures and training requirements.

ROLE OF INVESTIGATION

The role of investigation includes:

- Prevention of recurrence.
- Establish legal liability.
- Data gathering.
- Identification of trends.
- Discovery of underlying causes.

FUNCTION OF INVESTIGATION

Ideally all accidents should be investigated. A study of minor injuries and near misses can often reveal a major hazard, as the occurrence and severity of injury is a random happening. The degree of investigation may well vary with the degree of injury or damage, but should be based on the worst possible case of injury which is reasonably foreseeable as a result of the accident in question.

The objectives of any investigation will vary according to the circumstances, but it will always include the following points:

- The need to establish the causes of an accident, both immediate and underlying, in order that appropriate preventative action can be taken.
- Identify weaknesses in current systems so that standards can be improved.
- Determine economic losses.
- Recommend actions to prevent a recurrence.
- Determine compliance with statutory requirements or with company regulations.
- Improve staff relations by demonstrating commitment to health and safety.
- Acquire statistics.
- Prepare for criminal/civil action and provide insurance/worker compensation data.

The role and directive for the investigation of this nature should never seek to blame any individual or group of individuals. If human error is believed to be a significant cause, the reasons for this must be investigated. Lack of knowledge, training or unsuitability for the job may be the causes of this error. These are management and not worker failings. Only when these have been evaluated can the conclusion of wilful and intentional acts or omissions be considered.

Different types of incident

Incident can be defined as an output following an unplanned, uncontrolled event. This may include such things as injury, ill health, near miss or property damage.

INJURY

"Physical harm or damage done to or suffered by a person"

The term refers to physical harm to an individual. RIDDOR 1995 refers to types of injury in broad groups which translates as major, serious and minor. Major injuries include amputations, loss of sight and loss of consciousness *(full list is defined in RIDDOR 1995 Schedule 1)*. A serious injury is where a person is unable to do their normal work activities for more three consecutive days. The remainder are classified as minor injuries, where the incapacity lasts for less than three days.

ILL-HEALTH

"Harm to a person's health caused by their work"

The term refers to harm to a person's health caused by their work and will include harm to health in a physiological or psychological way. This will include the types of harm listed in RIDDOR 1995 as notifiable diseases, e.g. dermatitis.

DANGEROUS OCCURRENCE

"An accident not resulting in personal injury reportable to the enforcing authority"

The term is used in the RIDDOR 1995. A dangerous occurrence is an event specified in the schedules to the regulations, that the regulations require to be notified and reported to the appropriate enforcing authority (e.g. collapse of a scaffold of five metres high or more).

NEAR-MISS

"An accident that results in no apparent loss"

The term 'near-miss' refers to an event (accident) which did not result in personal injury, equipment damage or some other loss, but under slightly different circumstances could have done (e.g. building block falling off a scaffold and landing on the floor).

DAMAGE ONLY

The term 'damage only' is used in the Health and Safety Executive (HSE) guidance document HSG245 - 'Investigating Accidents and Incidents - A Workbook for Employers, Unions, Safety Representatives and Safety Professionals'. 'Damage only' describes damage to property, equipment, the environment or production losses. HSG245 though, focuses on events that have the potential to cause harm to people.

Basic incident investigation procedures

APPROACH TO INVESTIGATION (HSG245)

Guidance on the approach to be taken when investigating accidents is provided by the HSE in the document HSG245 'Investigating Accidents and Incidents'.

It suggests a step-by-step approach to investigations:

Step 1: Gathering the information - the where, when and who of the adverse event. The information gathered will include results of interviews, photographs of the equipment involved and the area in which it was positioned at the time, sketches of the workplace layout, weather conditions, etc.

Step 2: Analysing the information - the "what happened" and "why" stage. Analysing the information to find the immediate, underlying and root causes. At this stage it should be considered if human error is a contributory factor. This can be cross-referenced with the HSE guidance HSG48 'Reducing error and influencing behaviour'. Job factors, human factors and organisational factors can all influence human behaviour and will all need to be considered in the analysis.

Step 3: Identifying suitable risk control measures. Possible solutions can be identified. This will involve looking at the technical, procedural and behavioural controls, with the technical or engineering risk control measures being more reliable than those that rely on human behaviour.

Step 4: The action plan and its implementation to identify which risk control measures should be implemented in the short and long term. The risk control action plan should have SMART objectives, i.e. Specific, Measurable, Agreed and Realistic, with Timescales. This will also state which risk assessments need to be reviewed and which procedures need to be updated; any trends that need further investigation; and the adverse event cost.

HSG245 contains some useful investigation forms that could be used and developed for individual companies. It also has examples of simple, but effective investigation tools such as the accident/incident investigation tree.

PREPARING FOR THE INVESTIGATION

- Determine who should be involved in order that the investigator or team has all the necessary skills and expertise.
- Ensure that the accident scene remains undisturbed insofar as it is reasonable and safe to do so.
- Collate all relevant existing documents such as previous incident reports, maintenance records, risk assessments etc.
- Identify the persons (witnesses) who will need to be interviewed during the investigation.
- Check that relatives of any injured person have been notified.
- Check that legal reporting requirements have been met.
- Ascertain the equipment that will be needed e.g. measuring tape, camera.
- Determine the style and depth of the investigation.

TRAINING FOR THE REPORTING OF ACCIDENTS/INCIDENTS

To ensure that the investigation team has all the necessary information, training in some of the following areas may be required for workers:

- The importance of reporting accidents and incidents for legal, investigative and monitoring reasons.
- The types of incident that the organisation requires to be reported.
- The lines of reporting.
- How to complete internal documents and forms.
- Responsibilities for completing the accident book.

SCOPE AND DEPTH OF INVESTIGATION

Ideally all accidents should be investigated. A study of minor injuries and near misses can often reveal a major hazard, as the occurrence and severity of injury is a random happening.

The depth of investigation should depend on the severity of actual or potential loss, whichever is the greater.

TYPES OF INVESTIGATIONS

Supervisory investigations

As the person in immediate operating control of an area or activity it is logical to expect the supervisor to gather information on all accidents that happen in their area of responsibility. This investigation is normally all that is necessary for the majority of accidents.

It should result in swift remedial actions being implemented, and underlines the supervisor's responsibility for safety on a day to day basis.

Formal investigation

In some cases a formal investigation will be convened to carry out the functions described in the previous sections. The investigation committee should include the following people:

- A senior manager from another department who could act as an independent chairperson.
- A health and safety practitioner to advise on specific health and safety issues.
- An engineer or technical expert to provide any technical information required.
- A worker health and safety representative who, apart from having the statutory right to be involved if trade union appointed, could   represent the injured worker and his/her co-workers.

Any person whose responsibilities or actions may have been involved in the incident being investigated should be excluded from sitting on the investigation committee, but would be valuable as a witness. This may include a senior manager from the department where the accident occurred and any local manager or supervisor with detailed knowledge of the site of the accident and of the systems of work in place.

INVESTIGATION GUIDELINES

- The scene of the accident may still be highly hazardous. Anyone wishing to assist the injured party must take care, so that they too do not become a victim.
- The investigation must begin as soon as possible after the accident.
- Keep the objective clearly in mind, to discover the causes in order to initiate remedial action, not only to find someone to blame.
- Witnesses must be interviewed one at a time and not in the presence of any other witnesses to avoid influencing subsequent statements.
- Identify the root causes of the accident, not only immediate ones.
- Avoid making early unqualified assumptions.
- Approach witnesses without bias or pre-conceptions.
- Notes should be taken, so that the investigator is not relying on memory.

Interviews, plans, photographs, relevant records and checklists

INTERVIEWS

Interviews are of critical importance. The witnesses may be on guard and very defensive, feeling that blame could be directed their way, so it is important to put the person being interviewed at ease - state that the purpose of the interview is to help determine the facts to prevent a re-occurrence.

Good interview techniques will include:

- Interviewing witnesses promptly after the event, to avoid lapse of memory or confusion through witnesses discussing with each other.
- Conduct the interview in private with no interruptions.
- Not interviewing more than one person at a time.
- Protecting the reputation of the people interviewed.
- Setting a casual, informal tone during the interview to put the individual at ease.
- Asking probing questions, but being careful to avoid leading the witnesses.
- Recording the details: names of the interviewers, interviewee and anyone accompanying interviewees; place, data and time of the interview; and any significant comments or actions during the interview.
- Summarising your understanding of the matter.
- Expressing appreciation for the witnesses' information.

PLANS

Plans can be used to provide a clear indication of the accident scene including position of any injured person, witnesses, plant and equipment. The use of a sketch plan by the investigator, as well as any service or layout plans can assist in determining root causes of the event.

PHOTOGRAPHS

Cameras can be used to record and preserve images of accident scenes or resulting injuries. This can be especially useful if the situation changes with time through corrective actions, healing process, changes in environmental conditions etc. Until recently images from digital cameras were not accepted in Court, due to the potential for image manipulation by computer.

However, digital images can now be used, including those that have been enhanced for clarity, providing an original unaltered copy is archived in a read-only CD. A trail of authenticity is essential.

RELEVANT RECORDS

The amount of time and effort spent on information gathering should be proportionate to the level of the investigation, but should include all available and relevant information such as opinions, experiences, observations, measurements, check sheets, work permits, risk assessments, method statements and training records.

CHECKLISTS

Investigation report forms vary in design, layout and content. Many organisations recognise that a different report form may be necessary for first line managers' initial investigations (a level 1 report) and those done by other managers and health and safety practitioners (a level 2 report), the main difference being in the section relating to causes of the accident. The version used by other managers and practitioners often has more analysis in this area and causes greater investigation of underlying causes. In the same way, reports prepared by an investigation team would not tend to be on a pre-printed format, but would be designed around agreed headings and the content/extent of the report would depend on the matter being investigated and findings (a level 3 report). A common structure of a report tends to determine:

- What happened   - the loss.
- How it happened   - the event.
- Why it happened   - the causes, immediate and root causes.
- Recommendations - corrective and preventive action.

Drawings and photographs and statements as appendices usually support the report.

Immediate causes and root causes

IDENTIFYING IMMEDIATE CAUSES

The cause of injury should be identified. Injuries are caused by:

Unsafe acts by individuals e.g. not wearing the correct personal protective equipment such as goggles to prevent an eye injury.

Unsafe conditions in the workplace e.g. an electrical cable, supplying energy to a power tool, trailing across a busy walkway and presenting a trip hazard.

ROOT OR UNDERLYING CAUSES

The cause of the accident is often the result of many underlying or root causal failures. Typical root or underlying causes result:

- When people lack understanding or training, they are in a hurry and they are poorly supervised.
- When the wrong equipment is provided or the equipment is inadequate, not maintained or regularly inspected.

These are known as **management system failures** and occur when the organisation does not establish an adequate safety policy, incorporating an appropriate approach to risk identification and control for the organisation's activities. Research by Frank Bird and others into accident causation has led them to put forward an accident causation model based on a row of dominoes standing on one end. If any of the earlier dominoes fall, a chain reaction follows which results in a loss.

Figure 1-5-8: Domino theory of accident causation.   *Source: Frank Bird.*

Considering each stage separately:

"Loss"

This is the consequence of the accident and can be measured in terms of people (injuries), property (damage) or loss to the process (failed telecommunication) and hence loss of profit.

"Event (accident or incident)"

The event producing the loss involving contact with a substance or source of energy above the threshold limits of the body or structure.

"Immediate (direct) causes"

These are the substandard (unsafe) *acts* (e.g. using tools and equipment for tasks they were not designed to do) and substandard (unsafe) *conditions* (e.g. a trailing telephone cable in an office) which gives rise to an accident. These are physical symptoms which can be seen or sensed. Whilst these symptoms cannot be ignored, action solely at this level will not, by itself, ensure that recurrence is not prevented. Unsafe acts and conditions may be considered as workplace *hazards*.

"Indirect (root or underlying) causes"

These are the underlying or root causes of accidents. Identifying the root causes will explain why the substandard act happened or the condition arose. They are not always easy to identify. Indirect causes fall into three major categories:

- Organisational factors.
- Job factors.
- Personal factors.

Organisational factors:

- Work standards and procedures.
- Communication.
- Co-ordination.
- Supervision.

Job factors:

- Design of equipment and layouts.
- Maintenance.
- Purchase of materials and equipment.

Personal factors include:

- Physical capability.
- Mental capability.
- Physical stress.
- Mental stress.

- Knowledge.
- Skill.
- Motivation.
- Information.

"Lack of management control"

This is the initial stage, centred on the management functions of:

- Policy.
- Planning.
- Organising.

- Controlling.
- Monitoring.
- Reviewing.

It should be remembered that accident investigation experience confirms that there is usually more than one causative factor. Therefore each of the multiple causation factors may be seen as one domino in its own line of dominoes, just as the *roots* of a tree branch out.

Examples:

An accident involving an operator coming into contact with dangerous machinery could be the result of any of the following:

Immediate cause:

- Inadequate or non-existent safety devices.
- Poor housekeeping.

- Loose clothing.

- Machine malfunction.
- Operator error.

Root (underlying) cause:

- Poor design of guard.
- Inadequate training, instruction and/or supervision.
- Failure to provide appropriate personal protective equipment (PPE).
- Inadequate maintenance.
- A range of personal factors e.g. stress, fatigue, influence of drugs and alcohol.

A worker slipped on a patch of oil on a warehouse floor, was admitted to hospital and remained for several days. The oil was found close to a stack of pallets that had been left abandoned on the designated pedestrian walkway.

Immediate cause:

- Oil leaking onto the floor from equipment or being spilled by a co-worker.
- The floor remaining in a slippery condition because the spillage was not cleaned up.

- The abandoned pallets blocking the walkway causing the injured worker to make a detour.
- Inadequate lighting at the scene of the accident.

- The worker was wearing unsuitable footwear and not paying sufficient attention to where he was putting his feet.

Root (underlying) cause:

- The absence of adequate risk assessments and safe systems of work.
- Failure to introduce procedures for routine maintenance of equipment and cleaning up spillages.
- Poor warehouse design with inadequate walkways.
- Failure by management to monitor working conditions in the warehouse to ensure employees are not exposed to risks to their health and safety.
- Little training or instruction of employees in those procedures that might have been introduced.

Remedial actions

ACTION FOLLOWING A SERIOUS ACCIDENT

Immediately after an accident:

- Attend to the victim.
- Notify the next of kin.
- Secure the scene of the accident.
- Report to enforcing authority if necessary.

Longer-term actions will include:

- Identifying witnesses.
- Undertaking an investigation.
- Reviewing work procedures.

Reporting a death at work following an accident should include informing:

- The senior manager.
- Health and safety specialist.
- Coroner.
- Enforcing authority.
- Next of kin.
- Employee representatives.
- Other employees.
- Insurance company.

REPORTS AND FOLLOW-UP

The report should include a summarised version of the facts and recommendations for remedial action, together with discussion of controversial points and if necessary appendices containing specialist reports (medical and technical), photographs and diagrams. This virtually finishes the work of the investigator, but management is still responsible for seeing that the necessary remedial actions are implemented and monitored to ensure that the causes are satisfactorily controlled. The line manager, health and safety practitioner and health and safety committee/members should monitor the remedial actions.

SUMMARY

Throughout the process of investigation it must be clearly borne in mind that the objective is to prevent a recurrence of the accident, not to apportion blame. It is important to identify the true causes of the accident, not superficial ones. This cannot be achieved without the full commitment and assistance of witnesses and other persons who work in the area that the accident happened. It follows that recommendations must be put into action, even though they may take a considerable amount of time, trouble and money.

5.4 - Recording and reporting incidents

Major injuries, diseases and dangerous occurrences

MAJOR INJURIES (RIDDOR 1995 - SCHEDULE 1)

The list of major injuries includes:

- Any fracture, other than the finger or thumbs or toes.
- Any amputation.
- Dislocation of the shoulder, hip, knee or spine.
- Permanent or temporary loss of sight.
- Chemical, hot metal or penetrating eye injury.
- Electrical shock, electrical burn leading to unconsciousness or resuscitation or admittance to hospital for more than 24 hours.
- Loss of consciousness caused by asphyxia or exposure to a harmful substance or biological agent.
- Acute illness or loss of consciousness requiring medical attention due to any entry of substance by inhalation, ingestion or through the skin.
- Acute illness where there is a reason to believe that this resulted from exposure to a biological agent or its toxins or infected material.
- Any other injury leading to hypothermia, heat-induced illness or unconsciousness requiring resuscitation, hospitalisation greater than 24 hours.

DISEASES (RIDDOR 1995 - SCHEDULE 3)

Conditions due to physical agents and the physical demands of work

Conditions include:

- Inflammation, ulceration or malignant disease of the skin due to ionising radiation.
- Subcutaneous cellulitis of the hand (beat hand).
- Carpal tunnel syndrome.
- Hand-arm vibration syndrome.
- Decompression illness.

Conditions due to chemicals and other substances

Conditions include:

- Arsenic poisoning.
- Ethylene Oxide poisoning.
- Cancer of a bronchus or lung.
- Folliculitis.
- Acne.
- Pneumoconiosis.
- Asbestosis.
- Occupational dermatitis.

Infections due to biological agents

Infections include:

- Anthrax.
- Hepatitis.
- Legionellosis.
- Leptospirosis.
- Tetanus.

DANGEROUS OCCURRENCES (RIDDOR 1995 - SCHEDULE 2)

Dangerous occurrences are events that have the potential to cause death or serious injury and so must be reported whether anyone is injured or not. Examples of dangerous occurrences that must be reported are:

- The failure of any load bearing part of any lift, hoist, crane or derrick etc.
- The failure of any pressurised closed vessel.
- The failure of any freight container in any of its load bearing parts.
- Any unintentional incident in which plant or equipment either:
  - Comes into contact with an uninsulated overhead electric line.
  - Causes an electrical discharge from such an electric line by coming into close proximity to it.
- Electrical short-circuit or overload attended by fire or explosion which results in the stoppage of the plant involved for more than 24 hours.

Note: This information is a brief summary only. For full details consult HSE document L73 A Guide to RIDDOR 95.

Statutory requirements for recording and reporting incidents

There is a statutory duty for an employer to make available an accident book to employees so that they can record accidents that occur to them *(See figure ref 1-5-5)*.

Reporting and recording of certain accidents and ill health at work is a legal requirement. An employer, the self-employed or those in control of work premises, have duties under the Reporting of Injuries Diseases and Dangerous Occurrences Regulations (RIDDOR) 1995.

The information enables the enforcing authorities to identify where and how risks arise and to investigate serious accidents. The enforcing authorities can then help and advise on preventive action to reduce injury, ill health and accidental loss - much of which is uninsurable.

In April 2001, the Health and Safety Executive (HSE) launched the Incident Contact Centre (ICC) for all incidents currently reportable under RIDDOR 1995. The ICC provides a central point for employers to report incidents irrespective of whether their business is HSE or Local Authority enforced.

The primary objectives of the ICC are:

- To reduce the legislative burden.
- To improve the convenience of the current arrangements, by offering employers a single address and telephone number for all reports.
- To provide the option to report by telephone, fax, internet or hard copy.
- In the case of telephoned reports, provide a written confirmation on receipt.
- To allow injured persons a single point of contact for their rights under the Data Protection Act (DPA) 1998.

RIDDOR 1995 notifications received by the ICC are passed on to the appropriate enforcing authorities to alert them to individual incidents. These notifications also provide HSE with valuable information as to where and how risks arise, and to show up trends. Records held at the ICC are updated whenever new information about individual incidents reaches the centre, and are maintained accurate ongoing. A letter of confirmation of reports submitted on the ICC web site is forwarded to the responsible person (i.e. employer or person in control of the premises) under RIDDOR 1995.

Additional requirements for recording and reporting incidents

Organisational requirements for recording and reporting incidents will usually be wider than the statutory minimum, as statutory requirements tend to focus on the more serious incidents, those that clearly had or could have had serious consequences.

Organisations will have an interest in a wider range of incidents, some of which may not be reportable because they involve minor equipment damage or a near miss. The organisation should have a system to record and report these incidents, as well as the more serious ones, as they provide an opportunity to identify immediate and root causes that may lead to more serious incidents.

In addition, although there may not be statutory obligations to report incidents that can only have a minor potential, they still represent a loss to the organisation and if they occur frequently will warrant corrective and preventive action to avoid a reoccurrence.

Organisations may have separate recording and reporting forms for such things as near misses in order to ensure they are focused on or they may have a single form on which the type of incident is identified.

There are many important reasons why employers need to ensure that a wide range of incidents are recorded and reported, among them are the following:

- It is an implied requirement of the Management of Health and Safety at Work Regulations (MHSWR) 1999 (regulation 5).
- Reporting provides an opportunity for an investigation.
- The investigation, in turn, should help to identify flaws with existing controls and therefore assist in the implementation of improved controls.
- It enables analysis of reports which may identify trends or patterns that may emerge.
- It enables the gathering of statistical evidence to enable the employer to compare health and safety performance with industry and other standards (benchmarking).
- It provides evidence for use in legal actions that may ensue.
- It helps identify an increase in the number of incidents and should prompt a review of risk assessments.
- It will help the employer to comply with reporting requirements of RIDDOR 1995.

It must be borne in mind that many incidents go unreported. There are many reasons for this that managers should consider. The employee may fear disciplinary action; they might be embarrassed because the incident was caused by something they did wrong; there could be peer pressure; the employee might not want to break a long standing record for the period between incidents; they might not know what to report or the importance of reporting or how to report and who to report to.

Accident book

It is required by the Social Security (Claims and Payment) Regulations 1979 that all employers keep an Accident Book available to employees. All accident books will need to comply with the requirements of the Data Protection Act 1998 (DPA). It is not necessary that the employer use the book designed specifically for this purpose, the BI 510, so long as the same headings are used. The purpose of the book is to enable the employee to record accidents that have occurred to them at work and for which (industrial Injury) benefit may be payable. It is a duty placed on the employer that he investigate all recorded accidents to determine if they were accidents at work (for which benefit may be payable). Following this it is the duty of the employer to provide information to government organisations investigating an employee's claim for benefit. Accident record books (e.g. BI 510) must be kept for three years after the last entry and kept available for inspection.

Procedures for reporting under RIDDOR

RIDDOR covers the requirement to report certain categories of injury and disease sustained at work, along with specified dangerous occurrences and gas incidents, to the relevant enforcing authority. These reports are used to compile statistics to show trends and to highlight problem areas, in particular industries or companies.

THE MAIN POINTS OF RIDDOR 1995

Reporting

(1) When a person *dies or suffers any major injury* specified in Schedule 1 *(Reporting of Injuries)* and Schedule 2 *(Reporting of Dangerous Occurrences)* a responsible person must notify by the quickest practicable means (usually by telephone) the enforcing authorities and must send them a written report within 10 days (F2508). This means that If there is an accident connected with work and:

- An employee or a self-employed person at work is killed or suffers a major injury (including as a result of physical violence).
- A member of the public is killed or taken to hospital.

Notification to the enforcing authority must be made by the quickest practicable means.

(2) In cases of diseases which are linked to work activities listed in Schedule 3 *(Reporting of Diseases)* a responsible person must notify by the quickest possible means (usually by telephone) the enforcing authorities and must send them a written report forthwith (F2508A). If a doctor notifies an employer that an employed person at work suffers from any of the occupational diseases specified in column 1 of Part I of Schedule 3 and their work involves one of the activities specified in the corresponding entry in column 2 of that Part it must be reported to the enforcing authority.

(3) If there is an accident connected with work (including an act of physical violence) and an employee, or a self-employed person at work, suffers an over-three-day injury it must be reported to the enforcing authority within ten days. If personal injury results in *more than 3 days incapacity* from work away from normal duties, but does not fall in the category of "major injury", the written report alone is required. The day of the accident is not counted, but any days which would not have been working days are included.

(4) The enforcing authority is either the Health and Safety Executive or the Local Authority. The approved form for reporting is F2508 for injuries and dangerous occurrences and F2508A for diseases.

Summary of injuries that must be reported:

- Fatal injuries.
- Major injuries.
- Injuries that result in more than three days incapacity from normal duties.
- A member of the public is killed or taken to hospital.

Note:

"Accident" includes:

- An act of non-consensual physical violence done to a person at work.
- An act of suicide which occurs on or in the course of the operation of a relevant transport system.

Road traffic accidents

Road traffic accidents only have to be reported if:

- Death or injury results from exposure to a substance being conveyed by a vehicle.
- Death or injury results from the activities of another person engaged in the loading or unloading of an article or substance.
- Death or injury results from the activities of another person involving work on or alongside a road.
- Death or injury results from an accident involving a train.

Non employee

The responsible person must not only report non-employee deaths, but also cases that involve major injury or hospitalisation.

Recording

In the case of an accident at work, the following details must be recorded:

- Date and time.
- Name.
- Occupation.
- Nature of injury.
- Place of accident.
- Brief description of the event.

Copies of F2508 or suitable alternative records must be kept for at least 3 years. They may be held electronically provided they are printable.

Defences

A person must prove that he was not aware of the event and that he had taken all reasonable steps to have such events brought to his notice.

Internal systems for collecting, analysing and communicating data

COLLECTING DATA

Report form types

A number of report forms are utilised to identify and inform that accidents and ill-health have occurred. These include:

- Accident book, in the form of BI 510.
- First aid treatment reports.
- Medical treatment reports.
- Medical (doctor) reports of ill-health.
- Sickness absence reports.
- Event (accident) reports.
- Event (near miss) reports.
- Maintenance/repair reports.
- Insurance reports.
- RIDDOR reports - F2508, F2508A.

Reporting routes

Reporting of an accident or ill-health may be by a number of means and includes:

- Person receiving harm.
- Person causing loss.
- Person discovering loss.

Person receiving harm

This person is often the source of first reporting of less serious events. The reporting system must make available to them the means to make a report. They have a right to report in an 'accident book' BI 510 (or equivalent) any event that may cause them to claim Social Security benefit.

This might be fulfilled by using a copy of the BI 510 book or first aid/medical treatment documents/event report forms that are adapted to contain the same data. These reports should be under the control of a responsible person who would then initiate an investigation; this would usually require the completion of an event (e.g. accident) report.

Person causing loss

This person would be expected to bring the loss to the attention of a line manager who would fill in the appropriate event (e.g. accident) report and initiate an investigation to complete the remainder of the report that the person reporting the loss may not be able to do.

Person discovering the loss

If this person were not the manager responsible for the location in which the loss took place they would have to bring the loss to the attention of a line manager, as shown in the previous sections. If the person were the line manager they would initiate an investigation and report on the appropriate event form.

ANALYSING AND COMMUNICATING DATA

Reports from first line managers may be copied to the next line manager (middle manager), health and safety practitioner, worker health and safety representative. It is important that the originator retains a copy until action to prevent is complete, to encourage ownership and continued involvement. The copy passed to the next line manager is usually seen as the primary document. The manager confirms/adds to the investigation, retains a copy and passes the report to a central record point. Clearly this may be done in part or whole as a computer or paper system.

Records held by the line manager/health and safety practitioner may be held for varying periods depending on their role. Central records are usually maintained in accordance with the organisation's own practices. A minimum period is usually 3 years for accidents (in order to respond to civil claims) and 40 years for events resulting in ill-health (in order to deal with the long lived nature of the problem).

Collection of information and its availability in a civil claim

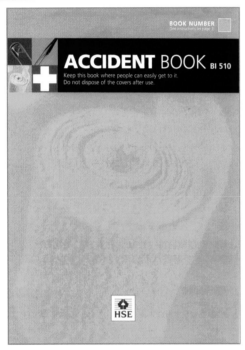

Figure 1-5-9: Examples from an accident book.   *Source: HSE.*

Figure 1-5-10: Example F2508 Forms.   *Source: HSE.*

Any accident may result in a claim. It is essential that organisations anticipate this and at the earliest opportunity assemble data necessary to consider whether a claim may be defended. The line manager plays an important role in promptly investigating accidents, and copying relevant data to file as part of the accident investigation. It is important to note that although one of the reasons that this data is being assembled is in readiness to defend a claim, its primary use is in prompting a thorough accident investigation. This and the identification of any preventive measures come before defending a claim.

Data prepared for accident investigation purposes remains discoverable in any legal action. Indeed, since the introduction of revised civil proceedings it is necessary to disclose to the other party evidence that will be relied on in court. This means that evidence may not be introduced at a later date. This reinforces the need to assemble all material data promptly.

Lessons learnt

It is important that lessons learned from incidents are shared with as many people who would benefit from it as is possible. As a minimum this must include different departments within an organisation. It would be regrettable if an accident happening in one department and it was seen as of no relevance to others, without considering the causes. The more that the root causes are examined the more likely the lessons are to be relevant to other departments. An incident in one department may reveal a need to improve job induction processes, which may affect all departments of an organisation.

In the same way, it is important to share lessons learned with other locations of the same organisation. Some industries share lessons learned across the whole of the organisations in an industry. This is very important as they may have similar practices or equipment.

Trade associations often take the lead in collating data on a non-attributable basis and sharing the lessons learned with participating member organisations. The collective experience of what is learned enables common problem activities and hazards to be identified and underlying causes, human, organisational and technical, to be examined. In some cases the lessons are shared as an immediate alert, in other cases quarterly reports provide analysis of recent experiences and trends. ***See figure ref 1-5-7*** which shows an example of a document which was circulated to all interested parties following investigations into an incident.

BN0901A1649 - Transport of Zip-Up (Mobile Tower) Scaffolding

Background

- A task had been carried out in the HAST 18 area of B215 which required the use of a zip-up scaffold.
- The type of scaffold used was a Planet Platforms Protec scaffold (GRP tower).
- The scaffold had been dismantled and the base frames (1.35m wide / 15-20 kg weight) were being carried up the HAST 15 stair case which is of an open nature.
- One of the adjustable legs with affixed castor (approx 5-6 kg) became detached from the bottom of one of the frames and fell approximately 9m, glanced off some lagging and came to rest on the landing of a lower floor.

Details

- The adjustable leg / castor assembly is inserted into the base frame which has an adjustment collar that is designed to be used to adjust the legs to level up a scaffold on an uneven surface.
- The adjustment collar has only a small range of movement between 'lock' and 'unlock' (approx one eight of a turn). When in the unlock position, the adjustable leg can be fully released in an uncontrolled manner if the castor is not resting on something.

Key Learning

- <u>Do not use this type of scaffold with the legs extended until investigations have been concluded</u>.
  - If the adjustable legs are used to raise the height of a scaffold there is the potential that if not properly locked or if the collar is in a poor state of repair, if knocked the collar could release resulting in the scaffold tipping.
- Remove the leg / castor assemblies from the base frame before transporting zip-up scaffolding.
- Do not carry zip-up scaffold on stair cases if possible – look for alternative routes where a lift can be used instead.
- If equipment has to be carried around Plant / on stair cases, ensure areas where personnel are at risk of falling items have barriers and signs are erected.

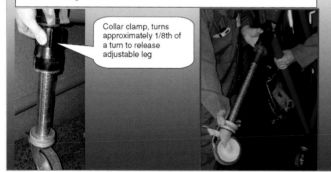

Collar clamp, turns approximately 1/8th of a turn to release adjustable leg

Figure 1-5-11: Incident lessons learned alert.   *Source: Jamie Lockie Sellafield Fellside site.*

It is important that the lessons learned from incidents are also considered as part of the regular review of an organisation's health and safety performance. The incidents may influence the organisation's policy, objectives and management system, therefore they should be considered by senior management in the organisation.

5.5 - Review of health and safety performance

Purpose of reviewing health and safety performance

The purpose of the health and safety performance review is to evaluate the effectiveness of what is being done when compared with experience and foreseeable factors that might affect future performance.

The Health and Safety Executive states that:

> *"Reviewing is the process of making judgements about the adequacy of performance and taking decisions about the nature and timing of the actions necessary to remedy deficiencies. [The purpose is that] the organisation learns from all relevant experience and applies the lessons".*

Figure 1-5-12: Reviewing performance.   *Source: HSE.*

Regulation 5 of the Management of Health and Safety at Work (MHSWR) 1999 requires:

"(1) Every employer shall make and give effect to such arrangements as are appropriate, having regard to the nature of his activities and the size of his undertaking, for the effective planning, organisation, control, monitoring and review of the preventive and protective measures."

Learning from all relevant experience (including that of the organisation and of other organisations) needs to be done systematically, through regular reviews of performance. The review draws on sources like data from monitoring activities and from independent audits. These form the basis of continuous improvement, necessary to maintain compliance and effectiveness. This helps to maintain a management system that is fresh, dynamic, appropriate and effective.

Who should take part in the review

Health and safety performance needs to be reviewed at each management level in an organisation, starting with the most senior management. Senior managers must guard against a culture of management, or measurement of health and safety, by exception. Management by exception would mean that unless a problem or deficiency is brought to senior management attention they presume that everything is working as intended, and do not inquire any further.

It is important that the most senior management of an organisation are involved in the process of reviewing health and safety performance as it may have an influence on policy, objectives, management system and resources. It may be that the review is done by a working party drawn from the senior management team, but all senior management must be involved with deciding the parameters of the review and considering the outcomes of the review process.

A more local level review of performance may take place by a manager of part of an organisation or location organising a review of performance by involving a number of people in a review team. This would usually involve the manager of that part of the organisation, another line manager who reports to the manager, someone who represents workers and someone who can give specific health and safety input. By using a team of this nature a wide range of experiences and perspectives can be taken into account and it will enable them to review the overall performance or focus on specific aspects of health and safety, such as transport accidents or manual handling.

Review at planned intervals

Reviewing health and safety performance is an ongoing activity, so in one sense the review process is continuous. But like any other activity, review should be both efficient and effective, so the frequency with which it takes place needs to be planned appropriately to ensure it happens on a timely basis, particularly where no monitoring activities have stimulated it to happen.

When considering when review should take place the following factors should be taken into consideration:

- Suitable intervals to ensure that specific planned objectives are achieved.
- The level of risk relating to the organisation and the consequences of ineffective performance.
- Where there are indicators of non-compliance or compliance.
- The potential for change, resources, external factors, legislation and standards.
- Where intervals for review are prescribed by standards, such as BS OHSAS 18001.
- If the review relates to a particular activity, the frequency at which the activity takes place.

Planned reviews may take place on the following basis:

Monthly	-	for individuals, first line managers or sections.
Quarterly	-	for middle managers or departments.
Annual	-	for senior managers, sites or the whole organisation.

The results of the reviews can be communicated to the next level of the organisation for consideration in the review at that level. If critical health and safety issues are identified during monthly reviews it is not necessary to wait to pass what has been learned to the next levels, if they require senior management input this can obtained outside the review structure.

Assessing opportunities for improvement and the need for change

Regular reviews of health and safety performance allow managers to identify success and deficiencies in performance. The need for improvement or change may not be apparent from individual incidents, but a review of accident statistics over time might show that certain control measures are not working as well as intended. For example, an organisation may have introduced a series of measures to reduce the risk of manual handling, but the statistics do not show an improvement in incidents to the level expected.

The review provides an opportunity to consider why this is and allows the organisation to make improvements on a timely basis. This may involve revising practical measures, improved training and supervision or the information gathered from the review might suggest that changes in policy and procedures are required if improvements are to be maintained.

Reviews conducted by senior management are important in helping to shape health and safety objectives for the following period and are essential for assessing opportunities for improvement and factors that may drive the need for change, such as changes in legislation, best practice and technology.

Review to consider

EVALUATION OF COMPLIANCE WITH LEGAL AND ORGANISATIONAL REQUIREMENTS

It is a well established principle that things like health and safety policy and risk assessments are reviewed. This is done when something it is believed may affect them has changed. Legislation may change and cause a review to determine if the arrangements and controls in place are relevant to the proposed change, for example, signage and work practices had to be changed when the exposure limits and action values were reduced by the Control Noise at Work Regulations 2005.

ACCIDENT AND INCIDENT DATA, CORRECTIVE AND PREVENTATIVE ACTIONS

Whilst review of accident and incident data is important it should be remembered it is after the event. Any analysis should consider the potential for each occurrence to have resulted in a more significant outcome. Two elements to consider when reviewing accident and incident data are:

- The quality of planning before the event.
- Any failure of controls. This will often include the review of current risk assessments.

When carrying out the review, it is important to consider the effectiveness of corrective and preventative actions taken following the analysis of accident/incident data. The review should also consider the timeliness of fulfilment of the corrective and preventive actions and if there was delay what caused it. The review of corrective and preventive actions applied following incidents may indicate a need for further strategic level action.

For example, a number of accidents may have led to action to provide refresher training for the specific risks associated with the hazards causing the accidents and this may indicate a need for a more organised, strategic approach to refresher training.

INSPECTIONS

The primary purpose of workplace planned general inspections is to identify general workplace hazards that are out of control before they result in any harmful outcome. Similarly, other inspections are necessary to prevent harmful outcomes for specific hazards, for example, inspections of scaffolds, excavations, lifting equipment and pressure systems. The presence of hazards or substandard condition of equipment identified at inspection might illustrate a need to review maintenance or use regimes.

SURVEYS, TOURS AND SAMPLING

Surveys, tours and sampling are active methods of measuring performance. The review of the outcome of these activities can provide information on the effectiveness of objectives in improving health and safety. For example a survey of attitudes of workers may confirm that action taken to improve communications and confidence of workers has had an effect. It is important to review what is working, as well as what is not, the approach taken to introducing the improvements may indicate how future improvements may be made with maximum acceptance of all people involved.

In some cases, organisations may pilot improvement strategies in one location or department, the outcome of this may be reviewed before extending it across the organisation. Surveys, tours and sampling may provide the data for the review which will determine if it is to go ahead on the same basis or following adjustments.

ABSENCES AND SICKNESS

Whilst physical injury will be recorded in the accident book and may have resulted in some investigation it should be remembered that some workplace hazards or working environments may result in absence, sickness or ill-health. Sickness or general absence data should be collected and reviewed to determine if it has resulted from work or working environment issues. Such review may determine causes such as shift working, overwork or poor environmental conditions, including inadequate ventilation or extremes of temperature or humidity.

QUALITY ASSURANCE REPORTS

Quality assurance reports are useful because they will identify the "normal or abnormal" features of a process and as such may be a useful indicator of the level of work performance in an area. The sort of problems that affect quality can also affect health and safety and the quality assurance reports may be the first indication of problems, particularly where quality has a stronger reporting and control ethic than health and safety. Quality assurance performance information, in its various forms, can provide a useful confirmation on the effectiveness of health and safety systems that work in parallel with quality. This is particularly useful in contributing to the process of health and safety performance review.

AUDITS

Audits are designed to determine the effectiveness of the management system and in particular the degree of management control.

Audits will examine all types of data, documents and records to determine the degree of system compliance and their suitability with the passage of time. Quality assurance audits may identify system non-compliance that can have an effect on health and safety, particularly where the organisation provides a service or product to an end user outside the organisation, for example, the defective manufacture of an electric drill intended for sale.

The review should consider information from audits because the audit process should provide a strong source of independent, verified data on the management system, implementation of objectives or specific risk being audited. This may provide a different perspective to that delivered by data from managers as it should be free from bias.

MONITORING DATA/RECORDS/REPORTS

Monitoring data may provide the review with information that supports the effectiveness of health and safety performance or, that objectives have not been met. Because monitoring is focussed on specific, aspects like the presence of a substance in the atmosphere or levels of blanching of a worker's fingers due to exposure to vibration, they are providing a very tangible perspective on the success or failure of effort applied to improve health and safety. The review process should consider the results of the monitoring and the action taken following them.

Monitoring data considered at review may also include reports of hazards identified in the workplace, particularly by workers. This can provide valuable feedback on how systems affect workers in practice. The reporting of hazards should be documented and actioned within an agreed time frame with appropriate feedback, in much the same way as customers complaints might be dealt with. The review should evaluate if this is being done effective.

EXTERNAL COMMUNICATION AND COMPLAINTS

Feedback on levels of performance should be encouraged from customers and neighbours; this will ensure that any health and safety issues are addressed before an incident occurs. Similarly any communication or complaints from the enforcement authorities will need to be taken into account. In addition, suppliers may provide information on the performance of things they supply, gathered from other users. All of this data informs the review process of the wider perspective of others that might be affected by the organisation or may have an opinion on how it is performing.

RESULTS OF PARTICIPATION AND CONSULTATION

At review it is important to involve employee representatives to ensure objectives have been met and appropriate actions from previous management reviews concerning identified legal/good practice developments have been taken into consideration following adequate consultation.

OBJECTIVES MET

It is essential that an organisation review its progress against its objectives in order that they can be successfully fulfilled. It could be that objectives set when implemented meet resource problems or are not as effective as planned. By identifying this through a review process, as they are implemented, they are more likely to be met and be effective.

ACTIONS FROM PREVIOUS MANAGEMENT REVIEWS

In a similar way to objectives, the actions identified from previous management reviews must be reviewed to determine their progress and effectiveness. This must be planned at intervals through the year to ensure they are completed effectively and on a timely basis. It is important that the lessons learned from the review process are acted on and progress made to improve performance through this.

LEGAL / GOOD PRACTICE DEVELOPMENTS

Innovation in health and safety is happening all the time and even well intending organisations can find themselves out of step with legislation and good practice. It is essential that formal reviews of changes take place and improvement plans are put into place to take account of them. Information on legislative changes is often communicated well in advance of the actual change being made. This provides an early opportunity for the possible impacts to be reviewed and plans put in place to deal with it on a timely basis.

Maintenance of records of management review

Every organisation must establish and maintain procedures for the maintenance of records of the management review. They should be maintained as appropriate to the system and the organisation.

Regulation 5 of the Management of Health and Safety at Work (MHSWR) 1999 requires:

"(2) Where the employer employs five or more employees, he shall record the arrangements", this includes arrangements for review.

Records of review will enable the organisation to consider the results of the review in following reviews and provide evidence of compliance with the Management of Health and Safety at Work Regulations. Records provide the necessary evidence that effort is being applied to ensure health and safety performance levels are being met. They should be legible, identifiable and traceable to the particular review activity in question.

Reporting on health and safety performance

The results of the review of health and safety performance should be reported at senior management level. This is particularly important in situations where the review has been conducted by a work group drawn from the senior management team as this will enable all of senior management to understand and accept the implications of the review.

The results of the review should be communicated widely in the organisation and in particular to those managers that have responsibility for responding to the actions arising from the review.

It is customary to include a statement of health and safety performance, along with other risks, within the annual report. Such reports should be available to all employees and other stakeholders.

Feeding into plans as part of continuous improvement

It is important that health and safety reviews take place in an analytical way, questioning if actions taken to date have been appropriate, effective and completed. From this review process objectives and actions to improve health and safety may be identified and fed into development and improvement plans. The strategic level plans enable the production of local level plans through information cascade. In this way health and safety in an organisation is maintained dynamically, leading to continuous improvement.

Health and safety objectives should be established for all development/improvement plans and be subject to key performance indicators (KPI's) in the same way as KPI's are established for the other key business objectives, such as production or quality.

For example, active reporting at meetings should be established for health and safety items such as the status of inspections and risk assessments.

Role of senior management

The senior management of the organisation carry the responsibility, on behalf of the organisation, to ensure reviews of performance are conducted. This will mean that the senior manager (Chief Executive or Managing Director) has overall responsibility, but the senior management team (Board) also share responsibility.

The role of the senior management team is to treat health, safety and the environment as equal partners to other business issues such as production (service) and quality. To this end, the review should assist in the establishment of goals and clear measurable objectives to achieve such goals.

"Safety is an integral part of business excellence and, together with product and service quality, and corporate health and profitability, is the foundation for our future success".

Figure 1-5-13: Policy Statement abstract.

Source: Standard Wire Corporation circa.1996.

Ref No.	Validation Material	Evaluation
1/1/05	**Health and safety as an equal partnership** Do managers readily accept that health and safety is a manageable item and should be seen to have equal standing with production and quality? ***Notes:***	***Consider:*** ■ Board commitment e.g. policy statement ■ Appointment of a Director for health and safety ■ Included in job descriptions/responsibility statements ■ Accepted as a line management responsibility ■ Included fully in all technical, procedural and behavioural standards of performance ■ Identified in appraisal documents ■ Planned allocation of time to health and safety issues ■ Health and safety performance measured and reported on equal basis with other management objectives

Figure 1-5-14: Extract from Audit 123 Level 3 Section 1 Auditor's Guidance [ISBN 978-1-900420-14-3].

Source: RMS.

The senior management team may appoint one of the team to take a lead with the review of health and safety performance, this person may have the role of health and safety director. The lead person would be conducting the review on behalf of the senior management team, against agreed parameters, and would report back to the senior management team, providing the outcome of the review for their consideration.

Senior management would provide data to and be involved in the senior management review process. Involvement in periodic reviews provides an opportunity for senior management to refresh their commitment to health and safety and to confirm the degree to which the organisation is being effective in managing health and safety risks. This in turn enables senior management to provide their input of views, experience and ideas to the review process and help to decide action to meet their responsibilities for health and safety.

This page is intentionally blank

Workplace hazards and risk control

Content

Sources of reference

Essential of Health and Safety at Work, HSE Books ISBN 0-7176-0716-X

The Workplace (Health, Safety and Welfare) Regulations 1992 (ACOP) (L24), HSE Books ISBN 0-7176-0413-6

Safe Use of Work Equipment (ACOP) (L22), HSE Books ISBN 0-7176-1626-6

Workplace Transport Safety - Guidance for Employers (HSG136), HSE Books ISBN 0-7176-0935-9

The Health and Safety (Safety Signs and Signals) Regulations 1996, Guidance on Regulations (L64), HSE Books ISBN 0-7176-0870-0

Lighting at Work (HSG38), HSE Books ISBN 0-7176-1232-5

Seating at Work (HSG57), HSE Books ISBN 0717612317

Work at Height Regulations 2005 (Amended) - A Brief Guide HSE Books (INDG401 rev1) 0-7176-6231-9

A pain in your workplace? Ergonomic Problems and Solutions (HSG121), HSE Books ISBN 0-7176-0668-6

Violence at work. A guide for employers HSE Books INDG69 HSE Books

Drug misuse at work a guide for employers HSE Books INDG91

Managing Health and Safety in Construction (ACOP) (HSG224), HSE Books ISBN 0-7176-2139-1

Health and Safety in Construction (Guidance) (HSG150rev), HSE Books ISBN 0-7176-6231-9

Relevant statutory provisions

The Workplace (Health, Safety and Welfare) Regulations (WHSWR) 1992

The Provision and Use of Work Equipment Regulations (PUWER) 1998 - Part III in particular

The Health and Safety (Safety Signs and Signals) Regulations (SSSR) 1996

The Work at Height Regulations (WAH) 2005

The Construction (Design and Management) Regulations (CDM) 2007

The Construction (Head Protection) Regulations (CHPR) 1989

1.1 - Health, welfare and work environment requirements

Health and welfare provisions

DRINKING WATER

Regulation 22 of the Workplace (Health, Safety and Welfare) Regulations (WHSWR) 1992 requires that an adequate supply of wholesome drinking water must be provided.

The supply needs to be accessible. If not provided in the form of a fountain, then drinking vessels must also be provided. The supply outlet from taps should be labelled, 'Suitable for drinking', or 'Unsuitable for drinking' as appropriate.

WASHING FACILITIES

Regulation 21 of WHSWR 1992 requires suitable and sufficient washing facilities, including showers where necessary because of the nature of the work or for health reasons. They must be provided at readily accessible places.

There must be a supply of clean, hot and cold or warm water, running water so far as is practicable, soap or other means of cleaning, towels or other means of drying and the rooms that contain these facilities must be kept clean, ventilated, lit and maintained.

SANITARY CONVENIENCES

Regulation 20 of WHSWR 1992 requires readily accessible, suitable and sufficient sanitary conveniences must be provided. The conveniences must be adequate for the numbers and gender employed, lit, kept clean and maintained in an orderly fashion.

Separate conveniences for male and female workers must be provided except where the convenience is in a separate room and the door of which is capable of being locked from the inside.

ACCOMMODATION FOR CLOTHING

Regulation 23 of WHSWR 1992 requires suitable and sufficient accommodation must be provided for personal clothing not worn at work and clothing worn at work but not taken home.

Such clothing accommodation must: be suitably secure when personal clothing not worn at work is being stored; separate work clothing and other clothing where necessary to avoid health risks or damage; be in a suitable location and so far as is reasonably practicable include drying facilities.

FACILITIES FOR CHANGING CLOTHING

Regulation 24 of WHSWR 1992 where special clothing must be worn at work, or for reasons of health or propriety a person cannot change in another room then suitable and sufficient changing facilities must be provided. Separate facilities or separate use of facilities for male and female workers must be taken into account.

The ACOP recommends that changing facilities should be readily accessible to workrooms (and eating facilities if provided) and should contain adequate seating arrangements. The facilities provided should be sufficiently large to enable the maximum number of workers to use them comfortably and quickly at any one time.

Figure 2-1-1: Accommodation for clothing.   *Source: RMS.*

Figure 2-1-2: Facilities for rest and to eat meals.   *Source: RMS.*

REST AND EATING FACILITIES

Regulation 25 of WHSWR 1992 requires readily accessible, suitable and sufficient rest facilities to be provided. Such rest facilities must be provided in one or more rest rooms (new and modified, etc. workplaces) or in rest rooms or rest areas (existing workplaces). Where meals are regularly eaten in the workplace, suitable and sufficient facilities must be provided for their consumption. Where food eaten in the workplace is liable to become contaminated, suitable facilities for eating meals must be included in the rest facilities. Suitable rest facilities must be provided for pregnant women and nursing mothers.

The ACOP recommends that rest facilities should include suitable and sufficient seats and tables for the number of workers likely to use them at any one time. Work seats in offices or other clean environments may be acceptable as rest facilities provided workers are not subjected to excessive disturbance during rest periods.

Eating facilities should include a facility for preparing or obtaining a hot drink, and where hot food cannot be readily obtained, means should be provided to enable workers to heat their own food. Canteens, etc. may be used as rest facilities providing there is no obligation to buy food.

SEATING

Suitable seats should be provided for workers who have to stand to carry out their work and occasionally have the opportunity to sit down. Seats should be provided for use during breaks. Rest rooms should have sufficient seats with backrests for the number of workers who may use them at one time. Seats in the work area can be counted as eating facilities provided the place is clean and there is a suitable surface to place food. There should also be facilities for pregnant and nursing mothers to lie down if required.

VENTILATION

The principal features of a ventilation system are:

- Provision and maintenance of the circulation of fresh air in every occupied part of a workplace.
- The rendering harmless of all potentially injurious airborne contaminants, e.g. dusts, fumes, vapours and gases.

HEATING

The level of heating should be appropriate to provide physical comfort. The nature of the work and the working environment will need to be assessed to achieve the correct level. Whenever possible the individual should be able to adjust their workplace to achieve this objective.

Workplaces can vary greatly:

- Very cold and exposed, such as an oil rig in the North Sea or a frozen food storage warehouse.
- General warehousing at ambient temperature.
- General office where the nature of the work is sedentary.
- High temperature processing such as a laundry.
- High temperature manufacturing such as with glass, steel or ceramics production.

Several factors should be considered such as personal capability, degree of hot or cold, wind speed and humidity.

LIGHTING

Lighting the task and workstation

In general, for each visual task we require a certain minimum quantity of light arriving on each unit area of the object in view (i.e. a minimum 'planar' illuminance). The value of this minimum luminance depends primarily on the size of the detail which must be perceived, but will also depend on the visual contrast that the task makes with the background against which it is seen, the duration of the task, whether or not errors may have serious consequences and the presence or absence of daylight.

Figure 2-1-3: Reflected light from window.   *Source: RMS.*   Figure 2-1-4: Light from windows controlled by blinds. *Source: RMS.*

Ideally the workstation should be designed in such a way as to make the task the brightest part of the field of view. Research has shown that favourable conditions exist when the task has a luminance, which is about three times that of its immediate surrounds, and when the immediate surrounds, again, have about three times the luminance of the general surrounds to the workstation. These conditions can be achieved by a combination of general and local lighting used to illuminate the work surfaces, which have appropriately chosen reflectance. For example, when a desk lamp provides local lighting for white paper seen against a grey-blotting pad placed on a desktop served by a general installation of ceiling-mounted fluorescent lighting, an approximation to these desirable conditions is then easily obtained.

Not all problems caused by poor lighting can be overcome simply by the provision of more light. When tasks are visually demanding, the quality of the available light is at least as important as its quantity.

Daylight has qualities which are difficult to imitate artificially. Moreover the provision of a distant view seen through a window will provide welcome relief to eyes which must focus at their 'near point' while work is in progress. Aspects of lighting quality, which should receive attention when lighting the workstation, are the control of glare, the provision of adequate modelling *(See below - 'Lighting the interior of the workplace')* and, where necessary, good colour rendering.

Lighting the interior of the workplace

The basic need is to provide sufficient and suitable light in the circulation areas to allow movement of personnel, materials and equipment between workstations to take place conveniently and in safety. The aim should be to provide conditions which remain comfortable to the eye as it passes from one zone of the workplace to another, and to make available all information relevant to the well being and safety of the workforce which can be received through the sense of sight. All the aspects of quantity and quality considered under task lighting would assume some significance in this larger scale application and so contribute to the achievement of these desirable conditions.

Attention should be drawn to accident black spots, such as changes in floor level or flights of stairs, with increased levels of illuminance served by luminaires which are carefully positioned to provide good three-dimensional modelling, while preventing any direct sight of the unshielded source, so as to avoid disabling glare. Machinery, which makes fast cyclic movements, should be carefully illuminated to prevent the occurrence of stroboscopic effects.

Sudden changes in lighting levels should not occur between neighbouring zones of the workplace. Levels should be graded to allow time for the eye to adapt. The processes of dark adaptation can take several minutes (more than half an hour in extreme cases) during which time the efficiency of the eye is severely reduced, making accidents more likely.

Differences in the colour characteristics of so-called 'white light' sources are sometimes apparent to the eye and although its ability to colour-adapt is considerable, the occurrence of frequent noticeable changes due to the use of various kinds of sources in the same interior may accelerate the onset of fatigue as well as making fine colour judgments impossible.

Exposure to extremes of temperature

TEMPERATURE

The body generates heat energy by the conversion of foodstuffs; energy is generated through muscle action. At rest, typically 80 watts of energy is produced, whereas during heavy physical exercise perhaps 500 watts is produced. The body loses (exchanges) heat energy by the process of sweat evaporation, conduction contact of the feet with the floor and by radiation (infra red energy loss).

EXTREMES OF TEMPERATURE

Exposure to the effects of cold temperature relies on high calorie diet, physical exercise and suitable protective clothing. Clothing should have a high tog rating of 20-25 tog, and prevent absorption of water and be suitably fastened to reduce the effects of wind chill.

The feet should be insulated to avoid loss through conduction. The head should be covered to the maximum extent to avoid excessive heat loss. Clothing should be light and white in colour to prevent heat loss through radiation.

Exposure to the effects of heat may be minimised by suitable clothing, such as light and loose or reflective clothing if working with very hot sources of heat.

Figure 2-1-5: Workplace temperature.   *Source: RMS.*

Issues such as conduction from hot surfaces and movement of heat will need to be considered. Consideration will need to be given to humidity levels and workload - increased humidity and workload will increase the worker's temperature rapidly.

EFFECTS

People working outside their thermal comfort range can suffer a dramatic loss of efficiency e.g. hot metal process working, working in refrigerated warehouses, working outdoors.

The precise effects will depend upon the type of work being carried out, the rate of air movement (wind chill) and temperature and humidity.

The main effects of working at high and low temperatures are outlined as follows:

General effects

Cold
- Loss of concentration in mental work.
- Reduced manipulative powers in manual work.
- Discomfort caused by shivering.

Hot
- Loss of concentration.
- Reduced activity rate.
- Discomfort caused by sweating.

Heat stress

■ Heat syncope	Fainting due to vasodilatation (widening of the blood vessels, especially the arteries, leading to increased blood flow or reduced blood pressure).
■ Heat rash or 'prickly heat'	Skin disorder.
■ Heat exhaustion	Fatigue, nausea, headache, giddiness.
■ Anhidrotic heat exhaustion	Insufficient moisture to sweat.
■ Heat cramps	Painful spasms of muscles - insufficient salt.
■ Heat stroke	Breakdown of control mechanisms, body temperatures soar, immediate cooling of body temperature required, otherwise death ensues.

Cold

- Hypothermia.
- Frost bite.
- Chilblains

- Trench foot, (also known as immersion foot) occurs when the feet are wet for long periods of time.
- Violent shivering.

RELEVANT FACTORS

One of the fundamental mechanisms by which the body regulates its temperature is by perspiration. Key factors which aid or hinder this process are airflow and humidity. Humidity relates to the moisture content in the air. Air with a relatively high humidity has little capacity to cool the body by 'wicking' away sweat, whereas low relative humidity can cause dry skin and has been identified as a possible factor in facial dermatitis (occasional itching or reddened skin) reported by some display screen equipment users. Industries and occupations particularly susceptible to extremes of temperature include foundries, cold stores, those who carry out hot work (e.g. burning and welding) or work in confined spaces where temperatures are often uncomfortably high. Likewise, those who work outdoors can be subject to extreme weather conditions. In winter the strength of the wind can significantly affect the temperature (wind-chill).

PREVENTIVE MEASURES

The approved code of practice (ACOP) which accompanies WHSWR 1992 states that a temperature of 16^0C should be maintained for sedentary work, for example in site offices, and a temperature of 13^0C for work that requires physical effort. Because these figures are stated in an ACOP, they should be regarded as minimum figures. Workers can be exposed to a varying degree of conditions and resultant temperatures. The effects of excessive cold or heat can have harmful effects on employees' health and accidents can result due to fatigue or thermal stress. Areas should be provided to enable workers who work in cold environments to warm themselves.

When work in hot environments or in controlled systems is required, it will be necessary for workers to be acclimatised slowly to the conditions. Drinks and the provision of refuge from heat may be necessary to reduce body temperatures.

Where the temperatures cannot be maintained, for example when working outside, areas should be provided to enable workers who work in cold environments to warm themselves. Practical measures and adequate protection must be provided against adverse conditions, for example workers may be provided with a sheeted area to work in order to protect them from the rain and wind.

Steps that employers should consider to reduce the effects of extremes of temperature should include regular work breaks with fluid intake. Preventative measures include improved ventilation and humidity control; screening of the work area; provision of suitable clothing; screening employees for individual susceptibility, for example, Reynard's syndrome (individuals who suffer with poor circulation to hands and feet). In the case of cold stores, removal of ice, particularly from floors, improved lighting and the provision of anti-locking devices to exit doors.

1.2 - Violence at work

Risk factors relating to violence at work

People who deal directly with the public may face aggressive or violent behaviour. They may be sworn at, threatened or even suffer physical violence. In addition, it is necessary to consider possible violence between co-workers. Maintenance and construction activities often need to be completed within a fixed timescale and can result in a lot of pressure on workers to work quickly and without error.

This can lead to a good deal of tension which might result in violent outbursts between co-workers including contractors.

> *"Any incident, in which a person is abused, threatened or assaulted in circumstances relating to their work".*

Figure 2-1-6: Definition of work related violence.

Source: HSE.

Verbal abuse and threats are the most common types of incident. Physical attacks are comparatively rare. Those professions most at risk are engaged in caring, education, cash handling, and representing authority.

The most common risk factors relating to violence are:

- The position a person holds - a worker may hold a position of authority over another person; how they use this authority and the effects on the person can cause disagreement, resentment and could cause the person to be more aggressive.
- The nature of the work - if a worker is working alone this may lead them to be more at risk of violence. The nature of the work may be dealing with people that are emotionally charged, and this may cause them to react to normal things in an unpredictable way.
- The location of the work - if the worker is working isolated from others this may leave them at risk. Some locations may have a tendency for violence, e.g. certain parts of a city centre or housing estates.
- The time of working - working during late evening and early morning may mean there are less people around and those people that are around may be more likely to have violent tendencies.
- Alcohol and drugs - can make some people more aggressive. Because their perception and behaviour is more unpredictable, it may lead to misunderstandings and violence.
- Visible appearance - violence may arise simply because someone does not like a worker's visible appearance and what this may represent. This can be accentuated if the appearance is one of privilege and wealth.
- The availability of weapons - if weapons, improvised or normal, are available to be used a sudden outburst that may have been verbal could escalate to involve major personal injury because a weapon was available, e.g. knives in a restaurant or home, shotgun on a farm or drinking glass in a public house.

DETERMINE THE SIZE OF PROBLEM

- Ask workers informally, through managers and health and safety representatives.
- Encourage workers to report all incidents and keep detailed records.
- Classify all incidents according to their actual or potential severity of outcome.
- Try to predict what might happen and how violence may arise.

Control measures to reduce risks from violence at work

POLICY

The policy for dealing with violence should be written into the safety policy statement so that all employees are aware of it. This will encourage employees to cooperate with the policy and report further incidents.

DETERMINE CONTROLS RELEVANT TO THE RISK

- Identify who might be harmed and how.
- Identify who is most vulnerable.
- Where appropriate, identify potentially violent people in advance.
- Evaluate the risk. Check existing arrangements.
- Train workers to recognise early signs of violence and how they can reduce the likelihood with their behaviour.
- Provide information - e.g. case histories, incidents.
- Improve the environment - e.g. better seating, lighting.

- Improve security - e.g. video cameras, coded locks, wider and higher counters for those who deal with members of the public, panic alarms.
- Redesign the job - e.g. use credit cards rather than cash, bank money more frequently. Check arrangements for lone workers and consider two workers where risks are high.
- Arrange safe transport or secure car parking for people who work late at night.
- Remove any items that could be used as a weapon.

MONITOR

Check regularly to see if the arrangements are working by consulting workers and worker health and safety representatives. If violence is still a problem, review work practices and risk controls.

DEALING WITH INCIDENTS

If there is a violent incident in the workplace it will be necessary to consider the following:

- Debriefing - victims might need to talk through their experience as soon as possible.
- Time off work - individuals may need differing times to recover.
- Support - in some cases victims might need counselling. Consider a phased return to work.
- Legal help - legal assistance may be appropriate in serious cases.
- Other workers - may need guidance or counselling to help them react appropriately.

1.3 - Substance misuse at work

Risks to health and safety of alcohol and drugs at work

The regular use of alcohol and drugs is becoming increasingly common in society. People who start consuming alcohol or drugs usually have a nil or low dependency and do so for recreational reasons. This however can escalate quickly into abuse when larger quantities of alcohol or drugs are consumed more frequently and become habitual. Drugs may be prescribed for a medical condition that a worker requires for treatment or of the controlled type whose general use is illegal, such as cocaine and heroin. The effects of alcohol or drugs can vary dependent upon the individual's state of health and fitness, and resilience to the chemicals. Alcohol and drugs can remain in the body for a considerable time after consumption and its effects still be present the next day when at work. Effects on health and safety include:

- Poor co-ordination and balance.
- Perception ability reduced.
- Overall state of poor health including fatigue, poor concentration and stress.
- Poor attitude, lack of adherence to rules.
- Increased risk of violence.
- Increased likelihood of transport incidents.

Specific legislation such as the Transport and Works Act (TWA) 1992 and the Road Traffic Act (RTA) 1988 specifically prohibit being unfit in specified circumstances through the use of alcohol and drugs. The TWA 1992 prohibits conducting safety critical work and RTA 1988 prohibits driving whilst unfit due to alcohol or drugs.

Control measures for the misuse of alcohol and drugs at work

The use of alcohol and drugs is a personal choice over which employers usually have little or no control when it is conducted in the worker's own time. However, employers should have a policy to deal with the issue should it start to impact on the worker's performance at work.

Control strategies often start with the identification of safety critical work, where the influence of drugs and alcohol would have a significant effect. It is usual that strategies do not presume use or non-use of alcohol and drugs for those that conduct safety critical work, treating them all equally. In a simple approach, all workers that come on to a site, such as a hospital, construction or power generation site, might be considered to be in safety critical work. All workers would work to the same rules, which included banning workers being under the influence of alcohol and drugs while at work, offering them opportunities to talk to someone about how this affects them and carrying out random drugs and alcohol tests. When accidents occur it is common to consider alcohol and drugs as factors. It may not always be possible to test an injured party to identify if they caused their own accident by being under the influence of alcohol or drugs, but, for example, it may be possible to test a driver of a fork lift truck that ran into someone on site.

1.4 - Safe movement of people in the workplace

Hazards in the workplace

TYPICAL HAZARDS

Slips, trips and falls on the same level

Figure 2-1-7: Trip hazard, damaged tile.   *Source: RMS.*

Figure 2-1-8: Slip hazard spilt liquid.   *Source: RMS.*

Slips, trips and falls on the same level are the most common causes of major injuries reported to the Health and Safety Executive (HSE) under the Reporting of Injuries, Diseases and Dangerous Occurrences Regulations (RIDDOR) 1995. Broken bones are the usual result when the following conditions are present.

- Poorly maintained surfaces - e.g. highly polished surfaces, damaged floor tiles, holes in roads, site debris, insecure ducting or grates, poor re-instatements of roads or walk ways.
- Changes in level caused by ramps, slopes, kerbs, or steps not clearly marked.

- Slippery surfaces caused by water, oils, fuels, silt, mud, or mixed compounds such as plaster.
- Inappropriate footwear.
- Rules not followed - e.g. running or not taking care when walking.
- General obstructions in walkways such as trailing cables, pipes and air hoses.

Falls from a height

- Inadequate access to and from the workplace, e.g. a flat roof, upper levels of a vehicle.
- Fragile roofs, e.g. asbestos cement composite roof panels.
- Inadequate barriers, e.g. no hand rails, edge protection.
- Unprotected trenches, e.g. no barriers/fences.

Figure 2-1-9: Falls from a height.   *Source: RMS.*

Figure 2-1-10: Fall from a height - roof used for storage. *Source: RMS.*

Collisions with moving vehicles

- Restricted space to allow for manoeuvring and passing - e.g. where there is a high volume movement of mobile plant and materials.
- Undefined routes to segregate site traffic - e.g. people with vehicles such as fork lift trucks or heavy goods vehicles.
- Traffic routes not defined.
- Vehicles reversing into loading bays without anyone providing assistance.
- Disregard for rules concerning vehicles - e.g. speed restrictions, competent operators.
- No or insufficient pedestrian warning devices fitted to vehicles and a general lack of maintenance.

Striking by moving, flying or falling objects

It is also important to consider precautions to prevent people being struck by moving, flying or falling objects. Situations that increase the likelihood of this hazard are:

- Stacking raw materials, finished products (sacks and drums) too high.
- Use of damaged or unsuitable pallets.
- Overloading of materials on racking.
- Loose materials stacked at too steep an angle e.g. soil, grain or vegetables.
- Faulty or inappropriate means of lifting or lowering materials to the workplace.
- Unstable loads on vehicles - e.g. not correctly supported, tied or shrink wrapped.
- Insecure components or work piece in moving machinery.
- Products of machining processes not contained - e.g. swarf or waste material ejected.
- Free dust from work processes or outside areas blown into the eyes of workers.

Figure 2-1-11: Obstructed designated walkway.   *Source: RMS.*

Figure 2-1-12: Insecure load, potential for falling objects. *Source: RMS.*

Striking against fixed or stationary objects

Whilst bumps and bruises are considered by many as "minor" injuries, they are painful and can be distressing for the sufferer. Therefore, the following situations should be avoided.

- Poorly sited machinery and furniture - avoid sharp corners protruding out.
- Insufficient space for storing tools and materials causing poor access and egress.
- Poor lighting.
- Work in enclosed areas.
- Walking into cranes or lifting devices with hanging hooks/slings.

CIRCUMSTANCES IN WHICH HAZARDS MAY ARISE

Conditions and environments that promote hazards

Conditions and environments that promote hazards include:

- Poor standards of housekeeping in the workplace. Allowing rubbish to accumulate also increases the risk of fire, and biological hazards from vermin.
- Adverse weather conditions - e.g. high winds, rain, and snow.
- Outdoor work, warehouses where vehicles operate alongside people or poorly laid out offices.
- Typical high risk work - maintenance, construction, demolition and excavating.
- Distribution centres, commercial vehicle depots, loading yards where fork lift trucks are used, freight and bus terminals.
- Activities that create a changing environment, for example, maintenance and construction activities.

Staircases

Staircases represent a high risk environment in which movement of people accidents are more likely to be caused. Reasons why accidents may occur on staircases include:

- Poor design of the staircase.
- Not using handrail (e.g. carrying).
- Slippery condition of the stairs (e.g. due to polish or water).
- Inadequate maintenance (e.g. worn or damaged stairs, tiles, carpets).
- Obstructions on the stairs (e.g. boxes of photocopy paper).
- Inadequate standards of lighting.
- Bad practice (carrying loads, inappropriate footwear, non-use of handrails or rushing).
- Too narrow for volume of people using it.

Maintenance work

- Operators often work in areas where the use of barriers excludes other people.
- Work is often carried out under severe time constraints.
- Plant or equipment may still be hot or cold, stuck at some point in its operating cycle, faulty or contaminated.
- Locking off the power supply may be difficult.
- Usually requires work in high risk areas such as confined spaces or at height.
- Often requires hot work such as welding or cutting.
- Asbestos is frequently encountered during maintenance work.
- Materials or liquids may be spilt while taking equipment apart.
- The work area may be restricted, untidy and the lighting may be poor.

Control measures for safe movement of people in the workplace

RISK ASSESSMENT

Some or all of the following issues might affect the hazards faced by pedestrians and should be considered when carrying out a risk assessment:

- Weather conditions - particularly snow and ice.
- Lighting - especially at night.
- Surfaces - the presence of holes in the floor or mud.
- Unusually high numbers of people. Consider, for example, busy periods such as pre-Christmas holiday sales in department stores causing large numbers of the public to be near street works and fluctuations in workloads which could lead to an influx of temporary workers.
- The effectiveness of existing controls - such as barriers.
- Unexpected movements of people - such as shortcuts, entry into restricted areas, emergency evacuation.
- Special needs for certain groups of people - such as people in wheel chairs, pregnant women and elderly people.

GENERAL CONTROLS FOR THE SAFE MOVEMENT OF PEOPLE IN THE WORKPLACE

Slip and trip hazards in the workplace may be controlled by:

- Designated slip resistant walkways.

- Using high grip surface coating.
- Highlighting changes in level with hazard warning strips.
- Providing good lighting.
- Introducing procedures for reporting defects and for dealing with spillage that might limit the slip resistance.
- Ensuring high standards of housekeeping to keep floors clear of obstructions, debris or spillage.
- Provision of made up roughened concrete walkways on construction sites and where outdoor work takes place.
- Fitting high grip grit sheets on the edge of steps and stairs.
- Provision of mats at the entrance to buildings.

Design features and/or safe practices intended to reduce the risk of accidents on staircases used as internal pedestrian routes within work premises:

- Adequate width of stair.
- Provision of handrails.
- The dimensions of treads and risers.
- Provision of landings.
- Special provisions for disabled persons.
- Possibility of using a lift as an alternative.
- Avoid the need to carry large or heavy items up or down stairs.
- Wear appropriate footwear.
- The provision of non-slip surfaces, together with reflective edging.
- Adequate lighting and effective maintenance.
- The removal of obstructions, with particular attention to emergency escape routes.

Figure 2-1-13: Slip resistance surface on steps.   *Source: RMS.*

SLIP RESISTANT SURFACES

In order to ensure the safe movement of people slip resistant surfaces should be provided:

- At the entrance of buildings, for example a mat that provides both slip resistance and can absorb water brought in on footwear.
- On designate walkways.
- On changes of level, such as stairs, steps, ladders, footholds to vehicles.
- On ramps or slopes.
- Where walkways intersect with internal transport routes and people may need to stop suddenly.

Figure 2-1-14: Anti-slip flooring.   *Source: RMS.*

- In work areas where spills of liquids or dry contaminants are likely.
- Where liquids are decanted or containers filled or stored.
- On access areas used for inspection or maintenance.
- Locations where workers need to go that are exposed to the weather and where surfaces may become covered in environmental grime or slippery growth.

When selecting a slip resistant surface consider:

- The consequences of slipping, a slip while holding a knife or at height could have major consequences.
- The type of contamination likely, for example, liquid or dry; water, oil or blood; visible or not.
- Ability to control contamination, e.g. drainage.
- Level of use of the surface.
- The range of people using the surface, age, disability.
- What people might be doing on the surface, e.g. walking, climbing, carrying, turning, moving fast.
- Environmental issues, weather, hot or cold.
- Level of control over footwear used.
- The surface option, for example, smooth or rough profile, wear durability.
- The slip resistance rating (SRV) and roughness (Rz) needed.

SPILLAGE CONTROL AND DRAINAGE

A procedure for spillage response for hazardous liquids should include:

- Raise the alarm and inform emergency services and relevant authorities (e.g. Fire Service, Water Company).
- Evacuate all personnel, seal off access from danger area.
- Quickly assess the nature and extent (if possible) of the incident.
- Do not approach the liquid if you do not know what it is.

- Raise first aid treatment for those who might have been affected.
- Provide bunding or some other form of spillage containment such as sand or special granules to contain the spillage.
- Isolate any ignition sources.
- Keep people away.
- For internal spills with no fire risk, ventilate the area by opening windows and isolate the material by closing doors.
- For external spills, cover drains to prevent the material going into drains and watercourses. Do not wash spillage into drains.
- Issue appropriate personal protective equipment to those involved and competent in carrying out the procedure.
- Ensure safe disposal of the spilled substance and any absorbent material used.

DESIGNATED WALKWAYS

The duty to provide a reasonably safe place of work relates to such matters as clearly marked walkways which are free of obstruction, the maintenance of floors and staircases, a safe working environment and safe means of access and egress together with the organisation of traffic routes (including pedestrian traffic). A critical consideration when considering traffic systems is the safety interface between pedestrians and traffic. The routes that people use should be clearly defined and marked. This is a requirement of the Workplace (Health, Safety and Welfare) Regulations (WHSWR) 1992 which states that every workplace shall be organised in such a way that pedestrian and vehicles can circulate in a safe manner.

The workplace may be some distance from the ground as with construction workers or several miles underground as with miners. Therefore, such things as approach roads, portable access equipment (ladders, etc.), and shoring of underground workings must be considered. Particular thought should be given to access and egress for emergency vehicles.

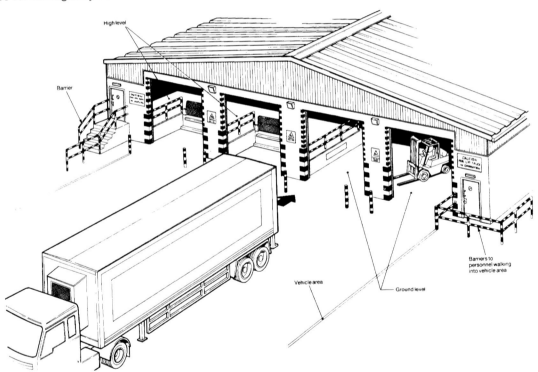

Figure 2-1-15: Vehicle unloading/loading showing separate pedestrian access, fencing and guarding barriers. *Source: HSG76.*

Control of hazards related to floors and gangways

Regulation 12 WHSWR 1992 requires that floors and traffic route surfaces must be constructed so that they are suitable for the purpose for which they are used. This means such things as having no holes or being slippery or uneven. Measures to control hazards related to floors and gangways may include:

- Being kept clean and free from obstructions that may hinder passage.
- Good drainage in wet process areas or wet weather conditions.
- Suitable footwear or working platforms provided where necessary.
- Ramps kept dry and with non-skid surfaces.
- Level, even ground without holes or broken boards.
- Floor load capacities posted in lofts and storage areas.
- Salting/sanding and sweeping of outdoor routes during icy or frosty conditions.
- Steps, corners and fixed obstacles clearly marked.
- Excavations and chambers kept covered when not in use and the edges clearly marked.

FENCING AND GUARDING

Fencing and guarding in the form of physical barriers should be erected to ensure that there is adequate protection for pedestrians who may be exposed to falls, falling objects and being struck by a moving object such as a vehicle.

"Every employer shall, where necessary to prevent injury to any person, take suitable and sufficient steps to prevent, so far as is reasonably practicable, the fall of any material or object".

Figure 2-1-16: Prevention of falling objects.   *Source: Regulation 10 of Work at Height Regulations (WAH) 2005.*

USE OF SIGNS AND PERSONAL PROTECTIVE EQUIPMENT

Signs must conform to the standards specified in the Health and Safety (Safety Signs and Signals) Regulations (SSSR) 1996. They must be clearly visible and be easily understood.

Safety signs should indicate the need to use personal protective equipment, such as hard hats, protective footwear or high visibility clothing, when entering certain work areas even if people are just visiting or passing quickly through. Signs to indicate the presence of a temporary hazard should be used to warn people who might be affected to keep clear of that area.

Hazard signs might be used where excavations are present, a change in height occurs or for the demarcation of a hazard area to assist with the provision of diversionary routes - for example, a vehicle unloading area where pedestrians are prohibited. Edges of steps, overhead obstructions and cables or pipes laid temporarily across walkways should also be clearly identified with hazard markings.

Appropriate footwear is important to avoid slips or trips or puncture wounds in the workplace.

The risk assessment process should consider the possibility of slips, trips and sharp material hazards, and where the decided control of this hazard includes the use of specific footwear this should be arranged.

Figure 2-1-17: Correct clothing and footwear.
Source: RMS.

If the footwear has particular properties, such as anti-slip soles or steel mid-plates, this would fall under the requirements of the Personal Protective Equipment Regulations (PPER) 1992 and as such the employer should provide them to employees without charge. Where specific personal protective footwear is not required but employees need to wear suitable personal shoes to work, this should be specified and would not normally be subject to the PPER 1992. In addition, footwear with a protective toe cap is necessary for those that may work in close proximity to vehicles. On sites where vehicles operate and for street works it is essential that workers are able to be seen, therefore it is essential that high visibility clothing be used. Though this is not a substitute for the separation of vehicles from people, for the many situations where workers work in close proximity to vehicles it will provide valuable assistance in preventing contact.

INFORMATION, INSTRUCTION, TRAINING AND SUPERVISION

The employer, through management, should ensure that rules, policies and procedures are followed and that people do not act irresponsibly. Certain circumstances may require specific information, instruction and training, for example, procedures for climbing ladders or wearing appropriate clothing (e.g. high visibility jackets).

The Health and Safety at Work Act etc (HASAWA) 1974 requires employers to provide supervision as necessary. This means that the employer must actively supervise the workplace and the work conducted in it, for example, if high visibility clothing is required or walkways are to be kept clear this must be supervised. The concept requires the supervisor to increase the level of supervision on a needs basis, for example, the higher the risk related to the work or workplace hazard or the more persistent the problem, the greater is the supervision necessary. If a large number of the public are to use a route after it has been cleaned the supervisor should make special effort to ensure that it is safe. If an obstruction of a walk route keeps returning, the supervisor will need to put in extra effort to bring it under control.

MAINTENANCE OF A SAFE WORKPLACE

Cleaning and housekeeping requirements

Maintenance of a safe workplace may be achieved through the development of a housekeeping procedure. Good housekeeping implies "a place for everything and everything in its place". Laid down procedures are necessary for preventing the spread of contamination, reducing the likelihood of accidents resulting in slips, trips, and falls and reducing the chances of unwanted fire caused by careless storage of flammable waste.

Access and egress

- Adequate space for easy movement, and safe plant or equipment use.
- No tripping hazards, e.g. trailing cables or pipes.
- Handholds or guardrails where people might fall from floor edges.
- Emergency provision, e.g. life belts/jackets for work near water or means of escape from confined spaces.
- Neat and tidy storage of tools, plant and equipment so that they do not present a hazard to passers-by.
- Identify storage areas.
- Mark areas to be kept clear.
- Pay particular attention to emergency routes.
- Vision panels in doors to avoid contact injuries.
- Emergency provision, e.g. life belts/jackets for work near water; means of escape from freezer rooms.

Figure 2-1-18: Vision panels in fire doors.   *Source: RMS.*

Lighting

Lighting plays an important part in health and safety, and in particular the safe movement of people in the workplace.

Factors to consider include:

- Good general illumination with no glare, especially where there are vehicle movements.
- Regular cleaning and maintenance of lights and windows.
- Local lighting for dangerous processes or movement areas and to reduce eye strain and fatigue.
- No flickering from fluorescent tubes (it can be dangerous with some rotating machinery and a distraction to people).
- Outside areas satisfactorily lit for work and access during hours of darkness - for security as well as safety.
- Adequate emergency lighting which is regularly tested and maintained.
- Specially constructed fittings for flammable or explosive atmospheres e.g. where paint spraying work is carried out.
- Light coloured wall finishes improving brightness, or darker colours to reduce glare, for example, from arc welding flash.

Care should be taken, in particular where temporary lighting is rigged during maintenance activities, to ensure that glare and shadows are minimised. Particular attention should be paid to changes in level, corners and where workers pass between the outside and inside where darkness occurs.

Factors to consider when assessing the adequacy of lighting within an open plan office:

- The types of task being undertaken (in particular the use of display screen equipment).
- The availability of natural light and emergency lighting, and the problems caused by glare.
- The effect of office layout (in terms of shadows cast, etc.) and the appropriateness of general lighting (its type, colour and intensity in relation to, for instance, the floor area), and the suitability and adjustability of local lighting in relation to specific tasks.

Regulation 8 of WHSWR 1992 requires that, as far as is reasonably practicable, suitable and sufficient lighting be provided. It should be noted that where there is a potential danger due to failure of artificial lighting that is provided emergency lighting is required. This would be particularly relevant where it was necessary for people to move away from machinery or to take or use a complex route of exit.

CONTROL MEASURES FOR MAINTENANCE WORK

Some maintenance activities may involve using large pieces of equipment which may compromise access and/or egress routes. It is important that all these are taken into consideration during the planning phase of the any activity and where required, temporary signage may be displayed. Barriers may also be required, if there is a need to protect other employees/contractors or the general public from other hazards i.e. noise, fumes, dusts or light (UV from welding). Competent supervision of the activity is essential to monitor and control any changes to the work, making sure any additional housekeeping is conducted at regular intervals to prevent slips/trips or falls from debris created during the work.

1.5 - Working at height

Work activities and injuries associated with falls from height

Falls are the most common cause of fatal injuries in the construction industry.

They account for more than half of those accidentally killed each year. Much of the work carried out on a building site is done above ground at height, commonly more than two metres.

Typical activities that involve working at height are:

- Steel erecting.
- Fixing of cladding, roof work.
- Painting and decorating.
- Demolition and dismantling.

- Bricklaying.
- Scaffold erection.
- Electrical installation and maintenance.

The risks of falls from height are substantial however long or short the work. Risks related to work activities at height are increased by the presence of fragile roofs, roof lights, voids, deteriorating materials and the weather. Some work though, only rarely involves height. Such as:

- Welding.
- Inspection.
- Machinery maintenance.

This means that, very often, people with little or no experience find themselves exposed to the dangers of working above ground level.

Basic hazards of working at height

VERTICAL DISTANCE

Though some construction work involves work activities to be carried out at a significant height (vertical distance), for example on a roof or scaffold, it should not be assumed that work at less significant heights is without risk. Major injuries can occur if a fall results whilst carrying out tasks at a height of less than 2 metres, for example fitting false ceilings or installing utilities inside buildings. This should not give the impression that people are not injured by falls from heights less than 2 metres; this remains a significant risk and many injuries result each year. Legislation, the Work at Height Regulations (WAH) 2005, reflects this risk and requires controls to be in place to manage the risk of falling, whatever the height. This legislation applies to workplaces in general, and therefore includes construction activities. Under these regulations the interpretation of 'work at height' includes any place of work at ground level, above or below ground level that a person could fall a distance liable to cause personal injury and includes places for obtaining access or egress, except by staircase in a permanent workplace.

WAH 2005 Regulation 6 states that work at height must only be carried out when it is not reasonably practicable to carry out the work otherwise. If work at height does take place, suitable and sufficient measures must be taken to prevent a fall of any distance, to minimise the distance and the consequences of any fall liable to cause injury. Employers must also make a risk assessment, as required by Regulation 3 of the Management of Health and Safety at Work Regulations (MHSWR) 1999.

ROOFS

Working at height and on roofs carries a high risk of accidents, unless proper procedures and precautions are taken. The danger of people or materials falling affects the safety of those working at height and those working beneath. Particular danger arises from two types of roof - fragile roofs and sloping roofs.

Fragile roofs

Materials such as asbestos, cement, glass or plastic are likely to be unable to bear the weight of a person. Asbestos sheet deteriorates over time leaving the remaining material in a particularly fragile state. Though the sheet looks intact it will only have a small fraction of its original strength. In a similar way plastic roof material, such as may be used in roof lights, will be affected by exposure to sunlight leaving it brittle. It should not be assumed that it is safe to walk on newly installed roof material though it will have its original strength, but this may not be enough to bear the weight of a worker. All fragile roofs and/or access routes to them should be marked with an appropriate warning sign.

The WAH 2005 Regulation 9 states that every employer shall ensure that suitable and sufficient steps are taken to prevent any person at work falling through any fragile surface; and that no work may pass across or near, or work on, from or near, fragile surfaces when it is reasonably practicable to carry out work without doing so. If work has to be from a fragile roof then suitable and sufficient means of support must be provided that can sustain foreseeable loads. No person at work should be allowed to pass or work near a fragile surface unless suitable and sufficient guard rails and other means of fall protection is in place. Signs must be situated at a prominent place at or near to works involving fragile surfaces, or persons are made aware of the fragile roof by other means.

Sloping roofs

Sloping roofs are those with a pitch greater than 10 degrees. Falls from the edge of sloping roofs can cause serious injury even when the eaves are relatively low. The hazard of sloping roofs is less obvious when the pitch is small causing people to underestimate the possibility of workers sliding off the edge. The material and therefore the surface of the roof have a significant influence on the hazard, for example, a smooth sheet metal surface can present a significant hazard even when the pitch is small.

The chances of an accident are increased when working on roofs that are wet or covered in moss growth and in extreme weather conditions such as high winds. The other significant influencing issue is the footwear used by the worker, smooth flat soled footwear may seem suitable in dry conditions but may not provide sufficient grip to deal with surface water in wet conditions. A build up of dry particles or grit on a roof can present a surface that leads to a high risk of slipping as the particles become free to move and form a mobile layer between the roof and the worker's foot.

DETERIORATION OF MATERIALS

The condition of the structure on which people are working can deteriorate with time. The rate of deterioration will accelerate if the structure is exposed to adverse weather conditions (including extremes of temperature) or attack by chemicals, animals, insects etc. It may not always be obvious that deterioration has occurred and this should be a factor to be considered at the pre-work assessment.

UNPROTECTED EDGES

Roofs, scaffolds, unfinished steel work and access platforms may sometimes have open sides. This increases the likelihood of someone or something falling, particularly if people have to approach them, work at them or pass by them repeatedly.

It is very easy in these circumstances to lose perception of the hazard and forget that it is there. Errors, such as stepping back over an edge, overreaching, or being pushed over the edge whilst manoeuvring materials can easily lead to fatal falls.

UNSTABLE/POORLY MAINTAINED ACCESS EQUIPMENT

An employer having committed to providing access to a height by the provision of work equipment might yet have employees using it who are at risk from basic hazards relating to its stability and maintenance. Working with mobile elevated work platforms (MEWPs), ladders and scaffolds have their own specific stability and maintenance issues, the hazard of falling from a height whilst using them being the common theme. Each is influenced by the problem of the stability of the ground conditions they are placed on and the height they are used at compared to their stability base. *See also - Mobile elevating work platforms - later in this Element.*

The effective working of the hydraulics of a MEWP is critical and failure to maintain this could lead to a sudden and catastrophic failure of the MEWP whilst it is extended. Scaffolds need periodic maintenance to ensure load bearing parts are still secured and those critical items such as brakes on mobile scaffolds are in place and effective. Failure to maintain them can quickly undermine the strength, integrity and stability of the scaffold leading to collapse or overturning.

All equipment, access equipment being no exception, can fail if not properly maintained. Cracks may occur in the sides of ladders and loose rungs can lead to failure. They may warp or rot if left exposed to the elements. Defects in ladders may be hidden if they are painted or covered in plaster.

WEATHER

Adverse weather can have a significant effect on the safety of those working at a height. Rain, snow and ice increase the risk of slips and falling from a roof. When handling large objects, such as roof panels, high wind can be a serious problem and may cause the person to be blown off the roof.

Extremely cold temperatures can increase the likelihood of brittle failure of materials and therefore increase the likelihood of failure of roof supports, scaffold components and plastic roof lights.

In addition, moisture can freeze; increasing the slipperiness of surfaces and on many occasions the presence of ice is not easily visible.

Figure 2-1-19: Working above ground level.   *Source: RMS.*

Workers exposed to the cold can lose their dexterity and when hot, sweat may cause them to lose their grip.

FALLING MATERIALS

Caused by:

- Poor housekeeping of people working above.
- Absence of toe boards or edge protection.
- Incorrect hooking and slinging.
- Incorrect assembly of gin wheels for raising materials.
- Surplus materials incorrectly stacked.
- Open, unprotected edges.
- Deterioration of structures causing crumbling masonry.

The risk of falling materials causing injury should be minimised by keeping platforms clear of loose materials. In addition, methods provided should prevent materials or other objects rolling, or being kicked off the edges of platforms.

This may be done with toe boards, solid barriers, brick guards, or similar being positioned at open edges. If working in a public place, nets, fans or covered walkways may be needed to give extra protection for people who may be passing below. High-visibility barrier netting is not suitable for use as a fall prevention device.

Materials such as old slates, tiles, etc. should not be thrown from the roof or scaffold - passers-by may be at risk of being injured. Enclosed debris chutes should be used or debris should be lowered in containers.

Methods of avoiding working at height

Where possible, work at height should be avoided by conducting the work at ground level. This means that organisations should review work done to determine a response to this requirement. This could be achieved by using different equipment or method of work. This may affect those that manually fill equipment hoppers located at height, requiring consideration of bulk delivery and automatic feed systems. Where workers have to lubricate or adjust equipment set at height by hand, options to automate or route the lubrication/adjustment mechanisms to ground level should be considered. Pre-assembly of materials such as roof trusses, either before delivery or on the ground on site, instead of assembly at a height should be considered. If materials are pre-painted or pre-drilled this can greatly reduce the work needed to be done at height, for example, decorative wooden panels for a building can be pre-treated to avoid weather treatment being brushed on at a height. Long reach handling devices can be used to allow cleaning or other tasks to be conducted from the ground. Where equipment, such as light units, requires maintenance an option may be to lower it sufficiently to enable bulbs to be changed and cleaning to be conducted from the ground.

Main precautions necessary to prevent falls and falling material

PROPER PLANNING AND SUPERVISION OF WORK

Fall of people

Regulation 4 of the Work at Height Regulations (WAH) 2005 states that all work at height must be properly planned, supervised and be carried out, so far as is reasonably practicable, safe. Planning must include the selection of suitable equipment, take account of emergencies and give consideration to weather conditions impacting on safety.

WAH 2005 Regulation 5 states that those engaged in any activity in relation to work at height must be competent; and, if under training, be supervised by a competent person.

WAH 2005 Regulation 6 states that work at height must only be carried out when it is not reasonably practicable to carry out the work otherwise. If work at height does take place, suitable and sufficient measures must be taken to prevent a fall of any distance, to minimise the distance and the consequences of any fall liable to cause injury. Employers must also make a risk assessment, as required by regulation 3 of the Management of Health and Safety at Work Regulations (MHSWR) 1999.

Fall of materials

WAH 2005 Regulation 10 states that every employer shall take reasonably practicable steps to prevent injury to any person from the fall of any material or object; and where it is not reasonably practicable to do so, to take similar steps to prevent any person being struck by any falling material or object which is liable to cause personal injury. Also, that no material is thrown or tipped from height in circumstances where it is liable to cause injury to any person. Materials and objects must be stored in such a way as to prevent risk to any person arising from the collapse, overturning or unintended movement of the materials or objects. WAH 2005 Regulation 11 states that every employer shall ensure that where an area presents a risk of falling from height or being struck from an item falling at height that the area is equipped with devices preventing unauthorised persons from entering such areas and the area is clearly indicated.

AVOIDING WORKING IN ADVERSE WEATHER CONDITIONS

Adverse weather can include wind, rain, sun, cold, snow and ice. Each of these conditions, particularly in extreme cases, can present a significant hazard to construction work. When long term projects are planned methods are often adjusted to minimise the effects. For example, road and walk routes that could quickly be affected by rain are made up into formal structures by the use of hardcore, concrete and tarmac. Work areas can be covered over at an early stage to enable work to be conducted in relative comfort. In some cases it may be that work is organised in an order that predicts expected adverse weather, allowing tasks to be adjusted until short term weather conditions improve. In some cases adverse weather must be considered formally and work may have to cease until conditions improve, for example, work on a roof in icy conditions or high winds. Similar approaches may have to be taken for operating a mobile elevating work platform (MEWP) in windy conditions or entering a sewer during a rain storm.

PRECAUTIONS TO PREVENT FALLS AND FALLING MATERIALS

Careful consideration during the risk assessment phase should establish which equipment is best suited for the working environment and work to be done. There are various types of edge protection which should be evaluated in relationship to the activity and environment. This could be edge protection in the form of scaffolding or barriers (temporary or fixed), or consideration of the building of temporary walls.

To safely maintain safe access and egress, temporary staircases should be considered before the use of ladders; if ladders are used it is more difficult to maintain a 'three-point contact' as staff carry or move items to different levels.

Guardrails, fencing and toeboards

Guardrails are designed to prevent people falling whilst toeboards prevent materials falling. Toeboards are usually planks laid on their edge to create a ledge which prevents rubble, tools and other materials from being kicked or knocked over the edge of the working platform. *See also - Scaffolding - later in this Element.* Brick guards, a form of fencing, provide more substantial protection to prevent larger amounts of material from falling and have the added advantage of providing protection for people. The Work at Height Regulations requires that these means of protection must:

- Be of sufficient dimensions, of sufficient strength and rigidity for the purposes for which they are being used, and otherwise suitable.
- Be so placed, secured and used as to ensure, so far as is reasonably practicable, that they do not become accidentally displaced.
- Be so placed as to prevent, so far as is practicable, the fall of any person, or of any material or object, from any place of work.

Working platforms

The Work at Height Regulations (WAH) 2005 defines a "working platform" as:

- Any platform used as a place of work or as a means of access to or egress from a place of work.
- Any scaffold, suspended scaffold, cradle, mobile platform, trestle, gangway, gantry and stairway which is so used.

Schedule 3 of WAH 2005 sets out requirements that work platforms must fulfil, and this comprises:

- Condition of surfaces on which the work platform rests.
- Stability of supporting structures.
- Safety on working platforms.
- Loading of platforms.
- Stability of working platforms.

The following practical precautions should also be considered:

- Wide enough - at least 600 mm wide - to allow people to pass back and forth safely and to use any equipment or material necessary for their work at that place.
- Free of openings and traps through which people's feet could pass and cause them to trip, fall or be injured in any other way.
- Constructed to prevent materials from falling. As well as toe boards or similar protection at the edge of the platform, the platform itself should be constructed to prevent any object which may be used on the platform from falling through gaps or holes, causing injury to people working below. For scaffolds, a close-boarded platform would suffice, although for work over public areas, a double-boarded platform sandwiching a polythene sheet may be needed. If a Mobile Elevated Work Platform (MEWP) or cradle is used and it has meshed platform floors, the mesh should be fine enough to prevent materials, especially nails and bolts, from slipping through.
- Kept free of tripping and slipping hazards. Where necessary, handholds and footholds should be provided. Platforms should be clean, tidy and mud should not be allowed to build up on them.

Access boards

Roof ladders (or crawling boards) spread across the supporting structures distribute the weight over a greater area so that the load can be sustained by the roof. They also provide hand and foot holds and may be equipped with guard rails and toe boards.

Figure 2-1-20: Ladder hoop with rest platform. *Source: RMS.*

Figure 2-1-21: Ladder hoops. *Source: RMS.*

Ladder hoops

Ladder hoops are attached to vertical or steeply sloping ladders to create a "tunnel" for safe climbing. Maintenance workers may make use of them to gain access to a roof or similar areas, they are often used where large process plant is installed over a number of floors and occasional access is required to parts of the

There is a risk of fatigue when climbing vertical ladders, because the climber needs to physically pull and step their body up the ladder. The ladder hoops are designed to prevent people falling away from the ladder through fatigue, but do not prevent sliding down the ladder. Hoops need to be used in conjunction with rest platforms, at intervals of 9 metres, to allow the climber to rest and recover from fatigue *(see figure ref 2-1-21)*.

Emergency rescue

When selecting work equipment for work at height, regulation 7 of the WAH 2005 requires the employer to consider the additional risks that may arise from evacuation and rescue from it. This will include the need to establish clear emergency escape routes from major scaffold installations, rescue arrangements for workers where a mobile elevated work platform fails in its raised position and rescue for those in harnesses or on a fall arrest net.

Steps must be taken to minimise the risk of injury due to the fall or contact with the safeguard. Even a short fall onto a net or other fall arresting safeguard could cause minor injuries or fractures. This should be anticipated and workers taught how to minimise the likelihood of injury.

Where an individual has fallen from height but has been protected by personal fall arrest equipment, such as a harness, significant health effects known as suspension trauma may be experienced if they are not rescued quickly. This is mainly due to blood pooling in the legs, reducing the amount circulating through the rest of the body, which has consequential effects for vital organs such as the brain, heart and kidneys. Unless the individual is rescued very quickly the lack of oxygenated blood to vital organs can be fatal. Therefore a rescue procedure and equipment must be available and practised. The procedure should also take into account that a sudden transition from a vertical to a horizontal position, when rescued and laid down, can lead to a massive amount of deoxygenated blood entering the heart, causing cardiac arrest.

Minimising the distance and consequences of a fall

EQUIPMENT

Personal protection systems

Fall arrest harnesses are useful when other means of fall protection are not reasonably practicable, such as work where open edges exist during steel erection. The harness itself may cause injury when the person comes to a sudden stop so that inertia reel harnesses (the same principle as a car seat belt) may be preferable.

When using harnesses in a mobile elevating work platform (MEWP), the harness should always be fixed to the inside of the cradle *(see figure ref 2-1-49)*.

WAH 2005 requires that a personal fall protection system shall be used only if:

- A risk assessment has demonstrated that:
  - Work can, so far as is reasonably practicable, be performed safely while using that system.
  - Use of other safer work equipment is not reasonably practicable.
- The user and a sufficient number of available persons have received adequate training specific to the operations envisaged, including rescue procedures.

In addition the WAH 2005 requires that a personal fall protection system shall:

- Be suitable and of sufficient strength for the purposes for which it is being used, having regard to the work being carried out and any foreseeable loading.
- Where necessary, fit the user.
- Be correctly fitted.
- Be designed to minimise injury to the user and, where necessary, be adjusted to prevent the user falling or slipping from it, should a fall occur.
- Be so designed, installed and used as to prevent unplanned or uncontrolled movement of the user.

Fall arresting systems

The WAH 2005 requires that a fall arresting safeguard shall be used only if:

- A risk assessment has demonstrated that the work activity can, so far as is reasonably practicable, be performed safely while using it and without affecting its effectiveness.
- Use of other, safer work equipment is not reasonably practicable.
- A sufficient number of available persons have received adequate training specific to the safeguard, including rescue procedures.

A fall arresting safeguard must be suitable and of sufficient strength to arrest safely the fall of any person who is liable to fall.

In addition it must:

- In the case of a safeguard which is designed to be attached, be securely attached to all the required anchor points.
- The anchors and the means of attachment must be suitable and of sufficient strength and stability for the purpose of supporting the foreseeable loading in arresting the fall and during any subsequent rescue.
- In the case of an airbag, landing mat or similar safeguard, be stable.
- In the case of a safeguard which distorts in arresting a fall, afford sufficient clearance.

Suitable and sufficient steps must be taken to ensure, so far as practicable, that in the event of a fall by any person the safeguard does not itself cause injury to that person. Fall arresting systems such as safety nets, air/bean bags or crash mats can be used to minimise the impact of falls through the gaps created within a structure. Safety netting is the preferred fall arrest option since it provides collective protection and, unlike a fall arrest harness, does not rely on individual user discipline to guarantee acceptable safety standards. They can simplify systems of work and can protect not only roof workers, but others such as supervisors. Where safety nets are used, they must be installed as close as possible beneath the roof surface, securely attached and able to withstand a person falling onto them. These must be installed and maintained by competent personnel.

TRAINING AND INSTRUCTION

Regulation 5 of the WAH 2005 requires:

"Every employer shall ensure that no person engages in any activity, including organisation, planning and supervision, in relation to work at height or work equipment for use in such work unless he is competent to do so or, if being trained, is being supervised by a competent person".

Source: The Work at Height Regulations (WAH) 2005.

Figure 2-1-22: Regulation 5 of WAH 2005.

Workers should receive full training and instruction on use of equipment and systems of working that will minimise the distance and consequences of a fall. Where harnesses are to be used this should include how to wear fall arrest harnesses, how to fit it to fixing points, what is a suitable fixing point, fixing at a height that minimises the fall (e.g. above the head where possible). Training should also include the checks that need to be made on fall arrest equipment before it is used, this will include checks on security of nets and the adequacy of airbags. Workers will also need to be trained in how to get off/out of this equipment safely when it has arrested a fall and on emergency arrangements for rescue where workers cannot assist themselves.

MINIMISING THE CONSEQUENCES

A fall arrest system must incorporate means of absorbing and limiting the forces applied to the user's body. Care should be taken to ensure that at time of use of the fall arrest system it is not at risk of the line being cut and that it is free to operate as intended. Consideration should be made to ensuring that there is a 'clear zone' available at all times it is in use and that this should take account of any pendulum effect. If work is being conducted near or over open water, then self-inflating life vests may be needed as well as a rescue boat.

Requirements for head protection

The Construction (Head Protection) Regulations (CHPR) 1989 make specific requirements about hard hats. *See also - Relevant statutory provisions section.* Hard hats are required where there is a foreseeable risk of injury to the head other than by falling e.g. struck by falling materials or where people might hit their heads.

Hazards to consider:

- Loose material kicked into an excavation.
- Material falling from a scaffold platform.
- Material falling off a load being lifted by a crane or goods hoist or carried on a site dumper or truck.
- Dropping a fitting while erecting or dismantling a scaffold.

Actions to be taken include:

- Decide on which areas of the site where hats have to be worn.
- Make site rules and tell everyone in the area.
- Provide employees with hard hats.
- Make sure hats are worn and worn correctly.
- A wide range of hats are available:
  - Let employees try a few and decide which is most suitable for the job and for them.
  - Some hats have extra features including a sweatband for the forehead and a soft, or webbing harness.
  - Although these hats are slightly more expensive, they are much more comfortable and therefore more likely to be worn.

Safe working practices for common forms of access equipment

LADDERS

Use of ladders

Ladders are primarily a means of vertical access to a workplace.

© RMS

However, they are often used to carry out work and this frequently results in accidents.

Many accidents involving ladders happen during work lasting 30 minutes or less. Ladders are often used for short jobs when it would be safer to use other equipment, e.g. mobile scaffold towers or MEWPs. Generally, ladders should be considered as access equipment and use of a ladder as a work platform should be discouraged. There are situations when working from a ladder would be inappropriate, for example:

- When two hands are needed or the work area is large.
- Where the equipment or materials used are large or awkward.
- Excessive height.
- Work of long duration.
- Where the ladder cannot be secured or made stable.
- Where the ladder cannot be protected from vehicles etc.
- Adverse weather conditions.

Figure 2-1-23: Ladder as access and workplace. *Source: RMS.*

Figure 2-1-24: Improper use of ladder. *Source: RMS.*

Figure 2-1-25: Inappropriate storage. *Source: Lincsafe.*

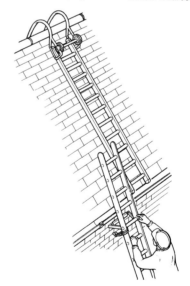

Figure 2-1-26: Use of roof ladders. *Source: HSG150, HSE.*

Before using a ladder to work from, consider whether it is the right equipment for the job. Ladders are only suitable as a workplace for light work of short duration, and for a large majority of activities a scaffold, mobile tower or mobile elevated work platform (MEWP) is likely to be more suitable and safer.

- Pre-use inspection. Make sure the ladder is in good condition. Check the rungs and stiles for warping, cracking or splintering, the condition of the feet, and for any other defects. Do not use defective or painted ladders.
- Position the ladder properly for safe access and out of the way of vehicles. Do not rest ladders against fragile surfaces.
- Ladders must stand on a firm, level base, be positioned approximately at an angle of 75^0 (1 unit horizontally to 4 units vertically), **(see figure ref 2-1-27)** (note means of securing omitted for clarity).

- Ladders must be properly tied near the top, even if only in use for a short time, while being tied a ladder must be footed. If not tied ladders must be secured near the bottom, footed or weighted.
- If the ladder is being used to gain access to a landing place it should extend about 1 metre above landing place.
- Both hands should be kept free to grip the ladder when climbing or descending, with only one person on the ladder at any time. Beware of wet, greasy or icy rungs and make sure soles of footwear are clean.

Step ladders

Stepladders require careful use. They are subject to the same general health and safety rules as ladders.

However, in addition, they will not withstand any degree of side loading and overturn very easily.

When using a step ladder over-reaching should be avoided at all times and care should be taken avoid side loading.

Care should be taken to ensure it is placed on a firm level surface to minimise the possibility of it overturning sideways.

Step ladder stays must be 'locked out' properly before use.

The top step of a stepladder should not be used as a working platform unless it has been specifically designed for that purpose.

Typically three clear steps should be left to ensure support and stability, depending on the size and design of the step ladder, *(see figure ref 2-1-29).*

Figure 2-1-27: Correct 1 in 4 angle. *Source: HSE.*

Figure 2-1-28: Incorrect use of a step ladder. *Source: HSE.*

Figure 2-1-29: Correct use of a step ladder. *Source: HSE.*

Figure 2-1-30: Incorrect use of a step ladder. *Source: RMS.*

Figure 2-1-31: Correct use of a step ladder. *Source: HSE.*

SCAFFOLDING

General points

Many accidents are due to simple faults, such as misuse of tools, use of a ladder left unfixed, or scaffold with a missing toeboard. Regrettably, some accidents are caused by failure to take due regard of the WAH 2005 and basic faults such as using a scaffold board which is seen to be defective, or using a scaffold board over an excessive span.

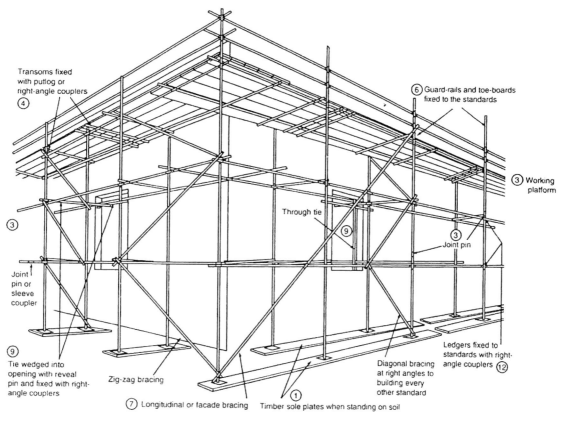

Figure 2-1-32: Independent tied scaffold.

Source: HSG150 Safety in Construction.

Reasons why scaffolds collapse

■ Incorrect erection.
■ Overloading.
■ Uneven distribution of loads.
■ Poor ground conditions.
■ Adverse weather.
■ Insufficient or inappropriate ties.
■ Interference with ties.
■ Incompatible components.
■ Unauthorised alteration.

Common misuse

■ Removal of bracings and ties.
■ Removal of scaffold boards.
■ Removal of handrails or toe boards.
■ Excavations near the scaffold.
■ Use of the scaffold for propping shuttering when it was not designed for that purpose.
■ Vehicle collision.

Figure 2-1-33: Independent tied scaffold. *Source: RMS.*

Scaffolding terms

Base Plate	Distribute the load from a standard or a raker (scaffold standard used as an outrigger).
Reveal Pin	A screw jack, fitting in the end of a tube.

Tubular members

Brace	A tube fixed diagonally across two or more members in a scaffold for stability.
Guard - Rail	A member incorporated in the structure to prevent personnel from falling.
Ledger	A tube spanning horizontally and tying the scaffold longitudinally. It may act as a

	support for putlogs or transoms.
Putlog	A tube with a flattened end, spanning from a horizontal member to a bearing in or on a brick wall. It may support scaffold boards.
Reveal Pin	A tube wedged by means of a reveal screw between two opposite surfaces (e.g. window reveals) to make a friction anchorage for tying a scaffold.
Standard / Column	A vertical or near vertical supporting member.
Tie	A member used for fixing the scaffold to the building or other structure for stability.
Transom	A tube spanning across ledgers to tie a scaffold transversely. It may also support boards.

Independent tied scaffold

This type of scaffold typically uses two sets of standards; one near to the structure and the other set at the width of the work platform. It is erected so that it is independent from the structure and does not rely on it for its primary stability. However, as the name suggests, it is usual to tie the scaffold to the structure in order to prevent the scaffold falling towards or away from the structure.

Base plates and sole boards

- A base plate must be used under every standard - it spreads the load and helps to keep the standard vertical.
- Sole boards are used to spread the weight of the scaffold and to provide a firm surface on which to erect a scaffold, particularly on soft ground. Sole boards must be sound and sufficient, and should run under at least two standards at a time.

Figure 2-1-34: Base plates and sole boards. *Source: Lincsafe.*

Figure 2-1-35: Base plate and protection. *Source: RMS.*

Standards

- All standards must be truly plumb, or leaning only a little ***towards*** the structure. One standard out of plumb will "bow" and push the others.
- Any joints in standards must be staggered.

Ledgers

- These must be truly horizontal, and not more than 2.7 metres above the ground or the ledgers below, on ***any*** scaffold.
- Any joints in ledgers must be made with sleeve couplers, and the joints must be staggered.
- Ledger bracings must be fixed to alternate standards, on every platform. They must ***not*** be fixed to the handrail.

Boards

- Boards supported by transoms or putlogs must be close fitting, free from cracks or splits or large knots, and must not be damaged in any way, which could cause weakness.

Working platforms

- However wide a working platform may be, if its height above ground or floor level is two metres or more, then it must be fitted with guardrails and toeboards. If it is also to carry materials, then the space between guardrails and toeboards must be reduced to a maximum 470 mm. This can be done with an intermediate rail, mesh or similar material.
- General access must not be allowed to any scaffold until its erection has been fully completed. Access must be blocked off to any section of any scaffold which is not yet finished.
- If a gap or opening is created in a platform for any reason, then it must immediately be blocked off and a warning notice displayed.
- Where a ladder passes through a working platform, the access must be as small as practicable.

- Any access point through a working platform must be covered when it is not being used, and clearly marked to show its purpose.
- Trestles *must not* be put up on any working platform.
- If a working platform becomes covered with ice, snow, grease or any other slippery material, then suitable action must be taken to reduce the hazard, by sprinkling sand, salt, sawdust, etc.
- Rubbish or unused materials must not be left on working platforms.
- Platforms must not be used for "storing" materials. All materials placed on a platform must be for immediate use only.
- Loadings must be evenly spread out over working platforms to the fullest extent possible.
- Where loadings cannot be distributed evenly (as with bricklayers' materials) then the larger weights should be kept nearest to the standards.
- Any platform near to fragile items should be sheeted out to the full height of the guardrail.
- Everything loose must be taken off the working platforms before any start is made on dismantling.

Toe boards

These are scaffold boards placed against the standards at right angles to the surface of the working platform. They help prevent materials from falling from the scaffold and people slipping under rails. They must be suitable and sufficient to prevent the fall of any person or any material or object from a place of work.

- The toe boards should be fixed to the inside of the standards with toe board clips.
- Joints must be as near as possible to a standard.
- Continuous around the platform where a guard-rail is required.
- Any toe board which is removed temporarily for access or for any other reason must be replaced as soon as possible.

Guardrails

These are horizontal scaffold tubes which help to prevent people falling from a scaffold.

- They must be fixed to the *inside* of the standards, at least 950 mm from the platform.
- An intermediate guard rail must be positioned such that the gap between it and the top guardrail and the toe boards is no more than 470 mm.
- Guardrails must always be fitted with load-bearing couplers.
- Joints in guard-rails must be near to a standard.
- Must be secured with sleeve couplers.
- Guardrail must go all round the work platform.
- Where there is a gap between the structures then a guardrail must be fitted to the inside of the working platform as well as the outside.
- Guardrails must always be carried round the end of a scaffold, to make a "stop end".

Figure 2-1-36: Scaffold boards - some defective. *Source: RMS.*

Brick guards

Suitable and sufficient to prevent the fall of people or materials.

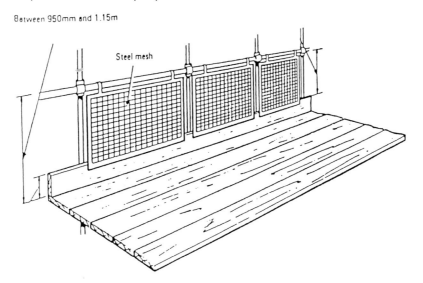

Between 950mm and 1.15m

Steel mesh

Figure 2-1-37: Brick guards.   *Source: HSG150 Safety in Construction.*

Ties and bracing

Ensuring stability of a scaffold is critical. In the case of an independent tied scaffold the scaffold is set a small distance away from the structure and ties connect it to the structure and prevent the scaffold falling away from or towards the structure.

One of the ways to do this is to use a 'through tie' which is set into place through an opening in the structure such as a window. In addition to this it is important that the scaffold is a rigid structure. A scaffold comprising standards, transoms and ledgers alone may not be rigid enough, particularly in the case of tall scaffolds. In order to improve rigidity a system of braces, scaffold poles set at a diagonal angle, is used. They are placed at the ends, in opposite diagonals for each level of scaffold, at intervals along the scaffold. In addition bracing is placed diagonally across the front of the scaffold.

Figure 2-1-38: Tie through window.   *Source: RMS.*

Figure 2-1-39: Ladder access.   *Source: RMS.*

Debris netting

Debris netting is often fixed to the sides of a scaffold to limit the amount of debris escaping from the scaffold that may come from work being done on it. It provides a tough, durable and inexpensive method of helping to provide protection from the danger of falling debris and windblown waste. It allows good light transmission and reduces the effects of adverse weather.

Debris netting may also be slung underneath steelwork or where roof work is being conducted to catch items that may fall. In this situation it should not be assumed that the debris netting is sufficient to hold the weight of a person who might fall.

Figure 2-1-40: Nets and sheets.   *Source: RMS.*

Figure 2-1-41: Nets.   *Source: RMS.*

Signs

Safety signs are used to provide people with information relating to the works being carried out, to control or divert people and most importantly of any dangers or hazards. Signs may be situated at a location in advance of the work area to give prior warning in addition to the works perimeter and actual work location.

Marking

Where equipment used to gain access to a height may be collided with it should carry hazard marking. For example, the standards of a scaffold at ground level on a street may be marked with hazard tape.

Lighting

Suitable and adequate lighting should be provided to allow the works being carried out and any possible hazards to be seen clearly in advance and allow people to take the required actions to avoid interference with the site. Scaffolds located near roads may be fitted with lighting to warn traffic of its presence.

Figure 2-1-42: Signs.   *Source: RMS.*

Figure 2-1-43: Marking.   *Source: RMS.*

Fans

Fans are scaffold boards fixed on scaffold tubes set at an upward angle out from a scaffold in order to catch debris that may fall from the scaffold. They may be provided at the entrances to buildings to protect persons entering and leaving the building that the scaffold is erected against. They are also used where a scaffold is erected alongside a pedestrian walkway where there is a need to have an increased confidence that materials that might fall cannot contact people below. In some cases it may be necessary for horizontal barriers to be erected to direct pedestrians under the fan.

Figure 2-1-44: Fans.   *Source: RMS.*

Figure 2-1-45: Mobile tower, wheels with brakes.   *Source: RMS.*

MOBILE TOWER SCAFFOLDS

Mobile scaffold towers are widely used as they are convenient for work which involves frequent access to a height over a short period of time in a number of locations that are spaced apart. However, they are often incorrectly erected or misused and accidents occur due to people/materials falling or the tower overturning / collapsing. They must be erected and dismantled by trained, competent personnel, strictly in accordance with the supplier's instructions. All parts must be sound and from the same manufacturer.

- The height of an untied, independent tower must never exceed the manufacturer's recommendations. A 'rule of thumb' may be:
  - Outdoor use - 3 times the minimum base width.
  - Indoor use - 3.5 times the minimum base width.
- If the height of the tower is to exceed these maximum figures then the scaffold *must* be secured (tied) to the structure or outriggers used.
- Working platforms must only be accessed by safe means. Use internal stairs or fixed ladders only and never climb on the outside.
- Before climbing a tower the wheels must be turned outwards, the wheel brakes "on", locked and kept locked.
- Never move a tower unless the platform is clear of people, materials, tools etc.
- Towers must only be moved by pushing them at base level. Instruct operators not to pull the tower along whilst on it. Pay careful attention to obstructions at base level and overhead.
- Never use a tower near live overhead power lines or cables.

■ Working platforms must always be fully boarded out. Guard rails and toe boards must be fitted if there is a risk of a fall of more than two metres. Inspections must be carried out by a competent person - before first use, after substantial alteration and after any event likely to have affected its stability.

Figure 2-1-46: Mobile tower scaffold. *Source: RMS.*

Figure 2-1-47: Mobile tower scaffold. *Source: RMS.*

MOBILE ELEVATING WORK PLATFORMS

Figure 2-1-48: Mobile elevated work platform (MEWP). *Source: RMS.*

Figure 2-1-49: Use of harness with a MEWP. *Source: HSG150.*

A mobile elevating work platform (MEWP) is, as the name suggests, a means of providing a work platform at a height. The equipment is designed to be movable, under its own power or by being towed, so that it can easily be set up in a location where it is needed. Various mechanical and hydraulic means are used to elevate the work platform to the desired height, including telescopic arms and scissor lifts. The versatility of this equipment, enabling the easy placement of a platform at a height, makes it a popular piece of access equipment. Often, to do similar work by other means would take a lot of time or be very difficult. They are now widely available and there is a tendency for people to oversimplify their use and allow people to operate them without prior training and experience. This places users and others at high risk of serious injury.

Some MEWPs can be used on rough terrain. This usually means that they are safe to use on uneven or undulating ground, *(see figure ref 2-1-50).* The MEWP's limitations should always be checked in the manufacturer's handbook before moving on to unprepared or sloping ground. They should only be operated within their defined stability working area. A harness with a lanyard attached to the platform provides extra protection against falls especially when the platform is being raised or lowered.

MEWPs and similar equipment used in poor lighting conditions on or near roads and walkways must use standard vehicle lighting.

Use of mobile elevating work platforms

Mobile Elevating Work Platforms (MEWPs) can provide excellent safe access to high level work.

When using a MEWP make sure:

- Whoever is operating it is fully trained and competent.
- The work platform is fitted with guard rails and toe boards.
- It is used on suitable firm and level ground. The ground may have to be prepared in advance.
- Tyres are properly inflated.
- The work area is cordoned off to prevent access below the work platform, *(see figure ref 2-1-48).*
- That it is well lit if being used on a public highway in poor lighting.
- Outriggers are extended and chocked as necessary before raising the platform.
- All involved know what to do if the machine fails with the platform in the raised position.

Do not

- Operate MEWPs close to overhead cables or dangerous machinery.
- Allow a knuckle, or elbow, of the arm to protrude into a traffic route when working near vehicles.
- Move the equipment with the platform in the raised position unless the equipment is especially designed to allow this to be done safely (the manufacturer's instructions should be checked).
- Overload or overreach from the platform.

Figure 2-1-50: Scissor lift MEWP. *Source: HSG150, HSE.*

Figure 2-1-51: Scissor lift MEWP. *Source: HSG150, HSE.*

Figure 2-1-52: Mobile elevated work platform (MEWP). *Source: RMS.*

TRESTLES

Trestles are pre-fabricated steel, aluminium or wood supports, of approximately 500 mm - 1 metre width, that may be of fixed height or may be height adjustable by means of sliding struts with varying fixing points (pin method) or various cross bars to suit the height required. They are used to span scaffold boards from one to the other in order to make a work platform.

These can only be used where work cannot be carried out from the ground but where a scaffold would be impracticable.

A good example would be a plasterer who is installing and plastering a new ceiling. Typical working heights when using a trestle system ranges from 300 mm to 1 metre but can be up to above 4 metres. Edge protection should be fitted wherever practical. As with any work carried out above ground level, a risk assessment, as required by the Management of Health and Safety at Work Regulations (MHSWR) 1999, should be carried out and consideration given to the application of the Work at Height Regulations (WAH) 2005 and/or the Construction (Design and Management) Regulations (CDM) 2007 and/or the Workplace (Health, Safety and Welfare) Regulations (WHSWR) 1992.

There are many configurations of locking and adjustable trestles. Platforms based on trestles should be fully boarded, adequately supported and provided with edge protection where appropriate. Safe means of access should be provided to trestle platforms, usually by stepladders.

Always	*Never*
■ Set up the equipment on a firm, level, nonslip surface.	■ Do anything that involves applying a lot of side force. The trestle could topple over.
■ On soft ground, stand the equipment on boards to stop it sinking in.	■ The maximum safe working load of a scaffold board is 150 Kg evenly spaced.

- Place each trestle at 1.5m intervals which allows the scaffold boards to be adequately supported.
- Then open each up to the height required, ensure the locking pins are properly located.
- The total weight of the user and tools must not exceed this.
- When moving to a new site, carry the equipment with care.
- Never use steps, boxes etc. to gain extra height.

STAGING PLATFORMS

Staging platforms can be made of metal alloy or wood and are often used for linking trestle systems or tower scaffolds together safely. They also provide a safe work platform for work on fragile roofs. They are produced in various lengths. The same rules apply for edge protection as with other scaffold platforms.

Ensure that the platform is:

- Of sufficient dimensions to allow safe passage and safe use of equipment and materials.
- Free from trip hazards or gaps through which persons or materials could fall.
- Fitted with toeboards and handrails; (if these requirements are not considered necessary for a specific platform, then this should be shown in the risk assessment i.e. that not installing a toe board and/or a guard rail had been considered and why it was not necessary).
- Kept clean and tidy, e.g. mortar and debris should not be allowed to build up on platforms.
- Not loaded so as to give rise to a risk of collapse or to any deformation that could affect its safe use. This is particularly relevant in relation to block work loaded on platforms.
- Erected on firm level ground to ensure equipment remains stable during use.

LEADING EDGE PROTECTION

Leading edges are created as new roof sheets are laid, or old ones are removed. Falls from a leading edge need to be prevented. Work at the leading edge requires careful planning to develop a safe system of work. Nets are the preferred method for reducing the risk of injury from falls at the leading edge, as they provide protection to everyone on the roof.

Nets should be erected by trained riggers and be strong enough to take the weight of people. Debris nets are only rigged to trap lightweight debris - therefore it is important to know which type is in use at a workplace. Staging platforms fitted with guard rails or suitable barriers and toe boards, in advance of the leading edge, can provide protection in some circumstances.

Figure 2-1-53: Edge protection and boards.   *Source: RMS.*

But these will need to be used in conjunction with harnesses attached to a suitable fixing.

Close supervision of this system of work will be needed as it is difficult for the harness to remain safely clipped at all times throughout the work activity.

Inspection requirements for work equipment

Inspection requirements for work equipment specified for use for work at height are set out in Regulation 12 of the WAH 2005. Requirements are:

- Where safety depends on how it is installed or assembled in any position - before used in that position.
- Where exposed to conditions causing deterioration which is liable to result in dangerous situations, to ensure that health and safety conditions are maintained and that any deterioration can be detected and remedied in good time - at suitable intervals and each time that exceptional circumstances which are liable to jeopardise the safety of the work equipment have occurred.
- Work platforms used for construction work in which a person could fall 2 metres or more - inspected in position, or if a mobile work platform inspected on the site, within the previous 7 days.

Results of an inspection must be recorded and kept until the next inspection. An inspection report containing the particulars set out below must be prepared before the end of the working period within which the inspection is completed and, within 24 hours of completing the inspection, and be provided to the person it was carried out for. The report must be kept at the site where the inspection was carried out until the construction work is completed and afterwards at an office of the person it was carried out on behalf of, for 3 months.

Reports on inspections must include the following particulars:

1) Name and address of person for whom the inspection is carried out.
2) Location of the work equipment.
3) Description of the work equipment.
4) Date and time of inspection.
5) Details of any matter identified that could give rise to a risk to the health and safety of any person.

6) Details of any action taken as a result of 5 above.
7) Details of any further action considered necessary.
8) Name and position of the person making the report.

1.6 - Excavations

Hazards of work in and around excavations

Work in excavations and trenches, basements, underground tanks, sewers, manholes etc., can involve high risks and each year construction workers are killed with some buried alive or asphyxiated.

Figure 2-1-54: Buried services.   *Source: RMS.*

Figure 2-1-55: Excavation hazards.   *Source: RMS.*

BURIED SERVICES

Although electricity cables provide the most obvious risk, gas pipes, water mains, drains and sewers can all release dangerous substances. Gas is particularly dangerous if there is a potential ignition source close by. Fibre-optic cables may carry laser light damaging to the eyes if severed accidentally; they are very expensive to repair.

Buried services (electricity, gas, water, etc) are not obvious upon site survey and so the likelihood of striking a service when excavating, drilling or piling is increased. The results of striking an underground service are varied, and the potential to cause injury or a fatality is high. As with overhead power lines, any underground service should be treated as live until confirmed dead by an authority (utility provider). Incidents can include shock, electrocution, explosion and burns from power cables, explosion, burns or unconsciousness from gas or power cables, impact injury from dislodged stones or flooding from ruptured water mains. Before groundwork is due to commence it is common and good practice to check for presence of any of the previously mentioned services or hazards by using a detection device. A common device used regularly is a cable avoidance tool more commonly known as a CAT scanner when utilised as a detection device in a particular area.

FALLS OF EQUIPMENT, MATERIALS AND PERSONS INTO THE EXCAVATION

When people are working below ground in excavations, the problems are very similar to those faced when people are working at a height - falls and falling objects. Particular problems arise when:

- Materials, including spoil, are stored too close to the edge of the excavation.
- The excavation is close to another building and the foundations may be undermined.
- The edge of the excavation is not clear, especially if the excavation is in a public area.
- Absence of barriers or lighting.
- Poor positioning or the absence of access ladders allowing people to fall.
- Absence of organised crossing points.
- Badly constructed ramps for vehicle access which can cause the vehicle to topple.
- No stop blocks for back filling of trenches or excavations.
- Routing of vehicles too close to the excavation.

COLLAPSE OF SIDES

Often, the soil and earth that make up the sides of the excavation cannot be relied upon to support their own weight, leading to the possibility of collapse. The risk can be made worse if:

- The soil structure is loose or made unstable by water logging.
- Heavy plant or materials are too close to the edge of the excavation.
- Machinery or vehicles cause vibration.
- There is inadequate support for the sides.

The consequences of even a minor collapse can be very serious. A minor fall of earth can happen at high speed and bring with it anything (plant and machinery) that may be at the edge. Even if the arms and head of a person are not trapped in the soil, the material pressing on the person can lead to severe crush injuries to the lower body and asphyxiation due to restriction of movement of the chest.

COLLAPSE OF ADJACENT STRUCTURES

Excavations that are carried out within close proximity to existing buildings or structures may result in their foundations becoming undermined and create the potential for significant settling damage to occur or even collapse.

Consideration should be given to the effects that excavation work might have on foundations of neighbouring buildings or structures, and control measures implemented to ensure that foundations are not disturbed or undermined. Building foundations that are at a distance of less than twice the excavation depth from the face of the excavation are more likely to be affected by ground movement; underpinning or shoring of such structures may be required to prevent structural damage.

WATER INGRESS

Ingress of water may occur through rainfall, flood (river, sea) or when an excavation continues below the natural groundwater level. Consideration must be given to the likelihood of water entering the excavation and the measures to be implemented in order to control water entering the excavation and water levels between it. When an excavation is liable to water ingress the stability of walls can be undermined; this will influence the choice of shoring, for example, close shoring rather than open shoring.

CONTAMINATED GROUND - HAZARDOUS SUBSTANCES

Digging may uncover buried materials that have the potential to be hazardous to health. The history of the site should be examined to try to identify if substances have been buried on the site during its previous use. Sites that once were used as steel works may contain arsenic and cyanide dating back many years; farmyards may have been used as graves for animals and to dispose of pesticides and organo-phosphates. There is always the presence of vermin to consider - this can increase the risk of diseases such as leptospirosis.

Excavations can under different circumstances be subject to toxic, asphyxiating or explosive atmospheres. Chalk or limestone deposits when in contact with acidic groundwater can release carbon dioxide, and gases such as methane or hydrogen sulphide can seep into excavations from contaminated ground or damaged services in built-up areas. These atmospheres can accumulate at the bottom of an excavation and result in asphyxiation, poisoning, explosion or potential fatalities.

MECHANICAL HAZARDS

Mechanical hazards of excavation work relate mainly to the equipment used to create the excavation and lay equipment/materials in place.

The principle mechanical hazard is the risk of being struck by this equipment as it moves its excavator arm or jib.

The risk is greatly increased as people move close to the equipment, for example, workers or pedestrians passing by. People particularly at risk are those that place themselves in close proximity to the equipment when it is operating.

This would include people directing the equipment movement or those supervising the work, particularly if they stand in or close to the excavation, near to where work is going on.

Figure 2-1-56: Mechanical hazard from excavator. *Source: RMS.*

The closing movements of parts of this equipment like an excavator arm or bucket present a significant crushing risk. In addition, as the plant is usually capable of easy movement there is a risk of people working in close proximity receiving crush injuries to their feet.

Control measures to prevent injury when working in and around excavations

"All practicable steps should be taken, where necessary, to prevent danger to any person, including, where necessary, the provision of supports or battering to ensure that; (a) any excavation or part of an excavation does not collapse; (b) no material from a side or roof of, or adjacent to, any excavation is dislodged or falls; and (c) no person is buried or trapped in an excavation by material which is dislodged or falls".

Figure 2-1-57: Precautions for working in and around excavations.   *Source: Regulation 31 of CDM 2007.*

BASIC METHODS OF SUPPORTING EXCAVATIONS

"Suitable and sufficient steps shall be taken to prevent any person, work equipment, or any accumulation of material from falling into any excavation".

Figure 2-1-58: Methods of shoring and battering.   *Source: Regulation 31 of CDM 2007.*

Precautions must be taken to prevent collapse. The methods of supporting (shoring) the sides of excavations vary widely in design depending on:

- The nature of the subsoil - for example, when wet may require close shoring with sheets.
- Projected life of the excavation - a trench box may give ready made access where it is only needed for short duration.
- Work to be undertaken, including equipment used - for example, the use of a trench box for shoring where pipe joints are made.
- The possibility of flooding from ground water and heavy rain - close shoring would be required.
- The depth of the excavation - a shallow excavation may use battering instead of shoring, particularly where shoring may impede access.
- The number of people using the excavation at any one time - a lot of space may be required so cantilever sheet piling may be preferred.

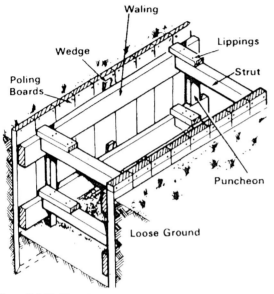

Figure 2-1-59: Close boarded excavation. *Source: BS6031.*

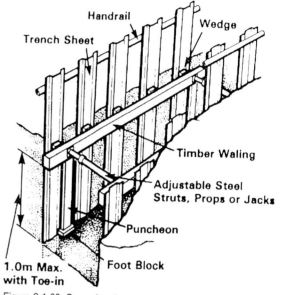

Figure 2-1-60: Open sheeting. *Source: BS6031.*

Figure 2-1-61: Trench box - for shoring. *Source: RMS.*

Figure 2-1-62: Battering. *Source: RMS.*

The options available as a means of shoring include, closed boarding / sheeting *(see figure refs 2-1-59 and 2-1-63)*, open sheeting *(see figure refs 2-1-60 and 2-1-64)* and where the shoring needs to be repositioned frequently, such as where services are being laid, a trench box *(see figure ref 2-1-61)*.

An alternative precaution to the use of shoring is where soil and material is removed from the sides of the excavation so that steps or a shallow slope is created in the sides; this is called battering, *(see figure ref 2-1-62)*. Battering relies on the material in the steps or slopes of the sides of the excavation creating minimal downward/sideways pressure, reducing the likelihood and effect of collapse.

MEANS OF ACCESS

Ladders are the usual means of access and egress to excavations. They must be properly secured, in good condition and inspected regularly. The ladder should extend about one metre or three rungs above ground level to give a good handhold.

To allow for emergency egress it is recommended that a minimum requirement of one ladder every 15 metres be provided.

CROSSING POINTS

Crossing excavations should only be allowed at predetermined points.

The crossing point should be able to withstand the maximum foreseeable load and be provided with guard rails and toe boards. The spacing or location of crossing points should be such that workers and others are encouraged to use them, rather than to attempt other means of crossing the excavation.

BARRIERS

Where people or materials can fall from height edge protection must be considered. In some cases the shoring method used can provide this barrier by ensuring the top of the shoring extends sufficiently above the edge of the excavation, *(see figure ref 2-1-63)*. It is also good practice to cover shallow trenches when they are left unattended.

Guardrails must meet the same standards as those provided for working platforms. Concrete or wooden blocks (usually old railway sleepers) can be placed some distance from the edge to prevent vehicles from getting too close, particularly when the excavation is being 'back filled'.

In this case the wooden blocks provide a 'stop block'. Large pieces of mobile plant and equipment that are commonly used on construction sites have the potential to cause serious harm to site workers and members of the public. In order to keep people and vehicles apart, exclusion zones identified by barriers *(see figure ref 2-1-63)*, fencing *(see figure ref 2-1-64)*, warning signs and lights should be provided.

Figure 2-1-63: Close sheeting.   *Source: RMS.*

Figure 2-1-64: Open sheeting.   *Source: RMS.*

LIGHTING AND SIGNS

Signs that comply with the Health and Safety (Signs and Signals) Regulations (SSSR) 1996 should be displayed to warn people of the excavation and any special measures to be taken. If working on a public highway, the police or the local authority must be consulted over the positioning of traffic lights.

Appropriate lighting should be provided; it must provide sufficient illumination for those at work but should not create glare or other distractions for passers by, especially motorists. Battery operated headlamps (to avoid trailing cables) may be considered for individual use. If excavations are present in dark conditions they must be suitably lit to prevent vehicles or people colliding or falling into them.

SAFE STORAGE OF SPOIL

Excavated material (spoil), other materials, plant and vehicles should never be stored or parked close to the sides of any excavation. The additional pressure distributed on the ground from spoil, vehicles, etc. significantly increases the likelihood of collapse occurring at the sides of the excavation. Though it will depend on the weight of the material it would normally be kept a minimum of 1 metre from the edge of the excavation, *(see figure ref 2-1-66)* which show heavy pipes set away from the excavation and spoil set to the side. In addition, spoil heaps consist of loose materials that have the risk of spilling into the excavation.

A means of preventing spillage of spoil into an excavation is by positioning scaffold boards as toe boards, fixed along the outside of trench sheets. This provides additional protection to combat the risk of loose materials spilling into the excavation. An alternative to this is to allow boards or sheeting to protrude above the top of the excavation sufficient to act as toe boards and prevent materials falling.

Unless sufficient control is implemented, workers can suffer injury from spoil or stored materials falling from ground level into an excavation. Head protection must be worn and this will provide protection for those working in the excavation from small pieces of materials falling either from above or from the sides of the excavation.

If stored at a suitable distance away from an excavation and at a suitable height, spoil heaps can form an effective barrier against vehicles travelling around the construction site and assist in preventing falls of vehicles and plant into an excavation and onto workers.

CHECKS FOR BURIED SERVICES

Excavation operations should not begin until all available service location drawings have been identified and thoroughly examined. Record plans and location drawings should not be considered as totally accurate but serve only as an indication of the likelihood of the presence of services, their location and depth. It is possible for the position of an electricity supply cable to alter if previous works have been carried out in the location due to the flexibility of the cable and movement of surrounding features since original installation of the cable.

In addition, plans often show a proposed position for the services that does not translate to the ground, such that services are placed in position only approximately where the plan says.

Figure 2-1-65: Marking of services.   *Source: RMS.*

It is important that 'service location devices' such as a cable avoidance tool (CAT) are used by competent, trained operatives to assist in the identification and marking of the actual location and position of buried services. When identified it is essential that physical markings be placed on the ground to show where these services are located.

POSITIONING AND ROUTING OF VEHICLES, PLANT AND EQUIPMENT

To prevent objects falling into excavations, the following precautions should be taken:

- Spoil and building materials must not be stacked near to the edge.
- The weight of stacks should not be enough to cause the sides to collapse.
- Designated operating areas for vehicles and machinery must be routed away from the excavation.
- Where vehicles have to approach, stop blocks must be provided to prevent overrunning.

Proximity to excavators

Large pieces of equipment have great potential for causing serious harm to not only site workers but also members of the public if work is carried out on a busy thoroughfare.

To keep people and vehicles apart, the following need to be considered:

- Exclusion zones identified by barriers.
- Warning signs and lights.
- Excavator cabs should have good visibility and operators properly trained.
- Workers should wear high visibility clothing.
- Work should be done under close supervision.

Figure 2-1-66: Materials storage and spoil.   *Source: RMS.*

Figure 2-1-67: Preventing water ingress.   *Source: RMS.*

CONTROL OF WATER

Usually water is abstracted from excavations and pumped to sumps for settlement from where it can be pumped out for disposal. It is permissible to distribute small quantities of pumped groundwater from within an excavation over grassy areas where any silt deposits can be absorbed and not have a detrimental effect on the environment.

However, when works are within close proximity to a watercourse, within 10 metres, then advice should be sought on the disposal of groundwater and a 'Consent for Works Affecting Watercourses' should be obtained from the Environment Agency.

SUBSTANCES

Excavations should be treated with similar caution to that applied to confined spaces, and an assessment should be carried out prior to work commencing in excavations to identify the risk of toxic gas, oxygen deficiency, and fire or explosion. It should also identify the appropriate risk control measures required, such as:

Figure 2-1-68: Water in excavation.   *Source: RMS.*

- Type of gas monitoring equipment to be provided.
- Testing of the atmosphere before entry into the excavation.
- Provision of suitable ventilation equipment.
- Training of employees.
- Use of a sufficient number of people, including one at ground level.
- Procedures and equipment needed for an emergency rescue.

PERSONAL PROTECTIVE EQUIPMENT

As well as the need for hard hats to limit the risks from falling materials, other personal protective equipment (PPE) may be necessary, such as:

- Breathing apparatus.
- Safety harnesses.
- Hearing protection.
- Clothing to protect from the rays of the sun.

- Masks and respirators.
- Face masks and gloves for welding and grinding.
- Footwear.

FILLING IN

On completion of use of the excavation experienced people should remove support materials. A competent person should inspect the site to ensure that all people and materials have been removed. The excavation may need water pumping from it before filling.

Where vehicles approach the excavation to add materials it is essential that stop barriers are used at the edge of the excavation to avoid vehicles falling into it. Materials added to the excavation must be sufficiently compacted to allow for the next use of the area, for example, as part of a roadway or to allow a scaffold to be placed on top of it. Only appropriate in-fill materials must be used. Uncontrolled tipping/burial is an offence.

Inspection requirements for excavation support

The Construction (Design and Management) Regulations (CDM) 2007 require inspections and reports to be carried out for excavations. A competent person must inspect excavations:

- At the start of each shift in which the work is to be carried out.
- After any event likely to have affected the strength or stability of the excavation.
- After any material unintentionally falls or is dislodged and the person who carried out the inspection is satisfied that the work can be carried out there safely.

The competent person must:

- Where the person who carried out the inspection has informed the person on whose behalf the inspection was carried out of any matter about which he or she is not satisfied; work shall not be carried out in the excavation until the matters have been satisfactorily remedied.
- Prepare a report and shall within 24 hours of completing the inspection to which the report relates; provide the report or a copy of it to the person on whose behalf the inspection was carried out.
- Where the person owing a duty is an employee or works under the control of another, his employer or, or as the case may be, the person under whose control he works shall ensure that he performs the duty.

The inspection report record must include the following information:

- Name and address of person on whose behalf the inspection was carried out.
- Location of the workplace inspected.
- Description of workplace or part of workplace inspected (including any plant and equipment and materials, if any).
- Date and time of inspection.
- Details of any matter identified that could lead to a risk to the health and safety of anyone.
- Details of any action taken as a result of any matter identified in the last point.
- Details of any more action considered necessary.
- The name and position of the person making the report.

UNIT NGC2
CONTROLLING WORKPLACE HAZARDS

Transport hazards and risk control

Learning outcomes

On completion of this element, candidates should be able to demonstrate understanding of the content through the application of knowledge to familiar and unfamiliar situations. In particular they should be able to:

2.1   Explain the hazards and control measures for the safe movement of vehicles in the workplace.

2.2   Outline the factors associated with driving at work that increases the risk of an incident and the control measures to reduce work-related driving risks.

Content

Sources of reference

Safe Use of Work Equipment (ACOP) (L22), HSE Books ISBN 0-7176-1626-6

Workplace Transport Safety - Guidance for Employers (HSG136), HSE Books ISBN 0-7176-0935-9

The Health and Safety (Safety Signs and Signals) Regulations 1996, Guidance on Regulations (L64), HSE Books ISBN 0-7176-0870-0

Driving at work, managing work-related road safety HSE INDG382

Relevant statutory provisions

The Provision and Use of Work Equipment Regulations (PUWER) 1998 - Part III in particular

The Health and Safety (Safety Signs and Signals) Regulations (SSSR) 1996

Road Traffic Act (RTA) 1988, 1991

2.1 - Safe movement of vehicles in the workplace

Hazards from workplace transport operations

There are five main kinds of accidents associated with vehicles; they form a significant part of the accidents that occur in workplace transport operations:

- Being struck by a moving vehicle.
- Injury caused by a vehicle collapse or overturn.
- Falling from a vehicle.
- Being hit by a load (materials) falling from a vehicle.
- Being hit against a vehicle whilst travelling in it.

Statistics provided by the Health and Safety Executive for 2008/09 show:

		Fatal injury	*Major injury*	*Over 3 day injury*
1	Struck by	25	605	1547
2	Collapse	9	46	25
3	Fall from	2	861	1205
4	Materials	5	172	342
5	Hit against	4	146	883
	Total	45	1830	4002

Figure 2-2-1: Workplace accident statistics 2008/09.   Source: HSE.

Figures reported for 2009/10 show that, as in 2008/09, there were 45 fatal injuries during the period.

OVERTURNING OF VEHICLES

Various circumstances that may cause a transport vehicle to overturn are insecure and unstable loads, manoeuvring with the load elevated, colliding with kerbs and other obstructions, cornering at speed, braking harshly, driving on uneven or soft ground, and mechanical failure.

Possible causes of a dumper truck overturning

- Overloading or uneven loading of the bucket.
- Cornering at excessive speed.
- Hitting obstructions.
- Driving too close to the edges of embankments or excavations.
- Mechanical defects that occur because of lack of maintenance.
- Inappropriate or unequal tyre pressures.
- Driving across slopes.

Possible causes of a fork lift truck overturning

- Driving too fast.
- Sudden braking.
- Driving on slopes.
- Driving over debris.
- Under-inflated tyres.
- Driving over holes in floor, such as drains.
- Driving with load elevated.
- Driving with the load incorrectly positioned on the forks.
- Overloading - exceeding maximum capacity.
- Collisions with buildings or other vehicles.

COLLISIONS WITH OTHER VEHICLES, PEDESTRIANS OR FIXED OBJECTS

People may unexpectedly appear from a part of a building structure or workers intent on the work they are doing may step away from where they are working to collect materials or tools. Often the space in workplaces such as warehouses is restricted. Racking is then increased in height to maximise the floor space. This in turn leads to restricted visibility especially at busy junctions where vehicles come together. This may lead to collisions with other vehicles and pedestrians or, in the avoidance of these, fixed objects such as roof and racking supports.

NON-MOVEMENT RELATED HAZARDS

Loading and un-loading

There is a risk of material falling on a vehicle driver where the vehicle is used to provide materials at a height or to remove materials from delivery vehicles. In addition, when vehicles are being unloaded by hand there is a possibility that the load has shifted and become unstable during transportation. This could mean that the load collapses onto the person unloading when a quantity of it is removed and this could lead to serious injury or death. Some loading and unloading tasks cause people to work at height, which creates the risk that people may fall from a vehicle. This may be more likely if the work is done in poor weather conditions, the load or vehicle surface is slippery or where there is no organised means of access to the vehicle.

People loading or unloading may loose awareness of the edge of the load/vehicle when they are paying particular attention to the task they are doing.

Regulation 37 of the Construction (Design and Management) Regulations (CDM) 2007 states that: *"No person shall remain or be required or permitted to remain on any vehicle during the loading or unloading of any loose material unless a safe place of work is provided and maintained for such person."*

Securing loads

The hazards relating to securing loads are work at height, slippery surfaces, weather conditions, and manual handling hazards. There is the additional hazard of a badly secured load shifting at some stage in the transport operation. Tasks to secure loads may cause the person to go onto the vehicle in order to fix straps and tighten devices to hold the load. This will present them with the risk of falling from the vehicle or from the load onto the vehicle. The vehicle may be contaminated with dirt, dust, oil or materials spilt from previous loads, which presents a risk of slipping. Load securing equipment will usually have to be placed in position and tightened by the person securing the load; this could expose them to manual handling hazards related to moving things and over-exertion.

Sheeting

Sheeting is the covering of a load with a sheet or net to secure it; prevents parts of it being disrupted by wind/air movement while being transported and protects it from the weather. If this is not a mechanised process, it involves the manually unrolling of the sheet over the load and the sides of the vehicle, so that the hazards of height, slips and manual handling exist. Though it may be possible to sheet some vehicles from the ground it is not unusual for the person sheeting to have to gain access to the top of the vehicle and sometimes the top of the load. As with securing the load, this can present risks of falling or slipping. As sheets are designed to be robust they are also quite heavy and it takes a considerable amount of exertion to pull sheets over the load, leading to risk of strains and back injury.

Coupling

The task of coupling a tractor unit to a trailer requires that the tractor unit is reversed towards the front trailer. The '5th wheel' is the connection between the tractor and the trailer. If the 5th wheel jaws are not located properly, this can lead to unexpected movement of the trailer.

Though most accidents during coupling involve drivers or other people being run over, hit or crushed by moving vehicles, a number of non-movement based hazards exist.

There is a significant risk of falling during coupling, especially in the dark, as the person coupling may be less able to see slippery surfaces, obstructions or steps.

A particular hazard is that the vehicle trailer could move or overturn. Though the ground may look flat it may be sufficient to cause the trailer to become unstable or move under its own weight. In addition, during uncoupling the trailer goes from being supported to bearing its own weight, and this can cause the trailer to sink into the ground and overturn.

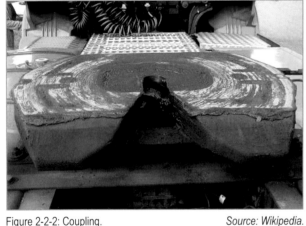

Figure 2-2-2: Coupling.   *Source: Wikipedia.*

Figure 2-2-3: Synchronised vehicle lifting system.   *Source: Rotala.*

Vehicle maintenance work

There are hidden hazards and associated risks with maintenance work from open pits, access gantries, oils and greases and fitting of replacement parts.

One of the particular hazards associated with large vehicle maintenance work is the hazard of being crushed by a falling cab that was tilted to gain access to parts of the vehicle for maintenance. Similar hazards exist at the rear of the vehicle where the vehicle has a tipping facility.

Hydraulic ramps and hoists can create crush hazards as they are lowered to the ground or if there is a sudden failure of the hydraulic or mechanical system. There is an additional hazard that a vehicle or equipment could fall from a lift system, particularly if not located correctly or if the lift system is not raised uniformly.

There are many manual handling and posture hazards associated with vehicle maintenance work, from leaning over to reach parts to the movement of large vehicle wheels.

The presence of flammable liquids, in the form of fuels, oils and paints present a hazard of fire and explosion.

Electrical hazards are present as portable electric equipment may be used, some operating at mains (230 volt) voltage. Where pneumatic equipment is used it presents the hazard of noise, flying particles and possible injection of air into the body.

It may be necessary to work on part of the vehicle at height, for example, to repair the top of a tanker trailer or to refill refrigerant for a chilled foods vehicle. This work can present falling hazards that can lead to major injury or death. The hazards are accentuated when working on vehicles that come straight from use and are wet and slippery.

Figure 2-2-4: Tilted LGV cab and prop. *Source: HSE.*

CONDITIONS AND ENVIRONMENTS IN WHICH HAZARDS MAY ARISE

Factors are:

- Inadequate lighting and direction signs.
- Inadequate signs or signals to identify the presence of vehicles.
- Drivers unfamiliar with site.
- Need to reverse.
- Poor visibility e.g. sharp bends, mirror/windscreen misted up.
- Poor identification of fixed objects e.g. overhead pipes, doorways, storage tanks, corners of buildings.
- Lack of safe crossing points on roads and vehicle routes.
- Lack of separate entrance/exit for vehicles and pedestrians.

- Lack of separation of pedestrians and vehicles.
- Pedestrians using doors provided for vehicle only use.
- Lack of barriers to prevent pedestrians suddenly stepping from an exit/entrance into a vehicle's path.
- Poor maintenance of vehicles e.g. tyres or brakes.
- Excessive speed of vehicles.
- Lack of vehicle management e.g. use of traffic control, 'banksman' (appointed individuals who control or direct plant).
- Environmental conditions e.g. poor lighting, rain, snow or ice.

Figure 2-2-5: Poor maintenance of vehicle tyres. *Source: RMS.*

Figure 2-2-6: Reduced risk of collision - people / vehicles. *Source: RMS.*

Control measures for safe workplace transport operations

The employer, through its managers, needs to carry out an assessment of risk with regard to the safe movement of vehicles and their loads as part of the overall health and safety policy. This includes the use of vehicles such as dumper trucks, lift trucks, and those used for delivery. Consideration should be given to the following.

SUITABILITY AND SUFFICIENCY OF TRAFFIC ROUTES

Design features of the vehicle intended to minimise the consequences of an overturn include rollover protection and seat belts. In addition, features designed to prevent overturning include increasing the width of the wheelbase and lowering the position of the centre of gravity of the vehicles.

- Traffic routes should be clearly marked and signed. These should incorporate speed limits, one way systems, priorities and other factors normal to public roads. Vehicles that are visiting the premises should be made aware of any local rules and conditions.
- Consideration should be given to adequate lighting on routes and particularly in loading/unloading and operating areas.
- Separate routes, designated crossing places and suitable barriers at recognised danger spots. As far as is practicable pedestrians should be kept clear of vehicle operating areas and/or a notice displayed warning pedestrians that they are entering an operating area.
- Clear direction signs and marking of storage areas and buildings can help to avoid unnecessary movement, such as reversing.
- Sharp bends and overhead obstructions should be avoided where possible. Hazards that cannot be removed should be clearly marked with black and yellow diagonal stripes, e.g. loading bay edges, and pits. If reasonably practicable barriers should be installed.
- Consideration to vehicle weight and height restriction on routes - signs, barriers and weight checks may be necessary.

MANAGEMENT OF VEHICLE MOVEMENTS

Many sites are complex in nature and require the careful management of vehicles in order to ensure that they are brought onto, move around and leave the site safely. Where materials are brought to site it may be necessary to manage deliveries to prevent too many vehicles arriving at the site at the same time causing them to back up into the public highway. Site security arrangements play a significant part in the management of vehicles on site and will assist with controlling vehicles so that they are routed correctly and safely. It is not uncommon for vehicles to be sent to a site that are too big or too heavy to access the roadways. Site security staff should be trained to identify these to prevent them accessing the site and causing harm.

Visiting drivers must be carefully managed. They must not be allowed to bring passengers (e.g. children during school holidays) onto the site.

Safe operation

- Appoint someone on site to be responsible for transport.
- Drivers properly trained.
- Ensure unauthorised people are not allowed to drive.
- Make sure visiting drivers are aware of site rules.
- Check vehicles daily and have faults rectified promptly.
- Avoid reversing where possible.
- If vehicles have to reverse, use a banksman.
- Keep keys secure when vehicles are not in use.
- Ensure safe movements - particularly when reversing.
- Keep roadways/gangways properly maintained and lit.
- Separate vehicles and pedestrians where practicable.
- Use of horns before entering doorways or at blind corners.

Factors to consider when planning traffic routes for internal transport

- The purpose of the routes, the types of vehicle using the routes.
- The likely volume of traffic, the layout of the area.
- The possible need for one-way systems or large turning circles.
- Speed limits.
- Markings.
- Crossing points and signs.
- The importance of separating pedestrians and vehicles possibly by the use of physical barriers.
- Suitability of floors as well as environmental issues such as lighting levels and ventilation when diesel-powered transport is to be used inside a building.
- Adequacy of lighting particularly at crossing points.
- Positioning of street furniture such as lights.
- Adequacy of road surfaces and, if necessary, provision for adverse weather.

ENVIRONMENTAL CONSIDERATIONS

Where vehicles operate, environmental conditions such as lighting and adverse weather will make a significant impact on their safe operation by affecting *visibility*. Where reasonably practicable a suitable standard of lighting must be maintained so that operators of vehicles can see to operate their vehicle and can be seen by others.

It is important to avoid areas of glare or shadow that could mask the presence of a person or vehicle. Similarly if vehicles travel from within buildings to the outside it is important that the light level is maintained at a roughly even level in order to give the driver's eyes time to adjust to the change in light. Fixed structure hazards should be made as visible as possible with additional lighting and/or reflective strips.

Roads, gangways and aisles should have sufficient width and overhead clearance for the largest vehicle. Attention should be paid to areas where they might meet other traffic, e.g. the entrance to the site. If ramps (sleeping policemen) are used a by-pass for trolleys and shallow draft vehicles should be provided. A one-way traffic system should be considered to reduce the risk of collision.

Gradients and changes in ground level, such as ramps, represent a specific hazard to plant and vehicle operation. Vehicles have a limit of stability dependent on loading and their wheelbase. These conditions could put them at risk of overturning or cause damage to articulated vehicle couplings. Any gradient in a vehicle operating area should be kept as gentle as possible.

Where *changes in level* are at an edge that a vehicle might approach, and there is risk of falling, it must be provided with a robust barrier or similar means to demarcate the edge. Particular care must be taken at points where loading and unloading is conducted.

In some workplaces, such as factories or chemical plants, process products may contaminate the *surface condition* of the road making it difficult for vehicles to brake effectively.

It is important to have a programme that anticipates this with regular cleaning or scarifying of the surface as well as means of dealing with spills. The floor surface should be in good condition, free of litter and obstructions.

Excessive ambient noise levels can mask the sound of vehicles working in the area; additional visual warning e.g. flashing lights should be used. Sufficient and suitable parking areas should be provided away from the main work area and located where the risk of unauthorised use of the vehicles will be reduced.

MAINTENANCE OF VEHICLES

All vehicles should be well maintained and 'roadworthy' with a formal system of checks and maintenance in place. A vehicle, such as one used for moving trailers in a transport yard, that does not usually go outside the site would be expected to be kept to the same good standard as one that was used on public roads for such critical items as tyres and brakes.

Vehicle maintenance should be planned for at regular intervals and vehicles taken out of use if critical items are not at an acceptable standard. In addition, it is important to conduct a pre-use check of the vehicle. This is usually done by the driver as part of their taking it over for a period of use such as a work shift or day. This would identify the condition of critical items and provide a formal system to identify and consider problems that may affect the safety of the vehicle.

If there is no nominated driver and the vehicle is for general use someone should be nominated to make these checks. A record book or card would usually be used to record the checks and the findings.

DRIVER PROTECTION AND RESTRAINT SYSTEMS

In many work vehicle accidents the driver is injured because the vehicle does not offer protection when it rolls over or it does not restrain the driver to prevent them falling out of the vehicle and being injured by the fall or the vehicle falling on them.

Vehicles such as dumper trucks, road rollers and forklift trucks are examples of equipment that may present this risk. PUWER 1998 Part 3 recognises the importance of this and now set out requirements for equipment to be adapted, where practicable, to provide this protection. New equipment must now be provided with protection and restraint systems, where relevant.

Figure 2-2-7: Roll bar and seat restraint.   *Source: RMS.*

Figure 2-2-8: Risk of falling materials.   *Source: RMS.*

SEGREGATING PEDESTRIANS AND VEHICLES

Means of segregation

"Every workplace shall be organised in such a way that pedestrians and vehicles can circulate in a safe manner".

Figure 2-2-9: Means of segregation.

Source: Regulation 17(1) of WHSWR 1992.

Clearly defined and marked routes should be provided for people going about their business at work. These should be provided for access and egress points to the workplace, car parks, and vehicle delivery routes. Safe crossing places should be provided where people have to cross main traffic routes. In buildings where vehicles operate, separate doors and walkways should be provided for pedestrians to get from building to building.

Meshed handrails can be used to channel people into the pedestrian route. Where it is not possible to have a pedestrian route with a safe clearance from vehicle movement, because of building and plant design, then a raised pedestrian walkway could be considered to help in segregation.

- Accidents can be caused where vehicles are unsafely parked as they can be an obstruction and restrict visibility. There should be clear entrance and exit routes in parking areas and designated parking areas to allow the load and sheeting of outgoing transport to be checked safely before leaving the site.
- There should be clear, well-marked and signposted vehicle traffic routes, which avoid steep gradients where possible, especially where fork lift trucks operate. It is important to have speed limits that are practicable and effective. Speed limit signs should be posted and traffic slowing measures such as speed bumps and ramps may be necessary in certain situations. Monitoring speed limit compliance is necessary, along with some kind of action against persistent offenders.

- Speed limits of 10 or 15 mph are usually considered appropriate, although 5 mph may be necessary in certain situations.
- Transport requires clear routes to be designated, marked with painted lines and preferably fenced off from pedestrians. Accidents can occur when plant and people collide: the pedestrian may be injured by contact and the driver injured if the vehicle overturns.
- Separate gates/doorways should be provided for vehicle entry and blind spots (where vision of the driver or pedestrian is restricted) should be dealt with by the careful positioning of mirrors on walls, plant or storage. Routes should be wide enough to allow manoeuvrability and passing.

Figure 2-2-10: Segregating pedestrians and vehicles.   *Source: RMS.*

- Where it is unavoidable that pedestrians will come into proximity with transport, people should be reminded of the hazards by briefings, site induction and signs, so they are aware at all times.

Any traffic route which is used by both pedestrians and vehicles should be wide enough to enable any vehicle likely to use the route to pass pedestrians safely.

On traffic routes in existence before 1 January 1993, where it is not practical to make the route wide enough, passing places or traffic management systems should be provided as necessary. In buildings, lines should be drawn on the floor to indicate routes followed by vehicles such as fork lift trucks.

On routes used by automatic, driverless vehicles that are also used by pedestrians, steps should be taken to ensure that vehicles do not trap pedestrians. The vehicles should be fitted with safeguards to minimize the risk of injury, sufficient clearance should be provided between the vehicles and pedestrians, and care should be taken that fixtures along the route do not create trapping hazards.

MEASURES TO BE TAKEN WHEN SEGREGATION IS NOT PRACTICABLE

Where pedestrians and vehicle routes cross, appropriate crossing points should be provided and used. Where necessary, barriers or rails should be provided to prevent pedestrians crossing at particularly dangerous points and to guide them to designated crossing places.

At crossing places where volumes of traffic are particularly heavy, the provision of suitable bridges or subways should be considered. At crossing points there should be adequate visibility and open space for the pedestrian where the pedestrian route joins the vehicle route.

Where segregation is not practicable and vehicles share the same workplace as pedestrians it is important to mark the work areas as being separate from vehicle routes to warn drivers to adjust their approach and be more aware of pedestrians.

Audible and visual warnings of the presence of the vehicle would also assist. Where vehicles are dominant but pedestrians need to access, similar means may be used but for the opposite reason. In this situation the added use of personal protective equipment that increases the ability to see the pedestrian, and safety footwear, are usually needed.

High visibility clothing is mandatory on the majority of construction projects. The reversing of large vehicles that have a restricted view should be controlled by the use of a banksman to guide them.

Summary of methods
- Defined traffic routes.
- One-way systems.
- Provision of refuges.
- Speed control.
- Mirrors/cameras.
- Good lighting.

- High visibility clothing.
- A good standard of housekeeping.
- Audible warnings on vehicles.
- Training and supervision of drivers.
- Drawing up and enforcement of site rules.

Figure 2-2-11: No segregation - high visibility clothing. *Source: RMS.*

Figure 2-2-12: Control of vehicle movement. *Source: RMS.*

PROTECTIVE MEASURES FOR PEOPLE AND STRUCTURES

It is important to anticipate that drivers of vehicles might misjudge a situation and collide with structures whilst operating. For this reason vulnerable plant and parts of the building should be provided with barriers that continuously surround the plant or alternatively posts can be provided at key positions. Clearly, important plant and structures that are at the same level of the vehicle should be protected. Care should also be taken of structures at a height, such as a pipe bridge, roof truss or door lintel. All of these could be damaged by tall vehicles or those that have tipping mechanisms that raise their effective height. Though it may not always be possible to protect all structures, such as a doorway, it is important to apply *markings* to make them more visible. In addition, *signs* warning of overhead structures or the presence of vehicles in the area will help increase awareness and avoid collisions. There is a need to alert people to the hazard when working in or near a vehicle operating area. Signs might help and these can be supplemented by *visual and audible warning systems* that confirm the presence of the vehicle. These may be operated by the driver, such as a horn on a dumper truck or automatically, such as an audible reversing signal on a large road vehicle. Visibility can be improved by mounting mirrors at strategic points. Consideration should be given to the provision of protective clothing - boots, helmets and high visibility clothing - for personnel working within areas where vehicles operate.

Barriers

Moving vehicles, and in particular large plant, have high impact energy when they are in contact with structures or people. It is essential that vehicles be separated from vulnerable people and structures. Because of the high energy involved the barrier used must reflect the type of thing in contact with it. If it is only people that might contact it a simple portable barrier may be adequate, but if it is heavy plant robust barriers including concrete structures may need to be considered. It is important to identify vulnerable locations that warrant protection, for example, storage tanks or bund walls.

Markings

Any structure that represents a height or width restriction should be readily identified for people and vehicle drivers. This will include low beams or doorways, pipe bridges and protruding scaffolds and edges where a risk of falling exists. These markings may be by means of attaching hazard tape or painting the structure to highlight the hazard.

Signs

Signs should be used to provide information, such as height restrictions, and to warn of hazards on site. Signs may be used to direct vehicles around workers at a safe distance.

Figure 2-2-13: Barriers and markings. *Source: RMS.*

Figure 2-2-14: Visual warning on a dumper truck. *Source: RMS.*

Warnings of vehicle approach and reversing

Warnings may be audible or visual or a combination of each. They are used to warn that the vehicle is operating in the area, such as a flashing light on the top of a fork lift truck or to warn of a specific movement, such as an audible warning that a large vehicle is reversing. These are designed to alert people in the area in order that they can place themselves in a position of safety. They do not provide the driver with authority to reverse the vehicle or to proceed in a work area without caution.

Measures to prevent accidents when pedestrians work in vehicle manoeuvring areas

- Segregated systems for vehicular and pedestrian traffic (barriers, separate doors).
- Maintaining good visibility (mirrors, transparent doors, provision of lighting, vehicle reversing cameras).
- Signs indicating where vehicles operate in this area.
- Audible warnings on vehicles and sometimes flashing lights on vehicles.
- Establish and enforce site rules.
- The provision of refuges.
- The wearing of high-visibility clothing.
- A good standard of housekeeping.
- Training for, and supervision of, all concerned, competency certificates, refresher training, trained banksman of direct cranes.
- Provision of parking areas.
- Provision of suitable battery charging or refuelling areas if necessary.
- Careful design of traffic routes.
- Maintenance of traffic routes.
- Traffic control e.g. identification of "no go" areas.

Precautions for reversing vehicles within the workplace

- Separation of vehicles and pedestrians.
- Warning signs.
- Audible alarms/vehicle cameras.
- Space to allow good visibility.
- Adequate mirrors that are kept clean.
- Refuges to protect banksman.
- Adequate lighting.
- Appropriate site rules adequately enforced.
- Procedural measures such as the use of trained banksman.
- Avoiding the need for vehicles to reverse (by the use of one-way and 'drive-through' systems or turning circles).

SITE RULES

It is important to establish clear and well understood site rules regarding vehicle operations. These may have to be communicated to drivers by security staff at the time they visit the site. They would often stipulate where the driver should be whilst vehicles are being loaded, where the keys to the vehicle should be, not reversing without permission and what access they have to areas of the site for such things as refreshment. Pedestrians should also know what the site rules are in order to keep themselves safe.

Site rules for pedestrians might include such things as using pedestrian exits/entrances or crossing points, not entering hazardous areas or the need to wear personal protective equipment in hazardous areas, and not walking behind a reversing vehicle. Where sites are made up of or join a highway, such as carriageway repairs on a motorway, it is important to identify who has priority - the vehicle or the worker. Site rules may clarify that once the site boundary is crossed the worker has priority - this has to be clear. The site rules may be re-enforced by the provision of additional signs to clarify a speed limit and the nature of the priority of workers.

SELECTION AND TRAINING OF DRIVERS

Only authorised persons should be permitted to operate plant or vehicles after they have been selected, trained and authorised to do so, or are undergoing properly organised formal training under competent supervision.

Selection

The safe usage of plant and vehicles calls for a reasonable degree of both physical and mental fitness. The selection procedure should be devised to identify people who have been shown to be reliable and mature enough to perform their work responsibly and carefully. To avoid wasteful training for workers who lack co-ordination and ability to learn, selection tests should be used.

Consideration must be given to any legal age restrictions that apply to vehicles that operate on the public road. A similar approach may be adopted for similar vehicles used on site though the law is not specific on age limitations in such cases.

Potential operators should be medically examined prior to employment/training in order to assess the individual's physical ability to cope with this type of work.

They should also be examined every five years in middle age and after sickness or accident.
Points to be considered are:

- General - normal agility, having full movement of trunk, neck and limbs.
- Vision - good eyesight in both eyes or corrected by spectacles, is important, as operators are required to have good judgement of space and distance.
- Hearing - the ability to hear instructions and warning signals with each ear is important.

Training

It is essential that immediate supervisors receive training in the safe operation of plant and vehicles and that senior management appreciates the risks resulting from the interaction of vehicles and the workplace.

For the operator/driver, safety must constitute an integral part of the skill-training programme and not be treated as a separate subject. The operator/driver should be trained to a level consistent with efficient operation and care for the safety of themselves and other persons. On completion of training they should be issued with a company authority to drive and a record of all basic training, refresher training and tests maintained in the individual's personal documents file. Certification of training by other organisations must be checked.

MANAGEMENT SYSTEMS FOR ASSURING DRIVER COMPETENCE

The trained operator/driver

It should not be assumed that employees who join as trained operators/drivers have received adequate training to operate safely in their new company. The management must ensure that they have the basic skills and receive training in company methods (local practices) and procedures for the type of work they are to undertake. They should be examined and tested before issue of company driving authority.

A copy of the site rules and any internal codes of practice must be given to all internal drivers and to external visitors such as delivery drivers preferably before they arrive at the site.

Testing

On completion of training, the operator/driver should be examined and tested to ensure that he/she has achieved the required standard. It is recommended that at set intervals or when there is indication of the operator/driver not working to required standards, or following an accident, formal check tests be introduced.

Refresher training

If high standards are to be maintained, periodic refresher training and testing should be considered.

A vigorous management policy covering operator training, plant maintenance and sound systems of work, supported by good supervision will reduce personal injury and damage to equipment and materials. This in turn will lead to better vehicle utilisation and increased materials handling efficiency.

Operator/driver identification

Many organisations operate local codes of practice and take great care to confirm the authority they have given to operators/drivers by the provision of a licence for that vehicle and sometimes a visible badge to confirm this. Access to vehicles is supervised and authority checked carefully to confirm that the actual class of vehicle is within the authority given. This is important with such things as rough terrain lift trucks that operate differently to a standard counterbalance truck. It is essential that access to keys for vehicles is restricted to those that are competent to operate/drive them; this is not just a practical point but enables compliance with PUWER 1998.

2.2 - Driving at work

Extent of work-related road injuries

The true cost of accidents to any organisation is nearly always higher than just the costs of repairs and insurance claims. This can include personal costs such as ill-health, time in hospital, stress on family members and possible penalty points being imposed on the driver's licences following an incident. There is also the potential for the driver to lose their licence. Therefore the benefits of managing driving activities through the introduction of policies, risk assessments and developing safe systems for work related driving is essential. This will ensure compliance with the Health and Safety at Work etc. Act (HASAWA) 1974 and the Management of Health and Safety at Work Regulations (MHSWR) 1999. The Health and Safety Executive (HSE) provide Guidance to assist management in managing driving risk, in the form of the document "Driving at work - Managing work-related road safety".

The HSE estimates that up to a third of all road traffic accidents involved somebody who was at work at the time. This may account for over 20 fatalities and 250 serious injuries per week.

"It has been estimated that between 800 and 1,000 road deaths a year are in some way work-related. Many bosses have ignored this problem in the past, but the Health and Safety Executive has now made it clear that employers have duties under health and safety law to manage the risks faced by their workers on the road".

Figure 2-2-15: Size of the road risk problem.

Source: RoSPA.

For the majority of people, the most dangerous thing they do while at work is drive on the public highway.

Figure 2-2-16: Road risk.   *Source: HSE 1996.*

Factors that increase risks of a road traffic incident

DISTANCE

Road conditions have improved over the years, which has allowed greater travel distances in shorter periods of time. However the fatigue encountered by drivers often increases due to other drivers' poor performance. This can be associated with poor or inappropriate training or monitoring of the driver's competence. Heavy goods vehicle drivers' travel distance is regulated by limitations on driving hours. However, there are no such limits on drivers of smaller vehicles and private cars. When assessing risk of any kind, an important consideration is the frequency and duration of exposure to hazards. It is logical then that the greater the distance of the journey (i.e. the duration of exposure to the hazard) the greater the risk. It is possible that scheduling of routes may extend or reduce the distance that has to be travelled and therefore affect the level of risk significantly.

DRIVING HOURS

If driving hours are excessive the driver is likely to be come fatigued, their attention and reaction levels will fall and they are at increased risk of making errors. The hours may be excessive because the driver has been driving too long without a break, their cumulative hours in a day have become too much or their rest period between days has become too little. For some drivers the driving hours is in addition to other work hours, for example, for someone travelling to a meeting these cumulative hours can have a significant effect on fatigue.

Most drivers of commercial vehicles will be fitted with tachometers, which record the time spent driving. These hours are limited by legislation, however most company car drivers do not have this specific monitoring imposed on them. Therefore safe systems of work and appropriate training should be given to all drivers concerning the hazards and associated risks with excessive hours. It is important that cumulative hours are monitored and controlled and that breaks are taken at intervals on longer journeys.

The Highway Code recommends that drivers should take a 15 minute break every two hours. The responsibility for monitoring hours and taking breaks is a shared responsibility of both the driver and the employer. Driving hours of goods vehicles over 3.5 tonnes and some passenger vehicles are regulated by European Community rules. These set limits on driver's hours:

- Daily driving limit: 9 hours.
- Maximum driving limit: 4 ½ hours.
- Daily rest period: 11 hours.
- Weekly driving limit: 56 hours.
- Fortnightly driving limit: 90 hours.
- Weekly rest period: 45 consecutive hours.

WORK SCHEDULES

Work schedules that are badly organised can put increased pressure on drivers to be in a place by a given time. This can lead to them being tempted to increase speed and take abrupt action to change lanes to improve their progress. This risky action can lead to higher risk of collision and reduced stopping distances.

Work schedules should take account of periods when drivers are most likely to feel sleepy. The high risk times are 2am to 6am and 2pm to 4pm. Employers should provide drivers with the means to stop and take a break if they feel sleepy, without the fear of recrimination. Where possible, schedules should be organised so that breaks can naturally and easily be taken, with agreed break points if travel is going as planned or if not. Driving to and from the place of employment does not form part of the working day, but may be an accident causation factor if travelling home follows a long working day.

STRESS DUE TO TRAFFIC

Nearly one in three UK drivers report feeling stressed whilst behind the wheel. Driving-related stress is likely to be experienced when the demands of the road/traffic environment exceed the driver's ability to cope with or control that environment. Sometimes driving stress can show itself as a 'road rage'. That is an irrational human mechanism that is activated to protect the sufferer from what they perceive to be actual or potential danger. A person may often resort to irrational behaviour in order to avoid certain situations or events. Others may perceive the circumstances which aggravate the 'road rage' as being either insignificant or trivial, but to the individual concerned they are 'very real' and 'very relevant'.

WEATHER CONDITIONS

Weather conditions have a significant impact on the risks of driving. Sudden rainfall or snow and fog can lead to poor visibility and sudden breaking. Snow and surface water conditions can increase stopping distances. Even good weather can have a negative effect as glare from the sun can limit visibility. This is particularly the case in early morning or evening and is most significant during the winter when the sun is lower in the sky for longer.

Managing work-related road safety

POLICY

A road safety policy should be incorporated into the health and safety policy. Whether employers provide vehicles or expect employees to drive their own for work purposes, all employers should have a policy to address the issues.

As part of any driving at work policy, employers should include:

- A requirement that the employee must maintain their vehicle in a roadworthy condition if they are to use their own vehicle for work.
- A requirement that if the vehicle is over three years old, it has a valid MOT certificate.
- A requirement that the employee has a current driving licence.
- A requirement that the employee has appropriate insurance (the employee should present copies of certificates annually for inspection).
- A requirement that the employee informs their line manager of any changes in circumstances such as penalty points, changes in insurer or vehicle used or use of any prescription medication or changes to health that affect their ability to drive safely.
- Assessment of risks.
- The management strategy to plan, organise, control, monitor and review work-related road risk.
- Driver training and competence.
- Taking breaks.
- Breakdown of the vehicle.
- Reporting problems and delays.
- Weather conditions.

SYSTEMS TO MANAGE WORK-RELATED ROAD SAFETY

Competent staff should be trained to manage and implement the work-related road safety policy. These should be developed using the guidance provided by professional organisations that have many years of experience and expertise around this subject e.g. the Automobile Association (AA), the RAC or ROSPA.

Many employers carry out internal assessments of driving skills in addition to the minimum legal requirements. This can be done in-house or carried out by an external assessor. If drivers are being asked to drive minibuses, etc. then employers can require additional qualifications, as proof of abilities. Some employers offer specific training in safe driving techniques for their employees.

It is important that systems are put in place to organise that driving distances are kept to a minimum, driving hours are controlled and work schedules are organised to reduce pressure on drivers to meet challenging times and in turn reduce undue road risk. Organisations should have systems in place to respond to inclement weather and enable drivers to take safe decisions about the effects of weather on their driving or journey.

MONITORING PERFORMANCE

It is a legal requirement to monitor health and safety systems to demonstrate compliance. Information which should be considered for effective monitoring includes:

- Legal responsibilities.
- Organisation and structure.
- Competence of drivers.
- Driving hours.
- Reporting of work-related road safety incidents.

Certain road traffic incidents are reportable under the Reporting of Injuries, Diseases and Dangerous Occurrences Regulations (RIDDOR) 1995. Employers should also monitor minor incidents to vehicle and premises.

ORGANISATION AND STRUCTURE

In a large organisation it is likely that various departments within the organisation will have different responsibilities for drivers at work. The despatch department will be responsible for planning journeys; the training department is responsible for driver competence; the human resources department could be responsible for driver selection and checking the validity of driving licences. The maintenance department is responsible for the upkeep of vehicles and ensuring the roadworthiness of vehicles and the occupational health department is responsible for carrying routine health surveillance of large goods vehicle (LGV) drivers.

It is therefore essential that the structure of the organisation allows for the free and simple interchange of information regarding legal standards and any changes in legislation and/or good practice. Responsibilities of different parts of the organisation should be defined, including the responsibility to co-operate with each other.

LEGAL RESPONSIBILITIES OF INDIVIDUALS ON PUBLIC ROADS

Vehicle condition

- Ensure the vehicle and trailer complies with the full requirements of the Road Vehicles (Construction and Use) Regulations (CUR) 1986 and Road Vehicles Lighting Regulations (RVLR) 1989.

Fitness to drive

- Drivers must report to the Driver and Vehicle Licensing Agency (DVLA) any health condition likely to affect their driving.
- Do not begin a journey if tired.

Vision

- Must be able to read (with the aid of vision corrected lenses) a vehicle number plate, in good daylight, from a distance of 20 metres (or 20.5 metres where the old style number plate is used).
- Slow down, and if necessary stop, if dazzled by bright sunlight.
- At night or in poor visibility, do not use tinted glasses, lenses or visors if they restrict vision.

Alcohol and drugs

- Do not drink and drive in excess of the legal limit for alcohol.
- Do not drive under the influence of drugs or medicine.

General

- Drivers must ensure they use all due care and attention for others when in charge of a vehicle.
- Divers must not tow more than their licence permits. Those who passed a car test after 1 January 1997 are restricted on the weight of trailer they can tow.
- Do not overload the vehicle or trailer.
- Secure the load and ensure it does not protrude out dangerously.
- Drivers and other passengers must wear a seat belt or suitable restraining device for babies or small children in cars, vans and other goods vehicles if one is fitted (exemptions are allowed for the holders of medical exemption certificates and those making deliveries or collections in goods vehicles when travelling less than 50 metres (approx 162 feet).

For detailed information refer to the Road Traffic Act (RTA) 1991 and the 'new' Highway Code and related legislation refer to www.direct.gov.uk.

Risk assessments

All work-related driving activity should follow the same principles as risk assessments for any other work activity. They should be carried out by a competent person with practical knowledge, qualifications and training relating to the work activity being assessed.

STEP 1 - IDENTIFY THE HAZARDS

Hazards will fall into the following categories:

The Driver   Competence, training, qualifications, fitness and health, alcohol and drug use, etc.

The Vehicle   Suitability, condition, safety equipment, ergonomic considerations, the load, security, etc.

The Journey   Route planning, scheduling, time, distance, driving hours, weather conditions, stress, volume of traffic, weather conditions, passengers, etc.

STEP 2 - DECIDE WHO MIGHT BE HARMED

Obviously the driver, but this might include any passengers, other road users and/or pedestrians. Consideration should also be given to other groups who may be particularly at risk, such as young or newly qualified drivers and those driving long distances.

STEP 3 - EVALUATE THE RISK AND DECIDED ON PRECAUTIONS

Risks may vary depending on whether driving is done at night or in the day, the type of vehicle or driving conditions. Decide the likelihood of the harm and severity (consequence) of any outcome. Consider risk factors such as distance travelled, driving hours, work schedules, traffic levels and weather conditions. Decide on appropriate precautions and once this has been established, decide whether the residual risk is acceptable.

STEP 4 - RECORD THE FINDINGS AND IMPLEMENT THEM

Significant findings need to be recorded and risk assessments findings should be made available to all drivers.

STEP 5 - REVIEW THE ASSESSMENT AND UPDATE IT IF NECESSARY

Monitoring and reviewing the assessments to ensure these risks are suitability controlled. Systems should be put into place to gather, monitor, record and analyse about incidents which might effect these risk assessments. The vehicle and driver's history should also be recorded. Any changes in the route, new equipment and changes in the vehicle specifications should be reviewed and recorded. This will ensure the effectiveness of controlling the risks.

Evaluating the risks

THE DRIVER

The level of risk is particularly affected by the driver's **competency**. If someone is new to driving their skill may be adequate to provide them with a national driving licence but their experience of driving will be low.

Drivers that only drive intermittently also present a high risk as any competence they may have may decay over the time between driving. The driver's competence has to be appropriate to the driving being expected of them an inexperienced driver driving in heavy traffic in complicated driving settings at night in the winter will present a particularly high risk. Similarly a person that is reasonably experienced in driving their small car may have difficulty when first driving a larger or faster accelerating vehicle. Some drivers will need to adjust to driving slower vehicles and ones with a different centre of gravity.

Driver *fitness* may influence their ability to see well when driving at night, their ability to travel distances without breaks and may put them in a high risk category for heart attack or other type of seizure. Pre-existing *health* conditions such as back injuries and late term pregnancy could influence the driver's ability to concentrate on road conditions.

The level of training that the driver has received may affect risk in that if no training is given a driver may have developed bad driving habits and not be aware of them. Refresher driver training may help to reduce risk.

THE VEHICLE

The size, weight, centre of gravity and power of a vehicle will all influence the functioning of the vehicle and therefore the risk that may arise from its use. It is important that the vehicle is *suitable* for the task and the driver. A large, powerful, fast acceleration car may be suitable for a specific task but very unsuitable for an inexperienced driver. The *condition* of the vehicle will have a significant effect on the level of risk. Vehicles that have poor brakes, lights, do not steer well and have poor suspension will represent a high risk in any driving situation. Vehicles with broken or missing mirrors will mean that the driver will not be able to see other road users adequately and will increase the risk when changing lanes.

Much of the *safety equipment* to prevent accidents, such as active breaking systems (ABS) should be built into most modern vehicles. Other items may be optional, such as run-flat tyres, these may reduce certain road risks. Other safety equipment is designed to reduce the consequences of accidents and can therefore reduce risk, such as airbags, escape kits, warning triangles and high-visibility vests. The absence of safety critical information, like the height of the vehicle, can have an immediate and significant effect on the level of risk.

Consideration has to be made of the *safety critical information* related to the vehicle, including its height, width, length, weight and load carrying/towing capacity.

Ergonomic considerations have an effect on both comfort and ability to control the vehicle effectively. The comfort issues can increase fatigue and ergonomic considerations like seat height adjustment can significantly affect the ability of the driver to see out of the vehicle properly.

THE JOURNEY

When evaluating the risk related to journeys it is important to take into account such factors as:

- The *route* being taken - motorways are safer than smaller roads; routes using motorways will be lower in risk.
- *Scheduling* - if the journey is to be made early in the morning their might be an increased level of risk due to tiredness but this may be offset by the reduced level of traffic.
- *Time* allowed for travel - if not enough time is allowed for the journey and normal delays the risk will be higher.
- *Weather* conditions - can rapidly increase risks, conditions such as ice and snow will have a significant effect.

Control measures to reduce work-related driving risks

Elimination of any driving activities should be the first consideration.

- Is the journey necessary, could there be a telephone or video conference instead of driving?
- Could the goods be sent by rail or air freight?

THE DRIVER

It is the employer's duty to ensure that drivers are competent, fit and in good health and capable of doing their work in a way that is safe for them. Employers must insist that all drivers produce evidence that they have a current licence to drive their vehicle. Without a current licence and/or test certificate the driver's insurance will be invalid. Regular assessments of driver competence and monitoring the validity of documentation such as insurance and driving licence should be carried out. Large goods vehicle (LGV) drivers and passenger carrying vehicle (PCV) drivers have to maintain a certificate of professional competence by undertaking 35 hours of training every 5 years.

THE VEHICLE

It is the employer's responsibility to ensure that the vehicle fits the purpose for which it is used. It is important that the vehicle is safe and in a fit condition and suitable for the task to be carried out this will include any safety equipment that is required being properly fitted and maintained. Any safety critical information should be displayed within the cab e.g. height or width of the vehicle. Ergonomics, such as the driver's seat should also be considered, it may require additional support e.g. lumbar cushions. Full body vibration should be considered and air-suspension seats may be required as a precaution.

Ensure safety equipment is used, for example:

■ Seat belts, air bags are installed, maintained and used correctly.
■ Two-wheeled vehicle users should have appropriate safety helmets and protective clothing.
■ Ensure vehicles do not exceed speed limits by fitting trackers to monitor the speed limits.

THE JOURNEY

Journey planning and scheduling is essential in ensuring the safety of employees who drive for work. Investing time in ensuring that journey planning is implemented as a component of the policy, will ensure that where possible, routes are planned thoroughly, schedules are realistic, and sufficient time is allocated to complete journeys safely. It may be required to plan overnight stopovers (provide hotel accommodation) if the journey time extends due to bad weather or traffic conditions. Delivery schedules should be adjusted so that unrealistic targets are not set. This will reduce the stress to drivers and will not encourage them to drive too fast for the conditions, or exceed speed limits.

INCIDENT REPORTING

Drivers must be required to record information about all incidents, whether minor or serious, for all journeys. A similar reporting procedure should be in place for reporting significant "near misses" with emphasis in training on how to recognise, analyse and learn from such events. The data provided should be analysed and any changes or improvements noted. These should be agreed fed back to those concerned and the policy procedures updated.

UNIT NGC2
CONTROLLING WORKPLACE HAZARDS

Musculo-skeletal hazards and risk control

Learning outcomes

On completion of this element, candidates should be able to demonstrate understanding of the content through the application of knowledge to familiar and unfamiliar situations. In particular they should be able to:

3.1 Explain work processes and practices that may give rise to work-related upper limb disorders and appropriate control measures.

3.2 Explain the hazards and control measures which should be considered when assessing risks from manual handling activities.

3.3 Explain the hazards, precautions and procedures to reduce the risk in the use of lifting and moving equipment with specific reference to manually operated load moving equipment.

3.4 Explain the hazards and the precautions and procedures to reduce the risk in the use of lifting and moving equipment with specific reference to mechanically operated load moving equipment.

Content

Sources of reference

Safe use of work equipment (ACOP) (L22), HSE Books ISBN 0-7176-1626-6

Manual Handling Operations Regulations 1992 (as amended), Guidance on Regulations L23 HSE Books ISBN 0-7176-2823

Safe use of lifting equipment (L113), HSE Books ISBN 0-7176-1628-2

Work Related Upper Limb Disorders - A Guide (HSG60), HSE Books ISBN 0-7176-1978-8

A pain in your workplace? Ergonomic problems and solutions HSG121 HSE Books 1994 ISBN 0-7176-0668-6

Work with display screen equipment: Health and Safety (Display Screen Equipment) Regulations 1992 as amended by the Health and Safety (Miscellaneous Amendments) Regulations 2002: Guidance on Regulations HSE Books ISBN: 9780717625826

The law on VDUs - An Easy Guide (HSG90), HSE Books ISBN 07176-2602-4

Relevant statutory provisions

The Health and Safety (Display Screen Equipment) Regulations (DSE) 1992

The Manual Handling Operations Regulations (MHOR) 1992

The Provision and Use of Work Equipment Regulations (PUWER) 1998

The Lifting Operations and Lifting Equipment Regulations (LOLER) 1998

3.1 - Work-related upper limb disorders

Meaning of musculo-skeletal disorders and work related upper limb disorders (WRULD's)

Work-related musculoskeletal disorders (MSD's) are disorders of parts of the body such as muscles, joints, tendons, ligaments, nerves, bones and the localised blood circulation system, that are caused by work and working conditions. Most work-related MSDs are cumulative disorders, resulting from repeated exposure to high or low intensity loads over a long period of time. These disorders mainly affect the back, neck, shoulders and upper limbs, but can also affect the lower limbs. Some MSDs, such as carpal tunnel syndrome in the wrist, are specific because of their well-defined signs and symptoms. Others are non-specific because only pain or discomfort exists without evidence of a clear specific disorder.

Work-related upper limb disorders (WRULD's) are that group of disorder that affect any part of the arm from the fingers to shoulders, or the neck. They can affect soft tissues, muscles, tendons, ligaments as well as the circulatory and nerve systems. Symptoms include aches, pains, tenderness, tingling, numbness, weakness, swelling, stiffness and cramp. Recognised WRULD conditions include carpel tunnel syndrome and tenosynovitis. Carpal tunnel syndrome is the painful inflammation of the nerves and tendons passing through the carpal bone in the wrist area and affects the whole hand. Tenosynovitis is inflammation of the synovial lining of the tendon sheath.

In 2008/09, an estimated 538,000 people in Great Britain, who had worked in the last year, believed they were suffering from a musculoskeletal disorder that was caused or made worse by their current or past work, according to the Labour Force Survey (LFS). This equates to 1800 per 100,000 people (1.8%) who worked in the last 12 months in Great Britain. Of these, about a third, 191,000 people, first became aware of their work-related musculoskeletal disorder in the previous 12 months. This equates to an estimated 630 per 100,000 people (0.63%) with a new work-related musculoskeletal disorder in 2008/09.

The LFS survey data suggests that despite fluctuations in the incidence rate in recent years, overall the incidence rate of self-reported work-related musculoskeletal disorder has fallen over the period 2001/02 to 2008/09.

The LFS shows that an estimated 9.3 million working days (full-day equivalent) were lost in 2008/09 through musculoskeletal disorders caused or made worse by work. On average, each person suffering took an estimated 17.2 days off in that 12 month period. This equates to an annual loss of 0.39 days per worker. Overall, the number of days lost per worker has fallen over the period 2001/02 to 2008/09, though in recent years the rate has fluctuated.

Examples of repetitive operations

Anyone who over-uses their back, arms and hands repeatedly may develop a musculo-skeletal disorder. Keyboard operators, workers on factory assembly lines, musicians, dressmakers, bricklaying, check out operators and cleaners are examples of workers at particular risk.

KEYBOARD OPERATION

Key board operations may have many thousands of movements an hour which will create repeated movement of the fingers. Many of the movements are centred on a small number of fingers where the operator is not fully proficient in using all fingers to operate the keyboard. Because of the amount of repeated movements, sometimes without taking breaks, the risks of WRULD are high, though the effects are cumulative.

ASSEMBLY OF SMALL COMPONENTS

Many light assembly tasks have a high risk of causing WRULDs. Typical are repetitive assembly tasks e.g. inserting a spring into a car radiator cap using one's thumb; operating a hand power press to insert ball bearings into a component; folding the lid of a cardboard box. Each task should be reviewed to determine the best technique is used to reduce fatigue or strain. In the case of the radiator cap an example of a change following review would be - providing a tool to replace the use of the thumb.

BRICKLAYING

Many building site trades are associated with WRULDs. Plasterers, joiners, electricians and bricklayers are commonly affected. Bricklayers are often self employed and therefore cannot afford to lose time from work. They will carry on working and ignore the warning signs. The size of the bricks being laid, the number of bricks they are expected to lay (often several hundred per day), and the position of the wall or structure are factors to consider when assessing the risk.

CHECKOUT OPERATORS

Checkout operations involve a large number of lifting and tracking movements that sweep from left to right or right to left. The item held in the operator's hands is frequently held at an extended distance from the body and will involve a large variety of sizes, shapes and weights of object.

The pace of work can be particularly high when working at peak times. This repeated movement involves the hands, arms, shoulders and lower back. Some of the movements will be particularly awkward and strenuous as it can involve large heavy items.

ASSESSMENT OF A DISPLAY SCREEN EQUIPMENT WORKSTATION

Assessment should take account of:

Equipment:	Screen.	Positioning, character definition, character stability.
	Keyboard.	Tiltable, character legibility.
	Desk.	Size, matt surface.
	Chair.	Adjustable back and height, footrest available.
Environment:	Noise.	Levels of noise not distractive.
	Humidity.	Low humidity, less 40% Relative Humidity (RH), may cause sore eyes, facial acne.
	Lighting.	Levels appropriate, contrast between surroundings balanced.
	Space.	Adequate for work conducted.
Person/software interface:	Software.	Easy to use.
	Work rate.	Not governed by software.
	Monitoring.	Operator/user informed.

Figure 2-3-1: Position of screen, reflective desk surface. *Source: RMS.*

Figure 2-3-2: Basic office chair, glare and limited work space. *Source: RMS.*

Matching the workplace to the individual needs of workers

The study of ergonomics is essential to good job design. It is the applied science of equipment design intended to maximise effectiveness by reducing worker fatigue and discomfort. It can be defined as "the study of the relationship between human beings, the equipment with which they work and the physical environment in which this human-machine system operates".

It is a broad area of study that includes the disciplines of psychology, physiology, anatomy and design engineering. Ergonomics has the human being at the centre of the study where individual capabilities and fallibilities are considered in order to, ultimately, eliminate the potential for human error and harm to effectiveness and efficiency.

Figure 2-3-3: Workstation design. *Source: RMS.*

This includes the minimisation of such things as work-related musculo-skeletal disorders which are caused by poorly designed machines, tools, task and workplace.

The aims of ergonomics, therefore, are to design the equipment and the working environment to fit the needs and capabilities of the individual, i.e. fitting the task to the individual, and to ensure that the physical and mental well-being of the individual is being met. This involves the consideration of psychological and physical factors, including the work system, body dimensions, capability, competence and the work environment (layout, noise, temperature and lighting).

Individuals, have different physical capabilities due to height, weight, age and levels of fitness. They also have different mental capabilities, memory retention and personalities. All these factors can influence ergonomic choices and the successful matching of the workplace to the individual.

The ill-health effects of poorly designed tasks and workstations

WORK RELATED UPPER LIMB DISORDERS [WRULD]

These were first defined in medical literature as long ago as the 19th century as a condition caused by forceful, frequent, twisting and repetitive movements. The body will be affected to a varying degree by tasks which involve bending, reaching, twisting, repetitive movements and poor posture. WRULD covers well-known conditions such as tennis elbow, flexor tenosynovitis and carpal tunnel syndrome. It is usually caused by repetitive tasks and movements and aggravated by excessive workloads, inadequate rest periods and sustained or constrained postures.

This can result in pain, soreness or inflammatory conditions of muscles and the synovial lining of the tendon sheath. Present approaches to treatment are largely effective, provided the condition is treated in its early stages. Clinical signs and symptoms are local aching, pain, tenderness, swelling, crepitus (a grating sensation in the joint). Some common WRULDs are:

Carpal Tunnel Syndrome	CTS occurs when tendons or ligaments in the wrist become enlarged, often from inflammation, after being aggravated. The narrowed tunnel of bones and ligaments in the wrist pinches the nerves that reach the fingers and the muscles at the base of the thumb. The first symptoms usually appear at night. Symptoms range from a burning, tingling numbness in the fingers, especially the thumb and the index and middle fingers, to difficulty gripping or making a fist, to dropping things.
Tenosynovitis	An irritation of the tendon sheath. It occurs when the repetitive activity becomes excessive and the tendon sheath can no longer lubricate the tendon. As a result, the tendon sheath thickens and becomes aggravated.
Tendinitis	Tendinitis involves inflammation of a tendon, the fibrous cord that attaches muscle to bone. It usually affects only one part of the body at a time, and usually lasts a short time, unless involved tissues are continuously irritated. It can result from an injury, activity or exercise that repeats the same movement.
Peritendinitis	Inflammation of the area where the tendon joins the muscle.
Epicondylitis	Tennis Elbow or Lateral Epicondylitis is a condition when the outer part of the elbow becomes painful and tender, usually because of a specific strain, overuse, or a direct bang. Sometimes no specific cause is found. Tennis Elbow is similar to Golfer's Elbow (Medial Epicondolytis) which affects the other side of the elbow.

The aches, pains and fatigue suffered doing certain tasks will eventually impair the operator's ability and lead to degradation in performance. It is therefore essential to consider the task in order to match it to the individual so the level of general comfort is maximised. For example, when carrying out manual handling assessments it is important to look at the relationship between the individual, the task, the load and the environment.

The factors giving rise to ill-health conditions

TASKS

Tasks should be assessed to determine the health risk factors.

If the task is **repetitive** in nature, i.e. the same series of operations are repeated in a short period of time, such as ten or more times per minute, then injury may occur to the muscles and ligaments affected. Similarly, work of a **strenuous** nature, such as moving heavy or difficult shaped objects, perhaps in limited space or hot environments, will cause fatigue, strains and sprains.

ENVIRONMENT

Poor working environments. Working in **extremes of temperature** or handling hot or cold items will make simple work more strenuous. Long hours of work in cold conditions causes problems with blood circulation which, in turn, may increase the likelihood of hand arm vibration syndrome. Fatigue will also occur to the eyes if the **lighting** levels are low, typically below 100-200 lux or bright, typically greater than 800 lux. Other lighting factors may need to be considered such as the stroboscopic effects associated with moving machinery, which may appear to be stationary when viewed under fluorescent light powered by alternating current.

The risk of injury increases with the **length of time** that a task is carried out. However, injury may occur over a short period if the work requires a lot of effort.

Working in **uncomfortable positions** such as working above head height or holding something in the same place for a long period of time increases the risk of injury. These factors will often be reduced if the worker is able to adjust the conditions to their personal needs.

There is robust scientific evidence of an association of increases in selected respiratory health effects with building dampness or visible mould. These health effects are asthma exacerbation in sensitized individuals, and cough, wheeze, and upper respiratory symptoms in otherwise healthy individuals.

Dampness in buildings is a concern because it often leads to growth of moulds and bacteria and to increased emissions of chemicals. In addition, dampness causes structural degradation on buildings. Building dampness problems have a number of causes. The way to reduce these problems and the risk of associated health effects is to improve the design, construction, operation, and maintenance of buildings. **Poor posture**. The position of the body and the way it has to move to carry out a particular function. This can be affected by such things as:

- Badly designed work methods (e.g. the need for regular bending or twisting).
- Poor layout of the workplace (e.g. having to kneel or stretch to put articles in a cupboard).

Figure 2-3-4: Poor posture.   *Source: Speedy Hire Plc.*

EQUIPMENT

All work factors that influence health issues should be under the influence of the operator as much as possible, such as the ability to adjust temperature and lighting, and the opportunity to take rest breaks. If this is not possible with continuous automated lines, such as with car assembly, then work should be designed to provide facilities for operators' work patterns to be rotated to reduce these effects. Consideration to automation should be given whenever possible. Equipment design should take into account the ergonomic **requirements of the user** and, where possible, allow the user to **adjust** any settings to suit their needs. Such things as workbench height and positioning of switches and buttons should be in the operator's easy control.

Appropriate control measures

A number of changes may need to be made and ergonomic solutions should be given first consideration. This means making the workplace and the work fit person, rather than making the person adapt to fit the workplace and work.

Workstation ■ Ensuring that working heights are appropriate for the full range of workers. ■ Relocating equipment to provide more space. ■ Relocating items that workers have to see clearly within their comfortable range of vision. ■ Providing adjustable workstations that allow postures to be varied between standing and sitting. ***Temperature*** ■ Avoiding handling or insulating cold items or equipment. ■ Directing warm/cool air flow (as appropriate) to the worker to increase thermal comfort. ***Hand tools*** ■ Providing tools with ergonomically designed handles. ■ Using lighter tools, or providing supports or counterbalances. ■ Ensuring tools are regularly maintained. ***Vibration*** ■ Using vibration-damped equipment. ■ Ensuring tools are regularly maintained. ■ Limiting exposure to agreed safe limits. ***Use of muscular force*** ■ Reducing the weight of items. ■ Using jigs or counterbalances to hold items. ■ Using stronger muscle groups to perform the task. ■ Using foot pedals as opposed to hand controls. ■ Using more effective tools that need less muscular power; for example, tools with engines or other mechanical advantage.	***Repetitive movements*** ■ Mechanising or automating repetitive processes. ■ Rotation of workers between tasks with high and low exposures. ■ Allowing adequate rest pauses. ***Postures*** ■ Relocating equipment or items that must be held to within easy reach. ■ Ensuring working heights are at or around waist level. ■ Ensuring workplaces and equipment are suitable for the full range of workers' sizes and strengths. ■ Providing jigs for re-positioning work pieces. ■ Ensuring that items that must be viewed clearly are within the normal visual range. ***Gloves*** ■ Providing gloves in a wide range of sizes to fit workers' hands. ■ Providing gloves made from flexible materials. ***Mechanical pressure*** ■ Providing suitable hand tools as effective substitutes for the use of inappropriate parts of the body. ■ Ensuring that edges on work pieces and equipment items are rounded to distribute pressure during contact with parts of the body. ***Organisation of work*** ■ Improving work flow to avoid production peaks and troughs through better planning and scheduling. ■ Encouraging better communication and team work. ■ Providing appropriate training.

Figure 2-3-5: Actions to be taken to control WRULD risks.   *Source: European Agency for Safety and Health at Work.*

3.2 - Manual handling hazards, risks and control measures

Common types of manual handling injury

Around 25% of all injuries reported to the appropriate enforcing authority have been attributed to the manual lifting and handling of loads. The injuries arise from such **hazards** as stooping while lifting, holding the load away from the body, twisting movements, frequent or prolonged effort, heavy/bulky/unwieldy/unstable loads, sharp/hot/slippery surfaces of loads, space constraints, and lack of capability of the individual.

Manual handling operations can cause many types of **injury**. The most common injuries are:

- Rupture of intervertebral discs ('slipped disc') in the lower spine.
- Muscle strain and sprain.
- Tendons and ligaments can also be over-stretched and torn.
- Rupture of a section of the abdominal wall can cause a hernia.
- Loads with sharp edges can cause cuts.
- Dropped loads can result in bruises, fractures and crushing injuries.

Assessment of manual handling risks

FACTORS TO CONSIDER

The Manual Handling Operations Regulations (MHOR) 1992 specify that the four factors to which the employer must have regard, and questions he must consider, when making an assessment of manual handling operations are:

- **L** oad.
- **I** ndividual capability.
- **T** ask.
- **E** nvironment.

Each factor in turn should be assessed to determine whether there is a risk of injury. When this has been completed the information can then be processed giving a **suitable and sufficient** risk assessment.

FACTORS	QUESTIONS	Level of Risk:		
		High	Med	Low
Load	Is it: ■ Heavy? ■ Bulky or Unwieldy? ■ Difficult to grasp? ■ Unstable, or with contents likely to shift? ■ Sharp, hot or otherwise potentially damaging?			
Individual Capability	Does the job: ■ Require unusual strength, height, etc.? ■ Create a hazard to those who have a health problem? ■ Require special knowledge or training for its safe performance? ■ Do clothing and footwear present an increased risk?			

Task	Does it involve:
	■ Holding load at distance from trunk?
	■ Unsatisfactory bodily movement or posture?
	  • Twisting the trunk.
	  • Stooping.
	■ Excessive movement of load?
	  • Excessive lifting or lowering distances.
	  • Excessive pushing or pulling distances.
	  • Risk of sudden movement of load.
	  • Frequent or prolonged physical effort.
	  • Insufficient rest or recovery periods.			

Working Environment	Are there: ■ Space constraints preventing good posture? ■ Uneven, slippery or unstable floors? ■ Variations in level of floors or work surfaces? ■ Extremes of temperature, humidity or air movement? ■ Poor lighting conditions?			

Figure 2-3-6: Manual handling risk assessment.   *Source: HSE Manual handling (Manual Handling Operations Regulations 1992) Guidance L23.*

The detailed consideration of each factor is necessary to achieve a suitable and sufficient risk assessment. The process of risk assessing includes observing the task as it is actually done; recording the factors that contribute to risk; assessing the level of risk that each factor represents (taking account of the circumstances and controls in place); and considering if the risks are different at different times and for different people. The following should be considered when making a risk assessment.

The load

- Consideration should be given to reducing the weight although this may mean increasing the frequency of handling.
- If there is a great variety of weight to be handled it may be possible to sort the loads into weight categories so that precautions can be applied selectively.
- Where the size, surface texture or nature of a load makes it difficult to grasp, consideration should be given to the provision of handles, hand grips, indents etc., to improve the grasp.
- Loads in packages should be such that they cannot shift unexpectedly while being handled.

Figure 2-3-7: Manual handling.   Source: RMS.

- Any loads to be handled should not have sharp corners, jagged edges, rough surfaces and the like.

Individual capability

- The individual's state of health, fitness and strength can significantly affect the ability to perform a task safely.
- An individual's physical capacity can also be age-related, typically climbing until the early 20's and declining gradually from the mid 40's.
- It is clear then that an individual's condition and age could significantly affect the ability to perform a task safely.

The task

- Ensure work and components in regular use are stored at waist height. Storage above or below this height should be used for lighter or less frequently used items.
- Layout changes should avoid the necessity for frequent bending, twisting, reaching, etc. and the lessening of any travel distances.
- Pay attention to the work routine i.e. fixed postures dictated by sustained holding or supporting loads, frequency of handling loads, with particular emphasis on heavy and awkward loads.
- Fixed breaks are generally less effective than those taken voluntary within the constraints of the work organisation.
- Handling while seated also requires careful consideration. Use of the powerful leg muscles is precluded and the weight of the handler's body cannot be used as a counterbalance. For these reasons, the loads that can be handled in safety by a person who is seated are substantially less than can be dealt with while standing.
- Team handling could be a solution for some tasks that are beyond the capability of one person. However team handling can create additional problems. The proportion of the load carried by each member of the team will vary; therefore, the load that can be handled in safety will be less than the sum of the loads with which an individual could cope.

The working environment

- Adequate gangways, space and working area should be provided in order to allow room to manoeuvre during handling.
- Lack of headroom could cause stooping and constrictions caused by a poor workstation, adjacent machinery etc. should also be avoided.
- In many cases problems are simply caused by lack of attention to good housekeeping.
- Whenever possible all manual handling tasks should be carried out on a single level. If tasks are to be carried out on more than one level, access should preferably be by a gentle slope, or failing that, properly positioned and well maintained stairs/steps. Steep slopes should be avoided.
- Workbenches should be of a uniform height, thus reducing the need for raising or lowering loads.
- Finally, look at the general working environment. A comfortable working environment (e.g. heating, ventilating and lighting) will help to reduce the risk of injury.

REVIEWING ASSESSMENTS

The assessment should be kept up to date. It should be reviewed whenever there is a reason to suppose that it is no longer valid, for example, because the working conditions or the personnel carrying out the operations have changed.

It should also be reviewed whenever there has been a significant change in the manual handling operations, for example, affecting the nature of the task or load.

GUIDELINES FOR ASSESSMENT OF MANUAL HANDLING OPERATIONS

Lifting

The MHOR 1992 set no specific requirements such as weight limits. The following guidelines set out an **approximate** boundary within which manual handling operations are unlikely to create a risk of injury sufficient to warrant assessment that is more detailed. This should enable assessment work to be concentrated where it is most needed.

The guideline figures are not weight or force limits. They may be exceeded where a more detailed assessment shows it is safe to do so. However, the guideline figures should not normally be exceeded by more than a factor of about two. The guideline figures for weight and force will give reasonable protection to nearly all men and between one half and two thirds of women.

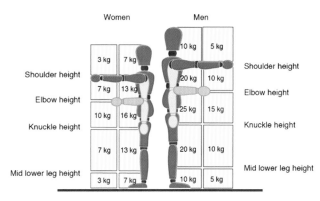

Figure 2-3-8: Lifting and lowering.   *Source: HSE Guidance, L23.*

Carrying

The guideline figures for manual handling operations involving carrying are similar to those given for lifting and lowering. It is assumed that the load is held against the body and is carried no further than about 10 metres without resting.

If the load is carried over a longer distance without resting, the guideline figures may need to be reduced. Where the load can be carried securely on the shoulder without attendant lifting (e.g. unloading sacks from a lorry) a more detailed assessment may show that it is safe to exceed the guideline figure.

Pushing and pulling

Guideline figures for manual handling operations involving pushing and pulling, whether the load is slid, rolled or supported on wheels, are as follows:

- The guideline figure for starting or stopping the load is a force of about 250 newtons (i.e. a force of about 25 Kg as measured on a spring balance).
- The guideline figure for keeping the load in motion is a force of about 100 newtons.
- No specific limit is intended as to the distances over which the load is pushed or pulled provided there are adequate opportunities for rest or recovery.

Handling while seated

The guideline figure for handling operations carried out while seated is given below and applies only when the hands are within the box zone indicated.

If handling beyond the box zone is unavoidable, a more detailed assessment should be made.

Twisting

The basic guideline figures for lifting and lowering should be reduced if the handler twists to the side during the operation.

As a rough guide, the figures should be reduced by about 10% where the handler twists through 45° and by about 20% where the handler twists through 90°.

Assumptions

The guideline figures should not be regarded as precise recommendations and should be applied with caution, noting particularly that they are based on the following assumptions:

- The handler is standing or crouching in a stable body position with the back substantially upright.
- The trunk is not twisted during the operation.
- Both hands are used to grasp the load.
- The hands are not more than shoulder width apart.

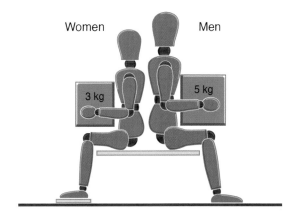

Figure 2-3-9: Handling while seated. *Source: HSE Guidance L23.*

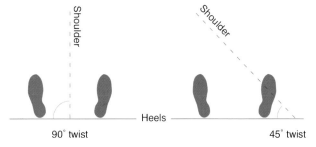

Figure 2-3-10: Twisting.   *Source: HSE Guidance L23.*

- The load is positioned centrally in front of the body and is itself reasonably symmetrical.
- The load is stable and readily grasped.
- The work area does not restrict the handler's posture.
- The working environment (heat, cold, wet, condition of floor) and any personal protective equipment used do not interfere with performance of the task.

Means of avoiding or minimising the risks from manual handling

Each manual handling operation should be examined and appropriate steps taken to minimise the risk of injury to the lowest level reasonably practicable in order to eliminate the potential for the creation or further degeneration of musculo-skeletal disorders (MSDs) i.e. problems to the back, bone, muscle and tissue injury. Wherever reasonably practicable, manual handling should be avoided or reduced by using mechanical handling aids, examples of which are shown below. Practical measures that may be taken to reduce the risk of injury can also be based on *LITE*. For example:

L OAD

By changing the load by lightening, reducing in size, provision of handles, elimination of sharp edges etc. employers must be mindful of the fact that reducing the weight of the load might encourage people to move more objects and attempt to move more than one at a time. The size and design of water dispensing bottles has changed over time. They are considerably smaller in size and have handles moulded into them.

I NDIVIDUAL

Address the individual factors such as selection, provision of information and training, provision of appropriate protective equipment and clothing. Individuals should be selected according to their capability. Personal factors such as height, build, physical condition, and pre-existing health conditions such as pregnancy must be considered.

T ASK

Redesign the task so that manual handling is eliminated or reduced by mechanisation, reducing carrying distances, team lifting, job rotation, etc. Some manufacturers have used technology to redesign cars so that the need to remove a spare wheel from the wheel well in the boot is no longer necessary.

E NVIRONMENT

Risks can be minimised by improving the working environment e.g. optimum heights of surfaces, improving floor conditions, increasing workspace, improving lighting, avoidance of changes in floor level etc.

DESIGN

The risks from manual handling may be minimised by the use of good design of the workplace. This can involve placing items where they can be conveniently handled, improving work layouts so that travel distances are minimised and arranging that items can be picked up or put down at a suitable height. The design of loads can also minimise risks. This can include designing the load to be smaller through concentration of substances contained in it or breaking the load up into suitable sized containers. It can also mean designing in handles or features that make it easier to grip the load, such as 'sticky grip' areas on plastic sacks.

AUTOMATION

Factors to consider here are high volume applications where unit costs of the items justify the large initial capital expense of automation. This is usually introduced where food processing or high volume component despatch is required. Examples include bottle or can filling, sorting, such as with letters and parcels and the transferring of materials into warehousing and then automated order picking for despatch, such as with electrical or automotive components. Systems will often combine a variety of techniques, but are particularly dependant on the movements of goods and material from one point to another using either conveyer systems and/or remotely operated material transfer trucks.

MECHANISATION

This involves the use of handling aids. Although this may retain some elements of manual handling, bodily forces are applied more efficiently. Examples are:

Levers	Reduces bodily force to move a load. Can avoid trapping fingers.
Hoists	Can support weights, allowing handler to position load.
Trolley, sack truck, truck roller or hoist	Reduces effort to move loads horizontally.
Chutes	A way of using gravity to move loads from one place to another.
Handling devices	Hand-held hooks or suction pads can help when handling a load that is difficult to grasp.

OTHER CONSIDERATIONS

Ergonomic approach

Emphasis must be given to all the factors involved in manual handling operations - task, load, working environment and individual capability. This should be carried out with a view to fitting the manual handling operation to the individual rather than the other way round.

Involving the workforce

Effort should be made to seek contributions from employees and, where applicable, safety representatives or representatives of employee safety.

Training

Employers should ensure that all employees who carry out manual handling operations receive the necessary training to enable them to carry out the task in a safe manner.

A training programme should include:

- How potentially hazardous loads may be recognised.
- How to deal with unfamiliar loads.
- The proper use of handling aids.
- The proper use of personal protective equipment.
- Features of the working environments that contribute to safety.
- The importance of good housekeeping.
- Factors affecting individual capability.
- Good handling techniques.

It should always be remembered that training should be kept under review. For training to be effective it should be on-going to reflect improved techniques developed by experienced workers and be supported by periodic refresher training and supervision.

Efficient movement principles for manually lifting loads

LIFTING TECHNIQUES USING KINETIC HANDLING PRINCIPLES

In order to avoid musculoskeletal disorders due to lifting, poor posture and repetitive awkward loads it is important to use recognised techniques. Many of these techniques use a kinetic handling approach, which seeks to use the body's natural movement to the advantage of lifting.

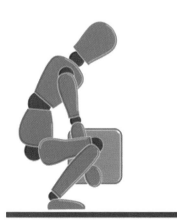

 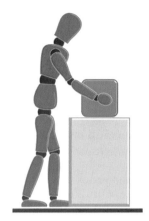

Figure 2-3-11: Basic lifting principles.   *Source: HSE Guidance L23.*

Putting it all into practice

a) Begin with the **load between the feet**, the leading foot should be in line with the side of the load, pointing in the direction of movement.

b) Bend your knees, tuck your chin in **and keep your back straight** (not vertical).

c) Generally grip the load at the upper outer corner on the side of the leading foot, tilt it slightly and grip the opposite corner with the other hand. **(Ensure the palm, not fingers, take the weight).**

d) Keep your **arms close to your body,** move rear hand forward along the lower edge of the load. Stand up in one movement, keeping the load in contact with the body at all times.

e) To lower the load, reverse the procedure, **bending your knees** whilst tilting the load to avoid trapping fingers.

Always remember:

- Assess the Load.
- Lift the load smoothly - do not jerk.
- Avoid twisting and stretching.

Poor posture

Injuries that are received as a result of carrying out activities that include manual handling operations need not necessarily arise solely from lifting large, awkward or heavy items. Poor posture can greatly increase the likelihood of suffering manual handling injuries. Examples of poor posture can include over-stretching, twisting, lifting with the spine (in bending position) or lifting whilst seated. Many construction and maintenance tasks can encourage the worker to take up a poor posture so they are bent over for a period of time, for example laying a floor.

Training should be given in correct manual handling techniques, adoption of the correct posture and ensuring that the 'kinetic' lifting method is used (feet slightly apart, straight back and use of the leg muscles to lift).

Guidance published by the Health and Safety Executive (HSE), indicates values of weights and ideal positions for these given weight values that should be adopted when manually handling **(see figure ref 2-3-8 earlier in this element).** It can be seen from the guidance that the ideal position for manually handling is waist height whilst standing; also to be noted are the different values given for the male and female gender. These figures are not strict and are quoted as maximum under guidance only and allowances must be made for individual differences in capability.

Whilst standing is seen to give the more suitable posture for lifting, it should also be noted that movements made in the standing or seating position can also reduce individual weight values and lifting zones significantly, as discussed earlier.

Repetitive movements

The aim of the regulations is to reduce the risk of injury from manual handling operations. One of the main methods used to reduce the load being manually lifted is to package smaller weights or break the bulk load down into smaller batches. This solution avoids the need to lift heavy items; however it will introduce increased frequency.

Injuries received from manual handling operations can either be immediate, resulting from over exertion and poor posture or also occur over time as a result of performing the manual handling task repeatedly, for example doing check-out tasks in a supermarket, sorting parcels, moving patients, digging an excavation or laying bricks. Whilst acute, painful injuries are typically more immediately noticeable, long-term effects from cumulative muscle strain can prove equally detrimental to individual health.

Where frequency is increased, in addition to training in the correct lifting method, regular breaks or job rotation must be introduced in order to share the workload suitably throughout the workforce. Mechanical assistance may also be introduced to prevent twisting or bending under strain (rollers, conveyors, air suction devices, and waist height benches).

Awkward movements

Training should be given in the correct lifting method (the kinetic method), that if used correctly, should eliminate incorrect posture and provide a means for lifting safely in most positions (floor level, waist height, not stretching). Awkward movements that should be avoided include, stretching, bending at the waist using the spine, twisting, lifting whilst seated, sudden movements, jerky movements, over exertion whilst pushing or pulling.

It should be remembered that many construction and maintenance tasks require a person to hold awkward positions for a period of time, for example the fitting of overhead lights or tiles. These awkward movements can lead to cumulative strain and it is important that there are sufficient rest periods or work rotation built into the work activity to allow relief of the muscles likely to be affected.

3.3 - Manually operated load handling equipment

SACK TRUCK

A sack truck is a simple fabrication fitted with two wheels on which the load is pivoted and supported when the truck is tilted back and pushed manually.

A risk assessment must be made of manual handling operations associated with using equipment of this type. As with the wheelbarrow there is still a need to manually handle materials when using a sack truck.

Hazard and control

Sack trucks are typically manually powered and as with the wheelbarrow the hazards arising from their use are generally of an ergonomic nature relating to posture and over exertion through manual handling.

Figure 2-3-12: Sack truck. *Source: RMS.*

Mechanical hazards are restricted to the wheels of the truck that only move when moved by the operator. Other associated hazards are tripping and falling whilst using the equipment and manual handling back and strain injuries.

Control measures include indicating a safe working load for the equipment and the provision of information/instruction in the safe loading and use of the equipment for the operator. A manual handling assessment may be required when using this equipment.

THE PALLET TRUCK

This truck has two elevating forks for insertion below the top deck of a pallet. When the forks are raised the load is moved clear of the ground to allow movement. This truck may be designed for pedestrian or rider control. It has no mast and cannot be used for stacking. Pallet trucks may be powered or non-powered.

Figure 2-3-13: Battery powered pallet truck. *Source: RMS.*

Figure 2-3-14: Manually operated pallet truck. *Source: RMS.*

Hazard and control

Pallet trucks can be driven both manually or by quiet running electric motor. Hazards include crush from moving loads or momentum of the equipment when stopping, crush and trap in the forks of the equipment, manual handling strain injuries and electricity hazards from battery power points.

In addition, some pallet trucks have a lifting mechanism to raise and lower the load. Control measures should include trained and authorised operatives; identification of safe working loads; inspection and maintenance; and designated areas for parking the equipment.

PEOPLE HANDLING HOISTS

To reduce the risk of manual handling injuries to carers, a patient hoist is often used where there is a need to lift and transfer the individual, or example, to transfer a patient from a chair to a bed; into a bathtub or onto a toilet.

There are various types of people handling devices; some designs use manual systems whereas others use a combination of manual and electrically driven mechanisms.

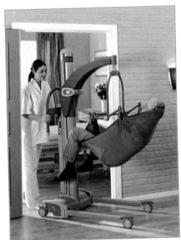

Figure 2-3-15: Mobile hoist. *Source: Arjo.*

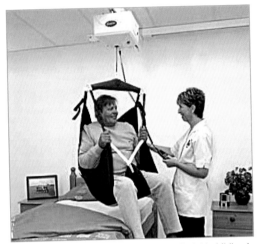

Figure 2-3-16: Ceiling hoist. *Source: Dolphin Midlands.*

Hazard and control

Mobile people handling hoists require some effort to move the device and patient, presenting a risk of manual handling injury to the carers back. Care should be taken to steer and locate the patient carefully, particularly when navigating around bends in corridors or doorways. The route to be travelled should be inspected to ensure there is no risk of collision with obstructions by the patient when being moved. The hoist wheels should always be locked before the loading or unloading of patients to prevent, uncontrolled movement of the lifting device.

Consideration should be given to the carers footwear; it needs to be appropriate to the task, with particular emphasis on non-slip soles and low heels to prevent slips and trips when transferring patients. There is an additional risk of crush injury to the toes or feet from the hoist transfer castors and shoes fitted with toe protection should also be worn ***(see figure ref 2-3-15)***.

Mobile hoists are not designed for long distance transfer and, if battery operated, the battery condition should be checked before use to avoid the risk of loss of power when transferring a patient. When not in use, they need to be stored safely out of the general work area. Hoists fitted with batteries will require a charging point for the battery. The charging should be carried out in a designated area to avoid trip hazards with the charging leads and risk of electric discharge or shock.

Ceiling hoists run on permanently fixed tracks ***(see figure ref 2-3-16)***. They offer less flexibility than a mobile system; they can only be used when there are robust joists available in the ceiling or the ceiling is made of concrete. However, they take up less floor space and may be operated by a remote control. They are better suited to long distance transfers.

Other safety factors need to be considered for both types of hoist:

- They should only be used by staff trained and authorised in their correct use and storage.
- The safe working load must be clearly marked and care should be taken to assess whether this is adequate for the patient to be lifted.
- The equipment (including patient slings) should be subject to regular maintenance and, because these devices are used to lift people, to comply with regulation 9 of LOLER 1998 they must be thoroughly inspected every six months.
- Care should be taken to inspect lifting slings for damage or tears and only cleaning agents recommended by the equipment manufacture should be used to avoid risk of physical degradation damage to the carrying harness.

PEOPLE HANDLING AIDS

Hazard and control

Lateral movement of patients is a common procedure in hospitals and care homes. Although manual handling is minimised where possible, performing this procedure so many times can amount to considerable strain on staff.

Problems are increased because the transfer surfaces may not be the same height or there could be obstacles or gaps between them.

Slide sheets allow basic handling without the need to lift the patient. They are invaluable (they reduce the friction significantly over conventional bedding sheets) when moving a patient on or off a bed, for turning the patient in bed, and as an aid to sitting the patient up in bed.

Slide sheets reduce manual handling effort and strain, minimising the risk of back and other injuries to carers. They reduce skin tears and bruising to patients and promote patient comfort and dignity.

The *walk belt* allows carers to assist those patients who can weight bear but may need extra support when walking. The belt encourages patients to walk more often, knowing that a carer is there to assist.

The use of a walk belt increases the risk to carers since they still have to support some of the patient's weight. Normally the belt should only be used when it is impracticable to use a stretcher or wheel chair. The task should involve two carers working together. When fitted properly the belt should not ride up as this can cause discomfort for the patient and increase the risk of instability. Fastenings (often velcro) should be checked for security and positioned so that the patient cannot unfasten them during transfer.

3.4 - Mechanically operated load handling equipment

Forklift trucks

HAZARDS

Although the forklift truck (FLT) is a very useful machine for moving materials in many industries, it features prominently in accidents. Every year about 20 deaths and 5,000 injuries can be attributed to forklift trucks and these can be analysed as follows:

- Injuries to driver   40%.
- Injuries to assistant   20%.
- Injuries to pedestrians   40% of which 80% were fractures with some 60% resulting in injuries to ankles and feet.

Unless preventative action is taken these accidents are likely to increase as forklift trucks are increasingly used in the workplace.

As about 45% of the accidents can be wholly or partly attributed to operator error, the need for proper operator training is underlined. There are, however, many other causes of accident including inadequate premises, gangways, poor truck maintenance, lighting etc.

- Overturning:
  - Driving too fast.
  - Sudden braking.
  - Driving on slopes.
  - Driving with load elevated.
- Collisions:
  - With buildings.
  - With pedestrians.
  - With other vehicles.

- Loss of load:
  - Insecure load.
  - Poor floor surface.
  - Passengers should not be carried.
- Overloading:
  - Exceeding maximum capacity.
  - Failure:
  - Load bearing part (e.g. chain).

PRECAUTIONS

Traffic routes

- Separate routes, designated crossing places and suitable barriers at recognised danger spots.
- Roads, gangways and aisles should have sufficient width and overhead clearance for the largest forklift truck.
- Clear direction signs.
- Sharp bends and overhead obstructions should be avoided.
- The floor surface should be in good condition.
- Any gradient in a forklift truck operating area should be kept as gentle as possible.

Parking areas

Sufficient and suitable parking areas should be provided away from the main work area.

Protection of personnel

There is a need to alert people to the hazard when working in or near a mechanical handling plant operating area. This is achieved by putting up signs and/or fitting audible warnings to vehicles.

PROCEDURES

Selection of equipment

There are many types of truck available for a range of activities. There are many situations when specialist trucks such as reach trucks, overhead telescopic or rough terrain trucks are required. Many accidents happen due to the incorrect selection and/or use of forklift trucks.

Figure 2-3-17: Rider operated fork-lift truck (reach type). *Source: RMS.*

Figure 2-3-18: Rider operated pallet truck. *Source: RMS.*

Figure 2-3-19: Rider operated fork-lift truck (counter-balance type). *Source: RMS.*

Figure 2-3-20: Width of traffic route and barriers. *Source: RMS.*

When choosing the right truck for the job the following factors should be taken into account:

- Power source - the choice of battery or diesel will depend on whether the truck is to be used indoors or outdoors.
- Tyres - solid or pneumatic depending on the terrain.
- Size and capacity - dependent on the size and nature of loads to be moved.
- Height of the mast.
- Audible and/or visual warning systems fitted according to the proximity of pedestrians.
- Protection provided for the operator dependent on rough terrain which might increase the likelihood of overturning or the possibility of falling objects say from insecure racking.
- Training given to operators must be related specifically to the type of truck.

Figure 2-3-21: Keys - unauthorised use not controlled. *Source: RMS.*

Figure 2-3-22: Pin pad to prevent unauthorised use. *Source: RMS.*

Mechanical handling equipment operators

No person should be permitted to drive a forklift truck or mobile plant unless they have been selected, trained and authorised to do so, or are undergoing properly organised formal training.

Selection of personnel

The safe use of forklift trucks calls for a reasonable degree of both physical and mental fitness and of intelligence. The selection procedure should be devised to identify people who have shown themselves reliable and mature during their early years at work.

Training

Training should consist of three stages, the last being the one in which the operator is introduced to his future work environment. This is illustrated by the stages of training of a fork lift truck operator.

Stage one - should contain the basic skills and knowledge required to operate the forklift truck safely, to understand the basic mechanics and balance of the machine, and to carry out routine daily checks.

Stage two - under strict training conditions closed to other personnel.

This stage should include:

- Knowledge of the operating principles and controls.
- Use of the forklift truck in gangways, slopes, cold-stores, confined spaces and bad weather conditions as appropriate.
- The work to be undertaken e.g. loading and unloading vehicles.

Stage three - after successfully completing the first two stages, the operator should be given further instruction in the place of work.

Testing - on completion of training, the operator should be examined and tested to ensure that he/she has achieved the required standard.

Refresher training - if high standards are to be maintained, periodic refresher training and testing is essential good practice.

SUMMARY OF CONTROLS

- Make someone responsible for transport.
- Select and train drivers thoroughly.
- Daily vehicle checks.
- Keep keys secure. *Do not leave in the ignition.*
- Maintain and light gangways.
- Separate vehicles and pedestrians.

A vigorous management policy covering operator training, vehicle maintenance and sound systems of work, supported by good supervision will reduce personal injury and damage to equipment and materials. This in turn will lead to better utilisation of plant and increased materials handling efficiency.

Lifts and hoists

HAZARDS

In general, the hazards associated with lifts and hoists are the same as with any other lifting equipment.

- The lift/hoist may overturn or collapse.
- The lift/hoist can strike persons, during normal operations, who may be near or under the platform or cage.
- The supporting ropes may fail and the platform/cage fall to the ground.
- The load or part of the load may fall.
- Persons being lifted may become stranded if the lift or hoist fails.
- The lift/hoist may fail in a high position.

PRECAUTIONS

Lifts and hoists for movement of goods require:

- Statutory safety devices.
- Holdback gears (for rope failure).
- Overrun tip systems.
- Guards on hoist machinery.
- Landing gates (securely closed down during operation).

In addition, passenger hoists require more sophisticated controls:

- Operating controls inside the cage.
- Electromagnetic interlocks on the cage doors.
- The enclosing shaft must be of fire-proof construction, if within a building.

Figure 2-3-23: Lift/hoist. *Source: HSG150, HSE books.*

The legislation governing the construction, use and thorough examination of lifts and hoists, is the Lifting Operations and Lifting Equipment Regulations (LOLER) 1998. *See also - Relevant statutory provisions section and later in this element for further details.*

PROCEDURES

Hoists

Only workers who have been trained in the proper use of hoists should be allowed to operate them. The lifting capacity of the hoist must be clearly marked and visible to the operator and cage-controlled hoists must be equipped with effective warning devices.

Before operation, operators should check that the hoist chains or ropes are of sufficient strength and length to safely lift or otherwise handle the load. On a chain hoist, they should make sure the hook has a safety clip so that if the chain is given slack the hook won't come loose. The oil level on hydraulic hoists should also be periodically checked. Operators should understand that they are prohibited from carrying loads over people and any hoist malfunction should be reported to their supervisor immediately.

Lifts

Passenger lifts are required to be examined every six months and goods lifts every twelve months or alternatively at intervals detailed in an examination scheme drawn up by a competent person based on an assessment of risks. The lift should be regularly serviced by a reputable maintenance company (approximately every three months). The service report provided should relate to the efficient working of the lift and is not a substitute for the thorough examination mentioned above. Any remedial work identified should receive prompt attention.

Safety checklist:

- Ensure that the lift is thoroughly examined by a competent person.
- Ensure that the lift is regularly serviced by a reputable company.
- Develop a system for rescuing people trapped in the lift car and where this is to be carried out by staff, provide adequate training on this procedure. Written rescue procedures should be displayed at appropriate locations.
- Ensure that the alarm bell can be activated.
- Ensure that there is adequate lighting at all lift landings to reduce the risk of persons tripping or falling.
- Ensure that the lift plant room door is secured and locked in order to prevent unauthorised access.
- The key to the plant room and the lift landing doors should be kept in a secure position, controlled by a responsible person and be available at all times to authorised personnel.

Conveyors

HAZARDS

- Drawing-in   -   Clothing or limbs being drawn in to in-running nips caused by moving parts.
- Contact   -   With moving parts (cut and abrasion).
- Entanglement   -   With rollers.
- Striking   -   Falling objects, especially from overhead conveyors.
- Manual Handling -   Loading and unloading components/packages.
- Noise   -   From mechanical movement.

TYPES OF CONVEYOR

The three basic types of conveyor are belt, roller and screw:

Belt

Materials are transported on a moving belt. Trapping points are created between the belt and the rotating drum. The 'head and tails' pulleys create the main risks. Guards can be fitted enclosing the sides or at each drawing in point (in-running nip).

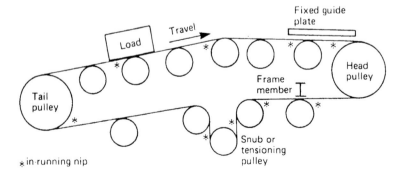

Figure 2-3-24: Diagrammatic layout of belt conveyor showing in-running nips. *Source: J Ridley; Safety at Work; Fourth Edition.*

Roller

- Power driven rollers: guards are required on power drives and drawing-in points (in-running nips).
- Powered and free running rollers: guards are required between each pair of powered and free running rollers.
- Free running rollers: no nips occur on these, but injuries can occur when people try to walk across them. Providing walkways can solve this problem.

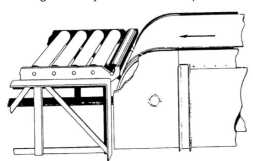

Figure 2-3-25: Preventing free running roller trap. *Source: J Ridley; Safety at Work; Fourth Edition - Courtesy HSE.*

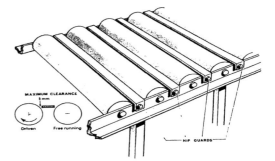

Figure 2-3-26: Guards between alternative drive-rollers. *Source: J Ridley; Safety at Work; Fourth Edition - Courtesy HSE.*

Screw

Materials are pushed forward by a rotating screw. Screw conveyors can cause terrible injuries and should be guarded or covered at all times. A locking-off system is required for maintenance and repairs.

PRECAUTIONS

- Fixed guards on drums.
- Enclosure of conveyed items by side guards.
- Trip wires, if necessary, along the full length of the conveyor.
- Emergency stop buttons.
- Keep all stopping/starting control devices free from obstructions.
- Safe access at regular intervals.

- Do not climb, step, sit or ride on conveyor at any time.
- Do not load conveyor outside of the design limits.
- Do not remove or alter conveyor guards or safety divides.
- Identify and train operators in the location and function of all stop/start controls.
- Avoid loose clothing and keep clothing, fingers, hair, and other parts of the body away from conveyor

Figure 2-3-27: Roller conveyor. *Source: RMS.*

Figure 2-3-28: Belt conveyor guard. *Source: RMS.*

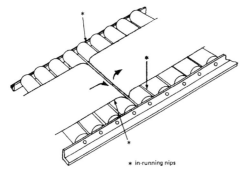

Figure 2-3-29: Drawing-in points on roller conveyor with belts. *Source: J Ridley; Safety at Work; Fourth Edition - Courtesy HSE.*

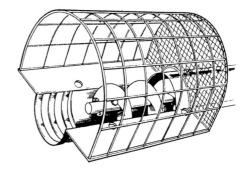

Figure 2-3-30: Screw conveyor guarding. *Source: J Ridley; Safety at Work; Fourth Edition - Courtesy HSE.*

PROCEDURES

- Regular maintenance by competent people.
- Do not perform service on conveyor until motor is disconnect and locked out.
- Wear bump caps.
- Keep area around conveyors clear of obstructions.
- All personnel must be clear of conveyor before starting.
- Operate conveyor with trained personnel only.
- Restrict access.

Cranes

HAZARDS

The principal hazards associated with any lifting operation are:

- **Overturning** which can be caused by weak support, operating outside the capabilities of the machine and by striking obstructions.
- **Overloading** by exceeding the operating capacity or operating radii, or by failure of safety devices.
- **Collision** with other cranes, overhead cables or structures.
- **Failure of load bearing part** - placing over cellars and drains, outriggers not extended, made-up or not solid ground, or of structural components of the crane itself.
- **Loss of load** from failure of lifting tackle or slinging procedure.

Factors which will affect all cranes

Ground condition:

- Level.
- Capable of bearing the load, underground voids or cellars.
- Load bearing capacity of the crane is sufficient for the task.

Positioning the crane:

- Sufficient room for the lift.
- Proximity to overhead power lines, buildings or other cranes.
- Personnel or members of the public nearby.
- Tower cranes (construction) near an airport or in a flight path.
- Adverse weather conditions:
- Rain, wind, temperature, signs of corrosion.
- Erecting and dismantling the crane - use of other cranes.

Figure 2-3-31: Safety latch on hook. *Source: Corel Clipart.*

PRECAUTIONS

General requirements for cranes

Lifting operations must be properly planned by a competent person, appropriately supervised and carried out in a safe manner.

No matter what type of crane, there are a number of common measures for safe operation that apply, including crane identification and capacity marking safe working load (SWL), and maintenance (preventative maintenance, as well as statutory implications). The main safety measures that should be incorporated for the safe operation of a crane include:

- Pre-use check by operator.
- Lifting equipment must be of adequate strength and stability for the load. Stresses induced at mounting or fixing points must be taken into account. Similarly every part of a load, anything attached to it and used in lifting must be of adequate strength.
- The safe working load (SWL) must be clearly marked on lifting machinery, equipment and accessories in order to ensure safe use. Where the SWL depends on the configuration of the machinery, it must be clearly marked for each configuration used and kept with the machinery. Equipment which is not designed for lifting persons, but which might be used as such, must have appropriate markings to the effect that it is not to be used for passengers.
- Load indicators - two types - a requirement with jib cranes, but beneficial if fitted to all cranes.
- Load/radius indicator - shows the radius the crane is working at and the safe load for that radius. Must be visible to the driver.
- Automatic safe load indicator - providing visible warning when SWL is approached and audible warning when SWL is exceeded.

- Controls - should be clearly identified and of the "hold to run" type.
- Over travel switches - limit switches to prevent the hook or sheave block being wound up to the cable drum.
- Access - safe access should be provided for the operator and for use during inspection and maintenance/emergency.
- Operating position - should provide clear visibility of hook and load, with the controls easily reached.
- Passengers - should not be carried without authorisation, and never on lifting tackle.
- Lifting tackle - chains, slings, wire ropes, eyebolts and shackles should be tested/examined.

Figure 2-3-32: Lifting operation.   *Source: RMS.*

Figure 2-3-33: Lifting points on load.   *Source: RMS.*

Accessories

Lifting accessories include slings, hooks, chains eyes and cradles. This equipment is designed with the aim of assisting in lifting items without the need for manual force. Because these accessories are in a constantly changing environment and are in and out of use they need to be protected from damage; a failure of any one item could result in a fatality. For example, lifting eyes need to be correctly fitted, slings have to be used with the correct technique and all equipment must be stored when not in use to prevent damage. Accessories must be attached correctly and safely to the load by a competent person, and then the lifting equipment takes over the task of providing the necessary required power to perform the lift. As with all lifting equipment, accessories must be regularly inspected and certificated and only used by trained authorised persons.

Figure 2-3-34: Safety latch on hook.   *Source: RMS.*

Figure 2-3-35: Accessories.   *Source: RMS.*

PROCEDURES

Operator training and practices

Crane operators and slingers should be fit and strong enough for the work. Training should be provided for the safe operation of the particular equipment. A safe system of work should be developed and communicated to all those involved. The planning should involve selecting competent persons including the mobile crane driver and appointed person who will supervise the lifting operation. A number of safety rules are suggested as a basis of a code of practice for the safe operation of mobile cranes. Circumstances differ from site to site and additional rules should be inserted to cover individual circumstances and conditions.

Site rules should apply before use, for example, before taking over a mobile crane the driver must always check around the crane, and check the pressure of tyres, the engine for fuel, lubrication oil, water and the compressed air system. All controls, such as clutches, brakes and safe load indicator, should be tested to see that all ropes run smoothly and check limit switches operate, where fitted.

The driver of a ***mobile crane*** should carry out the following:

- Before travelling unladen, lower jib onto its rest (if fitted) or to the lowest operating position and point in the direction of travel, but beware of steep hills.

- Understand the signalling system and observe the signals of the appointed banksman.
- Do not permit unauthorised persons to travel on the crane.
- Do not use the crane to replace normal means of transport, or as a towing tractor.
- Before lifting, check that the crane is on firm and level ground, and that spring locks and out-riggers are properly in position.
- Keep a constant watch on the load radius indicator. Do not lift any suspected overload. Overloads are forbidden.
- Ensure movements are made with caution. Violent handling produces excess loading on the crane structure and machinery.
- Make allowances for adverse weather conditions.
- Do not attempt to drag loads or cause loads to swing. Always position the crane so that the pull on the hoist rope is vertical.
- Ensure that the load is properly slung. A load considered unsafe should not be lifted.
- Ensure that all persons are in a safe position before any movement is carried out.
- Make certain before hoisting that the hook is not attached to any anchored load or fixed object.
- Do not drag slings when travelling.
- If the crane is slewing (swinging in a sideways or circular motion), the jib, hook or load must be in a position to clear any obstruction, but the load must not be lifted unnecessarily high.
- Be on a constant lookout for overhead obstructions, particularly electric cables.
- Never tamper with or disconnect safe load indicators.
- If the hoist or jib ropes become slack or out of their grooves, stop the crane and report the condition.
- Report all defects to the supervisor and never attempt to use a crane with a suspected serious defect until rectified and certified by a competent person that it is not dangerous.
- When leaving a crane unattended, ensure that the power is off, the engine stopped, the load unhooked, and the hook is raised up to a safe position.
- Where using special devices; e.g. magnets, grabs, etc. ensure they are used only for the purpose intended and in accordance with the instruction given.
- Keep the crane clean and tidy.
- When parking a crane after use, remember to apply all brakes, slew locks, and secure rail clamps when fitted. Some cranes, however, particularly tower cranes, must be left to weather vane and the manufacturers instructions must be clearly adhered to. Park the crane where the weather vaning jib will not strike any object. Lock the cabin before leaving the crane.
- When it is necessary to make a report this must be done promptly through supervision.
- Drive smoothly - drive safely. Remember that cranes are safe only when they are used as recommended by the makers. This applies in particular to speciality cranes.

Rules for safe operation of a crane

Always Ensure operators/slingers are trained and competent.

Always Select the right appliance and tackle for the job.

Always Ensure the appliance is stable when lifting - e.g. not outside lifting radius, firm, level ground, outriggers.

Always Use correct slinging methods.

Always Protect sling from sharp edges - pack out and lower onto spacers.

Always Ensure the sling is securely attached to the hook.

Always Ensure load is lifted to correct height and moved at an appropriate speed.

Figure 2-3-36: Crane operation.   *Source: RMS.*

Never Use standard signals - refer to the Health and Safety (Safety Signs and Signals) Regulations (SSSR) 1996.

Never Use equipment if damaged (check before use) - e.g. stretched or not free movement, worn or corroded, outside inspection date.

Never Exceed the safe working load.

Never Lift with sling angles greater than 120 degrees.

Never Lift a load over people.

Never Drag a load or allow sudden shock loading.

Requirements for lifting operations

CONTROL OF LIFTING OPERATIONS

Under regulation 8 of the LOLER 1998 employers have a duty to ensure that every lifting operation involving lifting equipment for the purposes of lifting or lowering of a load is organised safely. This will include ensuring the following:

- Lifting operations to be properly planned by a competent person.
- Provision of appropriate supervision.
- Work is to be carried out in a safe manner.

Figure 2-3-37: Lifting operations.   *Source: RMS.*

Figure 2-3-38: Lifting operations.   *Source: RMS.*

STRONG, STABLE AND SUITABLE EQUIPMENT

Strength

Regulation 4 of LOLER 1998 requires every employer shall ensure that:

- Lifting equipment is of adequate strength and stability for each load, having regard in particular to the stress induced at its mounting or fixing point.
- Every part of a load and anything attached to it and used in lifting it is of adequate strength.

When assessing whether lifting equipment has adequate strength for the proposed use, the combined weight of the load and lifting accessories should be taken into account. It is important to consider the load, task and environment in order to match the strength of the lifting equipment to the circumstances of use. For example, if the environment is hot or cold this can affect the lifting capacity of the lifting equipment. In order to counteract this effect equipment with a higher rated safe working load may be needed.

If the load to be lifted is a person, equipment with a generous capacity above the person's weight should be selected in order to provide an increased factor for safety. If the load is likely to move unexpectedly, because of the movement of an animal or liquids in a container, this sudden movement can put additional forces on the equipment and may necessitate equipment with higher strength to be selected. When lifting a load that is submerged in water, the initial lifting weight will be misleading because the load will be supported by the water. When the load emerges from the water the support will no longer be available and this sudden increase in weight can put additional stress on the crane and its lifting accessories.

When conducting the lifting task the lifting accessories may be used in such a way that may reduce its lifting capacity below its stated safe working load; sharp corners on a load and 'back hooking' can have this effect. In these circumstances accessories with a higher rated safe working load may be required.

It is essential to remember that in a lifting operation the equipment only has an overall lifting capacity equivalent to the item with the lowest strength. For example, in a situation where a crane with a lifting capacity of 50 tonnes is used with a hook of 10 tonnes capacity and a wire rope sling of 5 tonnes capacity this would give an overall maximum lifting strength/capacity of 5 tonnes.

Stability

A number of factors can affect the stability of lifting equipment, for example wind conditions, slopes/cambers, stability of ground conditions and how the load is to be lifted.

Lifting equipment must be positioned and installed so that it does not tip over when in use. Anchoring can be achieved by securing with guy ropes, bolting the structure to a foundation, using ballast as counterweights or using outriggers to bring the centre of gravity down to the base area.

Mobile lifting equipment should be sited on firm ground with the wheels or outrigger feet having their weight distributed over a large surface area. Care should be taken that the equipment is not positioned over cellars, drains or underground cavities, or positioned near excavations.

Sloping ground should be avoided as this can shift the load radius out or in, away from the safe working position. In the uphill position, the greatest danger occurs when the load is set down. This can cause the mobile lifting equipment to tip over. In the downhill position, the load moves out of the radius and may cause the equipment to tip forwards.

Suitability

Lifting equipment, and any accessories used for lifting, are pieces of work equipment under the Provision and Use of Work Equipment Regulations (PUWER) 1998.

Regulation 4 of PUWER 1998 states:

"Every employer shall ensure that work equipment is used only for operations for which, and under conditions for which, it is suitable in order to avoid any reasonably foreseeable risk to the health and safety of any person".

Figure 2-3-39: Regulation 4 of PUWER 1998.   *Source: The Provision and Use of Work Equipment Regulations (PUWER) 1998.*

In order for lifting equipment to be suitable it must be of the correct type for the task, have a safe working load limit in excess of the load being lifted, and have the correct type and combination of lifting accessories attached.

Lifting equipment used within industry varies and includes mobile cranes, static tower cranes and overhead travelling cranes. The type of lifting equipment selected will depend on a number of factors including the weight of the load to be lifted, the radius of operation, the height of the lift, the time available, and the frequency of the lifting activities. This equipment is often very heavy, which means its weight can cause the ground underneath the equipment to sink or collapse. Other factors like height and size may have to be considered as there may be limitations in site roads that are located between structures or where overhead restrictions exist. Careful consideration of these factors must be made when selecting the correct crane. Selecting lifting equipment to carry out a lifting activity should be done at the planning stage, where the most suitable equipment can be identified that is able to meet all of the lifting requirements and the limitations of the location.

POSITIONED AND INSTALLED CORRECTLY

Lifting equipment must be positioned or installed so that the risk of the equipment striking a person is as low as is reasonably practicable. Similarly, the risk of a load drifting, falling freely or being unintentionally released must also be considered and equipment positioned to take account of this.

All nearby hazards, including overhead cables and uninsulated power supply conductors, should be identified and removed or covered by safe working procedures such as locking-off and permit systems. The possibility of striking other lifting equipment or structures should also be examined.

Detailed consideration must be given to the location of any heavy piece of lifting equipment due to the fact that additional weight is distributed to the ground through the loading of the equipment when performing a lift.

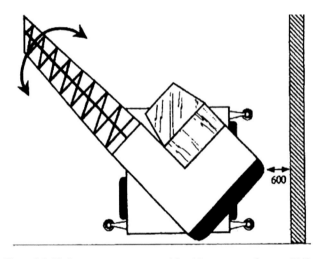

Figure 2-3-40: Danger zone - crane and fixed item.   *Source: RMS.*

Surveys must be carried out to determine the nature of the ground, whether soft or firm, and what underground hazards are present such as buried services or hollow voids. If the ground proves to be soft, then this can be covered using timber, digger mats or hard core to prevent the equipment or its outriggers sinking when under load. The surrounding environment must also be taken into consideration and factors may include highways, railways, electricity cables, areas of public interest. The area around where lifting equipment is sited should be securely fenced, including the extremes of the lift radius, with an additional factor of safety to allow for emergency arrangements such as emergency vehicle access or safety in the event of a collapse or fall.

Where practicable, lifting equipment should be positioned and installed such that loads are not carried or suspended over areas occupied by people. Where this is necessary appropriate systems of work should be used to ensure it is done safely.

If the operator cannot observe the full path of the load an appointed person (and assistants as appropriate) should be used to communicate the position of the load and provide directions to avoid striking anything or anyone.

VISIBLY MARKED

The safe working load (SWL) must be clearly marked on lifting machinery, equipment and accessories in order to ensure safe use. Where the SWL depends on the configuration of the machinery, it must be clearly marked for each configuration used and kept with the machinery. Accessories must be marked with supplementary information that indicates the characteristics for its safe use, for example safe angles of lift. Equipment designed for lifting people must be clearly marked as such and equipment which is not designed for lifting persons, but which might be used as such, must have appropriate markings to the effect that it is not to be used for lifting people.

PLANNED, SUPERVISED AND CARRIED OUT IN SAFE MANNER BY COMPETENT PEOPLE

Regulation 8 of LOLER 1998 requires that every employer shall ensure that every lifting operation involving lifting equipment is:

■ Properly planned by a competent person.
■ Appropriately supervised.
■ Carried out in a safe manner.

The type of lifting equipment that is to be used and the complexity of the lifting operations will dictate the degree of planning required for the lifting operation.

Planning combines two parts:

■ Initial planning to ensure that lifting equipment is provided which is suitable for the range of tasks that it will have to carry out.
■ Planning of individual lifting operations so that they can be carried out safely with the lifting equipment provided.

Factors that should be considered when formulating a plan include:

■ The load that is being lifted - weight, shape, centres of gravity, surface condition, lifting points.
■ The equipment and accessories being used for the operation and suitability - certification validity.
■ The proposed route that the load will take including the destination and checks for obstructions.
■ The team required to carry out the lift - competencies and numbers required.
■ Production of a safe system of work, risk assessments, permits to work.
■ The environment in which the lift will take place - ground conditions, weather, local population.
■ Securing areas below the lift - information, restrictions, demarcation and barriers.
■ A suitable trial to determine the reaction of the lifting equipment prior to full lift.

Completion of the operation and any dismantling required. It is important that someone takes supervisory control of lifting operations at the time they are being conducted. Though the operator may be skilled in lifting techniques this may not be enough to ensure safety as other factors may influence whether the overall operation is conducted safely, for example, people may stray into the area. The supervisor of the lifting operation must remain in control and stop the operation if it is not carried out satisfactorily.

Figure 2-3-41: Siting and stability. *Source: RMS.*

Lifting equipment and accessories should be subject to a pre-use check in order to determine their condition and suitability. In addition, care should be taken to ensure the lifting accessories used are compatible with the task and that the load is protected or supported such that it does not disintegrate when lifted.

Lifting operations should not be carried on where adverse weather conditions occur, such as fog, poor lightning, strong wind or where heavy rainfall makes ground conditions unstable. It is important that measures be used to prevent lifting equipment overturning and that there is sufficient room for it to operate without contacting other objects. Lifting equipment should not be used to drag loads and should not be overloaded. Special arrangements need to be in place when lifting equipment not normally used for lifting people is used for that purpose, for example, de-rating the working load limit, ensuring communication is in place between the people being lifted and the operator, and ensuring the operation controls are manned at all times.

The Health and Safety at Work etc Act (HASAWA) 1974 places a duty on employers to their employees for the provision of information, instruction, training and supervision as is necessary to ensure, so far as is reasonably practicable, the health and safety at work of the employees. In addition to this general duty, a further duty exists under The Provision and Use of Work Equipment Regulations (PUWER) 1998. Employers must ensure that any person who uses a piece of work equipment has received adequate training for purposes of health and safety, including training in the methods which may be adopted when using work equipment, any risks which such use may entail and precautions to be taken.

Drivers/operators of cranes and other lifting appliances, including others involved in lifting operations (e.g. those that direct the movement of the load), must be adequately trained, experienced and aged 18 years or over. The only exception is when under the direct supervision of a competent person for training requirements.

There are various appointments with specified responsibilities in order to ensure the safety of lifting operations on site. These are as follows:

■ Competent person   -   Appointed to plan the operation.

- Load handler   -   Attaches and detaches the load.
- Authorised person   -   Ensures the load safely attached.
- Operator   -   Appointed to operate the equipment.
- Responsible person   -   Appointed to communicate the position of the load (banksman).
- Assistants   -   Appointed to relay communications.

SPECIAL REQUIREMENTS FOR LIFTING EQUIPMENT FOR LIFTING PERSONS

Regulation 5 of PUWER 1998 requires every employer to ensure that lifting equipment for lifting persons:

- Is such as to prevent a person using it being crushed, trapped or struck or falling from the carrier.
- Is such as to prevent so far as is reasonably practicable a person using it, while carrying out activities from the carrier, being crushed, trapped or struck or falling from the carrier.
- Has suitable devices to prevent the risk of a carrier falling.
- Is such that a person trapped in any carrier is not thereby exposed to danger and can be freed.

In addition, every employer shall ensure that if the risk described above cannot be prevented for reasons inherent in the site and height differences:

- The carrier has an enhanced safety coefficient suspension rope or chain.
- The rope or chain is inspected by a competent person every working day.

Special arrangements need to be in place when lifting equipment not normally used for people is used for that purpose, e.g. de-rating the working load limit, ensuring communication is in place between the people and operator, and ensuring the operation controls are manned at all times. Lifting equipment for lifting people is subject to specific requirements for statutory examination.

Requirements for the statutory examination of lifting equipment

Statutory requirements are set out in Regulation 9 of the LOLER 1998.

Used lifting equipment must be thoroughly examined before being put into service for the first time by a new user. This does not apply to new lifting equipment (unless its safety depends on installation conditions) or equipment that conforms to European Community requirements and has been certified as being examined within the previous 12 months. Suppliers of used lifting equipment are obliged to certify that a thorough examination has been carried out. Where the safety of lifting equipment depends on the installation conditions it must be thoroughly examined prior to first use, after assembly and on change of location in order to ensure that it has been installed correctly and is safe to operate.

Lifting equipment exposed to conditions causing deterioration that is liable to result in dangerous situations is to be thoroughly examined by a competent person:

- At least every 6 months - lifting equipment for lifting persons and lifting accessories.
- At least every 12 months - other lifting equipment.
- In either case, in accordance with an examination scheme.
- On each occurrence of exceptional circumstances liable to jeopardise the safety of the lifting equipment.

Regulation 10 of LOLER 1998 requires those persons carrying out the thorough examination as specified under regulation 9 to, as soon as is practicable, make a written report of the results of the examination. This is to be signed by the competent person carrying out this task.

Regulation 11 of LOLER 1998 concerns the keeping of information in relation to examinations and specifies that any report written by a competent person, following an examination, must be kept available for inspection for the period of validity of the report.

Where appropriate to ensure health and safety, inspections must be carried out at suitable intervals between thorough examinations. Examinations and inspections must ensure that the good condition of equipment is maintained and that any deterioration can be detected and remedied in good time.

Figure 2-3-42: Marking of accessories.   *Source: RMS.*

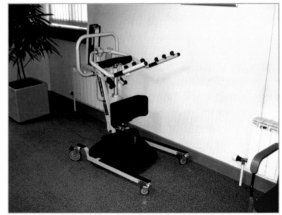

Figure 2-3-43: Mobile hoist for lifting people.   *Source: RMS.*

UNIT NGC2
CONTROLLING WORKPLACE HAZARDS

Element
4

Work equipment hazards and risk control

Learning outcomes

On completion of this element, candidates should be able to demonstrate understanding of the content through the application of knowledge to familiar and unfamiliar situations. In particular they should be able to:

4.1 Outline general requirements for work equipment.

4.2 Explain the hazards and controls for hand-held tools.

4.3 Describe the main mechanical and non-mechanical hazards of machinery.

4.4 Explain the main control measures for reducing risk from machinery hazards.

Content

Sources of reference

The Supply of Machinery (Safety) Regulations 1992 - scope and application, and relationship to CE marking

Safe use of work equipment, Provision and Use of Work Equipment Regulations 1998, Approved Code of Practice and guidance (L22), HSE Books ISBN: 9780717662951

Personal Protective Equipment at Work Regulations 1992 (as amended), Guidance on Regulations, (L25), HSE Books ISBN: 9780717661398

BS EN ISO 12100

Relevant statutory provisions

The Provision and Use of Work Equipment Regulations (PUWER) 1998 - Part II

The Personal Protective Equipment at Work Regulations (PPER) 1992

The Supply of Machinery (Safety) Regulations (SMSR) 1992

4.1 - General requirements for work equipment

Scope of work equipment

The Provision and Use of Work Equipment Regulations (PUWER) 1998 are concerned with most aspects relating to work equipment. The Regulations define work equipment as any machinery, appliance, apparatus, tool or assembly of components which are arranged so that they function as a whole. Clearly the term embraces many hand tools, power tools and machinery types.

Examples of work equipment commonly used in the construction industry include:

- Air compressor.
- Automatic car wash.
- Automatic storage and retrieval equipment.
- Blast furnace.
- Butcher's knife.
- Car ramp.
- Check-out machine.
- Circular saw.

- Lifting sling.
- Liquefied Petroleum Gas (LPG) filling plant.
- Mobile access platform.
- Overhead projector.
- Photocopier.
- Portable drill.
- Potato grading line.
- Power press.

Not work equipment:

- Livestock.
- Substances.

- Structural items (buildings).
- Private car.

Figure 2-4-1: Air compressor.   *Source: RMS.*

Figure 2-4-2: Vehicle lift.   *Source: RMS.*

Figure 2-4-3: Circular saw.   *Source: RMS.*

Figure 2-4-4: Photocopier.   *Source: RMS.*

Suitability as it relates to provision of equipment

PROVISION OF WORK EQUIPMENT REGULATIONS [PUWER] 1998

PUWER Regulation 4 - Suitability of work equipment

(1) Every employer shall ensure that work equipment is so constructed or adapted as to be suitable for the purpose for which it is used or provided.

(2) In selecting work equipment, every employer shall have regard to the working conditions and to the risks to the health and safety of persons which exist in the premises or undertaking in which that work equipment is to be used and any additional risk posed by the use of that work equipment.

(3) Every employer shall ensure that work equipment is used only for operations for which, and under conditions for which, it is suitable.

(4) In this regulation "suitable" means suitable in any respect which it is reasonably foreseeable will affect the health or safety of any person.

Suitability should consider:

■ Its initial integrity.
■ The place where it will be used.
■ The purpose for which it will be used.

Integrity - is equipment safe through its design, construction or adaptation? - Sharp edges removed from the pen tray of a flip chart stand; 'home made' tools; equipment adapted to do a specific task.

Place - is equipment suitable for different environments (risks)? - Wet or explosive. Account must be taken of the equipment causing a problem - a petrol generator used in a confined space; a hydraulic access platform used in a location with a low roof.

Use - is equipment suitable for the specific task? - A hacksaw being used to cut metal straps used to secure goods to a pallet (instead of a purpose designed tool); the use of a ladder to do work at a height (instead of a scaffold or other access platform); exceeding the safe working load of a crane or fork lift truck, a swivel chair used as a means of access to a shelf.

CONFORMITY WITH RELEVANT STANDARDS, CE MARKING

Section 6 of The Health and Safety at Work Act (HASAWA) 1974 requires those involved in the supply (including design and manufacture) of equipment to ensure that it is safe and healthy, so far as is reasonably practicable. This will require them to take account of all relevant standards.

PUWER Regulation 10 - Conformity with community requirements

(1) Every employer shall ensure that an item of work equipment has been designed and constructed in compliance with any essential requirements, that is to say, requirements relating to its design or construction in any of the instruments listed in Schedule 1 (being instruments which give effect to Community directives concerning the safety of products).

(2) Where an essential requirement is applied to the design or construction of an item of work equipment, the requirements of regulations 11 to 19 and 22 to 29 shall apply in respect of that item only to the extent that the essential requirement did not apply to it.

(3) This regulation applies to items of work equipment provided for use in the premises or undertaking of the employer for the first time after 31st December 1992.

Work equipment provided for use after 31 December 1992 must conform with legislation made in the UK in response to EC directives relating to work equipment. Only those directives listed in schedule 1 of PUWER 1998 are to be considered and then only those that have been translated to UK law. Examples relate to:

■ The amount of noise emitted from a variety of equipment (e.g. construction equipment or lawn mowers).
■ Electro-medical equipment.
■ Simple pressure vessels.
■ Machinery safety. ***See also - Supply of Machinery (Safety) Regulations (SMSR) 1992 - Relevant statutory provisions section.***
■ Personal protective equipment.

Directives, and in turn UK Regulations, tend to contain details of 'essential health and safety requirements' and a system whereby compliance may be demonstrated. Compliance is usually demonstrated by the attachment of a CE (Conformité Européenne) mark and the manufacturer/supplier holding an EC declaration of conformity.

FIT FOR PURPOSE

Equipment used for any activity must be suitable to fulfil the exact requirements of the task. This means considering the ergonomic requirements ***See following paragraph***, strength, durability, power source, portability, and protection against the environment, range of tasks to be carried out and the frequency and duration of use.

Equipment that is designed to perform a specific task must only be used for that task and not adapted for other tasks not considered in the manufacturer's design and instructions. An example of this is where a portable battery operated drill is rotated by hand or the back / butt of the drill is used as a hammer, clearly a task not meant for this equipment. Equipment used in these types of situation identifies a lack of forethought in the planning stage of a project when the correct equipment should have been sought and used.

The equipment may be used indoors or outdoors where consideration must be given to the dangers of damp, water and electricity or explosive atmospheres within confined spaces. The grade of equipment should be industrial or commercial type for work activities and not the type of equipment designed for personal use at home.

Whenever equipment is required, the full capacity and limitation requirements should be identified and it should be confirmed that the equipment provided can cope with the demands/limitations placed upon it. For example, construction sites use 110volt supply and it is important that workers only use equipment that suits this power supply.

ERGONOMIC CONSIDERATIONS

Ergonomic considerations involve the study of person-equipment interface, with an emphasis on adjustability of the machinery and equipment. The aim is to suit a variety of individual sizes and positions in order to provide the most comfortable position possible. In considering the ergonomic factors of a task that requires equipment to be used, it is essential to include the operator's individual attributes, and how they affect and may be affected by the process. Factors might include posture when seated or standing, height of the work station, how the equipment may be adjusted and frequency of the task being performed. It is essential that ergonomic considerations form an active part at the planning stage of a process to ensure the correct equipment is obtained and the reactive effects of poor ergonomics eliminated.

Prevention of access to dangerous parts of machinery

PUWER REGULATION 11 - DANGEROUS PARTS OF MACHINERY

(1) Every employer shall ensure that measures are taken in accordance with paragraph (2) which are effective:

(a) To prevent access to any dangerous part of machinery or to any rotating stock-bar.

(b) To stop the movement of any dangerous part of machinery or rotating stock-bar before any part of a person enters a danger zone.

See section 4.4 - Control measure for reducing risks from machinery hazards - for details of the steps to be taken to achieve these requirements.

Requirement to restrict the use and maintenance of equipment

PUWER REGULATION 7 - SPECIFIC RISKS

(1) Where the use of work equipment is likely to involve a specific risk to health or safety, every employer shall ensure that:

(a) The use of that work equipment is restricted to those persons given the task of using it.

(b) Repairs, modifications, maintenance or servicing of that work equipment is restricted to those persons who have been specifically designated to perform operations of that description (whether or not also authorised to perform other operations).

(2) The employer shall ensure that the persons designated for the purposes of sub-paragraph (b) of paragraph (1) have received adequate training related to any operations in respect of which they have been so designated.

For example, in view of the specific risks, it would be appropriate to restrict the use of a compactor, person handling hoist, fork-lift truck, brush cutter, tractor, abrasive wheel, nail gun, circular saw or mobile elevated work platform to those competent and authorised to use it. In the same way maintenance (replacement of a grinding wheel) of an abrasive wheel or (replacement of load bearing components) of a rough terrain fork lift truck should be restricted.

Information, instruction and training

INFORMATION AND INSTRUCTION

Whenever equipment is provided and used in the workplace there is a requirement to ensure that all operators are given adequate information and instruction in order that they can use the equipment safely.

The issues covered should include the safe operation of the equipment and also the capacities and limitations of the equipment. Specific information must be given on the particular hazards of equipment, and instruction and training given on how to implement, use and maintain control measures correctly.

PUWER Regulation 8 - Information and instruction

"Every employer shall ensure that all persons who use work equipment have available to them adequate health and safety information and, where appropriate, written instructions pertaining to the use of the work equipment.

Every employer shall ensure that any of his employees who supervises or manages the use of work equipment has available to him adequate health and safety information and, where appropriate, written instructions pertaining to the use of the work equipment, information and, where appropriate, written instructions on:

(a) The conditions in which and the methods by which the work equipment may be used.

(b) Foreseeable abnormal situations and the action to be taken if such a situation were to occur.

(c) Any conclusions to be drawn from experience in using the work equipment".

TRAINING

PUWER Regulation 9 - Training

"Every employer shall ensure that all persons who use work equipment have received adequate training for purposes of health and safety, including training in the methods which may be adopted when using the work equipment, any risks which such use may entail and precautions to be taken.

Every employer shall ensure that any of his employees who supervises or manages the use of work equipment has received adequate training for purposes of health and safety, including training in the methods which may be adopted when using the work equipment, any risks which such use may entail and precautions to be taken".

Training may be needed for existing staff as well as inexperienced staff or new starters (including temporary staff), particularly if they have to use powered machinery. The greater the danger, the better the training needs to be. For some high risk work such as driving forklift trucks, using a chainsaw and operating a crane, training should be carried out by specialist instructors. Remember that younger people can be quite skillful when moving and handling powered equipment, but they may lack experience and judgment and may require closer supervision to begin with.

Examples:

Users - how to carry out pre-use checks, report defects, only to use equipment for the purpose designed.

Maintenance - safe isolation, acceptable replacement parts and adjustments in accordance with manufacturer's manuals.

Managers - be aware of the hazards and controls and maintain effective supervision.

In addition, where the use of work equipment is likely to involve a specific risk to health and safety the employer must provide those restricted to repair, modify, maintain or service the equipment with adequate training.

Equipment to be maintained and maintenance conducted safely

EQUIPMENT TO BE MAINTAINED

Procedures for defective equipment

Under section 7 of the HASAWA 1974 and Regulation 14 of the management of Health and Safety at Work Regulations (MHSWR) 1999, employees have a duty and should notify any shortcomings in the health and safety arrangements, even when no immediate danger exists, so that employers can take remedial action if needed. The duties placed on employees do not reduce the responsibility of the employer to comply with his own duties. Regulation 5 of PUWER 1998 requires equipment to be maintained. With duties being placed upon both the employer and the employee to ensure the use of safe equipment, when identified in the workplace, faulty equipment should be isolated until such a time it can be repaired by a competent party.

PUWER Regulation 5 - Maintenance

"Every employer shall ensure that work equipment is maintained in an efficient state, in efficient working order and in good repair".

In order to achieve this, a system of maintenance should be in place which includes regular inspection, adjustment, replacement of parts and testing. Maintenance logs, where they exist, must be kept up to date.

Regulation 6 of PUWER 1998 lays down requirements for inspecting work equipment to ensure that health and safety conditions are maintained and that any deterioration can be detected and remedied in good time.

Figure 2-4-5: Inspection and examination.   *Source: RMS.*

PUWER Regulation 6 - inspection

"Every employer shall ensure that work equipment exposed to conditions causing deterioration which is liable to result in dangerous situations is inspected:

(a) At suitable intervals.

(b) Each time that exceptional circumstances which are liable to jeopardise the safety of the work equipment have occurred, to ensure that health and safety conditions are maintained and that any deterioration can be detected and remedied in good time.

Every employer shall ensure that the result of an inspection made under this regulation is recorded and kept until the next inspection under this regulation is recorded".

Equipment must be inspected on a regular basis in order to confirm the condition that it is in. The inspection required is more than a simple daily pre-use check carried out by the operator. The person using equipment, who should be confirmed as competent, should carry out operator checks prior to the use of any equipment. Operator checks should include guards, cables, casing integrity, cutting or machine parts and safety devices such as cut-outs.

The inspection required under this regulation should be significant and address a list of identifiable health and safety critical parts. The purpose of an inspection sheet is to record deterioration of specific parts, abuse and misuse and also to ensure that all items are considered at the time of inspection, by serving as an aide memoir. The results of the inspection will confirm whether or not a piece of equipment is in a safe enough condition to use.

Other regulations, such as the Lifting Operations and Lifting Equipment Regulations (LOLER) 1998 require and set certain statutory inspection requirements. Note also that Regulation 6(5) of PUWER 1998 has been amended by the Work at Height Regulations (WAH) 2005 to include 'work equipment to which regulation 12 of the WAH 2005 applies'. *See also - WAH 2005 - Relevant statutory provisions section.*

MAINTENANCE TO BE CONDUCTED SAFELY

PUWER Regulation 22 - Maintenance

No one should be exposed to undue risk during maintenance operations. In order to achieve this equipment should be stopped and isolated as appropriate before work starts. If it is necessary to keep equipment running then the risks must be adequately controlled. This may take the form of controlling running speed, range of movement or providing temporary guards. Consideration must be given to other legislation such as Electricity at Work Regulations (EWR) 1989 during the assessment of risk for maintenance.

Maintenance hazards

The principal sources of hazards are associated with maintenance work on:

- Conveyors.
- Lifts and hoists.
- Cranes.
- Concrete pumps.
- Live electrical equipment.

- Storage tanks.
- Hoppers.
- Chemical and degreasing plant.
- Compactors.
- X-ray machinery.

Typical hazards associated with maintenance operations

Mechanical	Entanglements, machinery traps, contact; shearing traps, in-running nips, ejection, unexpected start up.
Electrical	Electrocution, shock, burns.
Pressure	Unexpected pressure releases, explosion.
Physical	Extremes of temperature, noise, vibration, dust.
Chemical	Gases, vapours, mists, fumes, etc.
Structural	Obstructions and floor openings.
Access	Work at heights, confined spaces.

Typical accidents

- Crushing by moving machinery.
- Falls.
- Burns.

- Asphyxiation.
- Electrocution.
- Explosions.

One or more of the following factors causes maintenance accidents:

- Lack of perception of risk by managers/supervisors, often because of lack of necessary training.
- Unsafe or no system of work devised, for example, no permit-to-work system in operation, no facility to lock off machinery and electricity supply before work starts and until work has finished.
- No co-ordination between workers, and communication with other supervisors or managers.
- Lack of perception of risk by workers, including failure to wear protective clothing or equipment.
- Inadequacy of design, installation, siting of plant and equipment.
- Use of contractors with no health and safety systems or who are inadequately briefed on health and safety aspects.

Maintenance to be conducted safely

Isolation

This does not simply mean switching off the equipment using the stop button. It includes switching the equipment off at the start button and switching off the isolator for the equipment. In new workplaces, individual equipment isolators should be provided; i.e. each piece of equipment has its own isolator near to it. One isolator should not control several items of equipment as it is then impossible to isolate a single piece of equipment on its own.

Figure 2-4-6: Conveyor.   *Source: RMS.*

Figure 2-4-7: Electrical isolator with hole for padlock. *Source: RMS.*

Lock out and tag out

Isolation alone does not afford adequate protection, because there is nothing to prevent the isolator being switched back on, or removed fuses being replaced inadvertently while the person who isolated the item in the first place is still working on the equipment.

To ensure that this does not happen, the isolator needs to be physically locked in the off position (typically using a padlock, the key to be held by the person in danger). Multiple lock out devices are often used where multiple trades are carrying out work on the same equipment or plant; they are designed to carry a number of isolation padlocks for the different people working on the equipment, the equipment cannot be energised until all the padlocks are removed, thereby protecting the last worker on the job. It is also a good idea to sign *"Do not switch on..."* or tag on the equipment at the point of isolation.

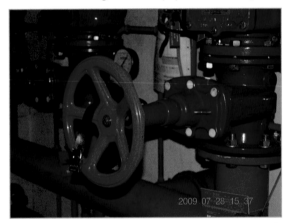

Figure 2-4-8: Physical isolation of valve.   Source: RMS.

Figure 2-4-9: Multiple (padlock) lock off device.   Source: RMS.

Summary of control measures

- Plan work in advance - provide safe access, support parts of equipment which could fail.
- Use written safe systems of work, method statements or permit to work systems as appropriate.
- Plan specific operations using method statements.
- Use physical means of isolating or locking off plant.
- Systems of working should incorporate two-man working for high risk operations.
- Integrate safety requirements in the planning of specific high risk tasks.
- Prevent unauthorised access to the work area by using barriers and signs.
- Ensure the competence of those carrying out the work.
- Ensure the availability and use of appropriate personal protective equipment (PPE) - gloves, eye protection.
- Prevent fire or explosion - thoroughly clean vessels that have contained flammable solids or liquids, gases or dusts and check them thoroughly before hot work is carried out.

Importance of operation and emergency controls, etc

OPERATION AND EMERGENCY CONTROLS

PUWER Regulation 14 - Controls for starting or making a significant change in operating conditions

(1) Every employer shall ensure that, where appropriate, work equipment is provided with one or more controls for the purposes of:

(a) Starting the work equipment (including re-starting after a stoppage for any reason).

(b) *Controlling any change in the speed, pressure or other operating conditions of the work equipment where such conditions after the change result in risk to health and safety which is greater than or of a different nature from such risks before the change.*

(2) *Subject to paragraph (3), every employer shall ensure that where a control is required by paragraph (1), it shall not be possible to perform any operation mentioned in sub-paragraph (a) or (b) of that paragraph except by a deliberate action on such control.*

Paragraph (1) shall not apply to re-starting or changing operating conditions as a result of the normal operating cycle of an automatic device.

Any change in the operating conditions should only be possible by the use of a control, except if the change does not increase risk to health or safety. Examples of operating conditions include speed, pressure, temperature and power.

The controls provided should be designed and positioned so as to prevent, so far as possible, inadvertent or accidental operation. Buttons and levers should be of appropriate design, for example, including a shroud or locking facility. It should not be possible for the control to 'operate itself' such as due to the effects of gravity, vibration, or failure of a spring mechanism.

PUWER Regulation 15 - Stop controls

(1) *Every employer shall ensure that, where appropriate, work equipment is provided with one or more readily accessible controls the operation of which will bring the work equipment to a safe condition in a safe manner.*

(2) *Any control required by paragraph (1) shall bring the work equipment to a complete stop where necessary for reasons of health and safety.*

(3) *Any control required by paragraph (1) shall, if necessary for reasons of health and safety, switch off all sources of energy after stopping the functioning of the work equipment.*

(4) *Any control required by paragraph (1) shall operate in priority to any control, which starts or changes the operating conditions of the work equipment.*

The primary requirement of this Regulation is that the action of the control should bring the equipment to a safe condition in a safe manner. This acknowledges that it is not always desirable to bring all items of work equipment immediately to a complete or instantaneous stop, for example, to prevent the unsafe build-up of heat or pressure or to allow a controlled run-down of large rotating parts. Similarly, stopping the mixing mechanism of a reactor during certain chemical reactions could lead to a dangerous exothermic reaction.

The Regulation is qualified by 'where necessary for reasons of health and safety'. Therefore, accessible dangerous parts must be rendered stationary. However, parts of equipment which do not present a risk, such as suitably guarded cooling fans, do not need to be positively stopped and may be allowed to idle.

PUWER Regulation 16 - Emergency stop controls

(1) *Every employer shall ensure that, where appropriate, work equipment is provided with one or more readily accessible emergency stop controls unless it is not necessary by reason of the nature of the hazards and the time taken for the work equipment to come to a complete stop as a result of the action of any control provided by virtue of regulation 15(1).*

(2) *Any control required by paragraph (1) shall operate in priority to any control required by regulation 15(1).*

Emergency stops are intended to affect a rapid response to potentially dangerous situations and they should not be used as functional stops during normal operation.

Emergency stop controls should be easily reached and actuated. Common types are mushroom-headed buttons, bars, levers, kick plates, or pressure-sensitive cables.

Figure 2-4-10: Controls and emergency stop.   *Source: RMS.*

Figure 2-4-11: Controls and interlocking guard.   *Source: RMS.*

PUWER Regulation 17 - Controls

(1) Every employer shall ensure that all controls for work equipment shall be clearly visible and identifiable, including by appropriate marking where necessary.

It should be possible to identify easily what each control does and on which equipment it takes effect. Both the controls and their markings should be clearly visible. As well as having legible wording or symbols, factors such as the colour, shape and position of controls are important.

(2) Except where necessary, the employer shall ensure that no control for work equipment is in a position where any person operating the control is exposed to a risk to his health or safety.

(3) Every employer shall ensure where appropriate:

> *(a) That, so far as is reasonably practicable, the operator of any control is able to ensure from the position of that control that no person is in a place where he would be exposed to any risk to his health or safety as a result of the operation of that control, but where or to the extent that it is not reasonably practicable.*

> *(b) That, so far as is reasonably practicable, systems of work are effective to ensure that, when work equipment is about to start, no person is in a place where he would be exposed to a risk to his health or safety as a result of the work equipment starting, but where neither of these is reasonably practicable.*

Figure 2-4-12: Controls.   Source: RMS.

> *(c) That an audible, visible or other suitable warning is given by virtue of regulation 24 whenever work equipment is about to start.*

(4) Every employer shall take appropriate measures to ensure that any person who is in a place where he would be exposed to a risk to his health or safety as a result of the starting or stopping of work equipment has sufficient time and suitable means to avoid that risk.

Warnings given in accordance with regulation 17(3)(c) should be given sufficiently in advance of the equipment actually starting to give those at risk time to get clear. As well as time, suitable means of avoiding the risk should be provided. This may take the form of a device by means of which the person at risk can prevent start-up or warn the operator of his/her presence. Otherwise, there must be adequate provision to enable people at risk to withdraw, e.g. sufficient space or exits. Circumstances will affect the type of warning chosen.

PUWER Regulation 18 - Control systems

(1) Every employer shall:

> *(a) Ensure, so far as is reasonably practicable, that all control systems of work equipment are safe.*

> *(b) Are chosen making due allowance for the failures, faults and constraints to be expected in the planned circumstances of use.*

(2) Without prejudice to the generality of paragraph (1), a control system shall not be safe unless:

> *(a) Its operation does not create any increased risk to health or safety.*

> *(b) It ensures, so far as is reasonably practicable, that any fault in or damage to any part of the control system or the loss of supply of any source of energy used by the work equipment cannot result in additional or increased risk to health or safety.*

> *(c) It does not impede the operation of any control required by regulation 15 or 16.*

Failure of any part of the control system or its power supply should lead to a 'fail-safe' condition (more correctly and realistically called 'minimised failure to danger'), and not impede the operation of the 'stop' or 'emergency stop' controls. The measures, which should be taken in the design and application of a control system to mitigate against the effects of failure, will need to be balanced against the consequences of any failure, and the greater the risk, the more resistant the control system should be to the effects of failure.

STABILITY

PUWER Regulation 20 - Stability

Every employer shall ensure that work equipment or any part of work equipment is stabilised by clamping or otherwise where necessary for purposes of health or safety.

Most machines used in a fixed position should be bolted or otherwise fastened down so that they do not move or rock during use. This is particularly important where the equipment is tall relative to its base or has a high centre of gravity, e.g. a pedestal mounted abrasive wheel, some diagnostic medical equipment and vertical cardboard compactors. It has long been recognised that woodworking and other machines (except those specifically designed for portable use) should be bolted to the floor or similarly secured to prevent unexpected movement.

LIGHTING

PUWER Regulation 21 - Lighting

Every employer shall ensure that suitable and sufficient lighting, which takes account of the operations to be carried out, is provided at any place where a person uses work equipment.

Local lighting may be needed to give sufficient view of a dangerous process or to reduce visual fatigue.

MARKINGS AND WARNINGS

PUWER Regulation 23 - Markings

Every employer shall ensure that work equipment is marked in a clearly visible manner with any marking appropriate for reasons of health and safety.

There are similarities between regulation 23 and 24 covering markings and warnings. Certain markings may also serve as a warning, e.g. the maximum working speed, maximum working load or the contents being of a hazardous nature (e.g. colour coded gas bottles or service mains.

PUWER Regulation 24 - Warnings

Every employer shall ensure that work equipment incorporates any warnings or warning devices which are appropriate for reasons of health and safety.

Warnings given by warning devices on work equipment shall not be appropriate unless they are unambiguous, easily perceived and easily understood.

Warnings and warning devices are introduced following the implementation of markings and other physical measures, where appropriate risks to health and safety remain. Warnings are usually in the form of a notice, sign or similar. Examples of warnings are positive instructions (hard hats must be worn); prohibitions (no naked flames) and restrictions (do not heat above 60°C). Warning devices are active units that give out either an audible or visual signal, usually connected to the equipment in order that it operates only when a hazard exists. Warning devices are also used where the equipment is mobile, such things as a flashing light can warn of the presence of a fork-lift truck and an audible device may warn of a vehicle reversing or a conveyor about to start.

CLEAR UNOBSTRUCTED WORKSPACE

Workplace (Health, Safety and Welfare) (WHSWR) Regulations 1992

Regulation 11 - Room dimensions and space

Every room where persons work shall have sufficient floor area, height and unoccupied space for purposes of health, safety and welfare.

Workrooms should have enough free space to allow people to get to and from workstations and to move within the room with ease. Workrooms should be of sufficient height (from floor to ceiling) over most of the room to enable safe access to workstations. In older buildings with obstructions such as low beams, the obstruction should be clearly marked.

The total volume of the room, when empty, divided by the number of people normally working in it, should be at least 11 cubic metres. In making this calculation a room or part of a room which is more than 3.0 m high should be counted as 3.0 m high. The figure of 11 cubic metres per person is a minimum and may be insufficient if, for example, much of the room is taken up by furniture.

Where work equipment, such as a circular saw, is used in a workplace care should be taken to ensure that adequate space exists around the equipment to ensure it is not overcrowded and does not cause risk to operators and those passing by the equipment when it is operating.

It is important that the workspace allocated for users of work equipment is maintained clear and unobstructed. Obstructions could lead to slips, trips and falls which could also involve contact with the equipment or moving parts of the equipment. Material being readied to be worked on, material worked on and any scrap material should not be allowed to build up in the workspace. Material such as dust, scraps of wood or metal can quickly build up as the equipment is used. Good control of the input, output and processing of material is essential. Scrap material must be removed from the workspace at suitable intervals, so that it does not build up and obstruct the workspace.

Responsibilities of users

MANAGEMENT OF HEALTH AND SAFETY AT WORK (MHSWR) REGULATION 14 - EMPLOYEES' DUTIES

"Every employee shall use any machinery, equipment, dangerous substance, transport equipment, means of production or safety device provided to him by his employer in accordance both with any training in the use of the equipment concerned which has been received by him and the instructions respecting that use which have

been provided to him by the said employer in compliance with the requirements and prohibitions imposed upon that employer by or under the relevant statutory provisions".

Employees have a duty under section 7 of the HASAWA 1974 to take reasonable care for their own health and safety and for that of others who may be affected by their acts or omissions and to co-operate with the employer to enable him to comply with statutory duties for health and safety. Employees should notify any shortcomings in the health and safety arrangements, even when no immediate danger exists, so that employers can take remedial action if needed. The duties placed on employees do not reduce the responsibility of the employer to comply with his own duties.

4.2 - Hand-held tools

Hand tools

HAZARDS AND MISUSE OF HAND TOOLS

Anyone who uses a hand-held tool may be at risk of injury, either accidentally, through misuse or equipment failure.

Injury hazards include hand-arm vibration, for example, caused by the use of hand-operated power tools. Employees who regularly use these as part of their job may be at risk of a permanent injury known as hand-arm vibration syndrome (HAVS).

In addition, there is a range of other risks for employees when using hand-held tools. For example, noise induced hearing loss from cutting or impact tools; respiratory disease from inhalation of dust from sanders; electric shock from faulty insulation; eye injury from material thrown off from grinding or cutting; punctures and cuts caused by sharp equipment such as scissors, paper guillotines, knives, chisels, saws, planes and screwdrivers. Heat-producing equipment such as blowtorches and irons can cause burns and permanent scarring.

Misuse includes using the wrong tool for the job, for example, a hammer to drive home a screw, rather than a screwdriver, or a file, which is brittle, as a lever.

REQUIREMENTS FOR SAFE USE, CONDITION AND FITNESS FOR USE, SUITABILITY FOR PURPOSE AND LOCATION

Hammers

Hammers are basic tools but they are also notorious for causing thumb and finger injuries. The following checklist will help to avoid incidents with hammers:

- Check the condition of the hammer - avoid split, broken or loose handles and worn or chipped heads. Heads should be properly secured to the handles.
- Grip the handle firmly.
- Hold the hammer at the end of the handle.
- Hit the surface squarely with the hammer.
- Use the whole arm and elbow.
- Place the work against a hard surface.
- Work in a natural position.
- Check area is clear around you before swinging the hammer.
- Practice good hammering technique.

Files

These should have a proper, well designed handle. The file should be held firmly in one hand with the fingers of the other hand used only to guide the file. The material being filed should be firmly held in clamps or a vice. File strokes should be made away from the user. Take care to avoid the file slipping on the surface of the material causing sudden forward movement of the user. Files must never be used as a lever – they are very brittle and will shatter easily. They should only be cleaned by using a cleaning card and not by striking them against a solid object as this can also cause the file to shatter.

Chisels

Choose a chisel large enough for the job, so the blade is used rather than only the point or corner. Never use chisels with dull blades - the sharper the tool, the better the performance. Chisels that are bent, cracked, or chipped should be discarded. The cutting edge should be sharpened to the correct angle. Do not allow the head of cold chisels to spread to a mushroom shape - grind off the sides regularly. Use a hand guard on the chisel and hit the chisel squarely. Chisels should not be used as a lever as they may break suddenly.

Screwdrivers

A screwdriver is one of the most commonly used and abused tools. The practice of using screwdrivers as punches, wedges, or levers should be discouraged as this practice dulls blades and may cause injury if the blade fractures or slips in use. Screwdrivers should be selected so the tip fits the screw. When working on electrical equipment screwdrivers must be equipped with insulated handles and blades. Screwdrivers with split handles or damaged tips should be taken out of use and discarded safely.

Spanners

Avoid spanners with splayed or damaged jaws. Use ring spanners or sockets where possible, as these are less likely to slip. Discard safely any spanners that show signs of slipping. Ensure enough spanners of the correct size are available. Do not improvise by using pipes, etc., as extensions to the handle. Where necessary use penetrating oil to loosen tight nuts.

Knives

Knives cause more disabling injuries than any other hand tool. The risks are that the hands may slip from the handle onto the blade or that the knife may strike the body or the free hand. Use knives with handle guards if possible. Make sure that the cutting stroke is always away from the body. Return the knife to a safe place and ensure it is sheathed before conducting other tasks, like moving a sack that the user has opened. Do not hold a knife with an open blade while carrying other things. Knives must be kept sharp and in their holders or sheaths when not in use.

Dirty or oily knives should be wiped clean to avoid the user's grip slipping. To clean the blade wipe with a towel or cloth with the sharp edge turned away from the wiping hand. Horseplay of any kind involving a knife (throwing, "fencing", etc.) must not be tolerated.

Where there is a potential for a flammable atmosphere to be present use alloy or bronze tools to prevent sparks.

Hazards of portable power tools

ELECTRIC DRILL

Electric drills are used for penetrating various materials and in construction are usually of a medium to heavy-duty nature. This equipment involves rotating shafts and tool bits, sharp tools, electricity and flying debris.

Hazards

Obvious hazards include shock and electrocution leading to possible fatalities; however this potential is reduced by using 110volt or battery operated equipment. Other hazards include puncture, entanglement, noise and dust.

Control measures

Control measures include using only equipment that is suitable for the task, ensuring equipment is tested and inspected as safe to use, suitable shut off and isolation measures, goggles, hearing protection. Care should be taken to ensure the drill bits are kept sharp as injuries can occur when the rotating drill bit gets stuck in material and the drill is caused to kick and rotate in the operator's hands.

SANDER

Hazards

Sanding equipment is available in a variety of sizes from hand held equipment to large industrial machines. Sanders are used to provide a smooth finished surface, using a mechanical abrasive action.

Sanding operations are carried out on a wide variety of materials including wood, minerals such as marble and man-made fibres. The main hazards associated with the sanding process are vibration and noise. Also, harm can be caused by the inhalation of respirable particles from dust. Where organic materials such as wood are being processed, fire may result from overheated surfaces or explosion from dust by-products.

Associated hazards may include electrocution if supply cables are damaged by hand held sanders, particularly if the sander is placed on the ground whilst still rotating. Other risks include trips from trailing leads, cuts from sharp surfaces and strains or sprains from manual handling of process materials.

Figure 2-4-13: Belt sander.   *Source: Clarke International.*

Control measures

When using sanding equipment, suitable personal respiratory protective equipment (RPE) is required to protect the user from dust exposure. Where possible, local exhaust ventilation equipment should be used to minimise dust in the atmosphere.

In order to protect against vibration injuries, the operator should be given regular breaks and the equipment maintained at intervals, including the renewal of sanding media to prevent the need for over exertion by the operator. Where hand held tools are used, suitable hand protection will also reduce injuries from vibration, cuts and manual handling. Pre-use inspections by the operator and regular thorough examinations should be carried out to identify potential electrical problems. Care should be taken to ensure that power leads do not create tripping hazards and they are positioned so that the likelihood of mechanical damage is minimised.

4.3 - Machinery hazards

Main mechanical and non-mechanical hazards

To meet requirements of the syllabus, machinery hazards are discussed in this section; *"control of hazards"* is considered in 'Application of protection methods to a range of equipment' *see section 4.4 – Control measure for reducing risks from machinery hazards.*

Mechanical and other hazards identified in BS EN ISO 12100 Part 1 are described as follows.

MECHANICAL HAZARDS

Entanglement

The mere fact that a machine part is revolving can constitute a very real hazard of entanglement. Loose clothing, jewellery, long hair, etc. increase the risk of entanglement.

Figure 2-4-14: Auger drill - entanglement. *Source: STIHL.*

Examples of entanglement hazards include couplings, drill chucks/bits, flywheels, spindles, shafts (especially those with keys/bolts) and rotating tools like abrasive wheels.

Friction and abrasion

Friction burns and encountering rough surfaces moving at high speed, as found in a sanding machine, grinding wheel or conveyor belt, can cause abrasion injuries.

Figure 2-4-15: Chop saw - cutting. *Source: Speedy Hire plc.*

Figure 2-4-16: Abrasive wheel - abrasion. *Source: RMS.*

Cutting

Saw blades, knives and even rough edges, especially when moving at high speed, can result in serious cuts and even amputation injuries. The dangerous part can appear stationary due to the stroboscopic effect under certain lighting conditions. Examples of cutting action hazards include saws, slicing machines, abrasive cutting discs and chainsaws.

Shear

When two or more machine parts move towards/past one another a "trap" is created. This can result in a crush injury or even an amputation. Examples of shearing action hazards include scissor lifts, power presses and guillotines.

Stabbing and puncture

The body may be penetrated by sharp pieces of equipment, or material contained in the equipment. Examples of stabbing and puncture hazards include fixing materials such as nails fired from a nail gun or a drill bit which could puncture the hand when operating the drill.

Impact

Impact is caused by objects that strike the body, but do not penetrate it. They may cause the person or part of the person to be moved, sometimes violently, resulting in injury. For example, a person could be struck by the jib of a crane/excavator or materials on a hoist or the moving platter of a machine like a surface grinder.

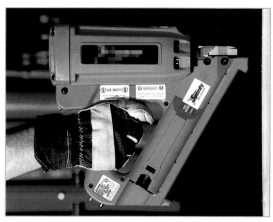

Figure 2-4-17: Stabbing and puncture. *Source: Speedy Hire plc.*

Figure 2-4-18: Shear. *Source: RMS.*

Crushing

Crushing is caused when part of the body is caught between either two moving parts of machinery or a moving part and a stationary object. Examples of crushing hazards include the platform of a hoist closing together with the ground or an overhead beam; moving parts of an adjustable hospital bed, a power press closing together or the callipers of a spot welding machine.

Figure 2-4-19: Crushing, on lowering of hoist ramp. *Source: RMS.*

Figure 2-4-20: Impact. *Source: RMS.*

Drawing-in

When a belt runs round a roller an 'in-running nip' is created between the moving parts, in the direction of travel of the belt. This inward movement draws in any part of the body presented to it. Examples of drawing-in hazards are chain drives of a fork lift truck lifting mast, V-belts on the drive from a motor to the drum of a cement mixer or the spindle of a drill, meshing gears and conveyors.

Figure 2-4-21: Drawing-in. *Source: RMS.*

Figure 2-4-22: Ejection. *Source: RMS.*

Ejection

When pieces of the material being worked on or components of the machinery are thrown or fired out of the equipment during operation, they represent an ejection hazard. Ejection hazards include parts of a shattered grinding wheel, waste metal turnings, and dust from a grinder/disc saw or a nail from a nail gun.

Figure 2-4-23: Disc saw - ejection. *Source: Water Active, Nov 06.*

Figure 2-4-24: Fluid injection. *Source: RMS.*

Injury by compressed air or high pressure fluid injection

Injection of fluids through the skin may lead to soft tissue injuries similar to crushing. Air entering the blood stream through the skin may be fatal. Examples of high pressure fluid injection hazards include diesel injectors, spray painting, compressed air jets for blast cleaning the outside of a building and a high pressure lance for cutting concrete.

OTHER (NON MECHANICAL) HAZARDS

Machinery may also present other hazards. The nature of the hazard will determine the measures taken to protect people from them.

The various sources of non-mechanical hazards include the following:

- Electricity - shock and burns.
- Hot surfaces/fire.
- Noise and vibration.
- Biological - viral and bacterial.
- High/low temperatures.
- Chemicals that are toxic, irritant, flammable, corrosive, explosive.
- Ionising and non ionising radiation.
- Access - slips, trips and falls; obstructions and projections.
- Manual handling.

SUMMARY - MACHINERY HAZARDS

Mechanical		Non -mechanical
Entanglement	e.g. Auger drill, drilling machine	Electricity
Friction and abrasion	e.g. Grinding wheel	Hot surfaces / fire
Cutting	e.g. Sharp edges of circular saw	Noise
Shear	e.g. Scissor lift mechanism	Vibration
Stabbing and Puncture	e.g. Nail gun	Noise / vibration
Impact	e.g. Moving arm of an excavator	Chemicals
Crushing	e.g. Platform of a hoist, ram of a forge hammer	Radiation
Drawing in	e.g. Conveyor belt	Access
Injection	e.g. High pressure hydraulic oil system	Manual handling
Ejection	e.g. Grinding wheel - sparks	Extremes of temperature

Figure 2-4-25: Summary - machinery hazards. *Source: RMS.*

Hazards presented by a range of equipment

OFFICE MACHINERY

Photocopier

Hazards are drawing-in, hot surfaces, fumes, toner dust, electrical, manual handling, noise and glare. These hazards are more likely to be encountered by people who carry out unauthorised maintenance work

Document shredder

The main hazards are drawing-in, cutting or crushing, also cuts from paper handling and electrical dangers. Although these machines are well designed and, therefore guarding is adequate, care has to be taken to ensure that loose clothing such as ties and scarves do not get caught in the blades. If the equipment is fitted with an interlock, there should be regular inspections to ensure that the device has not moved out of adjustment or has been overridden. Unauthorised electrical repairs should not be carried out.

Figure 2-4-26: Abrasive wheel (grinder). *Source: RMS.*

Figure 2-4-27: Document shredder. *Source: www.axminster.co.uk.*

MANUFACTURING/MAINTENANCE MACHINERY

Bench-top grinder

Bench-top grinders are typically found in workshops and are suitable for indoor use. Bench-top grinders are used for sharpening of tool bits (drills, chisels and blades), shaping steel, and de-burring cut steel components. Hazards include friction and abrasion from contact with the moving abrasive wheel, entanglement, drawing-in and possible ejections when parts of the wheel or work piece break and sparks are thrown off. Other hazards are electricity, heat and noise.

Pedestal drill

Hazards in setting up the equipment include failure to remove the chuck-key (which will be ejected if the equipment is stated) and failure to secure the guard to drive pulleys.

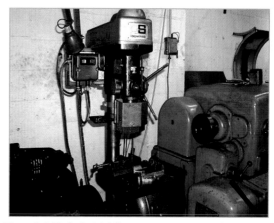

Figure 2-4-28: Pedestal drill. *Source: RMS.*

Hazards when the equipment is in use include entanglement, puncture and flying waste metal (swarf).

AGRICULTURAL/HORTICULTURAL MACHINERY

Cylinder mower

Hazards are:

- Contact with revolving blades.
- Potential for the machine to overturn when on inclines.
- Noise and vibration.
- Collision with road traffic or pedestrians.
- Manual handling.
- Combustion products from the petrol engine.
- Dust.
- Possibility of being struck by stones ejected from the machine.
- Exposure to sun.
- Attacks by insects.
- Fire or explosion associated with flammable fuel.

Figure 2-4-29: Brushcutter. *Source: www.kawasaki.co.uk.*

Petrol-driven strimmer/brush-cutter

Hazards are:

- Contact with the moving parts of the strimmer.
- Noise and vibration.
- Possibility of fire or explosion.
- Exposure to extreme weather conditions.
- Manual handling.
- Slips, trips and falls.
- Possibility of being struck by traffic.
- Struck by flying stones and fragments.

- Exposure to combustion products from the petrol engine.
- Struck by parts of the strimmer material broken off in the operation.

Chain-saw

Despite safety improvements, chainsaws can be dangerous, and injuries can arise from their use. The most common accident arises from "kickback", when a chain tooth at the upper quadrant of the guide bar tip cuts into wood without cutting through it. The chain cannot continue moving, and the bar is driven in an upward arc toward the operator. Kickback can result in serious injuries or death. Another dangerous situation occurs when heavy timber begins to fall or shift when a cut is nearly complete - the chainsaw operator can be trapped or crushed. Injury can also result if the chain breaks during operation due to poor maintenance or attempting to cut inappropriate materials.

In addition to the cutting hazard presented by this equipment, operation of chainsaws presents vibration and noise hazards. The equipment is often powered by a petrol motor which presents a fire hazard and exposure to combustion products from the exhaust. In addition, parts of the motor may get hot presenting a risk of burning to the skin of the operator and use of the equipment may cause the operator to take up awkward postures. Operation of the equipment may expose the user to other secondary hazards such as work at height, slips trips and falls, manual handling hazards, cuts and splinters.

RETAIL MACHINERY

Compactor

Compactors are used to reduce waste volume for transport and disposal. They can commonly be found in supermarkets and other workplaces where high volumes of packaging are used, such as food manufacture.

Mechanical hazards include crushing and impact injuries. Non-mechanical hazards include fumes, noxious substances (possibly biological hazards created by the presence of vermin) and manual handling issues.

Figure 2-4-30: Compactor.   *Source: RMS.*

Checkout conveyor system

Hazards include trapping and drawing-in between the rollers and belt, also crushing between the load and conveyor. Ergonomic hazards due to the working position of the operator and frequent repetitive actions may also be present.

CONSTRUCTION SITE MACHINERY

Cement mixer

Cement mixers are portable construction plant used for mixing a variety of aggregates and cement.

Hazards are:

- Exposure to fumes from petrol.
- Electricity, particularly as water is used in the mixing process.
- Risk of fire if fuel source is diesel or petrol.
- Slips and trips from spilt materials.

- Shovels and trowels caught in the mixer blades.
- Manual handling when loading.
- Exposure to cement dusts and wet cement.
- Entanglement risks from the rotating drum and drive shaft.

Figure 2-4-31: Cement mixer.   *Source: RMS.*

Figure 2-4-32: Bench cross-cut circular saw.   *Source: RMS.*

Bench-mounted circular saw

Cutting is the main hazard; together with electricity, noise, sawdust, splinters and musculo-skeletal disorders related to posture and materials handling.

4.4 - Control measure for reducing risks from machinery hazards

MACHINERY GUARDING

Objective of machinery guarding

- To prevent workpeople from coming into contact with dangerous parts of machinery.
- To prevent physical injury from power driven and manually operated machines.
- To enable machines to be operated safely without interference with production.

PUWER Regulation 11 - Dangerous parts of machinery

(1) Every employer shall ensure that measures are taken in accordance with paragraph (2) which are effective:

    (a) To prevent access to any dangerous part of machinery or to any rotating stock-bar; or

    (b) To stop the movement of any dangerous part of machinery or rotating stock-bar before any part of a person enters a danger zone.

(2) The measures required by paragraph (1) shall consist of:

    (a) The provision of fixed guards enclosing every dangerous part or rotating stock-bar where and to the extent that it is practicable to do so, but where or to the extent that it is not, then

    (b) The provision of other guards or protection devices where and to the extent that it is practicable to do so, but where or to the extent that it is not, then

    (c) The provision of jigs, holders, push-sticks or similar protection appliances used in conjunction with the machinery where and to the extent that it is practicable to do so, and

    (d) The provision of information, instruction, training and supervision as is necessary.

(3) All guards and protection devices provided under sub-paragraphs (a) or (b) of paragraph (2) shall:

    (a) Be suitable for the purpose for which they are provided.

    (b) Be of good construction, sound material and adequate strength.

    (c) Be maintained in an efficient state, in efficient working order and in good repair.

    (d) Not give rise to any increased risk to health or safety.

    (e) Not be easily bypassed or disabled.

    (f) Be situated at sufficient distance from the danger zone.

    (g) Not unduly restrict the view of the operating cycle of the machinery, where such a view is necessary.

    (h) Be so constructed or adapted that they allow operations necessary to fit or replace parts and for maintenance work, restricting access so that it is allowed only to the area where the work is to be carried out and, if possible, without having to dismantle the guard or protection device.

(4) All protection appliances provided under sub-paragraph c) of paragraph (2) shall comply with sub-paragraphs (a) to (d) and (g) of paragraph (3).

(5) In this regulation - "danger zone" means any zone in or around machinery in which a person is exposed to a risk to health or safety from contact with a dangerous part of machinery or a rotating stock-bar; "stock-bar" means any part of a stock-bar which projects beyond the headstock of a lathe.

- Regulation 11(2) gives the measures that an employer should take to fulfil the duty under regulation 11(1) a combination of measures may be necessary to satisfy regulation 11. When deciding on the appropriate level of safeguarding, risk assessment criteria (likelihood of injury, potential severity of injury, numbers at risk) need to be considered both in relation to the normal operation of the machinery and other operations such as maintenance, repair, setting, tuning, adjustment etc.

- Regulation 11(3) (c) applies to the maintenance of guards and protection devices and will include those which are not attached to the machine itself, e.g. perimeter fences.

The principles, merits and limitations of protection methods

HIERARCHY OF MEASURES FOR DANGEROUS PARTS OF MACHINERY

- Prevent access to dangerous parts by means of *F*ixed guard (preferably fully enclosing).
- When the above is not practicable protect by other guards (*I*nterlock, *A*utomatic) or safety devices (e.g. *T*rip device).
- When the above is not practicable protect by using safety appliances (e.g. push stick or jig).

- The various guards and safety devices can be summarised as follows:

  F ixed

  I nterlock

  A utomatic (including self-closing)

  T rip devices

FIXED GUARDS

A fixed guard/fence must be fitted such that it cannot be removed other than by the use of specialist tools which are not available to operators of the equipment.

A fixed guard may be designed to enable access by authorised personnel for maintenance or inspection, but only when the dangerous parts of the machine have been isolated.

A common example of a fixed guard is shown *(see figure ref 2-4-34)*. Not all fixed guards are of solid construction, some are made of mesh.

The holes in a mesh guard are of sufficient size to allow air circulation to cool the drive belt, but small enough to prevent the finger of the hand from penetrating the mesh and result in injury from the belt.

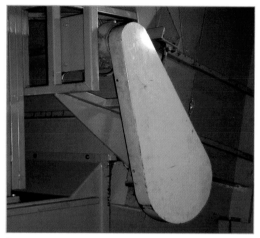

Figure 2-4-33: Total enclosure fixed guard.   *Source: RMS.*

Distance (fixed) guard

Fixed guards do not always completely cover the danger point but place it out of normal reach. The larger the opening (to feed in material) the greater must be the distance from the opening to the danger point. A tree shredding machine uses a fixed distance guard design to prevent operators reaching the dangerous part of a machine when in use.

Figure 2-4-34: Fixed guard - panel removed.   *Source: RMS.*

Figure 2-4-35: Fixed guard over fan - mesh too big. *Source: RMS.*

Merits of fixed guards

- Create a physical barrier.
- Require a tool to remove.
- May not protect against non-mechanical hazards such as dust/fluids which may be ejected.
- No moving parts - therefore they require very little maintenance.

Limitations of fixed guards

- Do not disconnect power when not in place, therefore machine can still be operated without guard.
- May cause problems with visibility for inspection.
- If enclosed, may create problems with heat which, in turn, can increase the risk of explosion.

INTERLOCKING GUARDS

An interlocking guard is similar to a fixed guard, but has a movable (usually hinged) part, so connected to the machine controls that if the movable part is in the open/lifted position the dangerous moving part at the work point cannot operate. This can be arranged so that the action of closing the guard activates the working part (to speed up work efficiently), e.g. the front panel of a photocopier. Interlocked guards are useful if operators need regular access to the danger area.

Everyday examples of interlocking guards are those found on domestic equipment such as dish washers, microwave cookers and automatic washing machines.

In the photograph opposite, the electrical interlock is positioned halfway down the right hand side of this panel.

The panel is made from transparent material to allow easy visual checks of the products that are manufactured by this equipment.

Merits of interlocking guards

- Connected to power source, therefore machine cannot be operated with guard open.
- Allow regular access.

Limitations of interlocking guards

- Have moving parts therefore need regular maintenance.
- Can be over-ridden.

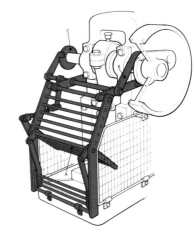

Figure 2-4-36: Interlocking guard. *Source: RMS.*

- If interlock is in the form of a gate, a person can step inside and close gate behind them (someone else could re-activate machine).
- Dangerous parts of machinery may not stop immediately the guard is opened. A delay timer or brake might need to be fitted as well, e.g. the drum on a spin drier does not stop instantly, and therefore a delay is fitted to prevent the door being opened until the drum is stationary.

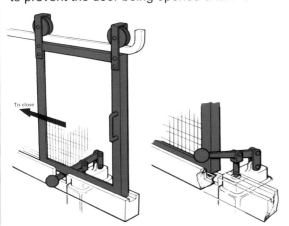

Figure 2-4-37: Open and closed interlock guard. *Source: BS EN ISO 12100.*

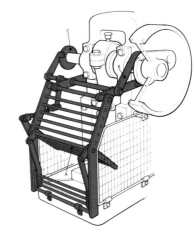

Figure 2-4-38: Power press - interlock guard. *Source: BS EN ISO 12100.*

Automatic guard

A guard which operates as the machine goes through its cycle. In some cases it physically moves the operator away from danger and is therefore only suitable for slow cycling equipment, e.g. on a guillotine or large panel press.

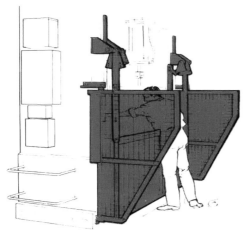

Figure 2-4-39: Automatic guard for a power press.

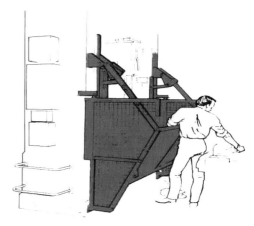

Source: BS EN ISO 12100.

Merits of automatic guards

- Guard becomes effective as part of the normal cycle of the equipment.
- Does not have to rely on human intervention.

Limitations of automatic guards

- Usually restricted to slow cycling machinery.

SELF-CLOSING GUARD

These are guards which close themselves over the dangerous parts and prevent accidental access by the operator, but allow entry of the material to the machine in such a way that the material forms part of the guarding arrangement itself. For example, a hand held circular saw.

Merits of self-closing guards

■ Close over the dangerous parts to provide protection without the need of the operator to do anything.

Limitations of adjustable guards

■ May obscure visibility when in use.
■ Are vulnerable to damage in the operation of the equipment.

Figure 2-4-40: Self adjusting (fixed) guard.   *Source: RMS.*

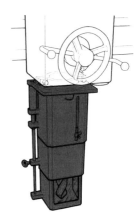

Figure 2-4-41: Adjustable (fixed) guard. *Source: BS EN ISO 12100.*

ADJUSTABLE GUARD

A fixed guard which incorporates an adjustable element (which remains fixed for the duration of a particular operation).

Merits of adjustable guards

■ Can be adjusted by operator to provide protection.

Limitations of adjustable guards

■ Are reliant on the operator to adjust to the correct position.
■ May obscure visibility when in use.

TWO-HAND CONTROL (2HC) DEVICE

They provide a level of protection where other methods are not practicable, helping to ensure the operator's hands remain outside the danger area. A two-hand control is a device that requires both hands to operate it, the controls must be operated simultaneously and help to assure that both hands are kept away from the dangerous parts.

'2HC' devices protect only the operator and then, only provided the assistance of a colleague is not solicited to activate one control. Everyday examples of two hand controls are a hedge trimmer and garment press.

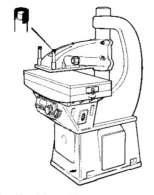

Figure 2-4-42: Two-Hand Control Device. *Source: BS EN ISO 12100.*

Figure 2-4-43: Hold-to-run device on hedge trimmer.   *Source: RMS.*

Merits of two hand control devices

■ Ensures both of the operator's hands are out of danger area when the machine is operated.

Limitations of two hand control devices

■ Only protects the operator from harm.
■ May limit speed of operation with delays if controls are not pressed at exactly same time.

HOLD-TO-RUN

The principle of this device is that the operator has to "hold" a button, stick or foot pedal to "run" a piece of equipment. A common application of this device is on a domestic lawn mower. It is essential that the hold-to-run device, which when released stops the machine, is located far enough away from the danger area to prevent the operator getting access to the moving parts without releasing it.

Merits of hold-to-run devices

- Ensures the operator is out of the danger area when the machine is operated.
- Provides distance between operator and hazard.

Limitations of hold-to-run devices

- Only protects the operator from harm.
- There may be residual movement of dangerous parts once the device has been released.

SENSITIVE PROTECTIVE EQUIPMENT

Sensitive protective equipment (sometimes called a trip device) comprises a sensitive rod, cable or other mechanism, which causes the device to activate a further mechanism which either stops or reverses the machine. It is important to note that this is not classed as a guard. A guard is something that physically prevents access to the hazard whereas sensitive protective equipment detects the person in the danger zone and responds to this, e.g. a pressure sensitive mat.

Merits of sensitive protective equipment

- Can be used as an additional risk control measure.
- Can minimise the severity of injury.

Limitations of sensitive protective equipment

- Can be over-ridden.
- May not prevent harm from occurring.

- May cause production delays and increase stress in users with false 'trips'.

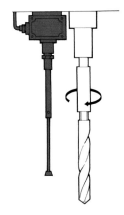

Figure 2-4-44: Trip device. *Source: BS EN ISO 12100.*

Figure 2-4-45: Trip device on radial drill. *Source: RMS.*

JIGS, HOLDERS AND PUSH-STICKS

When the methods of safeguarding mentioned above are not practicable then protection appliances such as jigs, holders and push-sticks must be provided. They will help to keep the operator's hands at a safe distance from the danger area. There is no physical restraint to prevent the operator from placing their hands in danger.

Figure 2-4-46: Notched push-stick. *Source: http://images.google.co.uk/.*

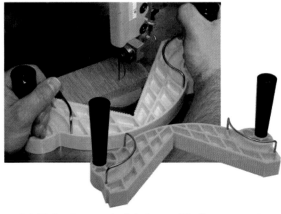

Figure 2-4-47: Band saw push-stick. *Source: http://images.google.co.uk/.*

Merits of protection appliances

■ Provide distance between operator and hazard.
■ Inexpensive and easily replaced if damaged.
■ May be shaped to suit work being carried out.

Limitations of protection appliances

■ Harm may still occur from other non-mechanical hazards.
■ Some designs can be awkward to use and may result in a lack of control.
■ Continuing adjustments have to be made e.g. when using different sizes of wood.
■ Failure of protection appliance (e.g. breaking or kickback) may present additional hazard to operator.

Figure 2-4-48: Fixed guard and push-stick.   *Source: Lincsafe.*

INFORMATION, INSTRUCTION, TRAINING AND SUPERVISION

PUWER 1998 requires every employer to ensure that all persons who use work equipment and any of his employees who supervises or manages the use of work equipment have available to them adequate health and safety information and, where appropriate, written instructions and appropriate training pertaining to the use of the work equipment.   This includes information and, where appropriate, written instructions that are comprehensible to those concerned on:

■ The conditions in which and the methods by which the work equipment may be used.
■ Foreseeable abnormal situations and the action to be taken if such a situation were to occur.
■ Any conclusions to be drawn from experience in using the work equipment.

Similarly, PUWER 1998 requires employers to ensure that all persons who use work equipment and any of his employees who supervises or manages work equipment have received training in any risks which such use may entail and precautions to be taken.

It is a requirement of both the HASAWA 1974 and PUWER Regulation 11 that supervision be provided as necessary. This will require extra supervision for new, inexperienced or less capable users of equipment.

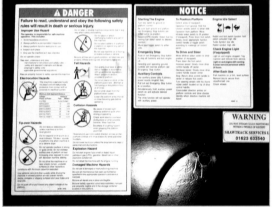

Figure 2-4-49: Information and instruction.   *Source: RMS.*

Figure 2-4-50: PPE and supervision.   *Source: RMS.*

Merits

■ Easy to reach a wide audience on a variety of subjects.
■ Can be applied immediately and adapted to suit specific needs of the user.

Limitations

■ Supervision may not prevent contact with the hazard.
■ Relies on the person concerned to follow the instruction.
■ May be misunderstood.
■ Supervision is needed to a sufficient degree to ensure health and safety, a high degree of supervision may be required for some equipment.

Application of protection methods to a range of equipment

To meet the requirements of the syllabus, protection methods are discussed in this section.

Specific *hazards* of the equipment listed are covered in *section 4.3 - machinery hazards.*

OFFICE MACHINERY

Photocopier

Because access to the moving parts by the user are likely to be required to remove paper, jams the use of interlocking guard is appropriate for these access panels. Fixed guards may also protect some dangerous parts inside the panels, such as heating elements.

Appropriate additional precautions are to avoid loose clothing i.e. ties, signage for hot components, well ventilated / suitable extraction, gloves, training in good practice when removing paper jams etc.

Shredder

Appropriate precautions are the use of interlocking guards that identify the removal of the shredding element of the equipment from the shredded paper collection area. Where the shredder has a large opening to the moving parts of the shredder to feed material in, it may be necessary to protect this with sensitive protective equipment that will detect the presence of the user's hand or clothing.

MANUFACTURING/MAINTENANCE MACHINERY

Bench grinder

Control measures include an adjustable fixed guard that is fitted over as much of the grinding wheel as is practicable, a workpiece rest, trained and competent users, high impact resistant goggles, respiratory protective equipment (depending on task) and personal hearing protection.

Pedestal drill

Appropriate precautions for pre-use are:

- Drive pulley entanglement prevented by isolation from power when adjusting speeds.
- Check that chuck key is removed before use.

Appropriate precautions during use are:

- Interlocking guard to cover the drive pulley and belts.
- Adjustable (fixed) guard provided round the chuck and drill bit, face shield/goggles for protection from flying metal pieces from the cutting process (swarf).
- Prevent entanglement - close fitting clothing, control of long hair and removal of jewellery.
- Puncture prevented by jigs or clamping devices.

Chain-saw

The equipment should have a hold to run device and sensitive protection equipment should be fitted in front of the operator's hand that will trip and stop operation if the chain-saw 'kicks-back'. The risks associated with chain-saw use mean that protective clothing and hearing protectors should be worn while operating them. In order to limit the effects of vibration careful selection of equipment with low vibration output is important. Training of operators is a critical element of the control strategy for use of this equipment.

AGRICULTURAL/HORTICULTURAL MACHINERY

Cylinder mower

Appropriate precautions are:

- Provision of fixed guards around any drive mechanisms, for example chains or shafts.
- Fitting of fixed guards to enclose as much of the blades as is practicable.
- Provision of personal protective equipment (e.g. ear defenders, eye protection and high visibility clothing).
- Coning off areas in close proximity to moving traffic.
- Training users in the operation of the machine on sloping ground and on re-fuelling procedures.

Petrol-driven strimmer/brush-cutter

Appropriate precautions are:

- Provision of fixed guards around any drive mechanisms and motor/engine.
- Fixed guards to enclose as much of the strimmer material or blade as is practicable.
- Personal protective equipment (eye and hearing protection).
- Appropriate storage of petrol.
- Regular maintenance by authorised people, including changing of cutters.

RETAIL MACHINERY

Compactor

Appropriate precautions are the provision of fixed guards around the sides and back of the compactor, where no access is normally required. Interlocked guards should be fitted to the opening where the material is placed in the compactor and access areas for removal. Good housekeeping around the compactor is essential to avoid slips, trips and falls.

Checkout conveyor system

Appropriate precautions are fixed guards around drive mechanisms, interlocked guards on panels that may need to be opened to remove material that has got stuck in the conveyor and sensitive protection equipment (trip devices) that identify items approaching the drawing-in point. The sides of the conveyor equipment should be sufficiently close to the belt to prevent abrasion contact and built up to prevent the fall of items.

CONSTRUCTION MACHINERY

Cement mixer

Fixed guards must be provided around drive mechanisms. Motor covers should be closed when in use. Operators should be warned of the dangers of shovels and trowels becoming caught in the mixer blades when charging. Electrical hazards are reduced by the use of low voltage (110volts) power (or residual current circuit breaker if 240volt supply), with suitable heavy duty protected cable. If petrol or diesel driven, equipment should be allowed to cool (e.g. exhaust system) before refuelling, no smoking should be observed. Other controls include manual handling training, good housekeeping of spilt materials, and avoidance of exposure to dust and fume.

Bench-mounted circular saw

Appropriate precautions are fixed, adjustable and/or self-adjusting guards, jigs, holders, push-sticks and personal protective equipment (eye, respiratory and hearing protection).

Basic requirements for guards and safety devices

PUWER REGULATION 11 PARAGRAPH 3 - EFFECTIVE GUARDS AND DEVICES

All guards and protection devices provided under sub-paragraphs (a) or (b) of paragraph (2) shall:

(a) *Be **suitable** for the purpose for which they are provided.*

(b) *Be of **good construction**, sound material and adequate strength.*

(c) *Be **maintained** in an efficient state, in efficient working order and in good repair.*

(d) *Not give rise to any increased risk to health or safety.*

(e) *Not be **easily bypassed** or disabled.*

(f) *Be situated at **sufficient distance** from the danger zone.*

(g) *Not unduly **restrict the view** of the operating cycle of the machinery, where such a view is necessary.*

(h) *Be so constructed or adapted that they allow operations necessary to fit or replace parts and for maintenance work, restricting access so that it is allowed only to the area where the work is to be carried out and, if possible, without having to dismantle the guard or protection device.*

COMPATIBLILITY WITH PROCESS

Compatibility with the material being processed - this is particularly important in the food processing industry where the guard material should not constitute a source of contamination of the product. Its ability to maintain its physical and mechanical properties after coming into contact with potential contaminants such as cutting fluids used in machining operations or cleaning and sterilising agents used in food processing machinery is also very important. In selecting an appropriate safeguard for a particular type of machinery or danger area, it should be borne in mind that a fixed guard is simple, and should be used where access to the danger area is not required during operation of the machinery or for cleaning, setting or other activities. As the need for access arises and increases in frequency, the importance of safety procedures for removal of a fixed guard increases until the frequency is such that interlocking should be used.

ADEQUATE STRENGTH

Guard mounting should be compatible with the strength and duty of the guard. In selecting the material to be used for the construction of a guard, consideration should be given to the following:

- Its ability to withstand the force of ejection of parts of the machinery or material being processed, where this is a foreseeable danger.
- Its ability to provide protection against hazards identified. In many cases, the guard may fulfil a combination of functions such as prevention of access and containment of hazards. This may apply where the hazards include ejected particles, liquids, dust, fumes, radiation, noise, etc. and one or more of these considerations may govern the selection of guard materials.

MAINTAINED

All guards must be maintained in effective order to perform their function. This will require a planned approach to checks on guards and work such as checking the security of fixed guards.

ALLOW FOR MAINTENANCE WITHOUT REMOVAL

Its weight and size are factors to be considered in relation to the need to remove and replace it for routine maintenance. If a guard has to be removed in order to carry out maintenance work, it increases the risks for maintenance workers and also increases the chances that the guard will not be replaced. This is especially the case if a piece of equipment has a history of regular break down.

NOT INCREASE RISK OR RESTRICT VIEW

Any guard selected should not itself present a hazard such as trapping or shear points, rough or sharp edges or other hazards likely to cause injury.

Power operated guards should be designed and constructed so that a hazard is not created or restrict the view of the process or machine by the user.

NOT EASILY BY-PASSED

Guards or their components must not be easily by-passed, in particular by operators. There is always a temptation to do so when under production or similar pressures. When positioning such protective devices as interlock switches; it is best to locate them away from the operator and preferably within the guard.

This page is intentionally blank

UNIT NGC2

CONTROLLING WORKPLACE HAZARDS

Electrical safety

Learning outcomes

On completion of this element, candidates should be able to demonstrate understanding of the content through the application of knowledge to familiar and unfamiliar situations. In particular they should be able to:

5.1   Outline the principles, hazards and risks associated with the use of electricity in the workplace.

5.2   Outline the control measures that should be taken when working with electrical systems or using electrical equipment in normal workplace conditions.

Content

Sources of reference

BS7671: 2008 IEE Wiring Regulations 17th Edition ISBN 978-0-86341-844-0

Electricity at Work - Safe Working Practices (HSG85), HSE Books ISBN 0-7176-2164-2

Maintaining Portable and Transportable Electrical Equipment (HSG107), HSE Books ISBN 0-7176-2805-1

Guidance on Safe Isolation procedures: http://www.select.org.uk/downloads/publications/Select%20-%20Safe%20Isolation%20Procedures.pdf

Relevant statutory provisions

The Electricity at Work Regulations (EWR) 1989

5.1 - Risks associated with electricity

Principles of electricity

Electricity is a facility that we have all come to take for granted, whether for lighting, heating, as a source of motive power or as the driving force behind the computer. Used properly it can be of great benefit to us, but misused it can be very dangerous and often fatal.

Electricity is used in most industries, offices and homes and our modern society could now not easily function without it. Despite its convenience to the user, it has a major danger. The normal senses of sight, hearing and smell will not detect electricity. Making contact with exposed conductors at the domestic supply voltage, 230V can be lethal.

Unlike many other workplace accidents, the actual number of electrical notifiable accidents is small. However, with a reported 10-20 fatalities each year, the severity is high. Accidents are often caused by complacency, not just by the normally assumed ignorance. It must be recognised by everyone working with electricity that over half of all electrical fatal accidents are to skilled/competent persons.

In order to avoid the causes of electric injury, it is necessary to understand the basic principles of electricity, what it does to the body and what controls are necessary.

BASIC CIRCUITRY

The flow of electrons through a conductor is known as a current. Electric current flows due to differences in electrical "pressure" (or potential difference as it is often known), just as water flows through a pipe because of the pressure behind it.

Differences in electrical potential are measured in volts. In some systems the current flows continually in the same direction. This is known as direct current (DC). However the current may also constantly reverse its direction of flow. This is known as alternating current (AC). Most public electricity supplies are AC.

The UK system reverses its direction 50 times per second and it is said to have a frequency of 50 cycles per second or 50 Hertz (50Hz). DC is little used in standard distribution systems but is sometimes used in industry for specialist applications. Although there are slight differences in the effects under fault and shock conditions between AC and DC it is a safe approach to apply the same rules of safety for the treatment and prevention of electric shock.

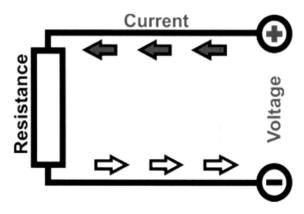

Figure 2-5-1: A basic electrical circuit.   Source: RMS.

As a current passes round a circuit under the action of an applied voltage it is impeded in its flow. This may be due to the presence in the circuit of resistance, inductance or capacitance, the combined effect of which is called impedance and is measured in ohms.

RELATIONSHIP BETWEEN VOLTAGE, CURRENT AND RESISTANCE

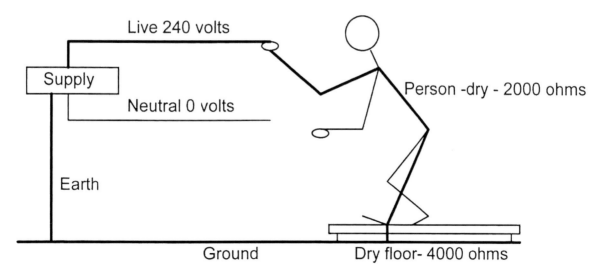

Figure 2-5-2: An electric circuit under fault conditions showing resistances in the path of a fault current.   Source: R. Gilmour.

There is a simple relationship between electrical pressure (Volts), current (measured in Amperes or milliamperes) and resistance (measured in Ohms) represented by Ohm's Law:

Voltage **(V)** = current **(I)** multiplied by the circuit resistance **(R).** $V = I \times R$ or $I = \dfrac{V}{R}$

Hence, given any two values the third can be calculated. Also, if one value changes the other two values will change accordingly. This basic electrical equation can be used to calculate the current that flows in a circuit of a given resistance.

This will need to be done to determine, for example, the fuse or cable rating needed for a particular circuit. Similarly, the current that will flow through a person who touches a live conductor can be calculated.

By Ohm's law:

Current = $\dfrac{\text{Voltage}}{\text{Resistance}}$ or $I = \dfrac{V}{R}$

Resistance in a circuit is dependent on many factors. Most metals, particularly precious metals (silver, gold and platinum), allow current to pass very easily. These have a low resistance and are used as conductors. Other materials such as plastics, rubber and textiles have a high resistance and are used as insulators.

If the person is on a dry concrete floor, resistance in the body will only be about 2,000 Ohms and the resistance in the floor about 4,000 Ohms, therefore the combined resistance would be 6,000 Ohms. Presuming the person is in contact with a live electrical supply at 230 Volts the current flowing through the person in this fault condition can be calculated.

$I = \dfrac{V}{R} = \dfrac{230 \text{ Volts}}{2,000 + 4,000 \text{ Ohms}} = 0.038$ Amperes

The current flowing through the operator will then be about 0.04 Amperes or 40mA (40 milliAmperes). This could result in a fatal shock.

Risks of electricity

ELECTRIC SHOCK AND ITS EFFECT ON THE BODY

Electric shock results from the current flowing through the body interfering with muscle and central nervous system functions. (For further details of the effects, see section "Current".)

Other consequences of contact with electricity are:

- ■ *Electrical burns*   -   resulting from the heating effect of the current which burns the body tissue.
- ■ *Electrical fires*   -   caused by overheating or arcing apparatus in contact with a fuel.
- ■ *Explosions*   -   from sparks in a flammable atmosphere.
- ■ *Secondary injuries*   -   falling from a ladder.

Causes of electric shock

Direct shock. Contact with a charged or energised conductor that is intended to be so charged or energised. In these circumstances the installation is operating in its normal or proper condition.

Indirect shock. Contact with a conductor or exposed conductive parts e.g. casing of the apparatus that is normally safe to touch but which, under fault conditions, could become dangerously live.

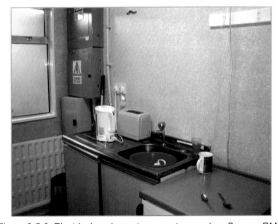

Figure 2-5-3: Electrical equipment near water supply. *Source: RMS.*   Figure 2-5-4: Contact with high voltage buried cable. *Source: RMS.*

Common causes of electric shock

- ■ Work on electrical circuits by unqualified persons.
- ■ Work on live circuits.
- ■ Replacement of fuses and light bulbs on supposedly dead circuits.
- ■ Working on de-energised circuits that could accidentally be re-energised.
- ■ Using electrical equipment in a wet environment.

FACTORS INFLUENCING SEVERITY

The severity of electric shock or the amount of current which flows for a given voltage will depend on the frequency of the supply voltage, on the level of the voltage which is applied and on the state of the point of contact with the body, particularly the moisture condition.

Current

The current that flows through the body provides the energy to do the harm, the more current flowing the more harm likely to be done. The body can tolerate small levels of current flowing through it, but as the level increases the current is able to have a greater effect on the body, in particular the muscles. As such, low currents tend to influence only the smaller muscles and the larger muscles need a larger current to influence them. The effects on the muscle will be to cause it to spasm, therefore small muscles in the hand may contract causing the hand to close or at higher current flow larger muscles in the chest may contract restricting breathing. When the heart is affected by the current flow its normal beat may be disrupted and it attempts to beat in a discordant manner; this effect is known as fibrillation. It should be remembered that the level of current necessary to cause harm to the body is much less than that required to run most equipment and is in mA rather than Amperes.

Effects of current flowing in the human body

Current (mA)	Length of time	Likely effects [mA = milliAmperes mS = milliseconds]
0-1	Not critical	Threshold of feeling. Undetected by person.
1-15	Not critical	Threshold of cramp. Independent loosening of the hands no longer possible.
15-30	Minutes	Cramp-like pulling together of the arms, breathing difficult. Limit of tolerance
30-50	Seconds to minutes	Strong cramp-like effects, loss of consciousness due to restricted breathing. Longer time may lead to fibrillation.
50-500	Less than one heart period (70 mS)	No fibrillation. Strong shock effects.
	Greater than one heart period	Fibrillation. Loss of consciousness. Burn marks.
Over 500	Less than one heart period	Fibrillation. Loss of consciousness. Burn marks.

Figure 2-5-5: Effects of current flowing in the human body.   Source: RMS.

Voltage

Voltage is the driving force behind the flow of electricity, somewhat like pressure in a water pipe. The correct name for this term is potential difference as a voltage is the measure of the difference in electrical energy between two points. Any electrical charge that is free to move about will move from the higher energy to the lower one, taking a quantity of that energy difference with it.

Frequency

The frequency of current flow in an alternating current supply, such as the mains supply in an office block, operates at 50 cycles per second in the UK. This frequency is close to that of the heart when functioning normally. It can have the effect of disrupting the operation of the heart causing it to beat in a discordant manner, to fibrillate.

Duration

For an electric shock to have an effect a person needs to be in contact with the current for sufficient time. At low current levels the body tolerates the current so the time is not material, however at higher current levels, e.g. 50mA, the person has to remain in contact for sufficient time to affect the heart, in the order of milliseconds. In general, the longer a person is in contact with the current the more harm may be caused.

Resistance

The amount of resistance in a circuit influences the amount of current that is allowed to flow, as explained above by Ohm's law. It is possible for a person to be in contact with a circuit and to present sufficiently high resistance that very little current is allowed to flow through their body. The example shown above illustrates this. It should be noted that the level of current is also dependent on the voltage; at high voltages an enormous amount of resistance is needed to ensure current flow will remain at a safe level. The human body contributes part of the resistance of a circuit, the amount it contributes depends on the current path taken and other factors such as personal chemical make-up (a large portion of the body is water), dryness and thickness of skin, and any clothing that is being worn, such as shoes and gloves.

Current path

The effect of an electric shock on a body is particularly dependent on the current path through the body. Current has to flow through from one point to another as part of a circuit. If the flow was between two points on a finger the effect on the body would be concentrated between the two points. If the current path is between one hand and another across the chest this means the flow will pass through major parts of the body, such as the heart, and may have a specific effect on it.

In a similar way a contact between hand and foot (feet) can have serious effects on a great many parts of the body, including the heart. These latter current paths tend to be the ones leading to fatal injuries. Although many people may experience shock from 230 volts this may not be fatal if they were, for example, standing on or wearing some insulating material. This may be a matter of fortune and as a rule for protection should not be relied on.

ELECTRICAL BURNS

Direct

There will be a heating effect along the route taken by electric current as it passes through body tissue. Whilst there are likely to be burn marks on the skin at the point of contact there may also be a deep seated burning within the body which is painful and slow to heal. As the outer layer of skin is burnt the resistance decreases and so the current will increase. The current flowing through the body can cause major injury to internal organs and bone marrow as it passes through them.

Indirect

If while working on live equipment the system is short-circuited by, for example, an un-insulated spanner touching live and neutral this will result in a large and sudden current flow through the spanner. This current will cause the spanner to melt and may throw molten metal out from the points of contact. When this molten metal contacts the parts of a person in the vicinity of the spanner, for example the hands or face, serious burns can take place as the molten metal hits and sticks to the person. With high voltages and the very low resistance of the spanner very large currents can flow. This rapid discharge of energy that follows contact with high voltages not only causes the rapid melting of the spanner but does so with such violent force that the molten particles of metal are thrown off with huge velocity.

It is not necessary to have high voltages to melt a spanner in this way - it can also occur with batteries with sufficient stored energy, such as those on a fork lift truck. There are many experiences of people suffering injury in this way when servicing lift truck batteries as a spanner falls out of their overall top pocket.

ELECTRICAL FIRES

Common causes

Much electrical equipment generates heat or produces sparks and this equipment should not be placed where this could lead to the uncontrolled ignition of any substance.

The principal causes of electrical fires are:

■ Wiring with defects such as insulation failure due to age or poor maintenance.
■ Overheating of cables or other electrical equipment through overloading with currents above their design capacity.
■ Incorrect fuse rating.
■ Poor connections due to lack of maintenance or unskilled personnel.

Electrical equipment may itself explode or arc violently and it may also act as a source of ignition of flammable vapours, gases, liquids or dust through electric sparks, arcs or high surface temperatures of equipment. Other causes are heat created by poorly maintained or defective motors, heaters and lighting.

Figure 2-5-6: Used coiled up - risk of overheating. *Source: RMS.*

Figure 2-5-7: Max current capacity exceeded. *Source: RMS.*

Figure 2-5-8: Worn cable - risk of electrical fire.   *Source: RMS.*

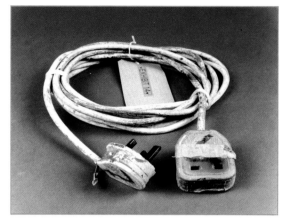

Figure 2-5-9: Evidence of overheating.   *Source: RMS.*

WORKPLACE ELECTRICAL EQUIPMENT INCLUDING PORTABLE ELECTRICAL EQUIPMENT

Conditions and practices likely to lead to accidents

Unsuitable equipment

- Unsuitable apparatus for the duty or the conditions.
- Misuse.
- Failure to follow operating instructions.
- Wrong connection of system - supply phase, neutral or earth reversed.
- Wrong voltage or rating of equipment.

Inadequate maintenance

- Inadequate maintenance of the installation and the equipment.
- Wrong or broken connection to portable apparatus.
- Inadequate earthing.
- Poor maintenance and testing.
- No defect reporting system.

Figure 2-5-10: Hazard - fuse wired out.   *Source: RMS.*

Figure 2-5-11: Continued use of defective equipment.   *Source: RMS.*

Use of defective apparatus

- Faulty cables, notably extension leads.
- Plugs and sockets.
- Damaged plug or socket.
- Protection devices, such as fuses or circuit breaker, incorrect rating, damaged or missing.
- Overloaded leading to damage or over-heating.
- Short circuit leading to damage, overheating or movement.
- Isolation procedures or systems of work wrong.
- Bad circuit connections.

General

- Lack of competence.
- Poor access, lighting and emergency procedures.
- No work planning, e.g. permit-to-work.

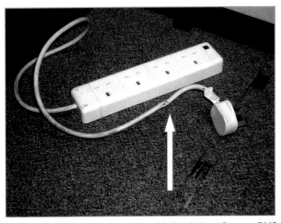

Figure 2-5-12: Hazard - damaged cable insulation. *Source: RMS.*

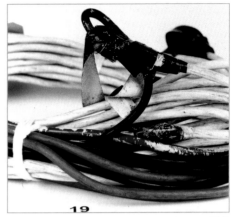

Figure 2-5-13: Hazard - taped joints.   *Source: RMS.*

SECONDARY EFFECTS

These occur where the injury results from the flow of electricity through the body's nerves, muscles and organs and causes abnormal function to occur. Muscular spasm may be severe, particularly if the leg muscles are affected, causing a person to be thrown several metres. Injuries may result from dislocation, impact with surrounding objects or fall from a height. In addition, a tool may be dropped causing such injuries as burns or impact injury to the user or others near by.

High risks associated with electricity

USE OF POORLY MAINTAINED ELECTRICAL EQUIPMENT

Regulation 4 of the Electricity at Work Regulations (EWR) 1989 states:

"All systems shall at all times be of such construction as to prevent, so far as reasonably practicable, such danger". "As may be necessary to prevent danger, all systems shall be maintained so as to prevent, so far as reasonably practicable, such danger".

Figure 2-5-14: Regulation 4 of EWR 1989.   *Source: The Electricity at Work Regulations (EWR) 1989.*

Many deaths and injuries result from poorly maintained electrical equipment and fires started by faulty electrical appliances. Around 1,000 electrical accidents at work are reported to the Health and safety Executive each year, of these, 30 people die of their injuries.

All electrical equipment should be maintained and checked at appropriate intervals (HSE Guidance "INDG236 Maintaining portable electrical equipment in offices and other low risk environments" gives some advice on inspection intervals) to ensure it is safe and in good repair. In particular, managers (and others, such as landlords) responsible for electrical equipment maintenance should ensure:

- Equipment is maintained in a safe condition.
- Information is available to equipment users to ensure safety.
- Safe procedures for inspection and testing are used.
- Records of inspection and testing are maintained.

WORK NEAR OVERHEAD POWER LINES

Contact with live overhead power lines kills a significant number of people and causes serious injuries every year. A high proportion -about one third - of inadvertent line contacts prove fatal. Overhead power lines may be confused with telephone lines, which can lead people not to identify the risk from contact. Lines may be hard to see at night or against a dark or very bright background. Power lines carry electricity at between 230 and 33,000 volts, even contact with a 230 volt line can kill. They are not normally covered in insulation so direct contact can easily be made. Contact can lead to current passing through a person, and the item that contacted the line, on a path to earth. Rubber-soled shoes would not provide protection from current flow and shock. Actual contact with a power line is not necessary to result in electric shock, a close approach to the line conductors may allow an arc to take place. The risk of arcing increases as the line voltage increases.

Many occupations may require workers to perform their job tasks near overhead power lines. Construction workers, truck drivers, tree service workers, mobile equipment operators, agricultural workers, and others find themselves carrying out their work in the vicinity of live overhead power lines. They may not be trained to recognise the dangers of electrocution if their bodies, equipment, tools, work materials, or vehicles come near to an overhead power line.

CONTACT WITH UNDERGROUND POWER CABLES DURING EXCAVATION WORK

Underground power cables are present in most locations that excavations are conducted, in the high street, on construction or re-development sites and even in the country. Their location may be marked, not identified or not known of at all. Their presence is not obvious when conducting a visual site survey and so the likelihood of striking a power cable when excavating, drilling or piling is increased. The results of striking an underground power cable can include shock, electrocution, explosion and burns. As with overhead power lines, any underground service should be treated as live until confirmed dead by a power authority. Maps showing the location of underground power cables need to be taken as an indication of their location not as 'pin-point' accuracy, which means that careful testing needs to take place until indicated power cables are located. Even then some degree of caution needs to be taken in case unmarked power cables are encountered.

WORK ON MAINS ELECTRICAL SUPPLIES (230 VOLT)

Mains electricity supplies can be treated complacently because of their prevalence and their relatively low voltage, however a number of deaths occur each year to people working on live mains electricity supplies. It is never absolutely safe to work on live electrical equipment. There are few circumstances where it is necessary to work live, and this must only be done after it has been determined that it is unreasonable for the work to be done dead. Even if working live can be justified, many precautions are needed to make sure that the risk is reduced 'so far as is reasonably practicable'.

USE OF ELECTRICAL EQUIPMENT IN WET ENVIRONMENTS

Use of electrical equipment in wet conditions increases the risk of harm because the wet conditions increase the conductivity of surrounding surfaces. Where a fault exists on electrical equipment in a wet environment it may not be necessary to make direct contact with it to receive an electric shock, the wet substance may act as a conductor making a circuit between the faulty equipment and the person. These conditions may exist where, for example, a plasterer plasters a wall around a faulty light socket or a pressure water cleaner has a damaged cable lying in the water run-off from the cleaning operation.

5.2 - Control measures

Protection of conductors

Conductors, whether live, neutral or earthed require protection from accidental or deliberate contact, interference, misuse or even abuse. This is often in the form of insulation. *Insulators* are materials that do not readily conduct electricity. Some common insulator materials are glass, plastic, rubber, air, and wood. Where conductors that are insulated are exposed to a higher risk of damage they may be further protected by a metal casing, which provides re-enforcement around the insulation, or ducting which provides a protective location for it to be placed.

CABLES AND LEADS

Insulation appropriate to the environment should be used to give resistance to abrasion, chemicals, heat and impact. The insulation must be in good condition. Flexible, multi-strand cables are required for portable tools and extension leads. Cables must be secured by the outer sheath at their point of entry into the apparatus, including plugs. The individual conductor insulation should not show through the sheath and conductors must not be exposed. Extension leads must be fused.

Temporary wiring should be used in compliance with standards and properly secured, supported and mechanically protected against damage. Taped joints in cables are not allowed and proper line connectors must be used to join cables. Connectors should be kept to a minimum to reduce earth path impedance. Many cables are set up on a temporary basis, but these improvised arrangements can get left for a considerable time. Care should be taken to identify true short term temporary arrangements and those that warrant full longer term arrangements, such as being placed in trunking for better protection.

Attention to cables in offices is particularly important to avoid tripping hazards with phone, computer, calculator and kettle leads growing in number. Conductors across roads or pedestrian ways should be covered to protect them from damage. Where they are to cross a doorway this is usually best done by taking it around the door instead of trailing it across the floor. Overhead cables likely to be hit by vehicles or persons carrying ladders, pipes etc. should be highlighted by the use of appropriate signs.

Regular examination should be made for deterioration, cuts (these are best identified by using the technique of systematic bending of short sections of cable by hand, progressing along the length of the cable). Cuts will be opened by this process revealing the conductor, kinks or bend damage (particularly near to the point of entry into apparatus), exposed conductors, overheat or burn damage, trapping damage, insulation embrittling or corrosion.

Strength and capability of equipment

Regulation 5 of the Electricity at Work Regulations (EWR) 1989 requires:

"No electrical equipment shall be put into use where its strength and capability may be exceeded in such a way as may give rise to danger".

Figure 2-5-15: Regulation 5 of EWR 1989.   Source: The Electricity at Work Regulations (EWR) 1989.

Strength and capability in this context has a wide meaning. This includes the requirement that any electrical equipment needs to be capable of standing normal and fault currents without failure.

In order for equipment to remain safe when subjected to sustained fault conditions it may require the inclusion of protective devices which detect the fault and break the circuit containing the fault.

It is also important to ensure that all electrical equipment is suitable for what it is used for in terms of its strength and capability. For example, if it is to be used for outdoor work on a construction site in conditions that it might get wet, equipment providing protection from the ingress of water must be selected. Many tools are designed and provided for use in a domestic situation and they may not be suitable for use in the more arduous conditions of a construction site, for example, cable entry grips may be more secure and outer protection of cables thicker on equipment designed for construction work.

The British Standard BS 7671, the Institute of Electrical Engineers (IEE) 17th edition requirements, Chapter 13 - 'Fundamental principles for safety' - specifies the following needs. Good workmanship and proper materials shall be used. Construction, installation, inspection, testing and maintenance shall be such as to prevent danger. Equipment shall be suitable for the power demanded and the conditions in which it is installed. Additions and alterations to installations shall comply with regulations. Equipment which requires operation or attention shall be accessible.

The Low Voltage (Safety) Regulations place a duty on the supplier of equipment to ensure that equipment using between 50 and 100 volts ac is safe. Construction, including flexible cables and cords, must be to European Union (EU) accepted good engineering practice standards. The Regulations are deemed satisfied if the equipment bears a recognised standard mark, certificate or other acceptable authorisation. Supply of unsafe equipment or components is prohibited.

Advantages and limitations of protective systems

FUSES

This is a device designed to automatically cut off the power supply to a circuit within a given time when the current flow in that circuit exceeds a given value. A fuse may be a rewirable tinned copper wire in a suitable carrier or a wire or wires in an enclosed cartridge.

In effect it is a weak link in the circuit that melts when heat is created by too high a current passing through the thin wire in the fuse case. When this happens the circuit is broken and no more current flows. A fuse usually has a rating in the order of Amperes rather than milli Amps which means it has *limited usefulness in protecting people from electric shock.* The fuse will operate (break the circuit) relatively slowly if the current is just above the fuse rating. Using too high a fuse means that the circuit will remain intact and the equipment will draw power. This may cause it to overheat leading to a fire or if a fault exists the circuit will remain live and the fault current may pass through the user of the equipment when they touch or operate it.

The following formula should be used to calculate the correct rating for a fuse:

$$\text{Current (Amperes)} = \frac{\text{Power (watts)}}{\text{Voltage (volts)}}$$

For example, the correct fuse current rating for a 2-kilowatt kettle on a 230-volt supply would be:

$$\frac{2,000 \text{ W}}{230 \text{ V}} = 8.69\text{A}$$

Typical fuses for domestic appliances are 3, 5, 10 and 13 Ampere ratings.

The nearest fuse just above this current level is 10A.

	Typical examples of power ratings are:	Suitable fuses at 230 Volts:
Computer processor.	350 Watts.	3 Amperes.
Electric kettle.	1,850-2,200 Watts.	10 - 13 Amperes.
Dishwasher.	1,380 Watts.	10 Amperes.
Refrigerator.	90 Watts.	3 Amperes.

Summary

- A weak link in the circuit that melts slowly when heat is created by a fault condition. However, this usually happens too slowly to protect people.
- Easy to replace with wrong rating.
- Needs tools to replace.
- Easy to override by replacing a fuse with one of a higher rating or putting in an improvised 'fuse', such as a nail, that has a high rating.

EARTHING

A conductor called an earth wire is fitted to the system; it is connected at one end to a plate buried in the ground and the other end connected to the metal casing of the equipment. If for any reason a conductor touches the casing so that the equipment casing becomes 'live' the current will flow to the point of lowest potential, the earth. The path to this point (earth) is made easier as the wire is designed to have very little resistance. This *may prevent electric shock* provided it is used in association with a correctly rated fuse, or better still a residual current device (RCD), and no one is in contact with the equipment at the time the fault occurs.

Figure 2-5-16: Plug-foil fuse no earth. *Source: RMS.*

Figure 2-5-17: Earthing. *Source: RMS.*

It should be remembered that earthing is provided where the casing can become live. If the equipment is designed so that this cannot be the case, such as double insulated equipment where the user touches non-conducting surfaces, earthing of the equipment is no advantage. In summary, earthing provides a path of least resistance for "stray" current and provides protection against indirect shock.

ISOLATION OF SUPPLY

Isolation of an electrical system is an excellent way of achieving safety for those that need to work on or near the system; for example, isolation of a power supply into a building that is to be refurbished or isolation of plant that is to be maintained. In its simplest form it can mean switching off and unplugging a portable appliance at times it is not in use. Care must be taken to check that the isolation has been adequate and effective before work starts; this can include tests on the system. It is also important to ensure the isolation is secure; 'lock off' and 'tag out' systems will assist with this.

DOUBLE INSULATION

This is a common protection device and consists of a layer of insulation around the live electrical parts of the equipment and a second layer of insulated material around this, commonly the casing of the equipment. Since the casing material is an insulator and does not conduct electricity, equipment having this type of protection does not normally have an earth wire.

To make sure that the double insulation is not impaired, it must not be pierced by conducting parts such as metal screws. Nor must insulating screws be used, because there is the possibility that they will be lost and will be replaced by metal screws. Any holes in the enclosure of a double Insulated appliance, such as those to allow ventilation, must be so small that fingers cannot reach live parts.

Each layer of insulation must be sufficient in its own right to give adequate protection against shock.

Equipment, which is double insulated, will carry the symbol shown in ***figure 2-5-21***.

Double insulated equipment has two layers of insulating material between the live parts of the equipment and the user. If a fault occurs with the live parts and a conductor touches the insulating material surrounding it no current can pass to the user, therefore ***no shock occurs.***

Figure 2-5-18: Residual current device. *Source: RMS.*

Figure 2-5-19: Plug-in residual current device. *Source: RMS.*

RESIDUAL CURRENT DEVICE (RCD)

An electro-mechanical switching device is used to automatically isolate the supply when there is a difference between the current flowing into a device and the current flowing from the device. Such a difference might result from a fault causing current leakage, with possible fire risks or the risk of shock current when a person touches a system and provides a path to earth for the current.

RCDs can be designed to operate at low currents and fast response times (usually 30 mA and 30 mSeconds) and thus they **reduce the effect of an electric shock**. Though they do not prevent the person receiving an electric shock they are very sensitive and operate very quickly and reduce some of the primary effects of the shock. It is still possible for a person to receive injury from the shock, not least some of the secondary injuries referred to earlier.

But the use of this type of device means the fault current should be isolated before sustained shock, and therefore before fibrillation, occurs. The equipment needs to be de-energised from time to time in order to be confident it will work properly when needed. This can easily be done by a simple test routine before use, as equipment is plugged into the RCD.

Summary

- Rapid and sensitive.
- Difficult to defeat.

- Easy and safe to test and reset.
- Does not prevent shock, but reduces the effect of a shock.

Figure 2-5-20: Double insulated 230V drill. *Source: RMS.*

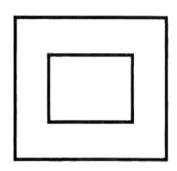

Figure 2-5-21: Double insulation symbol. *Source: HSG 107.*

Figure 2-5-22: 110V centre tapped earth transformer. *Source: RMS.*

Figure 2-5-23: Battery powered drill - 12V. *Source: RMS.*

REDUCED AND LOW VOLTAGE SYSTEMS

One of the best ways to reduce the risk from electricity is to reduce the voltage. This is frequently achieved by the use of a transformer (step down) which will reduce the voltage. A common reduction is from the mains voltage of 230V to 110V. Normally, transformers that are used to reduce voltage are described as "centre tapped to earth". In practice this means that any voltage involved in an electrical shock will be 55V.

Using the earlier example of Ohms Law, if the voltage is 230V then:

$$I = \frac{V}{R} = \frac{230 \text{ Volts}}{2,000+4,000 \text{ Ohms}} = 0.038 \text{Amperes or 38 mA}$$

However, if a centre tapped to earth transformer is used then,

$$I = \frac{V}{R} = \frac{55 \text{ Volts}}{2,000+4,000 \text{ Ohms}} = 0.009 \text{ Amperes or 9 mA}$$

Reference to **figures 2-5-2 and 2-5-5** will clearly show how this **reduces the effects of electric shock** on the body.

An alternative to reduction in voltage by means of a transformer is to provide battery-powered equipment; this will commonly run on 12V-24V but voltages may be higher. The common method is to use a rechargeable battery to power the equipment which eliminates the need for a cable to feed power to the equipment and gives a greater flexibility of use for the user, e.g. for drills and power drivers.

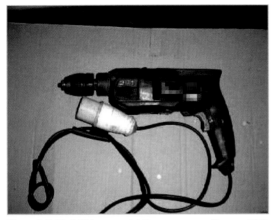

Figure 2-5-24: 110V powered drill.   *Source: RMS.*

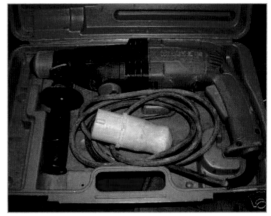

Figure 2-5-25: 110V powered drill.   *Source: RMS.*

Use of competent persons

It is particularly important that anyone who undertakes electrical work is able to satisfy the requirements of the Health and Safety at Work etc. Act (HASAWA) 1974 and the Electricity at Work Regulations (EWR) 1989. For work on electrical systems below 1000 volts ac they should be able to work within the guidelines set out in BS7671 'Requirements for electrical installations, IEE Wiring Regulations, Seventeenth edition'. Other work should be carried out according to the guidelines set out in the relevant industry standard.

Those who wish to undertake electrical testing work would normally be expected to have more knowledge and to be able to demonstrate competence through the successful completion of a suitable training course. More complex electrical tasks such as motor repair or maintenance of radio frequency heating equipment should only be carried out by someone who has been trained to do them.

Work on higher voltage systems must be carried out by specialist electrical engineers trained for this purpose. Work on live electrical systems must be controlled and requires specialist competence and systems of work to ensure safety.

Use of safe systems of work

LIVE ELECTRICAL WORK

The Electricity at Work Regulations (EWR) 1989, state that:

"No person shall be engaged in any work activity on or so near any live conductor that danger may arise, unless it is unreasonable in all the circumstances for it to be dead".

Figure 2-5-26: Work on live conductors, Regulation 14.   *Source: The Electricity at Work Regulations (EWR) 1989.*

This duty means that if danger could be present, work where possible, should be carried out with the electrical system dead. If it is necessary to work on live conductors, very strict controls must be in place and a safe system of work adhered to.

These will include:

- A full justification of why there is no reasonably practicable alternative to live working.
- A Live Electrical Permit to Work which will be valid for the stated task only.
- At least two competent persons must be present during the work and the more senior of these will sign off the permit when the work is complete and after all equipment has been restored to a fully safe condition.
- Restriction of work area to these competent people.
- Protection of the work area from other hazards, such as vehicles.
- Protection of workers from non-essential live conductors, by isolation or screening.
- Provision of information on the system and task.
- Use of suitable, insulated test equipment and tools.
- Adequate lighting and clear space to work.
- First aid service immediately available.
- Competent supervision.

ISOLATION

The Electricity at Work Regulations (EWR) 1989, state that:

"'Isolation' means the disconnection and separation of the electrical equipment from every source of electrical energy in such a way that this disconnection and separation is secure".

Figure 2-5-27: Isolation, Regulation 12 of EWR 1989.   *Source: The Electricity at Work Regulations (EWR) 1989.*

Health and Safety Executive (HSE) booklet 'Electricity at Work - Safe Working Practices (HSG85)' provides information on isolation procedures when working on both Low Voltage (LV) and High Voltage (HV) systems.

The requirement of the Electricity at Work Regulations (EWR) 1989 means that any isolation method used must be adequate and secure. This means that turning equipment off at a general on off switch or other mechanism is not adequate. Isolation therefore requires disconnection at the primary isolation mechanism for the equipment or circuit. In order to ensure a high level of security if work on the circuit or equipment takes the person away from constant site of the isolator mechanism, a lock may be added.

Isolation procedures, often referred to as 'lockout/tagout', in conjunction with a 'Permits-to-work' often form part of a 'Safe System of Work'. Various competences are required to ensure full compliance with these procedures, with specialist training and supervision required.

Figure 2-5-28: Multi-lock system.   *Source: RMS.*

If multi-lock systems are used *(see figure ref 2-5-28)* there must be a contingency plan to deal with the likelihood that someone will lose a key or even leave at the end of a shift without removing their personal pad lock.

LOCATING BURIED SERVICES

Excavation operations should not begin until all available service location drawings have been identified and thoroughly examined. Record plans and location drawings should not be considered as totally accurate but serve only as an indication of the likelihood of the presence of services, their location and depth. It is possible for the position of an electricity supply cable to alter if previous works have been carried out in the location due to the flexibility of the cable and movement of surrounding features since original installation of the cable. In addition, plans often show a proposed position for the services that does not translate to the ground, such that services are placed in position only approximately where the plan says.

Figure 2-5-29: Marking of services.   *Source: RMS.*

Before groundwork is due to commence it is common and good practice to check for presence of any of the services or hazards by using a detection device. A common detection device used is the cable avoidance tool more commonly known as a CAT scanner. It is important that 'service location devices' such as a cable avoidance tool (CAT) are used by competent, trained operatives to assist in the identification and marking of the actual location and position of buried services. When identified it is essential that physical markings be placed on the ground to show where these services are located.

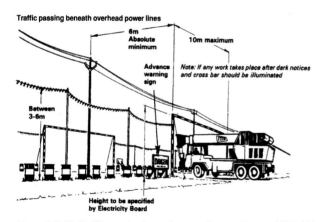

Figure 2-5-30: Traffic passing beneath power lines.   *Source: HSG 144.*

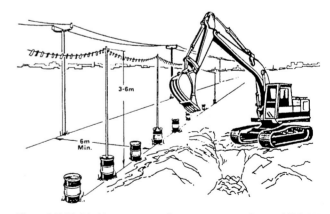

Figure 2-5-31: Working near power lines.   *Source: HSG 144.*

PROTECTION AGAINST OVERHEAD CABLES
- Isolate the supply.
- Erect 'goal-post' barriers to define clearance distances.

- Clearly mark danger zones with signs and/or bunting.
- Ensure safe access under lines.
- Use banksman or marshals where appropriate.
- Restrict the use of metal equipment such as ladders and scaffolds.

Emergency procedures following an electrical incident

Anyone working around electrical systems should be aware of what needs to be done for a casualty of electrical shock. If someone is lying unconscious and in contact with conductors the following actions should be taken in an order depending on the circumstances:

- Assess the situation.
- Summon help, including qualified medical support.
- If possible shut off the power.
- Do not touch the casualty - there may be enough voltage across the body of the casualty to shock the would-be rescuer. The problem with this rule is that the source of power may not be known, or easily found in time to save the casualty from shock.
- Remove the power. If possible prove the system is discharged and dead. If this is not possible take the following action.
- Remove the casualty from the power. It may be possible to dislodge the casualty from the circuit with a dry wooden board or piece of non-metallic material or using a jacket as a loop around the person, holding both sleeves and pulling away.

Figure 2-5-32: First aid sign. *Source: RMS.*

- Reassess the situation and any remaining danger to yourself and the casualty.
- Once the casualty has been disconnected from the source of electric power, the immediate medical concerns for the casualty should be respiration and circulation (breathing and pulse). If the rescuer is trained in cardio pulmonary resuscitation (CPR), they should follow the appropriate steps of checking breathing (including the airway) and pulse, then applying CPR as necessary to keep the casualty's body from de-oxygenating.
- If the casualty is conscious, lay them in the recovery position and keep them warm to reduce the chances of physiological shock until qualified medical personnel arrive on the scene.
- Keep the casualty under observation for secondary effects. Cool burns with water.

Further considerations:

- Do not go near the casualty until the electricity supply is proven to be off. This is especially important with overhead high voltage lines: keep yourself and others at least 18 metres away until the electricity supply company personnel advise otherwise.
- Do not delay - after 3 minutes without blood circulation irreversible damage can be done to the casualty.
- Do not wait for an accident to happen - train in emergency procedures and first aid, plan procedures for an emergency (calling for help, making calls to the emergency services, meeting ambulances and leading them to the casualty) and hold emergency drills.
- Establish if the incident has to be reported under the Reporting of Injuries, Diseases and Dangerous Occurrences Regulations (RIDDOR) 1995.

Figure 2-5-33: Risk of electric shock due to damage to cable resting on metal checker plate flooring. *Source: RMS.*

Figure 2-5-34: Restriction on work on live circuits. *Source: RMS.*

Inspection and maintenance strategies

THE LEGAL DUTY FOR INSPECTION AND MAINTENANCE

The Electricity at Work Regulations (EWR) 1989, Regulation 4(2) require that the owner shall 'as may be necessary to prevent danger, **maintain** all systems so as to prevent, so far as is reasonably practicable, such danger'. Danger is defined as the risk of injury from electric shock, electric burn, fire of electrical origin, electric arcing or explosion initiated or caused by electricity.

What is maintenance?

Guidance from the HSE document PM32, "The safe use of portable electrical apparatus (electrical safety)" 1990 and in the IEE Code of Practice for In-Service Inspection and Testing of Electrical Equipment indicates that maintenance is a general term that in practice can include visual inspection, repair, testing and replacement. Maintenance will determine whether equipment is fully serviceable or needing repair. It further suggests that cost effective maintenance can be achieved by a combination of:

■ Checks by the user.
■ Visual inspections by a person appointed to do this.
■ Combined inspection and tests by a competent person or by a contractor.

What needs maintenance?

The system

The Memorandum of Guidance on the EWR 1989 defines a system. In simple terms it will include any equipment which is, or may be, connected to a common source of electrical energy and includes the source and the equipment. Thus the distribution system in the plant and the apparatus connected to it are covered.

The IEE requirements apply similarly to the permanent installation in the building. It must be recognised that there is little benefit in having perfect portable apparatus if it is plugged into a defective socket which may be without proper insulation, with a switch that does not work properly, with the polarity reversed or with a high resistance earth connection.

Getting a maintenance programme started

In order to identify what systems will need maintenance, they should be listed. This same listing can be used as a checklist recording that the appropriate checks have been done. It may also include details of the type of the equipment, the checks and tests to be carried out.

USER CHECKS

The user of electrical equipment should be encouraged, after basic training, to look critically at apparatus and the source of power. If any defects are found, the apparatus should be marked and not be used again before examination by a competent person. Obviously, there must be a procedure by which the user brings faults to the attention of a supervisor and/or a competent person who might rectify the fault.

Checks by the user are the first line of defence but should never be the only line taken. Such inspections should be aimed at identifying the following:

■ Damaged cable sheaths.
■ Damaged plugs. Cracked casing or bent pins.
■ Taped or other inadequate cable joints.
■ Outer cable insulation not secured into plugs or equipment.
■ Faulty or ineffective switches.

■ Burn marks or discolouration.
■ Damaged casing.
■ Loose parts or screws.
■ Wet or contaminated equipment.
■ Loose or damaged sockets or switches.

FORMAL INSPECTON AND TESTS

Inspection

The maintenance system should always include formal visual inspection of all portable electrical equipment and electrical tests.

The frequency depends on the type of equipment and where it is used. The inspection can be done by a member of staff who has been trained in what to look for and has basic electrical knowledge. They should know enough to avoid danger to themselves or others.

Visual inspections are likely to need to look for the same types of defects as user checks but should also include the following:

Opening plugs of portable equipment to check for:

■ Use of correctly rated fuse.
■ Effective cord grip.
■ Secure and correct cable terminations.

Inspection of fixed installations for:

■ Damaged or loose conduit, trunking or cabling.

- Missing broken or inadequately secured covers.
- Loose or faulty joints.
- Loose earth connections.
- Moisture, corrosion or contamination.
- Burn marks or discolouration.
- Open or inadequately secured panel doors.
- Ease of access to switches and isolators.
- Presence of temporary wiring.

User checks and a programme of formal visual inspections are found to pick up some 95% of faults.

Testing

Faults such as loss of earth or broken wires inside an installation or cable cannot be found by visual inspection, so some apparatus needs to have a combined inspection and test. This is particularly important for all earthed equipment and leads and plugs connected to hand held or hand operated equipment. The system should be tested regularly in accordance with Institute of Electrical Engineers (IEE) requirements; tests may include earth continuity and impedance tests and tests of insulation material.

FREQUENCY OF INSPECTION AND TESTING

Question:	"I have been told that I have to have my desk lamp tested every six months. Is this correct?"
Answer:	"No. The law requires it to be maintained. It does not require any elaborate or rigorous system of frequent electrical testing".

Figure 2-5-35: Testing frequency.

Source: HSE Note INDG 160L.

Deciding the frequency

Many approaches to establishing frequency suggest that they should be done regularly. As can be seen above, the word 'regularly' is not specified in terms of fixed time intervals for all systems; a management judgment must be made to specify an appropriate timetable.

In effect, the frequency will depend on the condition the system is used in; for example, a test of office portable equipment may be sufficient if conducted every 3 years, whereas equipment used on a construction site may need to be tested every 3 months.

The system as a whole rather that just portable equipment must also be tested periodically and again this will depend on the conditions of use and may vary from 10 years to 6 months. Factors to be considered when deciding the frequency include:

- Type of equipment.
- Whether it is hand held.
- Manufacturer's recommendations.
- Its initial integrity and soundness.
- Age.
- Working environment.
- Likelihood of mechanical damage.

- Frequency of use.
- Duration of use.
- Foreseeable use.
- Who uses it.
- Modifications or repairs.
- Past experience.

RECORDS OF INSPECTION AND TESTING

In order to identify what systems and equipment will need inspection and testing they should be listed. This same listing can be used as a checklist recording that the appropriate checks, inspections and tests have been done. It would be usual to include details of the type of the equipment, its location and its age. It is important that a cumulative record of equipment and its status is held available to those that are responsible for using the equipment as well as those that are conducting the inspection or test.

In addition, it is common practice to add a label to the system or part of the system (e.g. portable appliances) to indicate that an inspection and/or test has taken place and its status following this.

Figure 2-5-36: PAT labels.

Source: RMS.

Some labels show the date that this took place; others prefer to show the date of next inspection or test. There is a growing trend, especially in offices, for employees to bring to work their own electrically powered equipment including calculators, radios, kettles and coffee makers.

The number of electrical accidents has grown accordingly and fires from calculator chargers left on overnight are growing in number. All such equipment should be recorded, inspected and tested by a competent person before use and at regular intervals, as if it were company property.

ADVANTAGES AND LIMITATIONS OF PORTABLE APPLIANCE TESTING (PAT)

The purpose of portable appliance testing is to periodically confirm the critical aspects of the electrical integrity of portable appliances. Three levels of inspection should be included in a maintenance and inspection strategy for portable electrical appliances:

- The first level of inspection would be that carried out by the operator before the appliance is used and would consist of an informal check of the condition of the appliance and its cable and plug.
- The second check would be supplemented by a more formal visual inspection by an appointed person which would follow a set down procedure and include other matters such as the correctness of the rating of the fuses fitted, security of cable grips, earth continuity, impedance and insulation.
- The third strategy would include the periodic combined inspection and testing of the appliance by a competent person.

It is important to keep centralised records of the results of portable appliance testing within an organisation. Such records can then be used for setting the frequency for appliance testing, to verify whether unlabelled equipment had been tested or had merely lost its label and to provide a record of past faults on all appliances that had been reported. This approach will demonstrate that the employer is in compliance with the regulations

The limitation with portable appliance testing is that people may have an over-reliance on the apparent assurance that the test indicates. They may be tempted to see it as a permanent assurance that the equipment is safe. This can lead to users not making their own pre-use checks of the appliance. In effect it is only a test, and therefore assurance, at a point in time. It does not assure that someone has not, for example, altered the fuse and put one in with an incorrect rating or that the cable grip has not come loose.

It must also be recognised that there is little benefit in having a perfect portable appliance if it is plugged into a defective socket which may be without proper insulation, with a switch that does not work properly, with the polarity reversed or with a high resistance earth connection.

UNIT NGC2
CONTROLLING WORKPLACE HAZARDS

Fire safety

Learning outcomes

On completion of this element, candidates should be able to demonstrate understanding of the content through the application of knowledge to familiar and unfamiliar situations. In particular they should be able to:

6.1   Describe the principles of fire initiation, classification and spread.

6.2   Outline the principles of fire risk assessment.

6.3   Describe the basic principles of fire prevention and the prevention of fire spread in buildings.

6.4   Identify the appropriate fire alarm system and fire-fighting equipment for a simple workplace.

6.5   Outline the factors which should be considered when implementing a successful evacuation of a workplace in the event of a fire.

Content

Sources of reference

Storage of Dangerous Substances (ACOP) (L135) HSE Books ISBN 0717622002

Dangerous Substances and Explosives Atmospheres Regulations 2002 (ACOP) (L135) HSE Books 0-7176-2200-2

Fire Safety Risk Assessment series, Communities and Local Government Publications:

Fire Safety Risk Assessment - Offices and shops ISBN-13: 978 1 85112 815 0

Fire Safety Risk Assessment - Factories and warehouses ISBN-13: 978 1 85112 816 7

Fire Safety Risk Assessment - Sleeping accommodation ISBN-13: 978 1 85112 817 4

Fire Safety Risk Assessment - Residential care premises ISBN-13: 978 1 85112 818 1

Fire Safety Risk Assessment - Educational premises ISBN-13: 978 1 85112 819 8

Fire Safety Risk Assessment - Small and medium places of assembly ISBN-13: 978 185112 820 4

Fire Safety Risk Assessment - Large places of assembly ISBN-13: 978 1 85112 821 1

Fire Safety Risk Assessment - Theatres, cinemas and similar premises ISBN-13: 978 185112 822 8

Fire Safety Risk Assessment - Open air events and venues ISBN-13: 978 1 85112 823 5

Fire Safety Risk Assessment - Healthcare premises ISBN-13: 978 1 85112 824 2

Fire Safety Risk Assessment - Transport premises and facilities ISBN-13: 978 1 85112825 9

Relevant statutory provisions

The Management of Health and Safety at Work Regulations (MHSWR) 1999

The Health and Safety (Safety Signs and Signals) Regulations (SSSR) 1996

The Regulatory Reform (Fire Safety) Order (RRFSO) 2005

Fire (Scotland) Act (FSA) 2005

Fire Safety (Scotland) Regulations (FSSR) 2006

Dangerous Substances and Explosives Atmospheres Regulations (DSEAR) 2002

6.1 - Fire initiation, classification and spread

Basic principles of fire

THE FIRE TRIANGLE

In order for combustion to take place the three essential elements of a fire have to be brought together - fuel, oxygen and source of ignition (heat) - this is called the fire triangle.

In order to prevent fires these elements, particularly the fuel and ignition sources, are kept apart. When they are brought together in the right proportions combustion takes place. It should be noted that it is only the vapour from a fuel that burns. A solid or liquid must be heated to a temperature where the vapour given off can ignite before combustion takes place.

This principle is important when considering combustible dusts as this combustion process happens so quickly it becomes an explosion.

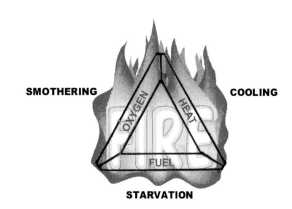

Figure 2-6-1: Fire triangle. *Source: RMS/Corel.*

This explosion can be caused by a source of ignition, for example, a spark; a small *dust explosion* can often disturb more dust to fuel a bigger explosion. The other important aspect of this combustion principle is that if one or more of these elements of the fire is removed the fire will be extinguished. This can be done by:

Cooling The fire to remove the heat - by applying water to the fire.

Starving The fire of fuel - by moving material from the area of a fire or closing off an area of combustible material from the fire e.g. isolating a gas valve to extinguish a gas fire.

Smothering The fire by limiting its oxygen supply - by closing a lid on a metal bin that contained a fire, covering a fire with a fire blanket or applying an extinguishing medium such as foam.

SOURCES OF IGNITION

Any source of heat is a possible ignition source. Examples could be:

- Discarded smokers' materials (not such a big problem now that smoking is prohibited in the workplace).
- Naked flames.
- Fixed or portable heaters - particularly those that use liquid fuel.
- Hot processes e.g. welding, cutting and grinding.
- Cooking.

- Electrical equipment - overloading electrical circuits.
- Machinery - sparks, overheating of drive belts due to over tightening.
- Static electricity - most commonly from lightning strikes although sparks from static charges are very dangerous in flammable and explosive atmospheres.

Figure 2-6-2: Illicit smoking. *Source: FSTC Ltd.*

Figure 2-6-3: Combustible materials - waste. *Source: RMS.*

SOURCES OF FUEL

Anything that burns is a fuel for a fire:

- Flammable liquids, e.g. petrol storage areas.
- Flammable gases, e.g. butane, liquefied petroleum gas (LPG), heater cylinders.

- Plastics, rubber and foam, e.g. furniture.
- Paper and card, e.g. stationery cupboards, waste paper.

- Flammable chemicals, e.g. paints and solvents.
- Wood, e.g. furniture, dust from manufacturing processes.
- Insulating materials, e.g. walls and partition components.
- Waste materials, chemicals, waste paper, and general waste.

The structure of the building should also be considered. The building itself could be made from wood or other flammable material or may contain flammable materials as part of the decoration e.g. wallpaper, etc.

SOURCES OF OXYGEN

The main source of oxygen for a fire is in the air around us. In an enclosed building this is provided by the ventilation system in use. This generally falls into one of two categories: natural airflow through doors, windows and other openings; or mechanical air conditioning systems and air handling systems. In many buildings there will be a combination of systems, which will be capable of introducing/extracting air to and from the building.

Leaks from oxygen supplies e.g. cylinders or piped supply which, combined with poor ventilation can lead to an oxygen enriched atmosphere. Materials that ordinarily will burn only slowly will burn very vigorously in an oxygen-enriched atmosphere. Others such as greases and oils may burst into flames in this kind of atmosphere. As well as the precautions outlined above for flammable gases, the following points should be remembered:

- Never use oxygen instead of compressed air.
- Never use oxygen to improve air quality in a working area or confined space.
- Never use grease or oil on equipment containing oxygen.

Classification of fires

A basic understanding of the classes of fire needs to be achieved because many fire extinguishers state the classes of fire on which they may be used.

Class A	Fire involving solids - wood, paper or plastics (usually material of an organic nature).
Class B	Fires involving liquids or liquefiable solids - petrol, oil, paint, fat or wax.
Class C	Fires involving gases - liquefied petroleum gas, natural gas, acetylene, methane, etc.
Class D	Fires caused by burning metals that combust easily on contact with air, such as magnesium and lithium. Such specialised fires require a specialised metal powder fire extinguisher to deal with them, and will be required in scientific labs or where manufacturing processes involve the risk of metal fires. For example, aluminium dust or swarf can catch fire, so any process involving cutting, drilling or milling aluminium holds potential risk.
Electrical fires	Though this is not a class of fire electricity is often a source of ignition and the presence of electricity is a very serious consideration where water is used as the extinguishing medium.
Class F	Fires involving cooking oils and fats usually found in commercial kitchens such as restaurants and fast food outlets.

Figure 2-6-4: Classification of fires. *Source: RMS.*

Principles of heat transmission

There are four methods by which heat may be transmitted:

1) Convection

The movement of hotter gases up through the air (hot air rises). Convection can quickly move hot gases to another part of a building where they raise the temperature of combustible materials to a point that combustion takes place e.g. hot gases rising up a staircase through an open door.

Control measure: protection of openings by fire doors and the creation of fire resistant compartments in buildings.

2) Conduction

The movement of heat through a material (usually solid). Some materials, such as metal can absorb heat readily and transmit it to other rooms by conduction, where it can set fire to combustible items that are in contact with the heated material e.g. metal beam or pipe transmitting heat through a solid wall.

Control measure: insulation of the surface of a beam or pipe with heat resistant materials.

3) Radiation

Transfer of heat as invisible waves through the air (the air or gas is not heated but solids and liquids in contact with the heat are). Radiation transfers heat in the air in the same way that an electric heater heats a room. Any material close to a fire will absorb the heat until the item starts to smoulder and then burn e.g. a fire in items or a waste container stored too near to a building may provide enough radiant heat to transfer the fire to the building.

Control measure: separation distances or fire resistant barriers.

4) Direct burning

Combustible materials in direct contact with a naked flame e.g. curtains or carpet tiles may be consumed by combustion and enable fire to be transferred along them to other parts of a building.

Control measure: the use of fire retardant materials.

Reasons why fires spread

FAILURE OF EARLY DETECTION

- No detection system or patrols.
- No alarm system in place.
- People not knowing or confusing the sound of an alarm.
- Not promptly extinguished due to no hoses or extinguishers.
- Fire starts in unoccupied area.
- Fire starts out of normal work hours.
- Building material waste may be being burnt as a normal routine and smoke and other signs of fire may not be seen as unusual.
- Numerous hot working tasks conducted - therefore smells of burning ignored.
- Frequent occurrence of small, local fires caused by hot work, and not seen as significant.

ABSENCE OF COMPARTMENTS IN BUILDING STRUCTURE

- Open plan office.
- False ceilings.
- The structure under construction or alteration is incomplete and has reduced separation between levels and/or sections on a level.

COMPARTMENTS UNDERMINED

- Fire doors wedged open.
- Poor maintenance of door structure.
- Holes may be designed to pass through compartments and are waiting fitment of services and subsequent sealing.
- Holes cut for ducts or doorways or to provide temporary access to locate/remove equipment.
- Compartments may be progressively created in buildings under alteration, thus increasing the risk of fire spread.

MATERIALS INAPPROPRIATELY STORED

- Flammable liquids not controlled - too much or in unsuitable containers.
- Boxes in corridors.

Figure 2-6-5: Compartment undermined-holes cut.   *Source: RMS.*

- Off cuts of wood and sawdust left in the areas where work has taken place.
- Packing materials used in the process, such as shredded paper, polystyrene, bubble wrap etc.
- Pallets and plastic covering left near to ignition sources.

Figure 2-6-6: Fire door wedged open. *Source: RMS.*

Figure 2-6-7: Materials inappropriately stored.   *Source: RMS.*

Common causes and consequences of fire

CAUSES

Causes may be split into four main groups.

These are:

Careless actions and accidents

E.g. hot works such as welding, cutting and grinding, discarded lighted cigarette end or match, smouldering waste, unattended burning of bonfires or poor electrical connections.

Misusing equipment

E.g. overloading electrical circuits and/or using fuses of too high a rating, failure to follow servicing instructions, failure to repair faulty machinery/equipment promptly.

Defective machinery or equipment

E.g. electrical short circuits, electrical earth fault can cause local overheating and electrical insulation failure may occur when affected by heat, damp or chemicals.

Deliberate ignition

The crime of maliciously and intentionally, or recklessly, starting a fire or causing an explosion e.g. insurance fraud, aggrieved persons, concealment of another crime, political activists or vandalism.

Figure 2-6-8: Careless action - hot work. *Source: RMS.*

Figure 2-6-9: Misusing equipment - overloaded electrical sockets. *Source: RMS.*

Figure 2-6-10: Defective electrical equipment. *Source: RMS.*

Figure 2-6-11: Potential for deliberate ignition. *Source: RMS.*

CONSEQUENCES

Consequences may be split into four main groups.

Human harm

Each year some 500 people die due to fires in the UK and around 15,000 non-fatal casualties are caused. Though most of these do not occur in the workplace, fire has the potential for major loss of life in the workplace due to direct contact with heat and flame or from the effects of smoke and toxic gases.

The radiant heat of a fire and contact with flames can give rise to the risk of heat stroke or burns. The degree of exposure to the heat or flames will influence greatly the effect on the body each will have, they could quickly lead to shock, coma or death.

Both the hot gases and smoke involved in fires represent separate hazards to a person involved in a fire. The hot gases and smoke can present a direct effect on the lungs causing restriction in breathing. In addition, toxic gases may be liberated as part of a fire; these may include carbon monoxide, which if breathed in sufficient quantities can lead to asphyxiation. Other toxic products of combustion can include hydrogen cyanide and chlorine.

Economic effects

The Association of British Insurers established that fire damage claims in the first half of 2009 cost £639 million - £3.6 million each day. This follows on from the £1.3 billion fire losses in 2008, a 16 percent rise on 2007 and the most expensive year ever. Between 2002 and 2008 the cost of the average fire claim for both commercial and domestic fires doubled, to £21,000 and £8,000 respectively. When fires do occur in the workplace the business is usually so badly affected it does not resume business again.

Legal effects

There is a legal requirement under the Regulatory Reform (Fire Safety) Order (RRFSO) 2005 to prevent fire, protect employees and other relevant persons from the effects of fire and to mitigate the effect of fire on anyone in the vicinity of premises on fire. Failure to comply with legislation could result in prosecutions and, if found guilty, fines.

Environmental

Large uncontrolled fires create pollutants, such as smoke, that enter the atmosphere. The fire itself may cause damage to storage areas with the subsequent leakage of chemicals onto land or into water courses and the run off from fire hoses may ultimately enter the water system. The photographs below show some of the damage caused by the Buncefield oil storage depot disaster in December 2005. The plume of smoke was so large it could be seen from space.

Figure 2-6-12: Buncefield - run off from fire hoses. *Source: RMS.*

Figure 2-6-13: Buncefield oil storage depot disaster. *Source: RMS.*

6.2 - Fire risk assessment

The requirement for a fire risk assessment

The purpose of a fire risk assessment (FRA) is to identify where fire may start in the workplace, the people who would be put at risk, and to reduce the risk where possible.

Specific legal duties to conduct risk assessments are set out in the Regulatory Reform (Fire Safety) Order (RRFSO) 2005, which require the following.

Every 'Responsible Person' (Employer, Person in control or Owner) must make a suitable and sufficient assessment of:

- The risks to the health and safety of his *employees* to which they are exposed whilst they are at work.
- The risks to the health and safety of *persons not in his employment* (Relevant Persons) arising out of or in connection with the conduct by him of his undertaking.

Similarly every self-employed person must make a suitable and sufficient assessment of:

- The risks to his *own* health and safety to which he is exposed whilst he is at work.
- The risks to the health and safety of *persons not in his employment* (Relevant Persons), arising out of or in connection with the conduct by him of his undertaking.

Factors to be considered in carrying out the risk assessment

The assessments must, at least, identify the measures needed to satisfy the 'General Fire Precautions' of the RRFSO 2005. This order requires fire and other emergency provisions to be in place; as such, risk assessments must be conducted to determine fire risks and the provisions necessary for the protection of people and the environment.

The measures would include:

- Reduction of the risk of fire.
- Prevention of fire spread.
- Adequate means of escape from fire.

- Maintenance measures to ensure means of escape available at all times.
- Means to fight fire.
- Means to detect and warn of fire.
- Fire actions/instructions and training.
- Actions to mitigate the effects of a fire.

Where the employer employs five or more employees they must record the significant findings of the assessment and any group of his employees identified by it as being especially at risk.

Assessments must be reviewed by the 'Responsible Person' if there is reason to suspect that it is no longer valid or there has been a significant change in the matters to which it relates.

Step 1 - Identify fire hazards

- *Identify sources of ignition* - smokers' materials, naked flames, heaters, hot processes, cooking, machinery, boilers, faulty or misused electrical equipment, lighting equipment, hot surfaces, blocked vents, friction, static electricity, metal impact and arson.
- *Identify sources of fuel* - flammable liquids, flammable chemicals, wood, paper and card, plastics, foam, flammable gases, furniture, textiles, packaging materials, waste materials including shavings, off cuts and dust.
- *Identify sources of oxygen* - natural ventilation, doors, windows, forced ventilation systems, air conditioning, oxidising materials, oxygen cylinders or piped oxygen systems.

Step 2 - Identify people at risk

- Consider people in the premises - staff, visitors, contractors, public, old, young, disabled, and their level of discipline and training.
- How could fire, heat or smoke spread to areas that people occupy? Convection, conduction, radiation or direct burning.
- Who and where are the people that may be at risk? People carrying out noisy tasks, placed high at the top of a building or in confined spaces conducting work, nearby workers or the public.
- Identify people who are especially at risk.
- How will people be warned of fire and could people be trapped be fire?

Step 3 - Evaluate, remove, or reduce and protect from risk

Risk reduction by prevention

- *Reduce sources of ignition* - remove unnecessary sources of heat or replace with safer alternatives, ensure electrical fuses etc are of the correct rating, ensure safe and correct use of electrical equipment, enforcing a 'hot work' permit system, safe smoking policy, arson reduction measures.
- *Minimise potential fuel for a fire* - remove or reduce amount of flammable materials, replace materials with safer alternatives, ensure safe handling, storage and use of materials, safe separation distances between flammable materials, use of fire resisting storage, repair or replace damaged or unsuitable furniture, control and removal of flammable waste, care of external storage due to arson, good housekeeping.
- *Reduce sources of oxygen* - close all doors and windows not required for ventilation particularly out of working hours, shutting down non essential ventilation systems, not storing oxidising materials near heat sources or flammable materials, controlling the use of oxygen cylinders and ensuring ventilation to areas where they are used.

Risk reduction by protection

Consider existing fire safety measures, risk reduction by protection (controls), in the workplace and consider possible improvements.

- Reducing unsatisfactory structural features.
  - Remove, cover or treat large areas of combustible wall and ceiling linings, improve fire resistance of workplace, install fire breaks into open voids.
- Fire detection and warning.
  - Can fire be detected quickly enough to allow people to escape?
  - Can means of warning be recognised and understood?
  - Do staff know how to operate the system?
  - Will staff know what to do if the alarm operates?
  - Are fire notices posted around workplace?
- Means of escape.
  - How long will it take for people to escape once they are aware of a fire?
  - Is this time reasonable?
  - Are there enough exits?
  - Are exits in the right places?
  - Is there suitable means of escape for all people, including disabled?

- Could a fire happen that would affect all escape routes?
- Are escape routes easily identifiable?
- Are exit routes free from obstructions and blockages?
- Are exit routes suitably lit at all times?
- Have staff been trained in the use of the escape routes?

■ Means of fighting fire.

- Is the fire fighting equipment suitable for the risk?
- Is it suitably located?
- Is it signed where necessary?
- Have people been trained to use equipment where necessary?

■ Maintenance and testing.

- Check all fire doors, escape routes, lighting and signs.
- Check all fire fighting equipment.
- Check all fire detectors and alarms.
- Check any other equipment provided to help means of escape arrangements.
- Are there relevant instructions to staff regarding maintenance and testing?
- Are those who carry out maintenance and testing competent?

■ Fire procedures and training.

- Is there an emergency plan?
- Does the emergency plan take account of all reasonably foreseeable circumstances?
- Are all employees familiar with the plan, trained in its use, and involved in testing it?
- Is the emergency plan made available to staff?
- Are fire procedures clearly indicated throughout the workplace?
- Have all people likely to be present, been considered?

Step 4 - Record, plan, inform, instruct and train

Where the employer employs five or more employees they must record the significant findings (actions already taken, plus actions that will be taken) of the assessment and any group of his employees identified by it as being especially at risk.

A record must also be kept of measures that have been or will be taken by the responsible person.

Emergency plans

Following completion of the fire risk assessment, an emergency plan should be devised. The plan should include the following:

- Action on discovery of fire.
- Action on hearing alarm.
- Details of the fire warning system.
- Details of the evacuation process.
- Means of escape - travel distances.
- Location of assembly points.
- Identification of escape routes - signs, emergency lighting.
- Details of fire fighting equipment.
- Specific staff duties.
- Safe evacuation of people who need assistance to escape.
- Safe working practices in high risk areas.
- Procedures for calling Fire Service.
- Staff training needs and arrangements for providing training.

Step 5 - Review and monitor

The assessment and the fire safety measures must be reviewed regularly.

In addition a review should be done if:

- Changes to workplace are proposed, e.g. increased storage of flammable materials.
- Changes to work process/activity are proposed, e.g. introducing a new night shift.
- Changes to number or type of people present are proposed, e.g. public are invited on site to buy goods.
- A near miss or a fire occurs.

See also NGC1 - Element 4 - Health and safety management systems 3 - planning; for more information on risk assessment technique.

Temporary workplaces and changes to workplaces

Many serious fires occur in existing buildings during maintenance and construction work. Due to the increased fire risks during these periods of time, additional fire precautions may be needed.

Dependant upon the nature of the work to be carried out and the size and use of the workplace, it may be necessary to carry out a new fire risk assessment to include all the new hazards that will be created during the construction work.

In some cases the increased risk will be due to the increase of sources of ignition or additional materials. In other cases it will be due to the effect on the controls in place at the premises. Some work may require the isolation of smoke detectors or an alarm system. Normally well controlled escape routes may become cluttered by equipment, materials or workers.

Attention should be paid to:

- Accumulation of flammable waste and building materials.
- The obstruction or loss of exits and exit routes.
- Fire doors being propped open, wedged open or removed.
- Openings created in fire resisting structures.
- Isolation of fire detection, or fixed fire fighting systems.
- Introduction of additional electrical equipment, or other sources of ignition.
- Use of hot work process.
- Introduction of flammable products e.g. adhesives or flammable gases.
- The addition of new people to the premises that may be unfamiliar with fire arrangements e.g. alarm, routes, roll calls, assembly points.
- People working in unusual locations e.g. the roof, basement or duct areas.
- People working outside normal working hours.

Figure 2-6-14: Materials in escape route.   *Source: Lincsafe.*

NEED FOR CONTINUAL REVIEW AS WORK PROGRESSES

In all workplaces there is a need to actively review and revise the fire risk assessment, the fire safety measures that apply and the fire/emergency plans. This aspect of fire safety is absolutely vital in construction sites or any other workplace where layout changes are constantly taking place. Dependant upon the state of the build, fire safety should be inspected at a frequency of weekly or daily.

Checks and assessment should be made to ensure that the fire plan for means of escape is still appropriate and that the following fire safety measures are not being compromised:

- Escape routes.
- Access to fire alarms.
- Audibility of fire alarm systems.
- Access and availability of fire fighting equipment.
- Suitability of fire safety signage.
- Need for and suitability of escape lighting.

- Fire protection/fire resistant structures within the building.
- Introduction of new fire hazards e.g. hot works.
- Correct storage/use of flammable materials.
- Site security/arson prevention.
- New staff and the need for 'fire induction'.

If, as a result of any works that need to be carried out, fire safety standards will be reduced then additional compensating factors may need to be introduced. For example, if detector heads need to be covered to prevent false alarms a fire watch system of patrols may be introduced to compensate. As can be seen, fire safety is a constantly changing factor which must be integral to the everyday management of site safety.

6.3 - Fire prevention and prevention of fire spread

Control measures to minimise the risk of fire in the workplace

USE AND STORAGE OF FLAMMABLE AND COMBUSTIBLE MATERIALS

Where possible employers should seek to *eliminate* the use of flammable materials in the workplace, for example, replacing adhesives that have a flammable content with those that are water based. Where this is not possible the amount used should be *reduced* and kept to the minimum.

Quantities of material stored in the workplace must be in suitable containers and controlled to the minimum for immediate work needs. Flammable materials not in use should be removed to a purpose designed store in a well ventilated area, preferably outside the building but in a secure area. Lids should be kept on containers at all times when they are not in immediate use.

Any waste containers, contaminated tools or materials should be treated in the same way and removed to a store in fresh air, until dealt with. Containers and contaminated materials need to be disposed of in a controlled manner so that they do not present a risk of fire.

Care has to be taken to control the delivery and therefore the storage of flammable and combustible materials to site. There is a temptation to have large quantities all delivered at the same time, but where possible deliveries should be staggered to reflect the rate of use in order to minimise the amount stored on site.

Terms used with flammable and combustible materials

Flashpoint

'Flashpoint' is defined as the lowest temperature at which, in a specific test apparatus, sufficient vapour is produced from a liquid sample for momentary or flash ignition to occur.

It must not be confused with ignition temperature which can be considerably lower.

Flammable

Liquids with a flash point between 32°C and 55°C are classified as flammable.

Highly flammable

Liquids with a flash point below 32°C are classified as highly flammable. The flash points of some common solvents are:

- Ethanol +12°C.
- Toluene +4°C.
- Methyl ethyl ketone - 9°C.
- Acetone -19°C.

General principles for storage and use of flammable liquids

When considering the storage or use of flammable liquids, the following safety principles should be applied:

V   Ventilation - plenty of fresh air.

I   Ignition - control of ignition sources.

C   Containment - suitable containers and spillage control.

E   Exchange - try to use a less flammable product to do task.

S   Separation - keep storage away from process areas, by distance or a physical barrier e.g. a wall or partition.

CONTROL OF IGNITION SOURCES

Welding

- Only use competent trained staff.
- Regulators should be of a recognised standard.
- Colour code hoses: **blue**   -   **oxygen**
             red   -   **acetylene**
             orange -   **propane.**
- Fit non-return valves at blowpipe/torch inlet on both gas lines.
- Fit flashback arrestors incorporating cut-off valves and flame arrestors fitted to outlet of both gas regulators.
- Use crimped hose connections not jubilee clips.
- Do not let oil or grease contaminate oxygen supply due to explosion hazard.
- Check equipment visually before use, and check new connections with soapy water for leaks.

Figure 2-6-15: Welding equipment.   Source: RMS.

- Secure cylinders in upright position.
- Keep hose lengths to a minimum.
- Follow a permit to work system.
- Do not store standby gases that are not connected to welding apparatus in the workplace.

Hot work

Hot work has been responsible for causing many fires. One of the most tragic fires due to hot work was Dusseldorf Airport Fire in 1996. The fire was started by welding on an open roadway and resulted in damage in excess of £200 million, several hundred injuries and 17 deaths.

It is imperative that good safe working practices are utilised. Combustible materials must be removed from the area or covered over. Consideration must be given to the effects of heat on the surrounding structure, and where sparks, flames, hot residue or heat will travel to. It is often necessary to have a fire watcher to spot any fires that may be started. Fire extinguishers need to be immediately available and operatives must know how to use them. The work area must be checked thoroughly for some time after the completion of work to ensure there are no smouldering fires. Strong consideration should be given to the use of hot work permits.

Smoking

It is now against the law to smoke inside any public buildings (includes the workplace). Prohibition of smoking may lead to illicit smoking and extra vigilance may be needed. Where smoking is allowed, provide easily accessible, non-combustible receptacles for cigarette ends and other smoking material and empty daily. Smoking should cease half an hour before close down.

Arson

Arson is the single greatest cause of fire (the arson detection rate is only 8 percent, compared to 24 percent for other offences) and as such simple but effective ways to deter the arsonist are by giving attention to security, both external and internal, which should encompass the following:

External security

- Control of people having access to the building/site.
- Use of patrol guards.
- Lighting the premises at night - linked to CCTV.
- Safety of keys.
- Structural protection.
- Siting of rubbish bins/skips at least 8m from buildings.

Internal security

- Good housekeeping and clear access routes.
- Inspections and audits.
- Visitor supervision.
- Control of sub-contractors.
- Control door access by keypad or electronic locks, *(see figure ref 2-6-17).*

Figure 2-6-16: Control arson by external security. *Source: RMS.*

Figure 2-6-17: Control arson by internal security. *Source: RMS.*

SYSTEMS OF WORK

Systems of work combine people, equipment, materials and the environment to produce the safest possible climate in which to work. In order to produce a safe system of work, it is essential to make an assessment of the area to determine where the hazards and risks arise and how best to control them.

The requirement to carry out a fire risk assessment should address the following:

- Identify potential fire hazards.
- Decide who may be in danger, and note their locations.
- Evaluate the risks and carry out any necessary improvement measures.
- Record findings and action taken.
- Keep assessment under review.

In addition to the fire risk assessment carried out, other measures may include implementing the following strategies.

1) A safe place

A safe place begins with ensuring that the fabric of the building is designed or planned in a way that will prevent ignition, suppress fire spread and allow for safe, speedy unobstructed evacuation with signs to direct people. Factors to consider will include compartmentalisation, fire resistant materials, proper and suitable means of storage, means of detection, means of raising the alarm good housekeeping and regular monitoring and review.

2) Safe person

A safe person begins with raising awareness to individuals of any risk of loss resulting from outbreak of fire. Information can be provided that will identify where to raise the alarm, what the alarm sounds like, how to evacuate and where to muster, responsibility for signing in and out of the site register, fire drill procedures, trained authorised fire appointed persons, use and storage of flammable materials, good housekeeping and use of equipment producing heat or ignition (including hot processes i.e. welding).

3) Safe materials

Safe materials begin with providing information and ensuring safe segregation and storage for materials and sources of ignition/heat. In addition, providing information on the correct way to handle materials and substances, including a COSHH register that will detail methods of tackling a fire involving hazardous substances, is necessary.

4) Safe equipment

Safe equipment begins with user information and maintenance to ensure good working and efficient order. Information should also provide the user with a safe method for use and the limitations of and risks from the equipment. Supervision may be necessary to ensure correct use and prevent misuse that may lead to short circuiting or overheating that could result in fire. Where work involves hot processes by nature (welding, grinding, casting, etc) then permit-to-work procedures may be necessary in order to tightly control the operations.

Other equipment required in relation to fire hazards and control may include smoke or heat detection equipment, alarm sounders/bells, alarm call points and appropriate fire extinguishing apparatus. It should be noted that in the event of a fire alarm, all the passenger lifts should not be used. Under normal circumstances the lift will return to the ground floor and remain in that position with the doors locked in the open position. All equipment should be regularly tested to ensure its conformity and be accompanied with a suitable certificate of validity.

Safe systems must also include consideration of who is at risk, including those persons with special needs such as the young, elderly, infirm or disabled. There may be a requirement to prevent smoking in the workplace or employ appointed persons to take control of the situation and co-ordinate emergency responses in the event of an alarm. If the building relies solely on internal artificial lighting, then the requirement to install emergency back-up lighting will be needed. All systems must be regularly monitored in order to reflect changes to the environment and put remedies in place to ensure full preparedness in the event of a fire.

Permit to work procedures

A permit to work is an official, documented safe system of work that is used for controlling high risk activities. Implementation is required prior to work beginning to ensure that all precautions are taken and securely in place to prevent danger to the workforce.

When managed correctly, a permit to work prevents any mistakes or deviations through poor verbal communication by stating the specific requirements of the project. For fire control, a permit to work is typically used where there is a requirement to use flammable materials or when hot work or processes are being carried out.

The authorised person shall issue the permit to work and will sign the document to declare that all isolations are made and remain in place throughout the duration of the project. In addition to this, the authorised person will make checks to ensure that all controls to be implemented by the acceptor are in place before work begins

The acceptor of the permit to work shall assume responsibility for carrying out the works. The acceptor shall sign the document to declare that the terms and conditions of the permit to work are understood and will be complied with fully at all times by the entire work team.

Compliance with a permit to work system includes ensuring the required safeguards are implemented and that the work will be restricted to the equipment only stated within the document.

Items included in a permit to work are:

- Permit issue number.
- Authorised person identification.
- Locations of fire fighting equipment.
- Locations of flammable materials.
- Warning information sign locations.
- Emergency muster points.
- Details of the work to be carried out.

- Signature of authoriser.
- Signature of acceptor.
- Signature for works clearance/extension/handover.
- Signature for cancellation.
- Other precautions (risk assessments, method statements, PPE).

Hot work permits

Hot work permits are formal management documents that control and implement a safe system of work whenever methods of work that utilise heat or flame systems are used. If the risk of fire is low, it may not be necessary to implement a hot work permit; however they should always be considered.

The hot work permit should be issued by an Authorised Person who ensures that the requirements stated in them are complied with before the permit is issued, and during duration of the work. Hot work permits should be issued for a specific time, for a specific place, for a specific task, and are issued to a designated competent person.

Figure 2-6-18: Hot work. *Source: Speedy Hire Plc.*

See also NGC1 - Element 4 - Health and safety management systems 3 - planning.

GOOD HOUSEKEEPING

By 'housekeeping' it means the general tidiness and order of the building. At first sight, this may seem a strange matter to discuss when considering fire safety, but as housekeeping affects so many different aspects of this subject, it cannot be ignored.

Housekeeping and its effect on fire safety

Fires need fuel. A build up of redundant combustible materials, rubbish and stacks of waste materials provide that fuel. All combustible materials cannot be eliminated, but they can be controlled. Any unnecessary build-up of rubbish and waste should be avoided.

If a fire starts in a neatly stacked pile of timber pallets, around which there is a clear space, the fire may be spotted and extinguished before it can spread. However, if the same pile were strewn around in an untidy heap, along with adjacent rubbish, the likelihood is that fire would spread over a larger area and involve other combustible materials.

Poor housekeeping can also lead to:

■ Blocked fire exits.
■ Obstructed escape routes.
■ Difficult access to fire alarm call points/extinguishers/hose reels.
■ Obstruction of vital signs and notices.
■ A reduction in the effectiveness of automatic fire detectors and sprinklers.

Checklists

Fire Prevention is a matter of good routine and the checklists shown below are a guide as to what to look out for:

List A - Routine checks

Daily at the start of business - including:

■ Doors which may be used for escape purposes - unlocked and escape routes unobstructed.
■ Free access to hydrants, extinguishers and fire alarm call points.
■ No deposits on electric motors.

List B - Routine checks

Daily at close-down - including:

■ Inspection of whole area of responsibility - to detect any incipient smoldering fires.
■ Fire doors and shutters closed.
■ All plant and equipment safely shut down.
■ Waste bins emptied.
■ No accumulation of combustible process waste, packaging materials or dust deposits.
■ Safe disposal of waste.
■ Premises left secure from unauthorised access.

List C - Periodic inspection

During working hours - weekly/monthly/quarterly as decided:

■ Goods neatly stored so as not to impede fire fighting.
■ Clear spaces around stacks of stored materials.
■ Gangways kept unobstructed.
■ No non-essential storage in production areas.
■ Materials clear of light fittings.
■ Company smoking rules known and enforced.

Storage of small quantities of highly flammable/flammable liquids

The objective in controlling the risk from these materials is to remove all unnecessary quantities from the workplace to a recognised storage area outside the building. This may be done as part of a close down routine at the end of the day. It is accepted that quantities of this material may need to be available in a workplace during normal working. This should not exceed 50 litres in any work area unless a full scale purpose constructed store is used. In other cases local small scale storage of up to **50 litres of highly flammable** or up to **250 litres of flammable** liquids may be kept within the workplace provided it is controlled and placed in a suitable store container. Highly flammable or flammable liquids removed from storage must be in suitable containers to prevent spills and loss of vapours.

STORAGE IN THE WORKPLACE

■ In a suitable sealed container.
■ In a suitable cabinet, bin or other store container.
■ In a designated area of the workplace.
■ Away from ignition sources, working or process areas.
■ Capable of containing any spillage.

- In a 30 min fire resistant structure.
- Provided with hazard warning signs to illustrate the flammability of the contents.
- Prohibition signs for smoking and naked flame.
- Not contain other substances or items.

STORAGE IN OPEN AIR

- Formal storage area on a concrete pad, with a sump for spills.
- Bunded all around to take content of largest drum plus an allowance of 10%.
- Away from other buildings.
- Secure fence and gate 2m high.
- Marked by signs warning of flammability.
- Signs prohibiting smoking or other naked flames.
- Protection from sunlight.
- If lighting is provided within store it must be flameproof.
- Provision for spill containment materials.
- Fire extinguishers located nearby - consider powder type.
- Full and empty containers separated.
- Clear identification of contents.

Figure 2-6-19: Poor storage of flammable liquids. *Source: RMS.*

Figure 2-6-20: Storage of flammable materials. *Source: RMS.*

Liquefied petroleum and other gases in cylinders

Liquefied Petroleum Gas (LPG) is a term that relates to gas stored in a liquefied state under pressure; common examples are propane and butane. LPG and other gas cylinders should be stored in line with the principles detailed below:

STORAGE

- Storage area should preferably be in clear open area outside.
- Stored in a secure compound - 2m high fence.
- Safe distance from toxic, corrosive, combustible materials, flammable liquids or general waste.
- Stored safe distance from any building.
- If stored inside building, kept away from exit routes, consideration should be given to fire resisting storage.
- Well ventilated area - 2.5% of total floor and wall area as vents, high and low.
- Oxygen cylinders at least 3m away from flammable gas cylinders.
- Acetylene may be stored with LPG if quantity of LPG less than 50Kg.
- Access to stores should be controlled to prevent LPG etc being stored unsafely in the general workplace.
- More than one exit (unlocked) may need to be available from any secure storage compound where distance to exit is greater than 12m.
- Lock storage compound when not in use.
- Protection from sunlight.
- Flameproof lighting.
- Empty containers stored separate from full.
- Fire extinguishers located nearby - consider powder and water types.

TRANSPORT

- Upright position.
- Secured to prevent falling over.
- Protection in event of accident e.g. position on vehicle.
- Transport in open vehicle preferably.
- Avoid overnight parking while loaded.
- Park in secure areas.

- 'Trem card' and warning signs.
- Driver training.
- Fire fighting equipment.

USE

General use

- Cylinder connected for use may be stored in the general workplace; any spare cylinders must be secured in a purpose built store until required for use.
- Fixed position to prevent falling over, or on wheeled trolley - chained.
- Well ventilated area.
- Away from combustibles.
- Kept upright unless used on equipment specifically designed for horizontal use - e.g. gas powered lift truck.
- Handled carefully - do not drop.
- Allow to settle after transport and before use.
- Consider manual handling and injury prevention.
- Turn off cylinder before connecting, disconnecting equipment.
- Check equipment before use.
- Any smell of gas during use, turn off cylinder and investigate.
- Use correct gas regulator for equipment/task.
- Use equipment in line with manufacturers' instructions.

Use in huts

- Only allow cylinders in a hut if it is part of a heater (cabinet heater).
- Pipe into site huts from cylinder located outside where possible.
- If cylinder is outside the hut use the shortest connecting hose as possible.
- Hut to be adequately ventilated high and low.
- Heaters fitted with flame failure devices.
- Turn off heater and cylinder after use and overnight.
- Be aware of danger of leaks inside huts, especially overnight as a severe risk of fire or explosion may occur.
- Keep heaters away from clothing and other combustibles.

Figure 2-6-21: Gas cylinders for huts. *Source: RMS.*

Structural measures to prevent spread of fire and smoke

PROPERTIES OF COMMON BUILDING MATERIALS

Brickwork/blockwork

Both brickwork and blockwork perform well in fires. Dependent upon the materials, workmanship, thickness, and the load carried, fire resistance of 30 minutes to 2 hours may be achieved.

Steelwork

Steel and other metals are extensively used in modern building structures. Generally they can be affected by fire at relatively low temperatures unless they are protected from the effects of the fire by some form of fire retardant materials. This may be done by encasing in concrete, fire retardant boards or spray coatings.

Timber

Timber performs very well in fires as long as it is of sufficient size that, as its outer coat burns away, there is still sufficient strength to do its task. Generally timber does not fail rapidly in a fire, unlike steel.

Glass

Glass generally performs poorly in a fire unless it is fire resistant glass. At high temperatures glass will melt and sag, which is why the traditional fire resistant glass has wire within it.

STRUCTURAL MEASURES TO PREVENT SPREAD

Measures to prevent spread of fire and smoke include:

- Fire resisting structures.
- Compartmentalisation to confine the fire to a predetermined size.
- Fire stopping of ducts, flues and holes in fire resistant structures.
- Fire resisting doors.

- Smoke seals and intumescent (a material which expands and insulates the surface, when heat is applied) materials on doors.
- Early and rapid detection of a fire by use of 'intelligent' fire alarm systems.
- Sprinklers in large compartments, in particular 'rapid response' systems to limit the size of the fire.
- Control of smoke and toxic fumes by ventilation systems, so that clear air is maintained at head height level, to enable persons to escape.

Figure 2-6-22: Magnetic door holder linked to alarm. *Source: RMS.*

Figure 2-6-23: Door stop with automatic release. *Source: RMS.*

PROTECTION OF OPENINGS AND VOIDS

Consideration should be given to the protection of openings and voids by the use of fire barriers such as fire shutters, cavity barriers and fire curtains. It is important that when construction or maintenance work takes place it is managed to minimise the effect on the structure being worked on to keep fire precautions intact as much as possible. This will involve planning for the prompt re-instatement of protection of openings and voids as soon after their breach to do work as is possible. The temptation to leave all breaches to the end of work and then re-instate them should be avoided - the longer that breaches are left open the higher the risk from fires.

Use of suitable electrical equipment in flammable atmospheres

The Dangerous Substances and Explosive Atmospheres Regulations (DSEAR) 2002 apply to most workplaces where a potentially explosive atmosphere may occur. DSEAR 2002 requires employers to eliminate or control the risks from potentially explosive atmospheres.

CLASSIFICATION OF AREAS WHERE EXPLOSIVE ATMOSPHERES MAY OCCUR

Employers must classify areas where hazardous explosive atmospheres may occur into zones. The classification given to a particular zone, and its size and location, depends on the likelihood of an explosive atmosphere occurring and its persistence if it does occur. Schedule 2 of DSEAR 2002 contains descriptions of the various classifications of zones for gases and vapours and for dusts.

There are three zones for gases and vapours:

- Zone 0   Flammable atmosphere highly likely to be present - may be present for long periods or even continuously.
- Zone 1   Flammable atmosphere possible but unlikely to be present for long periods.
- Zone 2   Flammable atmosphere unlikely to be present except for short periods of time - typically as a result of a process fault condition.

Similarly, there are three zones for dusts:

- Zone 20   Dust cloud likely to be present continuously or for long periods.
- Zone 21   Dust cloud likely to be present occasionally in normal operation.
- Zone 22   Dust cloud unlikely to occur in normal operation, but if it does, will only exist for a short period.

SELECTION OF EQUIPMENT AND PROTECTIVE SYSTEMS

Areas classified into zones must be protected from sources of ignition. Electrical equipment for use in hazardous explosive atmospheres needs to be designed and constructed in such a way that it will not provide a source of ignition. Equipment intended to be used in zoned areas should be selected to meet the requirements of the Equipment and Protective Systems Intended for Use in Potentially Explosive Atmospheres Regulations (EPS) 1996. Zone zero and zone 20 are the zones with the highest likelihood of an explosive atmosphere occurring and persisting; electrical equipment for this zone needs to be very well protected against providing a source of ignition. There are a number of ways in which electrical equipment can be designed to prevent ignition of explosive atmospheres, each achieves this in different ways. The types of protection include intrinsically safe (cannot produce a spark with sufficient energy to cause ignition), flameproof (ingress of explosive atmosphere is controlled and any ignition is contained in the equipment) and Type 'E' equipment (do not produce sparks or hot surfaces).

6.4 - Fire detection, fire alarm and fire-fighting equipment

Common fire detection and alarm systems

FIRE DETECTION

Heat detection

Sensors operate by the melting of a metal (fusion detectors) or expansion of a solid, liquid or gas (thermal expansion detectors).

Radiation detection

Photoelectric cells detect the emission of infra-red/ultra-violet radiation from the fire.

Smoke detection

Using ionising radiations, light scatter (smoke scatters beams of light), obscuration (smoke entering a detector prevents light from reaching a photoelectric cell).

Figure 2-6-24: Smoke detector.   *Source: RMS.*

Flammable gas detection

Measures the amount of flammable gas in the atmosphere and compares the value with a reference value.

ALARM SYSTEMS

The purpose of a fire alarm is to give an early warning of a fire in a building for two reasons:

- To increase the safety of occupants by encouraging them to escape to a place of safety.
- To increase the possibility of early extinction of the fire thus reducing the loss of or damage to the property.

TYPES OF FIRE ALARMS

Voice	Simplest and most effective type but very limited because it is dependent upon the size of the workplace and background noise levels.
Hand operated	Rotary gong, hand bell or triangle and sounder but limited by the scale of the building.
Call points with sounders	Standard system, operation of one call point sounds alarm throughout workplace.
Automatic system	System as above, with added fire detection to initiate the alarm.

Single-stage alarm

The alarm sounds throughout the whole of the building and calls for total evacuation.

Two-stage alarm

In certain large/high rise buildings it may be better to evacuate the areas of high risk first, usually those closest to the fire or immediately above it. In this case, an evacuation signal is given in the affected area, together with an alert signal in other areas. If this type of system is required, early consultation with the Fire Service is essential.

Figure 2-6-25 Easy operation alarm call point.   *Source: RMS.*

Figure 2-6-26: Alarm point identified and well located. *Source: RMS.*

Staff alarms

In some premises, an immediate total evacuation may not be desirable, e.g. nightclubs, shops, theatres, cinemas. A controlled evacuation by the staff may be preferred, to prevent distress and panic to the occupants. If such a system is used, the alarm must be restricted to the staff and only used where there are sufficient members of staff and they have been fully trained in the action of what to do in case of fire.

Alarms must make a distinctive sound, audible in all parts of the workplace (sound levels should be 65 dB (A) or 5dB (A) above any other noise - which ever is the greater). The meaning of the alarm sound must be understood by all. They may be manually or automatically operated.

Portable fire fighting equipment

SITING

Portable fire extinguishers should always be sited:

- On the line of escape routes.
- Near, but not too near, to danger points.
- Near to room exits inside or outside according to occupancy and/or risk.
- In multi-storey buildings, at the same position on each floor e.g. top of stair flights or at corners in corridors.
- Where possible in groups forming fire points.
- So that no person need travel more than 45 metres to reach an extinguisher.
- With the carrying handle about one metre from the floor to facilitate ease of handling, removal from wall bracket, or on purpose designed floor stand.
- Away from excesses of heat or cold.

MAINTENANCE AND INSPECTION

Any fire fighting equipment provided must be properly maintained and subject to examination and test at intervals such that it remains effective.

Maintenance

This means service of the fire extinguisher by a competent person. It involves thorough examination of the extinguisher (internal/external) and this is usually done annually.

Inspection

A monthly check should be carried out to ensure that extinguishers are in their proper place and have not been discharged, lost pressure or suffered obvious damage. It may be necessary to increase the frequency of checks made for fire extinguishers on a construction site to a weekly basis, due to the less structured or controlled work environment that they are sited in. This could mean that there is a higher risk of them being damaged or used without notification.

FIRE FIGHTING EQUIPMENT TRAINING REQUIREMENTS

The 'Responsible Person' must take measures for fire-fighting as necessary. They should nominate competent persons to implement these measures and provide training and equipment accordingly. It would be good practice to make sure that those that may need to take a lead in operating fire extinguishers can do this competently and for most people this would mean practising how to use them in a situation that reproduces the circumstances of a fire. Training should include:

- Understanding of principles of combustion and classification of fires.
- Identification of the various types of fire extinguisher available to them.
- Principles of use and limitations of extinguishers.
- Considerations for personal safety and the safety of others.
- How to identify if the extinguisher is appropriate to the fire and ready to use.
- How to attack fires with the appropriate extinguisher(s).
- Any specific considerations related to the environment the extinguishers are kept or used in.

Training has to clarify the general and specific rules for use of extinguishers:

General - aim at the seat of the fire and move the extinguisher across the fire to extinguish it - this is particularly appropriate for Class A fires.

Specific - if using a foam extinguisher for Class B fires the foam is allowed to drop onto the fire by aiming just above it. If this is for a flammable liquid fire contained in an open tank it is possible to get good results by this process or aiming it to the back of the tank and allowing the foam to float over the liquid. For other specific limitations or approaches to the use of individual types of extinguishing media see section below.

Extinguishing media

WATER (PORTABLE EXTINGUISHER - COLOUR CODE - RED)

Water should only be used on Class A fires - those involving solids like paper and wood. Water works by cooling the burning material to below its ignition temperature, therefore removing the heat part of the fire triangle, and so the fire goes out. Water is the most common form of extinguishing media and can be used on the majority of fires involving solid materials. It must not be used on liquid fires or in the vicinity of live electrical equipment.

Figure 2-6-27: Fire point sign.
Source: BCW Office Products.

Figure 2-6-28: Water extinguisher colour coded red by label and sign.
Source: RMS.

Figure 2-6-29: Fire point sign.
Source: Warning Signs Direct.

Figure 2-6-30: Cream colour coded extinguisher.
Source: Low Cost Fire.

FOAM (PORTABLE EXTINGUISHER - COLOUR CODE - CREAM)

Foam is especially useful for extinguishing Class B fires - those involving burning liquids and solids which melt and turn to liquids as they burn. Foam works in several ways to extinguish the fire, the main way being to smother the burning liquid, i.e. to stop the oxygen reaching the combustion zone. Foam can also be used to prevent flammable vapours escaping from spilled volatile liquids and also on Class A fires. It is worth noting that the modern spray foams are more efficient than water on a Class A fire. *It must not be used in the vicinity of live electrical equipment, unless electrically rated.*

Figure 2-6-31: Fire point sign.
Source: Warning Signs Direct.

Figure 2-6-32: Blue colour coded extinguisher.
Source: The Sharpedge.

Figure 2-6-33: Fire point sign.
Source: BCW Office Products.

Figure 2-6-34: Black colour coded extinguisher.
Source: Blazetec Fire Protection.

DRY POWDER (PORTABLE EXTINGUISHER - COLOUR CODE - BLUE)

Designed for Class A, B and C fires but may only subdue Class A fires for a short while. One of the main ways in which powder works to extinguish a fire is the smothering effect, whereby it forms a thin film of powder on the burning liquid, thus excluding air. The extinguishing media is also excellent for the rapid knock down (flame suppression) of flammable liquid spills.

Powders generally provide extinction faster than foam, but there is a greater risk of re-ignition. If used indoors, a powder can cause problems for the operator due to the inhalation of the powder and obscuration of vision.

This type of extinguishing media may be used on live electrical equipment.

CARBON DIOXIDE (CO^2) (PORTABLE EXTINGUISHER - COLOUR CODE - BLACK)

Carbon dioxide (CO^2) is safe and excellent for use on live electrical equipment. It may also be used for small Class B fires in their early stages of development, indoors or outdoors with little air movement. CO^2 replaces the oxygen in the atmosphere surrounding the fuel and the fire is extinguished.

CO^2 is an asphyxiant and should not be used in confined spaces. As it does not remove the heat there is the possibility of re-ignition. CO^2 extinguishers are very noisy due to the rapid expansion of gas on release; this can surprise people when they operate a portable extinguisher. This expansion causes severe cooling around the discharge horn and can freeze the skin if the operator's hand is in contact with the horn. As most carbon dioxide portable extinguishers last only a few seconds, only small fires should be tackled with this type of extinguisher.

EXTINGUISHING MEDIA FOR SPECIFIC CLASSES OF FIRE

Class C fires

Except in very small occurrences, a Class C fire involving gas should not normally be extinguished. If a gas fire is to be extinguished, then isolation of the gas supply must also take place.

Class D fires

Class D metal fires are a specialist type of fire and they cannot be extinguished by the use of ordinary extinguishing media. In fact, it may be dangerous to attempt to fight a metal fire with ordinary extinguishing media as an explosion of the metal may take place or toxic fumes may be produced. Metal fires can be extinguished by smothering them with dry sand.

However, the sand must be absolutely dry or an explosion may occur. Other extinguishing media used may are pyromet, graphite, talc or salt. All of these extinguishing media basically operate by the smothering principle.

Class F fires (Wet chemical) (Portable extinguisher - Colour code - Yellow)

New style wet chemical extinguishing media have been designed to specifically deal with Class F *cooking oil* fires.

This type of extinguishing media congeals on top of the oil and excludes the oxygen. It may also be used on Class A fires depending upon the manufacturer's instructions.

Figure 2-6-35: Fire point sign. *Source: Midland Fire Ltd.*

Figure 2-6-36: Yellow colour coded extinguisher. *Source: Midland Fire Ltd.*

SUMMARY MATRIX - FIRE EXTINGUISHING MEDIA

	Method	Class 'A'	Class 'B'	Class 'C'	Class 'D'	Electric	Class 'F'
Water	Cools	Yes	No	No	No	No	No
Spray Foam	Smothers	Yes	Yes	No	No	No	No
Wet Chemical	Chemical	No	No	No	No	No	Yes
Dry Powder	Smothers and Chemical	Yes	Yes	Yes and Isolate	Special Powders	Yes - Low Voltage	No
Vapourising Liquids	Chemical and Smothers	Special uses					
Carbon Dioxide	Smothers	No	Yes - Small Fires	No	No	Yes	No

Figure 2-6-37: Summary matrix - fire extinguishing media.

Source: RMS.

6.5 - Evacuation of a workplace

Means of escape

The Regulatory Reform (Fire Safety) Order (RRFSO) 2005 requires the responsible person to "make and give effect to such arrangements as are appropriate, having regard to the size of his undertaking and the nature of its activities, for the effective planning, organisation, control, monitoring and review of the preventive and protective measures".

The RRFSO 2005 also sets out the type of requirements necessary with regard to emergency routes and exits. An adequate means of escape is essential for all premises.

The following general factors should be taken into consideration when planning means of escape.

TRAVEL DISTANCES

Travel distance is a significant component of a successful means of escape plan.

Travel distances are judged on the basis of distance to a place of safety in the open air and away from the building; the distance needs to be kept to the minimum.

The distance includes travel around obstructions in the workplace and may be greatly affected by any work in progress on a construction site.

If someone is outside on a scaffold it is unlikely to be considered as a place of safety and the distance would usually be taken as that to reach the ground away from the building (for example, at an assembly point).

The route must be sufficiently wide and of sufficiently short distance to allow speedy and safe evacuation.

Figure 2-6-38: Fire escape - hazard of falling on exit due to height from ground. *Source: RMS.*

There should normally be alternative routes leading in different directions. Everyone should be able to escape unaided (if able bodied).

The distance between work stations and the nearest fire exit should be minimised.

STAIRS

Staircases form an integral part of the means of escape from fire in most buildings. If they are to be part of the escape route, the following points must be ensured:

■ Fire resistant structure.
■ Fitted with fire doors.
■ Doors must not be wedged open.
■ Wide enough to take the required number of people.
■ Must lead direct to fresh air, or to two totally separate routes of escape.
■ Non slip/trip and in good condition.
■ No combustible storage within staircase.

PASSAGEWAYS

■ The route should lead directly to the open air via a protected route (where necessary).
■ Route to be kept unobstructed.

DOORS

■ Exit doors are to open outwards easily (unless small numbers of people involved).
■ Provide fire doors along the escape route.
■ Fire doors along with fire resistant structures serve two purposes:
  • Prevent the spread of fire.
  • Ensure that there is means of escape for persons using the building.
■ They should not be wedged open.
■ Lead to open air - safety.

EMERGENCY LIGHTING

Emergency lighting should be considered if escape is likely to be required in dark conditions. This could mean late afternoon in winter time, not just at night time.

EXIT AND DIRECTIONAL SIGNS

Fire escape signs are provided to guide escape from wherever people are in a building, via a place of relative safety (the escape route) to the place of ultimate safety (the assembly area). Fire escape signs are not needed on the main route into or out of a building (the one used by people for normal arrival and exit), but alternative escape routes and complicated escape routes do need to be signed.

It must not be assumed that everyone will know all safe routes through the building or that once people are out of the building they will know how to get to the assembly point. Signs directing to the assembly point will also be needed.

(See also NGC1 - Element 4 - Health and safety management systems 3 - planning; Safety signs).

Figure 2-6-39: Fire escape sign. *Source: RMS.*

ASSEMBLY POINTS

The assembly point is a place of safety where people wait whilst any incident is investigated, and where confirmation can be made that everyone has evacuated the premises. The main factors to consider are:

- Safe distance from building.
- Sited in a safe position.
- Not sited so that staff will be in the way of Fire Brigade.
- Must be able to walk away from assembly point and back to a public road.
- Clearly signed.
- More than one provided to suit numbers and groups of people.
- Communications should be provided between assembly points.
- Measures provided to decide if evacuation successful.
- Person must be in charge of assembly point and identified.
- Person to meet/brief the fire and rescue service.

Figure 2-6-40: Assembly point. *Source: RMS.*

Emergency evacuation procedures

Article 15 of the RRFSO 2005 requires that the responsible person:

> *"Establish and, where necessary, give effect to appropriate procedures, including safety drills, to be followed in the event of serious and imminent danger to relevant persons".*

Figure 2-6-41: Article 15 of RRFSO 2005. *Source: The Regulatory Reform (Fire Safety) Order (RRFSO) 2005.*

Furthermore, it sets out a requirement to nominate a sufficient number of competent persons to implement evacuation procedures.

The danger which may threaten people if an emergency occurs at work depends on many different factors; consequently it is not possible to construct one model procedure for action in the event of fire and emergency for all premises. Evacuation procedures need to reflect the type of emergency, the people affected and the premises involved. Many of the different issues to consider for different emergencies have common factors, for example, evacuation in an efficient/effective manner, an agreed assembly location (which may be different for different emergencies) and checks to ensure people are safe. These factors are considered below with regard to fire emergencies.

ROLE AND APPOINTMENT OF FIRE MARSHALS

In all premises a person should be nominated to be responsible for co-ordinating the fire evacuation plan. This may be the same person that organises fire instruction and training and drills and co-ordinates the evacuation at the time of the fire. They may appoint persons such as fire marshals to assist them in fulfilling the role. This involves the appointment of certain staff to act as fire marshals to assist with evacuation. The way in which they assist will vary between organisations; for example, some will check areas of the building in the event of a fire to ensure no person is still inside and others will lead the evacuation to show where to go. The fire marshals' appointment should be made known to workers and they should be clearly identifiable at the time of emergency so that those that are asked to evacuate understand the authority of the person requiring them to do so. The appointment of fire marshals contributes to an employer's compliance with the requirement to establish competent persons to assist with health and safety.

FIRE INSTRUCTION NOTICES

At conspicuous positions in all parts of the location, and adjacent to all fire alarm actuating points (e.g. break glass operated call points), printed notices should be exhibited stating, in concise terms, the essentials of the action to be taken upon discovering a fire and on hearing the fire alarm. It is usual to also state what someone must do when they discover a fire.

Fire action

The action in the event of a fire and upon discovery needs to be immediate, and a simple fire action plan should be put into effect. A good plan of action would include the following points.

On discovering a fire

- Sound the fire alarm (to warn others).
- Call the fire service.
- Go to the assembly point.

On hearing the alarm

- Leave the building by the nearest exit.
- Close doors behind you.
- Go to the assembly point.
- Get out of the building and stay out.

On evacuation

- Do not take risks.
- Do not stop for personal belongings.
- Do not use lifts.
- Do not return to the building unless authorised to do so.
- Report to assembly point.
- Consider the wording on notices that are posted and ensure that workers are instructed and trained to do what is asked of them.

Figure 2-6-42: Fire instruction notice.   Source: RMS.

FIRE TRAINING

Typical issues to be included in a fire training programme relating to emergency action are:

- Fire prevention.
- Recognition of fire alarms and the actions to be taken.
- Understanding the emergency signs.
- Location of fire escape routes and assembly points.
- Requirements for safe evacuation (e.g. non-use of lifts, do not run etc.).
- Location and operation of call points and other means of raising the alarm.
- How the fire service is called.
- Location, use and limitations of fire fighting equipment.
- Consideration of people with special needs.
- Identity and role of fire marshals.

FIRE DRILLS

A fire drill is intended to ensure, by means of training and rehearsal, that in the event of fire:

- The people who may be in danger act in a calm, orderly and efficient manner.
- Those designated with specific duties carry them out in an organised and effective manner.
- The means of escape are used in accordance with a predetermined and practised plan.
- An opportunity for management leadership.

The fire drill enables all people involved in the evacuation to practice and learn under as near realistic circumstances as possible. This can identify what works well in the evacuation procedure and what does not. Practice in the form of a drill helps people to respond quickly to the alarm and, because they have done it before, to make their way efficiently to the assembly point. At least once a year a practice fire drill should normally be carried out simulating conditions in which one or more of the escape routes from the building are obstructed. This will assist in developing an awareness of the alternative exits that can be taken and assist in ensuring people understand the unpredictability of fires.

ROLL CALL

The traditional method of undertaking a roll call is by use of a checklist of names. Very few workplaces can now operate this system as they do not have such a static workforce as this system requires. Where they can operate they will provide a speedy and efficient means of identifying who has arrived at the assembly point and who has not. Where strict security control to a construction site is used, with signing in and out, this may make this process more viable. This requires people on site to report to their allocated assembly point and for someone (e.g. a Fire Marshal) to confirm that they have arrived safely and determine if anyone is missing.

If it is not known exactly who is in a building a system of Fire Marshals who can make a check of the building at the time of their own evacuation (without endangering their own safety) may be employed. This can assist with the process and may identify people that have not evacuated. However, this system may not be able to provide an absolute confirmation that everyone has evacuated as there may be limited opportunity for the Fire Marshal to check the whole of the area allocated to them. Any doubt or confirmed missing persons should be reported to the person nominated to report to the fire service, who in turn will provide a report to the fire service as soon as they arrive.

PROVISIONS FOR THE DISABLED

When planning a fire evacuation system employers need to consider who may be in the workplace, their abilities and capabilities.

Any disability e.g. hearing, vision, mental or mobility impairment must be catered for. Some of the arrangements may be to provide the person with a nominated assistant(s) to support their speedy escape, for example, with the use of a specially designed evacuation chair to enable them to make their way out of a building down emergency exit stairs.

Part of the provision is to make sure they are capable of knowing that an emergency exists. This may mean providing them with special alarm arrangements that cater for their disability, for example, a visual and or vibrating alert for the hearing impaired.

Figure 2-6-43: Fire refuge sign for disabled people.
Source: Safety Selector.

In some cases, disabled people may need to use a refuge area, a relatively safe waiting area for short periods. A refuge area is separated from the fire by a fire-resisting structure and has access via a safe route to a fire exit. It provides a temporary space for disabled people to wait for others who will help them to evacuate. Some buildings may be equipped with an evacuation lift, which has been specifically designed within a fire resisting enclosure and having a separate power supply.

BUILDING PLANS TO INCLUDE RECORD OF EMERGENCY ESCAPE

Building plans should be drawn up to aid the emergency services. These will help identify the quickest and shortest route through the building, but can also be used to aid search and rescue. Plans should clearly identify call points, the siting of fire fighting equipment/sprinklers (if fitted), fire doors, travel distances, escape routes, refuge areas for the disabled, assembly points.

This page is intentionally blank

UNIT NGC2
CONTROLLING WORKPLACE HAZARDS

Element

7

Chemical and biological health hazards and risk control

Sources of reference

Step by Step Guide to COSHH Assessment (HSG97), HSE Books ISBN 0-7176-2785-3

Occupational Exposure Limits (EH40), HSE Books (updated annually)

Control of Substances Hazardous to Health (ACOP) (L5), HSE Books ISBN 0-7176-2981-3

Personal Protective Equipment at Work (Guidance) (L25), HSE Books ISBN 0-7176-6139-3

An Introduction to Local Exhaust Ventilation (HSG37), HSE Books ISBN 0-7176-1001-2

Respiratory Protective Equipment at Work - A Practical Guide (HSG53), HSE Books ISBN 0-7176-2904-X

The management of asbestos in non-domestic premises, Regulation 4 of the Control of Asbestos Regulations 2006 Approved Code of Practice and guidance (L127) ISBN 0717662098

Relevant statutory provisions

The Control of Substances Hazardous to Health Regulations (COSHH) 2002

The Chemicals (Hazard Information and Packaging for Supply) Regulations (CHIP) 2009

The Personal Protective Equipment at Work Regulations (PPER) 1992

The Control of Asbestos Regulations (CAR) 2006

The Hazardous Waste (England and Wales) Regulations (HWR) 2005

The Special Waste Regulations (SWR) 1996

The Special Waste Amendment (Scotland) Regulations (SWASR) 2004

7.1 - Health risks from hazardous substances

Forms of chemical agent

The form taken by a hazardous substance is a contributory factor to its potential for harm. Principally the form affects how easily a substance gains entry to the body, how it is absorbed into the body and how it reaches a susceptible site.

Chemical agents take many forms, the most common being as follows:

DUSTS

Dusts are solid airborne particles, often created by operations such as grinding, crushing, milling, sanding or demolition - e.g. silica, asbestos, cotton fibres, flour, cement, etc.

FUMES

Fumes are solid particles formed by condensation from the gaseous state - e.g. lead fume, welding fume.

SMOKE

Smoke is particles that result from incomplete combustion. A combination of gases and very small particles that can be either solid or liquid state.

GASES

Gases are formless fluids usually produced by chemical processes involving combustion or by the interaction of chemical substances. A gas will normally seek to fill the space completely into which it is liberated - e.g. chlorine gas, carbon monoxide, methane, etc.

MISTS AND AEROSOLS

Mists are finely dispersed liquid droplets suspended in air. Mists are mainly created by spraying, foaming, pickling and electro-plating - e.g. mist from a water pressure washer, paint spray, pesticides, oil, etc.

VAPOUR

Vapour is the gaseous form of a material normally encountered in a liquid or solid state at normal room temperature and pressure; typical examples are solvents - e.g. trichloroethylene which releases vapours when the container is opened.

LIQUIDS

Liquids are substances which are liquid at normal temperature and pressure.

SOLIDS

Solids are materials which are solid at normal temperature and pressure.

Forms of biological agents

FUNGAL

Fungi are a variety of organisms that act in a parasitic manner, feeding on organic matter. Most are either harmless or positively beneficial to health; however a number causes harm to humans and may be fatal. An example of a fungi organism is the mould from rotten hay called Aspergilla, which causes Aspergillosis (Farmer's Lung). Farmer's lung is an allergic reaction to the mould. This occurs deep in the lungs in the alveoli region. It leads to shortness of breath, which gets progressively worse at each exposure. The resulting attack is similar to asthma. Aspergilla can also cause short-term effects of irritation to the eyes and nose and coughing. Moulds from the same family can cause ringworm and Athlete's Foot.

ALGAE

Microscopic plants deposited in pool or spa water by wind, rain, and dust. They thrive in sunlight and warm water, clogging filters, increasing the need for sanitisers and oxidisers, and causing slippery surfaces. The presence of algae can increase the risk of Legionella.

BACTERIAL

Bacteria are single cell organisms. Most bacteria are harmless to humans and many are beneficial. The bacteria that can cause disease are called pathogens. Examples of harmful bacteria are leptospira (causing Weil's disease), bacillus anthracis (causing anthrax), and legionella pneumophila (causing legionnaires disease).

VIRUSES

Viruses are the smallest known type of infectious agent. They invade the cells of other organisms, which they take over and make copies of themselves, and while not all cause disease many of them do. Examples of viruses are hepatitis which can cause liver damage and the Human Immunodeficiency Virus (HIV) which causes acquired immune deficiency syndrome (AIDS).

Main classification of substances hazardous to health

Indication of danger	Symbol orange background)	Category of danger	Characteristic properties and body responses
Irritant		Irritant.	A non-corrosive substance which, through immediate, prolonged or repeated contact with the skin or mucous membrane, can cause inflammation e.g. butyl ester, a severe irritant which can cause abdominal pain, vomiting and burning of the skin and eyes.
		Sensitising (by contact).	May cause an allergic skin reaction which will worsen on further exposures (allergic dermatitis), e.g. nickel or epoxy resin.
Corrosive		Corrosive.	May destroy living tissues on contact e.g. sulphuric (battery) acid or sodium hydroxide (caustic soda).
Harmful		Harmful.	If inhaled or ingested or it penetrates the skin, has an adverse effect on health e.g. some solvents causing narcosis or central nervous system failure.
	 Figure 2-7-1: Harmful, toxic.　　Source: RMS.	Sensitising (by inhalation).	May cause an allergic respiratory reaction, which will progressively worsen on further exposures (asthma), e.g. flour dust, isocyanates.
		Carcinogenic (category 3).	Only evidence is from animals, which is of doubtful relevance to humans, e.g. benzyl chloride.
		Mutagenic (category 3).	Evidence of mutation in Ames Test and possible somatic cell mutation.
		Toxic to reproduction (category 3).	Animal data, not necessarily relevant.
Toxic		Toxic.	If inhaled or ingested or it penetrates the skin, may involve serious acute or chronic health risks and even death e.g. arsenic, a systemic poison.
		Mutagenic (categories 1 and 2).	May cause genetic defects, e.g. 2-Ethoxyethanol may impair fertility.
		Toxic to reproduction (categories 1 and 2).	May cause harm to the unborn child, e.g. lead suspected of causing restricted development of the brain of the foetus.
Very Toxic			If inhaled or ingested or it penetrates the skin, may involve extremely serious acute or chronic health risks and even death e.g. cyanide, a severe irritant and systemic poison.
Carcinogenic		Category 1. Substances known to cause cancer on the basis of human experience.	May, if inhaled or it penetrates the skin, induce uncontrolled cell division (cancer) or increase its incidence, e.g. benzene affects bone marrow causing leukaemia.
		Category 2. Substances which it is assumed can cause cancer, on the basis of reliable animal evidence.	Carries the risk phrase R45.

Category 3.

Not included in the COSHH definition of carcinogen although they are subject to the general requirements of COSHH. If purchased from a supplier carries the "harmful" (Xn) symbol and the Risk Phrase R40 (limited evidence of a carcinogenic effect).

Source: The Chemicals (Hazard Information and Packaging for Supply) Regulations (CHIP 3) 2002.

Difference between acute and chronic health effects

The effect of a substance on the body depends not only on the substance, but also on the dose, and the susceptibility of the individual. No substance can be considered non-toxic; there are only differences in degree of effect.

ACUTE EFFECT

Is an immediate or rapidly produced, adverse effect, following a single or short term exposure to an offending agent, which is usually reversible (the obvious exception being death). Examples of acute effects are carbon monoxide or cyanide poisoning, radiation burns and sickness.

CHRONIC EFFECT

An adverse health effect produced as a result of prolonged or repeated exposure, with a gradual or latent, and often irreversible, effect that may often go unrecognised for a number of years. Examples of chronic effects are lead or mercury poisoning, cancer and asthma.

Other common terms used in the context of occupational health are:

Toxicology	The study of the body's responses to substances. In order to interpret toxicological data and information, the meaning of the following terms should be understood.
Toxicity	The ability of a chemical substance to produce injury once it reaches a susceptible site in or on the body. A poisonous substance (e.g. organic lead), which causes harm to biological systems and interferes with the normal functions of the body. The effects may be acute or chronic, local or systemic.
Dose	The level of environmental contamination multiplied by the length of time (duration) of exposure to the contaminant.
Local effect	Usually confined to the initial point of contact. Possible sites affected include the skin, mucous membranes or the eyes, nose or throat. Examples are burns to the skin by corrosive substances (acids and alkalis), solvents causing dermatitis.
Systemic effect	Occurs in parts of the body other than at the point of initial contact. Frequently the circulatory system provides a means to distribute the substance round the body to a target organ/system.
Target organs	An organ within the human body on which a specified toxic material exerts its effects e.g. lungs, liver, brain, skin, bladder or eyes.
Target systems	Central nervous system, circulatory system, and reproductive system. Examples of substances that have a systemic effect and their target organs are:

Alcohol - central nervous system, liver.
Lead - bone marrow and brain damage.
Mercury - central nervous system.

It must be noted that many chemicals in use today can have both an acute and chronic effect. A simple everyday example is alcohol. The acute effect of drinking too much wine in a single evening is vomiting and headache whereas the chronic effect of drinking wine in smaller quantities but over a prolonged period is cirrhosis, a systemic effect with the liver as the target organ.

7.2 - Assessment of health risks

Routes of entry of hazardous substances into the body

INHALATION

The most significant industrial entry route is inhalation. It has been estimated that at least 90% of industrial poisons are absorbed through the lungs. Harmful substances can directly attack the lung tissue causing a local affect or pass through to the blood system, to be carried round the body and affect target organs such as the liver. Typical effects of substances that enter the body through inhalation are:

Local effect

For example Silicosis, caused by inhalation of silica dust - where dust causes scarring of the lung leading to inelastic fibrous tissue to develop reducing lung capacity.

Systemic effect

For example Anoxia, caused by inhalation of carbon monoxide - the carbon dioxide replaces oxygen in the bloodstream affecting the nervous system.

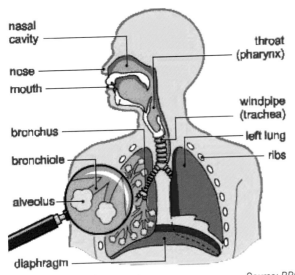

Figure 2-7-2: Respiratory system.

Source: BBC.

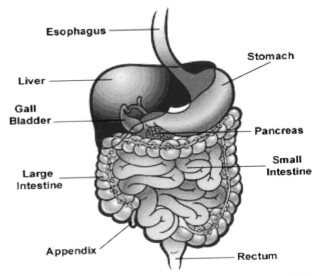

Figure 2-7-3: Digestive system.

Source: STEM.

INGESTION

This route normally presents the least problem as it is unlikely that any significant quantity of harmful liquid or solid will be swallowed without deliberate intent. However, accidents will occur where small amounts of contaminant are transferred from the fingers to the mouth if eating, drinking or smoking in chemical areas is allowed or where a substance has been decanted into a container normally used for drinking. The sense of taste will often be a defence if chemicals are taken in through this route, causing the person to spit it out. If the substance is taken in, vomiting and/or excretion may mean the substance does not cause a systemic problem, though a direct effect, for example ingestion of an acid, may destroy cells in the mouth, oesophagus or stomach.

ABSORPTION (SKIN CONTACT)

Substances can enter through the skin, cuts or abrasions and conjunctiva of the eye. Solvents such as organic solvents, e.g. toluene and trichloroethylene, can enter either accidentally or if used for washing. The substance may have a local effect, such as de-fatting of the skin resulting in inflammation and cracking of the horny layer, or pass through into the blood system causing damage to the brain, bone marrow and liver.

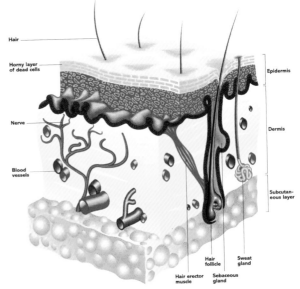

Figure 2-7-4: Skin layer.

Source: SHP.

Dermatitis

Dermatitis is caused by exposure to substances which interfere with normal skin physiology leading to inflammation of skin, usually on the hands, wrists and forearms. The skin turns red and in some cases may be itchy. Small blisters may occur and the condition may take the form of dry and cracked skin.

Contact dermatitis

Figure 2-7-5: Dermatitis.

Source: SHP.

If a person is frequently in contact with some substances or is exposed for a long duration the persistent contact can lead to dermatitis.

There are many chemicals which may irritate the skin leading to this condition; including cement, soaps, detergents, industrial chemicals, some metals, cosmetics and plants

Removal from contact with the substance usually allows normal cell repair. A similar level of repeat exposure results in the same response. This class of dermatitis is called contact dermatitis.

Sensitisation dermatitis

A second form of dermatitis is called sensitisation dermatitis. In cases of sensitisation dermatitis a person exposed to the substance develops dermatitis in the usual way.

When removed from exposure to the substance the dermatitis usually repairs, but the body gets ready for later exposures by preparing the body's defence mechanisms. A subsequent small exposure is enough to cause a major response by the immune system. The person will have become sensitised and will no longer be able to tolerate small exposures to the substance without a reaction occurring.

Dermatitis can be prevented by:

- Clean working conditions and properly planned work systems.
- Careful attention to skin hygiene principles.
- Prompt attention to cuts, abrasions and spillages onto the skin.
- Use of protective equipment.
- Barrier cream can help.
- Pre-employment screening for sensitive individuals.

INJECTION

A forceful breach of the skin, perhaps as a result of injury, can carry harmful substances through the skin barrier; for example, handling broken glass which cuts the skin and transfers a biological or chemical agent. On construction sites there are quite a few items that present a hazard of penetration, such as nails in broken up false work that might be trodden on and penetrate the foot presenting a risk of infection from tetanus.

In addition, some land or buildings being worked on may have been used by intravenous drug users and their needles may present a risk of injection of a virus, such as hepatitis. The forced injection of an agent into the body provides an easy route past the skin, which usually acts as the body's defence mechanism and protects people from the effects of many agents that do not have the ability to penetrate.

When identifying possible routes of entry, it must be remembered that many substances have multiple possibilities. Trichloroethylene, for example is denoted "sk" in EH40, that is, it will absorb through the skin. However, when in use, it also gives off very harmful vapours and, because it is liquid, there is the possibility of accidental ingestion.

BODY RESPONSE TO AGENTS AND PROTECTIVE MECHANISMS

The body's response against the invasion of substances likely to cause damage can be divided into external or superficial defences and internal or cellular defences.

Superficial defence mechanisms

Respiratory (inhalation):

Nose	On inhalation many substances and minor organisms are successfully trapped by nasal hairs, for example, the larger wood dust particles.
Respiratory tract	The next line of defence against inhalation or substances harmful to health begin here, where a series of reflexes activate the coughing and sneezing mechanisms to forcibly expel the triggering substances.
Ciliary escalator	The passages of the respiratory system are also lined with mucus and well supplied with fine hair cells which sweep rhythmically towards the outside and pass along large particles. The respiratory system narrows as it enters the lungs where the ciliary escalator assumes more and more importance as the effective defence. Smaller particles of agents, such as some lead particles, are dealt with at this stage. The smallest particles, such as organic solvent vapours, reach the alveoli and are either deposited or exhaled.

Gastrointestinal (ingestion):

Mouth	For ingestion of substances. Saliva in the mouth provides a useful defence to substances which are not excessively acid or alkaline or in large quantities.
Gastrointestinal tract	Acid in the stomach also provides a useful defence similar to saliva. Vomiting and diarrhoea are additional reflex mechanisms which act to remove substances or quantities that the body is not equipped to deal with.

Skin (absorption):

Skin	The body's largest organ provides a useful barrier against the absorption of many foreign organisms and chemicals (but not against all of them). Its effect is, however, limited by its physical characteristics. The outer part of the skin is covered in an oily layer and substances have to overcome this before they can damage the skin or enter the body.

The outer part of the epidermis is made up of dead skin cells. These are readily sacrificed to substances without harm to the newer cells underneath. Repeated or prolonged exposure could defeat this. The skin, when attacked by substances, may blister in order to protect the layers beneath. Openings in the skin such as sweat pores, hair follicles and cuts can allow entry and the skin itself may be permeable to some chemicals, e.g. toluene.

Cellular mechanisms

The cells of the body possess their own defence systems.

Scavenging action	A type of white blood cell called macrophages attack invading particles in order to destroy them and remove them from the body. This process is known as phagocytosis.
Secretion of defensive substances	Is done by some specialised cells. Histamine release and heparin, which promotes availability of blood sugar, are examples.
Prevention of excessive blood loss	Reduced circulation through blood clotting and coagulation prevents excessive bleeding and slows or prevents the entry of bacteria.
Repair of damaged tissues	Is a necessary defence mechanism which includes removal of dead cells, increased availability of defender cells and replacement of tissue strength, e.g. scar tissue caused by silica.
The lymphatic system	Acts as a 'form of drainage system' throughout the body for the removal of foreign bodies. Lymphatic glands or nodes at specific points in the system act as selective filters preventing infection from entering the blood system. In many cases a localised inflammation occurs in the node at this time.

Other practical measures to complement the body's protection mechanisms

- Good personal hygiene.
- Do not apply cosmetics in the workplace.
- No eating or drinking in the workplace.
- Provision and use of appropriate personal protective equipment.
- Taking care when removing contaminated protective clothing.
- Proper containers / storage for food and drink.

Factors to be taken into account when assessing health risks

In order to assess the risks to health it is necessary to know the following:

- The form the substance is in: solid, liquid, dust, gas, etc.
- The classification of the hazard: very toxic, toxic, corrosive, etc.
- How much of the substance will be present and its concentration.
- The routes of entry onto and into the body: inhalation, ingestion, skin pervasion, absorption.
- Whether the substance has an acute or chronic affect or both.
- The extent to which the body's defences will deal with the substance.
- The first signs of damage or ill-health.
- The vulnerability of the people involved in the process: young persons, pregnant workers; anyone who has existing health problems, such as skin problems or bronchitis.
- The effectiveness of existing control measures.

Considering the previous issues will help the assessor decide whether the risks to health are tolerable or acceptable or further controls are needed.

Sources of information

PRODUCT LABELS

All substances available for use in the workplace should be labelled in accordance with the Chemicals (Hazard Information Packaging for Supply) Regulations (CHIP) 2009 e.g. toxic, harmful, corrosive, irritant, and sensitising.

Where a dangerous chemical is supplied in a package, the package must be labelled. Packaging must be safe and able to withstand the conditions. The label must state the hazards and precautions required.

More useful information to help ensure the safe use of dangerous substances comes in the form of risk phrases and safety phrases. These are often displayed either on the container label (if it is large enough) or in the safety data sheet.

There are currently 122 risk phrases and 74 safety phrases, some examples can be seen in the following table and detailed information can be found in the ACOP to CHIP 2009.

	Risk Phrase		Safety Phrase
R3	Extreme risk of explosion by shock, friction, fire or other sources of ignition.	S2	Keep out of reach of children.
R20	Harmful by inhalation.	S20	When using do not eat or drink.
R30	Can become highly flammable in use.	S25	Avoid contact with eyes.
R45	May cause cancer.	S36	Wear suitable protective clothing.
R47	May cause birth defects.	S41	In cases of fire and/or explosion do not breathe fumes.

Figure 2-7-6: Risk and safety phrase table.   *Source: RMS.*

Absence of hazard symbols or risk and safety advice does not mean the item is harmless.

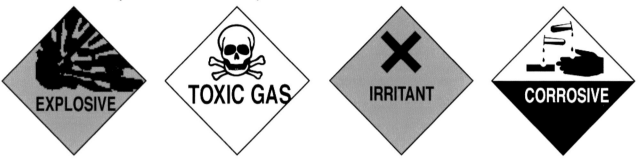

Figure 2-7-7: Product labels.   *Source: Stocksigns.*

HSE GUIDANCE NOTE EH40

EH40, which is prepared and published annually by the Health and Safety Executive (HSE), contains the lists of Workplace Exposure Limits (WEL) for use with the Control of Substances Hazardous to Health Regulations (COSHH) 2002, a description of the limit setting process, technical definitions and explanatory notes. EH40 is mostly guidance but does contain sections of special legal status; some sections have been approved by the Health and Safety Executive (HSE) and are statutory requirements that must be complied with.

MANUFACTURERS' HEALTH AND SAFETY DATA SHEETS

Section 6 of HASAWA 1974 requires manufacturers, importers and suppliers to provide information on substances for use at work; this is usually provided in the form of a data sheet. REACH (Registration, Evaluation, Authorisation and restriction of Chemicals) is the system for controlling chemicals in Europe. It became law in the UK on the 1st June 2007. REACH adopts some of the older aspects of the chemicals system in Europe, including Safety Data Sheets (SDS).

Safety Data Sheets established in accordance with REACH require the following to be included:

- Identification of the substance/mixture and of the company/undertaking.
- Hazards identification.
- Composition/information on ingredients.
- First-aid measures.
- Fire fighting measures.
- Accidental release measures.
- Handling and storage.
- Exposure controls/personal protection.

- Physical and chemical properties.
- Stability and reactivity.
- Toxicological information.
- Ecological information.
- Disposal considerations.
- Transport information.
- Regulatory information.
- Other information

SDS information does not have to be provided for:

- The offer or sale of dangerous substances or mixtures to the general public provided sufficient information is provided to enable users to take the necessary measures as regards safety, protection of human health and the environment.
- Unless a SDS is requested by a downstream user or distributor.
- If the substances/mixtures are supplied in the UK and not classified as dangerous.
- For certain products intended for the final user, e.g. medicinal products or cosmetics.

LIMITATIONS OF INFORMATION IN ASSESSING RISKS TO HEALTH

Information provided by manufacturers and contained within the HSE Guidance Note EH40 may be very technical and require a specialist to explain its relevance to a given activity. Some substances have good toxicological information, usually gained from past experience of harm; many others have a limited amount of useful toxicological information available to guide us as to the harm it may produce. This can lead to a reliance on data that is only our best understanding at the time and this may have to be revised as our knowledge on the substance changes. This is reflected in the use of WELs. Individual susceptibility of workers differs by, for example, age, gender or ethnic origin. Exposure history varies over the working life of an individual and current exposure may not indicate that the individual may suffer due to a cumulative effect from the earlier exposures.

For example, an individual may have been or be engaged in a number of processes within a variety of workplaces or personal pastimes.

Role and limitations of hazardous substance monitoring

The role of hazardous substance monitoring is to determine the level of likely exposure of workers to substances in order to establish the likely effects on the worker. Hazardous substance monitoring can help to determine what controls are required, if current controls are adequate to limit exposure and assist in choosing appropriate personal protective equipment (PPE). Monitoring can also confirm compliance with workplace exposure limits (WEL).

As described previously, the health effects of exposure to toxic substances can be acute or chronic. It is therefore necessary to use appropriate methods of measurement to distinguish these effects. It is also important to understand the limitation of any hazardous substance monitoring method used, for example, the risk of cross contamination of similar substances being measured and the fact that general workplace monitoring may not represent specific worker exposure.

When embarking upon a monitoring campaign to assess the risk to which an individual may be exposed, it is necessary to ask several questions.

1)   What to sample?

This involves a review of the materials, processes and operating procedures being used within a process, coupled with discussions with management and health and safety personnel. A brief 'walk-through' survey can also be useful as a guide to the extent of monitoring that may be necessary.

Health and safety data sheets are also of use. When the background work has been completed it can then be decided what is to be measured.

2)   On whom?

This depends on the size and diversity of the group that the survey relates to. From the group of workers being surveyed the sample to be monitored should be selected; this must be representative of the group and the work undertaken. Selecting the individual with the highest exposure can be a reasonable starting point. If the group is large then random sampling may have to be employed, but care has to be exercised with this approach. The group should also be aware of the reason for sampling.

3)   How long should the sample be for?

There are many considerations when answering this question: what are the control limits; is the hazard acute or chronic; what is our limit of detection; or simply what resources are available?

4)   How is monitoring done?

The particular sampling strategy, based on the hazard presented, is outlined in the following table:

Measurements to determine	Suitable types of measurement
Chronic hazard.	Continuous personal dose measurement. Continuous measurements of average background levels. Short term readings of containment levels at selected positions and times.
Acute hazard.	Continuous personal monitoring with rapid response. Continuous background monitoring with rapid response. Short term readings of background contaminant levels at selected positions and times.
Environmental control status.	Continuous background monitoring. Short term readings of background contaminant levels at selected positions and times.
Whether area is safe to enter.	Direct reading instruments.

Figure 2-7-8: Sampling strategy.   Source: RMS.

Basic monitoring equipment

SHORT TERM SAMPLERS

Stain tube detectors (multi-gas/vapour)

Simple devices for the measurement of contamination on a grab (short term) sampling basis. It incorporates a glass detector tube, filled with inert material. The material is impregnated with a chemical reagent which changes colour ('stains') in proportion to the quantity of contaminant as a known quantity of air is drawn through the tube. There are several different manufacturers of detector tubes including Dräger and Gastec. It is important that the literature provided with the pumps and tubes is followed. These provide a quick and easy way to detect the presence of a particular airborne contaminant. However they possess inherent inaccuracies and tube manufacturers claim a relative standard deviation of 20% or less (i.e. 1ppm in 5ppm).

Types of tube construction

- Commonest is the simple stain length tube, but it may contain filter layers, drying layers, or oxidation layers.
- Double tube or tube containing separate ampoules, avoids incompatibility or reaction during storage.
- Comparison tube.
- Narrow tube to achieve better resolution at low concentrations.

The previously shown list illustrates the main types of tubes; however there are more variations and the manufacturer's operating instructions must be read and fully understood before tubes are used.

Pumps

There are four types:

- Bellows pump.
- Piston pump.
- Ball pump.
- Battery operated pump.

Pumps and tubes of different manufacturers should not be missed.

How to use tubes

- Choose tube to measure material of interest and expected range.
- Check tubes are in date.
- Check leak tightness of pump.
- Read instructions to ensure there are no limitations due to temperature, pressure, humidity or interfering substances.
- Break off tips of tube, prepare tube if necessary and insert correctly into pump. Arrows normally indicate the direction of air flow.

Figure 2-7-9: Gas detector pump. *Source: Drager.*

- Draw the requisite number of strokes, to cause the given quantity of air to pass through the tube.
- Immediately, unless operating instructions say otherwise, evaluate the amount of contaminant by examining the stain and comparing it against the graduations on the tube. If there is any doubt when reading the tube, always err on the safe side (higher end of the scale of discolouration).
- Remove tube and discard according to instructions.
- Purge pump to remove any contaminants from inside the pump.

Advantages of short term samplers:

- Quick and easy to use.
- Instant reading without further analysis. Does not require much expertise to use.
- Relatively inexpensive.

Disadvantages of short term samplers:

- Tubes can be cross sensitive to other contaminants.
- Accuracy varies - some are only useful as an indication of the presence of contaminants.
- Is only a grab sample (taken at a single location point and may not represent the workplace as a whole).
- Relies on operator to accurately count pump strokes (manual versions).
- Only suitable for gases and vapours (not dusts).

Direct reading dust sampler

Simple methods are by direct observation of the effect of the dust on a strong beam of light e.g. using a Tyndall Lamp. High levels of small particles of dust show up under this strong beam of light. Other ways are by means of a direct reading instrument. This establishes the level of dust by, for example, scattering of light. Some also collect the dust sample. The advantages and disadvantages are:

Advantages of direct reading dust samplers:

- Instant reading.
- Continuous monitoring.
- Can record electronically.
- Can be linked to an alarm.
- Suitable for clean room environments.

Disadvantages of direct reading dust samplers:

- Some direct reading instruments can be expensive.
- Does not differentiate between dusts of different types.
- Most effective on dusts of a spherical nature.

LONG TERM SAMPLERS

Personal samplers

Passive personal samplers

Passive samplers are so described to illustrate the fact that they have no mechanism to draw in a sample of the contaminant but instead rely on passive means to sample. As such they take a time to perform this function, for example, acting as an absorber taking in contaminant vapours over a period of a working day. Some passive samplers, like gas badges, are generally fitted to the lapel and change colour to indicate contamination.

Active personal samplers

Filtration devices are used for dusts, mists and fumes. A known volume of air is pumped through a sampling head and the contaminant filtered out. By comparing the quantity of air with the amount of contaminant a measurement is made.

Sampling head in consistent position (eg mid point on shoulder seam)

Battery operated sampling pump

Figure 2-7-10: Personal sampling equipment. *Source: ROSPA OS&H.*

The filter is either weighed or an actual count of particles is done to establish the amount, as with asbestos. The type of dust can be determined by further laboratory analysis. Active samplers are used in two forms, for personal sampling and for static sampling.

Static sampling

These devices are stationed in the working area. They sample continuously over the length of a shift, or longer period if necessary. Mains or battery-operated pumps are used. Very small quantities of contaminant may be detected. The techniques employed include absorption, bubblers, and filtration; they are similar in principle to personal samplers, but the equipment is tailored to suit static use.

Advantages of long term samplers:

- Will monitor the workplace over a long period of time.
- Will accurately identify 8 hour time weighted average.

Disadvantages of long term samplers:

- Will not generally identify a specific type of contaminant.
- Will not identify multiple exposure i.e. more than one contaminant.
- Does not identify personal exposure.

Unless very sophisticated, will not read peaks and troughs.

SMOKE TUBES

Smoke tubes are simple devices that generate a 'smoke' by means of a chemical reaction. A tube similar in type to those used in stain tube detectors is selected, its ends broken (which starts the chemical reaction) and it is inserted into a small hand bellows. By gently pumping the bellows smoke is emitted. By watching the smoke air flow can be studied. This can be used to survey extraction and ventilation arrangements to determine their extent of influence.

7.3 - Workplace exposure limits

Purpose of workplace exposure limits

The purpose of workplace exposure limits is to control the exposure of workers to a variety of substances which can have harmful effects. If exposure is not controlled this can lead to many forms of ill-health. Therefore, it is important to know in advance how to protect people at work. The Health and Safety Executive set Workplace Exposure Limits (WELs) for hazardous substances and these are published in EH40, which is updated annually. These WEL's establish limits that employers work to when controlling exposure of workers to substances.

Workplace exposure limits (WELs) are occupational exposure limits set under COSHH 2002 (amended) to protect the health of persons in the workplace. They are concentrations (either parts per million or per cubic meter of air) of airborne substances averaged over a period of time known as a Time Weighted Average (TWA). The two periods that are used are 8-hours and 15-minutes. The 8-hour TWA is known as an LTEL (long-term exposure limit), used to help protect against chronic ill-health effects. 15-minute STELs (short-term exposure limits) are to protect against acute ill-health effects such as eye irritation, which may happen in minutes or even seconds of exposure. Many substances have both a LTEL and STEL allocated to them.

Airborne substances can be solid (dust), liquid (mist/aerosol), gas, vapours or fumes. Solids and liquids can be measured by weight (milligrams - mg); therefore the WEL for cement dust is expressed as 10 mg/m3. Gas, vapours and fumes are weightless. Therefore, the WEL is expressed as a concentration in the atmosphere - the long term WEL for trichloroethylene is 100 parts per million (PPM). COSHH 2002 (amended) states that exposure to hazardous substances should be prevented where it is reasonably practicable. Where this cannot be done by, for example changing the process, substituting it for something safer or enclosing the process, exposure should be reduced by other methods.

TOTAL INHALABLE DUST AND RESPIRABLE DUST

'Total inhalable dust' approximates to the fraction of airborne material, which enters the nose and mouth during breathing and is, therefore, available for deposition in the body. 'Respirable dust' approximates to the fraction, which penetrates to the gas exchange region of the lung. Where dusts contain components which have their own assigned occupational exposure limits, all the relevant limits should be complied with. Many cases of exposure can consist of a complex mixture of chemicals, such as a welding fume. The effects of these can be difficult to assess as simultaneous exposure to two or more chemicals may alter toxicity in several ways. In additive effects the combined effects are equal to the sum of its parts. EH40 provides advice on assessing the effects of mixed exposures.

Long-term and short-term exposure limits

LONG-TERM EXPOSURE LIMITS

LTEL   These are WELs that are concerned with the total intake averaged over a reference period (usually 8 hours) and is therefore appropriate for protecting against the effects of long term exposure (chronic effects). Some examples:

Benzene	1ppm
Formaldehyde	2ppm
Chlorine	0.5ppm
Phenol	2ppm
Trichloroethylene	100ppm
Trichloroethylene	550 mg/m3

SHORT-TERM EXPOSURE LIMITS

STEL   These are WELs primarily aimed at avoiding the acute effects or at least reducing the risk of occurrence. They are averaged over a 15 minute reference period. Some examples:

Phosgene	0.02ppm
Trichloroethylene	150 ppm
Trichloroethylene	820 mg/m3

It can be seen from the examples shown that trichloroethylene has both a long and short term WEL to accommodate its acute effect (narcosis) and its chronic effect (possible cancer). It is also expressed as parts per million to protect from its harmful vapours and, because processes that use trichloroethylene can create mists, it is also regulated by milligrams per cubic meter.

Limitations of exposure limits

There are many reasons why control of exposure should not be based solely on WELs:

- **Inhalation only.** Many substances (e.g. trichloroethylene) have the ability to absorb through the skin. WELs do not account for these compound routes of entry.
- **Personal susceptibility.** The majority of the work has been based on the average male physiology from the countries in which studies were conducted. Some work has been done where specific health related effects have been noted amongst females e.g. exposure to lead compounds.
- **Adopted from American TLV.** Work done to date has been based upon exposure to individuals in the developed countries e.g. Europe and USA.
- **Variations in control.** Local exhaust ventilation systems may not always work consistently because of lack of maintenance, overwhelming levels of contamination, etc.
- **Errors in monitoring.** Measuring microscopic amounts of contamination requires very accurate and sensitive equipment. Lack of maintenance and misuse can lead to inaccuracies in monitoring.
- **Synergistic effects.** The standards that are available relate to single substances and the effects of multiple substances in the workplace need to be considered.

Reducing exposure levels

Though WELs may be set for substances the Health and Safety at Work Act (HASAWA) 1974 and COSHH 2002 require reduction of exposure to as low as is reasonably practicable. Existing data on exposure limits may not reflect the safe levels that should be achieved to ensure the health of people exposed to substances in the workplace. It is important to review work practices and control strategies to reduce levels of exposure whenever possible. Control strategies should be constantly reviewed to ensure the lowest levels of exposure are achieved. If the levels of exposure are to be maintained below the WEL, with confidence, it will be necessary to work below them sufficiently to account for changes in work situation. This is particularly important with those WELs that are set for substances that are carcinogens or sensitisers. By working "at the limit" employers do not allow for sensitive people who may be affected by relatively low exposures. Nor do they account for variations or inaccuracies in monitoring, sudden surges of contaminant or partial failures of control measures.

Regulation 7 (7) of COSHH 2002 states that control will be treated as adequate if:

(a)   *The principles of good practice for the control of exposure to substances hazardous to health set out in Schedule 2A are applied.*

(b)   *Any workplace exposure limit approved for that substance is not exceeded.*

(c)   *For a substance:*

(i)   *Which carries the risk phrase R45, R46 or R49 (i.e. carcinogens), or for a substance or process that is listed in Schedule 1.*

(ii)   *Which carries the risk phrase R42 or R42/43 (i.e. respiratory sensitisers), or which is listed in section C of HSE publication "Asthmagen? Critical assessments of the evidence for agents implicated in occupational asthma", exposure is reduced to as low a level as is reasonably practicable.*

7.4 - Control measures

Duty to prevent exposure or adequately control it

"Every employer shall ensure that the exposure of his employees to substances hazardous to health is either prevented or, where this is not reasonably practicable, adequately controlled".

Figure 2-7-11: Regulation 7(1).   *Source: The Control of Substances Hazardous to Health Regulations (COSHH) 2002 (amended).*

The eight principles of good practice for the control of exposure to substances hazardous to health are set out in Schedule 2A of COSHH 2002 (amended) ACOP and guidance. A summary of the main points is given here and further detail can be found in the section *'Principles of good practice as regards control of exposure'* later in this element.

- Design and operate processes and activities to minimise emission, release and spread of substances hazardous to health.
- Take into account all relevant routes of exposure - inhalation, skin absorption and ingestion - when developing control measures.
- Control exposure by measures that are proportionate to the health risk.
- Chose the most effective and reliable control options which minimize the escape and spread of the substances hazardous to health.
- Where adequate control of exposure cannot be achieved by other means, provide, in combination with other control measures, suitable personable protective equipment.
- Check and review regularly all elements of control measures for their continuing effectiveness.
- Inform and train all employees on the hazards and risks from the substances with which they work and the use of control measures developed to minimize the risks.
- Ensure that the introduction of control measures does not increase the overall risk to health and safety.

Ensuring the workplace exposure limit is not exceeded

If exposure cannot be prevented, preferably by avoiding the use of a hazardous substance, then employers must adequately control exposure. To achieve this, the employer must apply protection measures appropriate to the activity and consistent with the priority order specified by COSHH 2002:

- Provision of a high level of inherent health and safety by careful design, selection and use of appropriate work processes, systems and engineering controls, and use of suitable work equipment and materials, e.g. systems and processes which reduce to the minimum required for the work the amount of hazardous substance used or produced, or equipment which totally encloses the process.
- Controlling exposure at source, e.g. by including adequate ventilation systems and appropriate organisational measures such as reducing to a minimum the number of employees exposed and the level and duration of their exposure.
- Using personal protective equipment in addition to the previous measures where those measures alone cannot achieve adequate control.

The selection of protection measures should be determined by the level of the ill health risk resulting from exposure to the hazardous substance and the scope for reducing the risk to a minimum. It is important to ensure that protection measures are put in place that protects those directly affected by the substance and maintenance workers. Protection measures need to be supported by the provision of information, instruction, training and supervision to ensure exposure limits are met and protection measures not undermined. It is essential that the protection measures are monitored for effectiveness by the provision of workplace and worker monitoring.

Principles of good practice as regards control of exposure

The principles of good practice are detailed in schedule 2A of The Control of Substances Hazardous to Health Regulations (COSHH) 2002 (amended). Employers have a responsibility to manage and minimise the risks from work activities. They must develop suitable and sufficient control measures and ways of maintaining them. They should:

- Identify hazards and potentially significant risks.
- Take action to prevent and control risks.
- Keep control measures under regular review.

To be effective in the long-term, control measures must be practical, workable and sustainable. Principles of good practice in the control of substances hazardous to health are outlined in the forthcoming sections.

MINIMISING EMISSION, RELEASE AND SPREAD OF HAZARDOUS SUBSTANCES THROUGH DESIGN AND OPERATION OF PROCESSES AND TASK ACTIVITIES

A useful approach to control exposure to hazardous substances is to reduce the actual quantity of the substance which can become airborne; for example, prevention of large volumes of airborne vapours by use of a paint brush rather than an aerosol can of paint or paint spraying equipment. In the case of disposal of acids, the risk of acid burns or corrosion will be removed by neutralisation with a suitable alkali.

Changes in work patterns can ensure that fewer employees are exposed. It might be possible that some work takes place at night or weekend when fewer people are present.

Change of work patterns to reduce length of time of exposure forms the basis of occupational exposure limits, i.e. long-term exposure limits (8 hours time weighted average value) and short-term exposure limits (15 minutes weighted average value). This is particularly relevant when considering shift patterns, where 12 hour shifts are common and the individual operators' work arrangements may need to be rotated, within a shift, to ensure 8 hours time weighted averages are not exceeded.

Remove contaminant at source so that its range of contamination is minimised. Removal is usually achieved by mechanical air handling. Local exhaust ventilation or dilution ventilation are the options available depending on the amount and toxicity of the contaminant.

EFFECTIVENESS AND RELIABILITY OF CONTROL OPTIONS

A set of integrated control measures that are effective and reliable enough to control exposure adequately has to be developed. It is important that the 'hierarchical' approach to reliability and effectiveness is not viewed so rigidly that some control options are seen as 'good', while others are seen as ineffective.

Some control measures are more reliable than others. There is a general hierarchy of controls available:

- **Elimination of the substance** - This is the most effective though least realistic option. If elimination can be achieved it means that no exposure can take place and there is no residual risk to manage.
- **Reduction of exposure** - By substituting a less harmful substance or reducing the number of people exposed and/or the frequency and duration of exposure. This method protects all employees but there will be residual risk to deal with.
- **Isolation of the substance** - Secure storage facilities with limited access.
- **Controls** - Engineering controls such as local exhaust ventilation. These have to be carefully monitored to ensure, for example, that the captor hood is correctly positioned.
- **Personal protective equipment** - Or other devices worn by individuals such as exposure monitors. The main disadvantage of this method is that it only protects the user. Furthermore, it will only protect the user if the equipment/device is worn correctly, if at all.

Employers should consider the consequences of failure of the control measure when making their selection. If failure of the control measure would lead to exposure of workers to a high risk of harm and failure of the control measure to control harm was likely, it would be preferable to use a control that was more reliable. Decisions to use personal protective equipment as a control measure should be taken with regard to its likely level of success in preventing harm. When working with high risk substances it would be preferable to use controls that are more reliable than personal protective equipment.

EXPOSURE CONTROL TO BE PROPORTIONAL TO HEALTH RISK

The principle of "so far as is reasonably practicable" allows employers to balance cost against the degree of risk. This principle has to be applied when selecting adequate control measures to protect employees from harmful exposures. Control measures have to take into account the nature of the hazard, the frequency and duration of exposure and the number and type of people exposed. If the risk is low and not likely to cause long-term harm, the control measures may be simple procedural issues such as replacing the lid tightly on tins and vessels or a regime of regular cleaning. However, if the consequences are likely to be diseases such as dermatitis, asthma or cancer then more robust and reliable measures must be implemented.

USE OF PERSONAL PROTECTIVE EQUIPMENT IN CONJUNCTION WITH OTHER MEASURES

When adequate control of exposure cannot be achieved by other means, a combination of control measures and personal protective equipment may be applied. *The use of personal protective equipment is considered in more detail later in this element and also in NGC1 - Element 4 - Health and safety management systems 3 - planning.*

REGULAR CHECKS AND REVIEW OF CONTROL MEASURES TO CONFIRM CONTINUED EFFECTIVENESS

All control measures require regular checks and review to ensure their effectiveness and efficiency. There are a number of reasons why this approach should be adopted.

- Statutory obligations.
- To comply with WELs.
- Provision of information to employees.

- To indicate the need for health surveillance.
- For insurance purposes.
- To develop in-house exposure standards.

Exactly what checks should be carried out depends on such factors as:

- The control measures in use.
- The reliability of the controls.

- The consequences of failure.

PROVISION OF INFORMATION AND TRAINING TO THOSE WORKING WITH HAZARDOUS SUBSTANCES

For control measures to be effective, people need to know how to use them. Furthermore, employees should be consulted during the development of control measures. Employees who have been actively involved in the design of controls are more likely to appreciate the need for their use and, therefore, more likely to use them correctly.

Regulation 12 of the Control of Substances Hazardous to Health Regulations (COSHH) 2002 requires:

"That the instruction and training must ensure that people at work on the premises do not put themselves, or others at risk through exposure to substances hazardous to health. In particular, the instruction must be sufficient and suitable for them to know:

(a)   How and when to use the control measures.

(b)   The defined methods of work.

(c)   How to use the personal protective equipment and especially respiratory protective equipment, e.g. the correct method of removing and refitting gloves and masks and determining how long protective gloves should be worn before any liquid contamination is liable to permeate them.

(d)   The cleaning, storage and disposal procedures they should follow, why they are required and when they are to be carried out, e.g. cleaning contaminated PPE with water or a vacuum fitted with a high-efficiency particulate arrester (HEPA) filter, and not with an airline, or the risks of using contaminated PPE.

(e)   The procedures to be followed in an emergency".

Training should include elements of theory as well as practice. Training in the use and application of control measures and PPE should take account of recommendations and instructions supplied by the manufacturer.

CONTROL MEASURES NOT TO INCREASE OVERALL RISK TO HEALTH AND SAFETY

People designing control measures have to consider the possibility that the new measures might introduce new risks. For example, personal protective equipment can affect mobility and interfere with the senses. The introduction of local exhaust ventilation means that it will have to be maintained and, therefore, will introduce the hazards attendant to maintenance operations and the use of enclosures might increase the chances of an explosion.

Common measures used to implement principles of good practice

REDUCED TIME EXPOSURE AND SIGNIFICANCE OF TIME WEIGHTED AVERAGES

There is a close relationship between exposure and time. At a fixed level of contamination the effect will be proportional to the time exposed. This is the basis of occupational exposure limits, i.e. long-term exposure limits (8 hours time weighted average value) and short-term exposure limits (15 minutes weighted average value). The strategy is also encompassed in the approach to control noise exposure whereby the total noise dose over an eight hour day, 5-day week, must not exceed 85 dB(A). It may be possible to organise work so that exposure to any one person is controlled by means of job/task rotation.

ENCLOSURE OF HAZARDS

In its simplest sense this can mean putting lids on substances that have volatile vapours, such as tins of solvent based products. In this way the strategy is to enclose the hazard so that vapours are not given off. In this case, this is best done when the substance is not in use, this does not just mean at the end of the day but at intervals when the substance is not actually in use. It makes a very simple and effective control of exposure to hazards.

SEGREGATION OF PROCESS

This strategy is based on the containment of an offending substance or agent to prevent its free movement in the working environment. It may take a number of forms, e.g. acoustic enclosures, pipelines, closed conveyors, laboratory fume cupboards. In construction situations this is used in processes such as asbestos removal where the work being done is enclosed in plastic sheeting in order to segregate the work from the surrounding areas. In a similar way this may be for building cleaning processes using shot or for spray protection being applied to a structure.

SEGREGATION OF PEOPLE

Segregation is a method of controlling the risks from toxic substances and physical hazards such as biological or toxic substances. It can take a number of forms:

By physical separation

This can be a relatively simple method such as where the minimum number of employees are working with biological or toxic substances and are distanced (segregated) from the general workforce. If the hazards cannot be enclosed close to their source it may be preferable that the workforce be segregated from the hazard by providing physical separation in the form of a refuge, for example, a control room of a chemical process.

By worker characteristics

The protection of young workers in certain trades is still valid today, a good example being lead. In this case the Control of Lead at Work Regulations (CLAW) 2002 excludes the employment of young persons in lead processes. There remains the possibility of gender linked vulnerability to certain toxic substances such as lead; segregation affords a high level of control in these circumstances.

By time

Concentrations of airborne substances averaged over a period of time known as a Time Weighted Average (TWA). The two periods that are used are 8-hours and 15-minutes. The 8-hour TWA is known as an LTEL (long-term exposure limit), used to help protect against chronic ill-health effects. 15-minute STELs (short-term exposure limits) are to protect against acute ill-health effects such as eye irritation, which may happen after minutes or even seconds of exposure.

LOCAL EXHAUST VENTILATION

General applications and principles

Various local exhaust ventilation (LEV) systems are in use in the workplace, for example:

- Receptor hoods such as are used in fume cupboards and kilns.
- Captor hoods (used for welding and milling operations). *See figure ref 2-7-13* which clearly shows the fixed captor hood, flexible hose and rigid duct.
- High velocity low volume flow systems e.g. as used on a grinding tool.

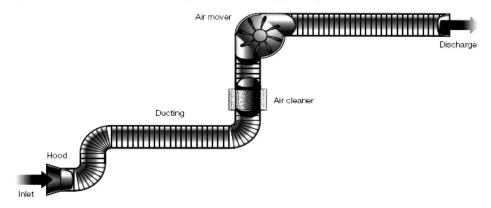

Figure 2-7-12: Common elements of a simple LEV system.   *Source: HSE indg408.*

Components of a basic system

- *Hood(s)* to collect airborne contaminants at, or near, where they are created (the source).
- *Ducts* to carry the airborne contaminants away from the process. *See figure ref 2-7-17* which shows the length of ducting with curves not corners.
- *Air cleaner* to filter and clean the extracted air.
- *Fan* must be the right size and type to deliver sufficient 'suck' to the hood. *See figure ref 2-7-14* as it clearly shows the size of a fan and motor required for industrial scale LEV.
- *Discharge* the safe release of cleaned, extracted air into the atmosphere.

Figure 2-7-13: Captor system on circular saw.   *Source: RMS.*

Figure 2-7-14: LEV fan and motor.   *Source: RMS.*

Figure 2-7-15: Flexible hose and captor hood.   *Source: RMS.*

Figure 2-7-16: Portable self contained unit.   *Source: RMS.*

Factors that reduce a LEV system's effectiveness

The efficiency of LEV systems can be affected by many factors including the following:

- Damaged ducting.
- Unauthorised alterations.
- Incorrect hood location. **See figure ref 2-7-15** which shows how a captor hood can be repositioned to suit the work activity by the use of a flexible hose.
- Too many bends in ducts.
- Blocked or defective filters.
- Leaving too many ports open.
- Process changes leading to overwhelming amounts of contamination.
- Fan strength or incorrect adjustment of fan.

The cost of heating make up air may encourage some employers to reduce extraction rates. When arranging installation of LEV it is vital that the pre and post ventilation contamination levels are specified and the required reduction should be part of the commissioning contract.

Figure 2-7-17: Length of ducting with curves.   *Source: RMS.*

Figure 2-7-18: Shows a number of ports at the end of one duct - not all ports being used. *Source: RMS.*

Requirements for inspection

COSHH 2002 Regulation 9(2) and schedule 4 set out requirements for inspection of LEV systems. A thorough examination and test must take place once every 14 months (more frequently for those processes listed in schedule 4). Records must be kept available for at least 5 years from the date on which it was made.

The majority of ventilation systems, although effective in protecting workers' health from airborne contaminants, can create other hazards. One of the main hazards that need to be considered when designing LEV systems is that of noise. Even if it has been considered as a design feature when establishing LEV systems, it should be monitored on a periodic basis.

USE AND LIMITATIONS OF DILUTION VENTILATION

Dilution ventilation is a system designed to induce a general flow of clean air into a work area. A particularly simple approach to providing dilution ventilation is to open a window and door and allow natural air flow to dilute the workplace air. This is not a reliable means of dealing with toxic contaminants and may be over relied on in the construction industry. On its own it may prove inadequate but supported by respiratory protection equipment it may be acceptable for some substances.

Dilution ventilation may be achieved by driving air into a work area, causing air flow around the work area, dilution of contaminants in the work area and then out of the work area through general leakage or through ventilation ducts to the open air.

A variation on this is where air may be forcibly removed from the work area, but not associated with a particular contaminant source, and air is allowed in through ventilation ducts to dilute the air in the work area. Sometimes a combination of these two approaches is used; an example may be general air conditioning provided into an office environment.

Because dilution ventilation does not target any specific source and it relies on dispersal and dilution instead of specific removal, it can only be used with nuisance contaminants that are themselves fairly mobile in air. Dilution ventilation systems will only deal with general contamination and will not prevent contaminants entering a person's breathing zone. Local exhaust ventilation is the preferred means of controlling a person's exposure to substances.

Dilution ventilation may only be used as the sole means of control in circumstances where there is:

- Non toxic contaminant or vapour (not dusts).
- Contaminant which is uniformly produced in small, known quantities.
- No discrete point of release.
- No other practical means of reducing levels.

RESPIRATORY PROTECTIVE EQUIPMENT

Purpose, application and effectiveness

Damage to health and death can be caused by breathing in hazardous substances, such as dusts, fumes, vapours, gases or even micro-organisms. If direct prevention or control of exposure is not possible then respiratory protective equipment (RPE) may be needed; this should always be seen as a measure of last resort in the hierarchy of control measures. RPE includes a very wide range of devices from simple respirators offering basic protection against low levels of nuisance dusts to self-contained breathing apparatus.

The effectiveness of respiratory protection depends on using the proper equipment for the specific task. Before selecting respiratory protection equipment, the following issues should be considered:

- Operations and work sites where there is any kind of contamination.
- Jobs where a lack of oxygen is a problem.
- Specific contaminants that is present at the work site.
- Harmful properties of the contaminants.
- Form of the contaminant material: dust, mist, spray, gas, vapour, fume, or some combination of these.
- Concentrations of each contaminant.

Types of respiratory protection equipment

There are two main categories of respiratory protection:

1) Respirators.
2) Breathing apparatus.

Respirators

Respirators filter the air breathed but do not provide additional oxygen. There are a number of types of respirator that provide a variety of degrees of protection from dealing with nuisance dusts to high efficiency respirators for solvents or asbestos.

Some respirators may be nominated as providing non-specific protection from contaminants whereas others will be designed to protect from a very specific contaminant such as solvent vapours. There are five main types of respirators:

1)   Filtering face piece.
2)   Half mask respirator.
3)   Full face respirator.
4)   Powered air purifying respirator.
5)   Powered visor respirator.

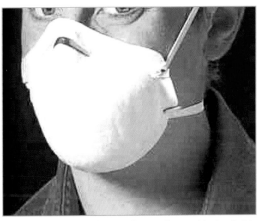

Figure 2-7-19: Paper filter respirator. *Source: Haxton Safety.*

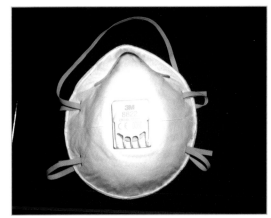

Figure 2-7-20: 3M disposable respirator. *Source: RMS.*

Advantages

- Unrestricted movement.
- Often lightweight and comfortable.
- Can be worn for long periods.

Limitations

- Purify the air by drawing it through a filter to remove contaminants. Therefore, can only be used when there is sufficient oxygen in the atmosphere.
- Requires careful selection by a competent person.
- Requires regular maintenance.
- Knowing when a filter or cartridge is at the end of its useful life.
- Requires correct storage facilities.
- Can give a 'closed in' / claustrophobic feeling.
- Relies on user for correct fit/use etc.
- Incompatible with other forms of personal protective equipment (PPE).
- Performance can be affected by beards and long hair.
- Interferes with other senses, e.g. sense of smell.

Breathing apparatus

Breathing apparatus provides a separate source of supply of air (including oxygen) to that which surrounds the person. Because of the self-contained nature of breathing apparatus it may be used to provide a high degree of protection from a variety of toxic contaminants and may be used in situations where the actual contaminant is not known or there is more than one contaminant.

There are three types of breathing apparatus:

1) Fresh air hose apparatus - clean air from uncontaminated source.
2) Compressed air line apparatus from compressed air source.
3) Self-contained breathing apparatus - from cylinder.

Figure 2-7-21: Full face canister respirator. *Source: Haxton Safety.*

Figure 2-7-22: Breathing apparatus. *Source: Haxton Safety.*

Advantages

- Supplies clean air from an uncontaminated source. Therefore, can be worn in oxygen deficient atmospheres.
- Has high assigned protection factor (APF). Therefore may be used in an atmosphere with high levels of toxic substance.
- Can be worn for long periods if connected to a permanent supply of air.

Limitations

- Can be heavy and cumbersome which restricts movement.
- Requires careful selection by competent person.
- Requires special training.
- Requires arrangements to monitor / supervise user and for emergencies.

- Can give a 'closed in' / claustrophobic feeling.
- Relies on user for correct fit/use etc.
- Incompatible with other forms of PPE.
- Performance can be affected by e.g. long hair.
- Interferes with other senses, e.g. sense of smell. Requires correct storage facilities.

Selection, use and maintenance

There are a number of issues to consider in the selection of respiratory protective equipment (RPE) not least the advantages and limitations shown in the previous list.

A general approach must not only take account of the needs derived from the work to be done and the contaminant to be protected from but must include suitability for the person. This will include issues such as face fit and the ability of the person to use the equipment for a sustained period, if this is required. One of the important factors is to ensure that the equipment will provide the level of protection required.

This is indicated by the assigned protection factor given to the equipment by the manufacturers - the higher the factor the more protection provided. With a little knowledge it is possible to work out what APF is needed using the following formula.

$$APF = \frac{\text{Concentration of contaminant in the workplace}}{\text{Concentration of contaminant in the face-piece}}$$

It is important to understand that this factor is only an indication of what the equipment will provide. Actual protection may be different due to fit and the task being conducted. Every employee must use any personal protective equipment provided in accordance with the training and instructions that they have received.

Where respiratory protective equipment (other than disposable respiratory protective equipment) is provided the employer must ensure that thorough examination and where appropriate testing, of that equipment is carried out at suitable intervals.

OTHER PROTECTIVE EQUIPMENT AND CLOTHING

Hand/arm protection including gloves

There are numerous types of glove and gauntlet available that offer protection from hazards:

- Chemical hazards such as acids, alkalis etc.
- Thermal hazards such as hot surfaces.
- Mechanical hazards in the form of splinters and sharp edges.

The materials used in the manufacture of these products are an essential feature to consider when making the selection. There are several types of rubber (latex, nitrile, PVC, butyl) all giving different levels of protection against aqueous chemicals; leather affords protection against heat , splinters and cuts; space age technology in the form of Kevlar (a tough, lightweight material) protects against cuts from knife blades and is used in the sleeves of jackets for those using chainsaws.

Figure 2-7-23: Gloves. *Source: Speedy Hire plc.*

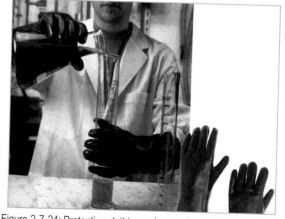

Figure 2-7-24: Protective clothing - gloves. *Source: Haxton Safety.*

Protective clothing - overalls

1) Head protection - safety helmets or scalp protectors (bump caps) - scalp protectors give limited protection and are unsuitable for confined spaces. Safety helmets have a useful life of three years and this can be shortened by prolonged exposure to ultra-violet light. There is specific legal requirement on construction sites to wear head protection where there is risk of injury from falling objects.
2) Protective outer clothing - normally PVC, often high visibility to alert traffic.
3) Protective inner clothing - overalls, aprons.

Eye protection

When selecting suitable eye protection, some of the factors to be considered are:

Type and nature of hazard (impact, chemical, ultra violet (UV) light, etc.), type/standard/quality of protection, comfort and user acceptability issues, compatibility, maintenance requirements, training requirements and cost.

Figure 2-7-25: Eye and ear protection. *Source: Speedy Hire plc.*

Figure 2-7-26: Arc welding visor - UV reactive. *Source: RMS.*

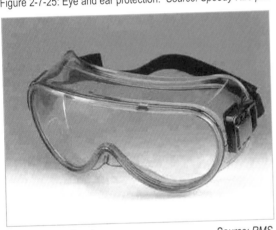

Figure 2-7-27: Goggles. *Source: RMS.*

Figure 2-7-28: Spectacles. *Source: RMS.*

Types	Advantages	Limitations
Spectacles	■ Lightweight, easy to wear. ■ Can incorporate prescription lenses. ■ Do not 'mist up'.	■ Do not give all round protection. ■ Relies on the wearer for use.
Goggles	■ Give all round protection. ■ Can be worn over prescription lenses. ■ Capable of high impact protection. ■ Can protect against other hazards e.g. dust, molten metal.	■ Tendency to 'mist up'. ■ Uncomfortable when worn for long periods. ■ Can affect peripheral vision.
Face shields (visors)	■ Gives full face protection against splashes. ■ Can incorporate a fan which creates air movement for comfort and protection against low level contaminants. ■ Can be integrated into other PPE e.g. head protection.	■ Require care in use, otherwise can become dirty and scratched. ■ Can affect peripheral vision. ■ Unless the visor is provided with extra sealing gusset around the visor, substances may go underneath the visor to the face.

© RMS

Footwear - safety boots/shoes

The importance of foot protection is illustrated by the fact that around 21,000 foot and ankle injuries are reported annually. Inadequate protection and a lack of discipline on the part of the wearer commonly cause these.

There are many types of safety footwear on the market, many of them offering different types of protection. It is vital that the nature of the hazard is considered when selecting appropriate footwear.

Here are some common examples:

- Falling objects   - steel toe-caps.
- Sharp objects   - steel in-soles.
- Flammable atmospheres   - anti-static footwear.
- Spread of contamination   - washable boots.
- Electricity   - rubber soles.
- Wet environments   - impermeable wellingtons.
- Slippery surfaces   - non-slip soles.
- Cold environments   - thermally insulated soles.

Figure 2-7-29: Personal protective equipment. *Source: RMS.*

Ear protection

See also NGC2 - Element 8 - Physical and psychological health hazards and risk control - for details of ear protection.

PERSONAL HYGIENE AND PROTECTION REGIMES

Personal hygiene and good housekeeping have an important role in the protection of the health and safety of the people at work. Laid down procedures and standards are necessary for preventing the spread of contamination. The provision of adequate washing/showering facilities is important to remove contamination from the body. The provision of laundry facilities for overalls and PPE reduces the effect of contamination. Barrier creams and suitable hand protection are important considerations for chemical and biological risks.

Where personal hygiene is critical, for example, when stripping asbestos, a 'three room system' is employed. Workers enter the 'clean end' and put work clothes on, leaving by means of the 'dirty end'. When work has been completed they return by means of the 'dirty end', carry out personal hygiene and leave by means of the 'clean end'.

Vaccination

Certain occupations, such as water treatment/sewage workers, medical profession, have a higher than average risk from some biological hazards. Staff from these occupations may need to be immunised against common high risks e.g. hepatitis B. Whilst vaccination can be an effective way of preventing ill health as a result of exposure to biological agents, it is important that employers are aware of problems that can arise. In the first instance, vaccination is intrusive.

Employers need the permission of employees before adopting this method - this may not always be forthcoming. Secondly, it is possible that some people will suffer adverse effects from the vaccination. Finally, not all diseases are treatable by vaccination and, for those that are, vaccination might not be available.

HEALTH SURVEILLANCE AND BIOLOGICAL MONITORING

The Management of Health and Safety at Work Regulations (MHSWR) 1999, Regulation 6, deals with health surveillance and gives employers a duty to provide it where it is appropriate. Further details on health surveillance are contained in other Regulations e.g. COSHH 2002. *(Details can be found in the Approved Code of Practice Schedule 6; Extracts from the ACOP follow).*

Substances for which health surveillance is appropriate		Processes
Vinyl Chloride Monomer (VCM).		In manufacturing, production, reclamation, storage, discharge, transport, use or polymerization.
Nitro or amino derivatives of phenol and of benzene or its homologues.		In the manufacture of nitro or amino derivatives of phenol and of benzene or its homologues and the making of explosives with the use of any of these substances.
Orthotolidine and its salts.	Dianisidine and its salts Dichlorbenzidene and its salts.	In manufacture, formation or use of these substances.

Auramine.	Magenta.	In manufacture.
Carbon Disulphide. Disulpher Dichloride. Benzene, including benzol.	Carbon Tetrachloride. Tricholoroethylene.	Process in which these substances are used, or given off as a vapour, in the manufacture of indiarubber or of articles or goods made wholly or partially of indiarubber.
Pitch.		In manufacture of blocks of fuel consisting of coal, coal dust, coke or slurry with pitch as a binding substance.

Figure 2-7-30: Schedule 6 medical surveillance.   *Source: COSHH AcoP.*

Other than the cases stated in the COSHH 2002 schedule, surveillance may be appropriate where exposure to hazardous substances is such that an identifiable disease or adverse health effect may be linked to the exposure. There must be a reasonable likelihood that the disease or effect may occur under the particular conditions of work prevailing and that valid techniques exist to detect such conditions and effects. The employer must keep records of surveillance in respect of each employee for at least 40 years. This requirement still applies where companies cease to trade, in which case the records must be offered to the HSE.

Biological monitoring guidance values

Biological monitoring may be particularly useful in circumstances where:

- There is likely to be significant skin absorption and/or gastrointestinal tract uptake following ingestion.
- Control of exposure depends on respiratory protective equipment.
- There is a reasonably well-defined relationship between biological monitoring and effect.
- It gives information on accumulated dose and target organ burden which is related to toxicity.

Biological Monitoring Values (BMGVs) are set where they are likely to be of practical value, suitable monitoring methods exist and there are sufficient data available. BMGVs are non-statutory and any biological monitoring undertaken in association with a guidance value needs to be conducted on a voluntary basis (i.e. with the fully informed consent of all concerned). Where a BMG is exceeded it does not necessarily mean that any corresponding airborne standard has been exceeded nor that ill health will occur. It is intended that where they are exceeded this will give an indication that investigation into current control measures and work practices is necessary. Similarly a low BMGV should not suggest that there is no need to reduce workplace exposure further.

Table 2 EH40/2005 lists BMGVs, a few examples of common substances can be seen in **figure ref 2-7-30**.

Substance	Biological Monitoring Guidance Value	Sampling time
Butan-2-one.	70µmol butan-2-one/L in urine.	Post shift.
Carbon monoxide.	30ppm carbon monoxide in end-tidal breath.	Post shift.
Lindane. (Organo chlorine pesticide).	35nmol/L(10µg/L of Lindane in whole blood (equivalent to 70nmol/Lidane in plasma).	Random.
Xylene, o-, m-, p- or mixed isomers.	650 mmol methyl hippuric acid/mol creainine in urine.	Post shift.

Figure 2-7-31: Biological Monitoring Values (BMGVs).   *Source: EH40/2005 Workplace exposure limits.*

Control of substances with specific effects

CARCINOGENS

Carcinogens are substances that have been identified as having the ability to cause cancer. Examples of these include arsenic, hardwood dusts and used engine oils.

OCCUPATIONAL ASTHMA

Occupational asthma is caused by substances in the workplace that trigger a state of specific airway hyper-responsiveness in an individual, resulting in breathlessness, chest tightness or wheezing. These substances are known as asthmagens and respiratory sensitisers. Exposure to these substances should be prevented, and where that is not possible, kept as low as reasonably practicable. Control measures used should take account of long term time weighted averages and short term peak exposures to the substance. If an individual develops occupational asthma, their exposure must be controlled to prevent any further attacks. Employees who work with asthmagens must have regular health surveillance to detect any changes in respiratory function.

GENETIC DAMAGE

Substances known as mutagens have been identified that cause changes to DNA, increasing the number of genetic mutations above natural background levels. These changes can lead to cancer in the individual affected or be passed to their offspring genetic material, for example thalidomide and plutonium oxide.

Due to the serious and irreversible nature of cancer and genetic changes, an employer's first objective must be to prevent exposure to carcinogens and mutagens. These substances should not be used or processes carried out with them, if a safer alternative less hazardous substance can be used instead. Where this is not feasible suitable control measures should include:

- Totally enclosed systems.
- Where total enclosure is not possible, exposure to these substances must kept to as low level as possible through the use of appropriate plant and process control measures such as handling systems and local exhaust ventilation (these measures should not produce other risks in the workplace).
- Storage of carcinogens/mutagens must be kept to the minimum needed for the process, in closed, labelled containers with warning and hazard signs, including waste products until safe disposal.
- Areas where carcinogens/mutagens are present must be identified and segregated to prevent spread to other areas.
- The number of people exposed and the duration of exposure must be kept to the minimum necessary to do the work.
- Personal protective equipment is considered a secondary protection measure used in combination with other control measures.
- Measures should be in place for monitoring of workplace exposure and health surveillance for work involving carcinogens and mutagens.

7.5 - Specific agents

Health risks and controls associated with asbestos

HEALTH RISKS

Asbestos is a general term used to describe a range of mineral fibres (commonly referred to by colour i.e. white, chrysotile; brown, amosite and blue, crocidolite). Asbestos was mainly used as an insulating and fire resisting material. Asbestos fibres readily become airborne when disturbed and may enter the lungs, where they cause fibrosis (scarring and thickening) of the lung tissue, asbestosis or mesothelioma (thickening of the pleural lining).

Asbestosis typically takes more than 10 years to develop. Research suggests that 50 per cent of asbestos sufferers will also develop cancer of the lung or bronchus. Asbestosis is often classified separately from pneumoconiosis even though asbestos is a dust - but it is a special form of fibrous dust. Like silicosis, asbestosis is a serious condition which is incurable and can result in death at an early age. The primary symptom of asbestosis is generally the slow onset of shortness of breath on exertion. In severe, advanced cases, this may lead to respiratory failure. Coughing is not usually a typical symptom, unless the patient has other, concomitant respiratory tract diseases.

Figure 2-7-32: Asbestos label. *Source: Scaftag.*

Symptoms of mesothelioma may not appear until 20 to 50 years after exposure to asbestos. Shortness of breath, cough, and pain in the chest due to an accumulation of fluid in the pleural space are often symptoms of pleural mesothelioma.

CONTROLS

The Control of Asbestos Regulations (CAR) 2006 prohibit the importation, supply and use of all forms of asbestos. They also prohibit the second-hand use of asbestos products such as asbestos cement sheets and asbestos tiles. If existing asbestos containing materials are in good condition they may be left in place and their condition monitored and managed.

- The presence of asbestos must be identified and must be labelled.
- An assessment must be done of work which exposes employees to asbestos.
- Training is mandatory for those that may be exposed to asbestos fibres at work, including maintenance workers, cable installers or others that may come into contact with or disturb asbestos.
- A written plan of work is required for work with asbestos.

Regulation 3 requires that employers who work with asbestos must be licensed unless the circumstances are that:

(a)   The exposure of employees to asbestos is sporadic and of low intensity.

(b)   It is clear from the risk assessment that the exposure of any employee to asbestos will not exceed the control limit.

(c)   The work involves:

(i)   *Short, non-continuous maintenance activities.*

(ii)   *Removal of materials in which the asbestos fibres are firmly linked in a matrix.*

(iii)   *Encapsulation or sealing of asbestos-containing materials which are in good condition, or*

(iv)   *Air monitoring and control, and the collection and analysis of samples to ascertain whether a specific material contains asbestos.*

- Work with asbestos other than that listed previously must be notified to the employer's enforcing authority.
- Exposure must be prevented or reduced by controls.
- Controls must be used and maintained.
- The employer is responsible for the cleaning of personal protective clothing.

DUTY TO MANAGE ASBESTOS

The duty to manage asbestos is covered by Regulation 4 of the Control of Asbestos Regulations (CAR) 2006.

In many cases, the duty holder is the person or organisation that has clear responsibility for the maintenance or repair of non-domestic premises through an explicit agreement such as a tenancy agreement or contract. Where there are domestic premises such as flats the duty holder will be responsible for common areas such as corridors or walkways.

The duty holder has the responsibility to:

- Take reasonable steps to find out if there are materials containing asbestos in non-domestic premises and if so, amount, location and condition.
- Presume materials contain asbestos unless there is strong evidence that they do not.
- Record the location and condition of the asbestos containing materials or materials which are presumed to contain asbestos.
- Assess the risk of anyone being exposed to fibres from the materials identified.
- Prepare a plan that sets out in detail how the risks from these materials will be managed.
- Take the necessary steps to put the plan into action.
- Periodically review and monitor the plan.
- Provide information on the location and condition of the materials to anyone who is liable to work on or disturb them.

There is also a requirement on anyone to co-operate as far as is necessary to allow the duty holder to comply with the requirements shown previously.

Health risks and controls associated with other specific agents

BLOOD BORNE VIRUSES (BBVS)

BBVs are mainly found in blood or bodily fluids. The main BBVs of concern are Human Immunodeficiency Virus (HIV), Hepatitis B and Hepatitis C.

Health risks

HIV

HIV is transmitted through contact with body fluids, in particular blood, semen, vaginal secretions and breast milk. It is not transmitted through casual contact, coughing, sneezing, by sharing a toilet, by eating utensils, or by consuming food or beverages handled or prepared by someone with HIV. The main method of transfer at work is through laceration or puncture of the skin or contamination of the eyes; therefore, a co-worker with HIV in the workplace is not a risk to others.

Hepatitis

Hepatitis means inflammation of the liver. Viruses can cause this by infecting the liver. There are a number of different hepatitis viruses. Two of the most common are Hepatitis B and C.

Hepatitis B and C are easily transmitted through contaminated blood. Most people do not know if they are infected. They may live for many years without symptoms. A proportion take 20 to 30 years to develop severe liver disease, some recover completely with treatment, others recover without any treatment at all. A small proportion develops liver cancer.

Hepatitis B is mainly transmitted through contact body fluids, such as, blood, semen, vaginal fluid and breast milk. Importantly, there is an effective vaccination against Hepatitis B.

Hepatitis C is mainly transmitted through blood, with a low risk of transmission through semen and vaginal fluid. There is no vaccine against Hepatitis C and current treatments for it are not effective in all cases.

Risk occupations

Workers who come into contact with bodily fluids from other humans are at risk from BBVs, particularly if their work also involves sharp or abrasive implements or substances that may break the skin.

Healthcare workers are at an obvious risk. Less obvious, perhaps, are those who work for cleansing or recreation/parks departments and staff who conduct bodily searches or searches of personal effects. Staff who works in these circumstances may come into contact with used needles.

Risk factors

The level of risk will depend on:

- Frequency and scale of contact with bodily fluids.
- The type of fluid or material they come into contact with.
- The activity the person must conduct in relation to the infectious material.
- The nature of the infection contained in the material.

Risks controls

Where a risk of exposure to BBVs has been identified, simple, inexpensive measures to prevent or control risks can be taken:

- Ensure good personal hygiene practices are observed, in particular hygienic hand-washing.
- Use procedures such as avoiding the use of sharps such as needles, blades, glass, etc.
- Also consider using equipment with built-in safety devices.
- Use personal protective equipment such as gloves, eye protection, face masks, etc.
- Ensure contaminated waste is disposed of in a safe manner, e.g. sharps disposal bin.
- Use disposable equipment where there is a risk of BBV contamination, otherwise decontamination procedures must be strictly complied with.
- Ensure employees are aware of immediate steps to be followed upon contamination with blood or other body fluids.

CARBON MONOXIDE

Is a chemical asphyxiant produced as a by-product of incomplete combustion of carbon fuels e.g. gas water heaters, compressors, pumps, dumper trucks or generators. It is a particular risk when operated in poorly ventilated confined areas where workers are forced to breathe it. Carbon monoxide has a great affinity (200 times that of oxygen) for the haemoglobin red blood cells which means it will inhibit oxygen uptake by red blood cells resulting in chemical asphyxiation, leading to collapse and death.

Acute effects: The earliest symptoms, especially from low level exposures, are often non-specific and readily confused with other illnesses, typically flu-like viral syndromes, depression, chronic fatigue syndrome, and migraine or other headaches. This often makes the diagnosis of carbon monoxide poisoning difficult. If suspected, the diagnosis can be confirmed by measurement of blood carboxyhemoglobin. Common problems encountered are difficulty with higher intellectual functions and short-term memory, dementia, irritability, gait disturbance, speech disturbances, parkinson-like syndromes, cortical blindness, and depression.

Chronic effects: Long term, repeat exposures present a greater risk to persons with coronary heart disease and in pregnant patients. Chronic exposure may increase the incidence of cardiovascular symptoms in some workers, such as motor vehicle examiners, firefighters, and welders. Patients often complain of persistent headaches, light-headedness, depression, confusion, and nausea. Upon removal from exposure, the symptoms usually resolve themselves.

CEMENT

Cement is used extensively in the construction industry as part of the mix for mortar and concrete. It is mildly corrosive and can cause harm in the following ways:

- Skin contact - causing contact dermatitis. If it is trapped inside a worker's boot or glove then it can cause severe chemical burns.
- Eye contact - causing irritation and inflammation.
- Inhalation - causing irritation of the nose and throat. Possible long term respiratory problems.

The accompanying image shows severe burns a worker sustained from kneeling in wet cement for 3 hours; his right leg had to be amputated. Gloves, protective overalls, boots and masks should be worn. Wash skin thoroughly after contact with cement.

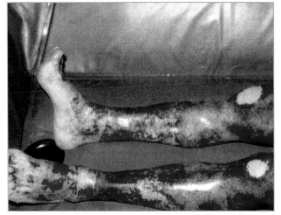

Figure 2-7:33: Cement burns.   *Source: SHP.*

LEGIONNELLA/LEGIONNAIRES' DISEASE

Legionnella/Legionnaires' disease is a type of pneumonia caused by Legionella Pneumophila, a bacterium. The organism is ubiquitous in water and frequently present in water cooling systems and domestic hot water systems. Large workplace buildings are therefore susceptible to infected water systems, especially hotels and hospitals.

The organism is widespread in the environment, but needs certain conditions to multiply, for example the presence of sludge, scale, algae, rust and organic material plus a temperature of 20-50°C. Transmission is from inhalation of the organism in contaminated aerosols. Smoking, age and alcohol may increase susceptibility.

Symptoms are aching muscles, headaches and fever followed by a cough. Confusion, emotional disturbance and delirium may follow the acute phase. The fatality rate in the UK is about 12%.

Greatest risk areas are from showers used for bathing, air conditioning sprays, water cooling towers and recirculating water cooling systems. The hazard can be controlled by proper design of water systems, disinfection/chlorination of water or heating water to 55-60^{0}C.

LEPTOSPIRA

The bacteria Leptospira, spiral shaped bacteria, penetrates the skin and causes leptospirosis (Weil's Disease). Rodents represent the most important reservoir of infections, especially rats (also gerbils, voles, and field mice). Other sources of infection are dogs, hedgehogs, foxes, pigs, and cattle. These animals are not necessarily ill, but carry leptospires in their kidneys and excrete it in their urine. Infection can be transmitted directly via direct contact with blood, tissues, organs or urine of one of the host animals or indirectly by contaminated environment. Infection enters through broken skin or mucous membrane. Symptoms vary but include flu-like illness, conjunctivitis, liver damage (including jaundice), kidney failure and meningitis. If untreated infection may be fatal.

Construction workers most at risk are those who work where rats prevail and will include water and sewage work, demolition or refurbishment of old unoccupied buildings, and those working on sites adjoining rivers and other watercourses. The bacteria's survival depends on protection from direct sunlight, so it survives well in water courses and ditches protected by vegetation.

SILICA

Silica exists naturally as crystalline minerals. A common variety is quartz (tridymite, cristobalite). Industrially silica is used in the morphous (after heating) form e.g. fumed silica, silica gel. In construction activities it may be encountered in stone work or work with quartz based tiles. Inhalation of silica can result in silicosis, a fibrosis of the lung.

Silicosis (also known as Grinder's disease and Potter's rot) is a form of occupational lung disease caused by inhalation of crystalline silica dust, and is marked by inflammation and scarring in forms of nodular lesions in the upper lobes of the lungs. Silicosis (especially the acute form) is characterised by shortness of breath, fever, and cyanosis (bluish skin). It may often be misdiagnosed as pulmonary oedema (fluid in the lungs), pneumonia, or tuberculosis.

WOOD DUST

Exposure to wood dust has long been associated with a variety of adverse health effects, including dermatitis, allergic respiratory effects, mucosal and non-allergic respiratory effects, and cancer. Contact with the irritant compounds in wood sap can cause dermatitis and other allergic reactions. The respiratory effects of wood dust exposure include asthma, hypersensitivity pneumonitis, and chronic bronchitis. The main operations likely to produce high dust levels in the woodworking industry are:

- Machining operations, particularly sawing, routing and turning.
- Sanding, by machine and by hand.
- Using compressed air lines to blow dust off furniture and other articles before spraying.
- High airborne dust levels can also occur during the bagging of dust from dust extraction systems and during factory cleaning, especially when compressed air lines are used for blowing dust from walls, ledges and other surfaces.

7.6 - Safe handling and storage of waste

Basic environmental issues relating to waste disposal and effluent

Environmental pollution is a major issue today with the industrialised countries of the world concerned about the long-term effects on Earth's resources and on plant, animal and human life. Major concerns on health are often blamed on pollution and there are many pressure groups that focus on environmental issues, particularly pollution.

The problem of pollution is not new; it has been with us since Roman times and the land around old lead mines is still contaminated with the heavy metal today. Since the industrial revolution industry has relied on the capacity of the environment to dilute and disperse pollutants by discharging them to the ground, water and air. This has left a legacy of polluted areas, land pollution being the most persistent, but the discharges to air and water are more global in their effect.

An example of an intentional release of pollution is the emission of sulphur dioxide (SO_2) and nitrogen oxides (NO_x) into the atmosphere by coal-fired power stations. This example also illustrates the global, as well as local, impact that such emissions have which, in this case, results in acid rain falling in Scandinavia, a country which emits very little sulphur dioxide itself. A further impact by the same power station is caused by the carbon dioxide emissions that lead to global warming.

The local effects of the emission of particulates and sulphur dioxide is illustrated by the London smogs of the 1950s, and more recently by the increase in road traffic - many cities in Britain now have pollutants above recommended limits, especially in warm, still conditions.

Plant failure and accidents can lead to abnormal releases following higher than expected temperatures and pressures. This has led to a loss of process control with uncontrolled venting to the environment.

Lack of control when filling tankers with waste effluent can lead to losses through overfilling or bad coupling, either of which could lead to a release to the environment.

PERONAL PROTECTIVE EQUIPMENT

The hazards that might be encountered during the collection, storage and disposal of waste are:

- Chemicals.
- Biological agents.
- Gases, vapours and fumes.
- Dusts.
- Oil, grease.

- Paint, solvents.
- Asbestos.
- Flammable, explosive substances.
- Radioactive materials.

When selecting suitable personal protective equipment it is essential that these issues are considered.

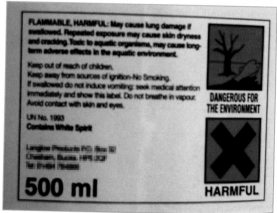

Figure 2-7-34: Hazard label - environment. *Source: RMS.*

Figure 2-7-35: Environmental hazard. *Source: RMS.*

SEPARATE STORAGE OF INCOMPATIBLE WASTE STREAMS

In addition to general safe storage practices, segregated storage of incompatible materials is a must. As a minimum, wastes should be segregated according to similar hazards, such as flammability, corrosivity, sensitivity to water or air, and toxicity.

When establishing a storage scheme, the main consideration should be the flammability characteristics of the material. If the material will contribute significantly to a fire (i.e. oxidisers) it should be isolated from the flammables. If a fire were to occur, the response to the fire with water would exacerbate the environmental situation.

Consider the toxicity of the material, with particular attention paid to regulated materials. In some cases, this may mean that certain wastes will be isolated within a storage area, for instance, a material that is an extreme poison but is also flammable, should be locked away in the flammable storage area to protect it against accidental release. There will always be some chemicals that will not fit singularly into one category or another, but with careful consideration of the hazards involved most of these cases can be handled in an appropriate manner. For the safety of all personnel and to protect the integrity of the facilities, hazardous materials must be segregated.

Principles of protection against accidental release

Leaking and spillage can result from a number of sources: faulty valves or flanges to pipework; containers such as tins, drums or bags; loss from tanks (typically one tonne) of solids and liquids; road or rail freight containers; cargo vessels etc.

Typical techniques to contain spillage include: curbed areas for drum storage, tanker loading of liquids, bunded areas to contain sited tanks and drip trays at piped systems and drum decanting points.

Portable tanks are available with two skins (a tank within a tank) to contain any leaks from the internal tank. They are often used where there is a need for portability such as with storing fuels on construction sites. Similarly, cargo vessels may have double skinned tanks or hulls.

Bunding

A bund, sometimes called a secondary containment system, often consists of an area contained by a rectangular wall built upon a concrete slab. The bund floor and walls should be treated to be impervious to any spillage or water that may be present. Storage tanks are located within this confined area. The bund must provide storage of at least 110% of the tank's maximum capacity.

If more than one tank is stored, the bund system must be capable of storing 110% of the volume of the biggest of the tank's capacity, or 25% of the total capacity of all the tanks within the bund, whichever is the greater.

It is necessary to consider the potential escape of any spillage beyond the bund area in the event of the tank developing a hole (known as jetting).

The risk of this can be minimised by:

- Keeping the primary container as low as possible.
- Increasing the height of the bund wall.
- Leaving sufficient space between the tank and bund walls.
- Not sitting one tank above another.
- Providing screens or curtains.
- Ensure there is no direct uncontrolled outlet connecting the bund to any drain, sewer, watercourse, yard or unmade ground.

Ideally, pipework should not pass through the bund wall. If unavoidable, the pipe should be sealed into the bund with a material that is resistant to attack by the substance stored, to ensure the bund remains leak-proof.

UNIT NGC2
CONTROLLING WORKPLACE HAZARDS

Physical and psychological health hazards and risk control

Learning outcomes

On completion of this element, candidates should be able to demonstrate understanding of the content through the application of knowledge to familiar and unfamiliar situations. In particular they should be able to:

8.1   Outline the health effects associated with exposure to noise and appropriate control measures.

8.2   Outline the health effects associated with exposure to vibration and appropriate control measures.

8.3   Outline the health effects associated with ionising and non-ionising radiation and outline appropriate control measures.

8.4   Outline the causes and effects of stress at work and appropriate control measures.

Content

Sources of reference

Essentials of Health and Safety at Work, HSE Books ISBN 0-7176-0716-X

Personal Protective Equipment at Work (Guidance) (L25), HSE Books ISBN 0-7176-6139-3

Controlling Noise at Work (L108), HSE Books ISBN 0-7176-6164-4

Work Related Upper Limb Disorders - A Guide (HSG60), HSE Books ISBN 0-7176-1978-8

Hand-arm vibration - Control of Vibration at Work Regulations 2005 (L140), HSE Books ISBN 0-7176-6125-3

Whole-body vibration - Control of Vibration at Work Regulations 2005 (L141), HSE Books ISBN 0-7176-6126-1

Real Solutions, real people:A manager's guide to tackling work-related stress, HSE Books ISBN 0-7176-2767-5

HSE Stress Management Standards www.hse.gov.uk/stress/standards

Tackling Work-related Stress (HSG218), HSE Books

Radon in the workplace: http://www.hse.gov.uk/radiation/ionising/radon.htm#testingradon

Relevant statutory provisions

Control of Noise at Work Regulations (CNWR) 2005

The Personal Protective Equipment at Work Regulations (PPER) 1992

The Ionising Radiations Regulations (IRR) 1999

The Control of Vibration at Work Regulations (CVWR) 2005

8.1 - Noise

Physical and psychological effects on hearing of exposure to noise

The ear senses **sound**, which is transmitted in the form of pressure waves travelling through a substance, e.g., air, water, metals etc. Unwanted sound is generally known as **noise**.

The ear has 3 basic regions **(see figure ref 2-8-1)**:

a) The **outer** ear channels the sound pressure waves through to the eardrum.

b) In the **middle** ear, the vibrations of the eardrum are transmitted through three small bones (hammer, anvil and stirrup) to the inner ear.

c) The cochlea in the **inner** ear is filled with fluid and contains tiny hairs (nerves) which respond to the sound. Signals are then sent to the brain via the acoustic nerve.

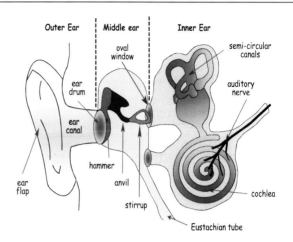

Figure 2-8-1: Inner ear diagram.   Source: www.echalk.co.uk.

PHYSICAL EFFECTS

Excessive noise over long periods of time can cause damage to the hairs (nerves) in the cochlea of the ear. This results in **noise induced hearing loss (deafness)**, which can be of a temporary or permanent nature. Also, a single high pressure event can damage the ear by dislocation of a bone or rupturing the ear drum. It has been shown that high levels of noise can cause, or increase the onset of, **tinnitus** ('ringing in the ears').

PSYCHOLOGICAL EFFECTS

Noise is often linked with adverse psychological effects such as stress, sleep disturbance or aggressive behaviour, and is frequently cited as the cause of friction between workers, particularly in a noisy office environment where there is a need for some individuals to concentrate on complex issues but they find this difficult or impossible because of background noise levels.

The meaning of common sound measurement terms

SOUND POWER AND PRESSURE

For noise to occur power must be available. It is the sound power of a source (measured in Watts) which causes the sound pressure (measured in Pascals) to occur at a specific point.

INTENSITY AND FREQUENCY

The amplitude of a sound wave represents the intensity of the sound pressure. When measuring the **amplitude** of sound there are two main parameters of interest **(as shown in figure ref 2-8-2)**. One is related to the energy in the sound pressure wave and is known as the 'root mean square' (rms) value, and the other is the 'peak' level. We use the rms sound pressure for the majority of noise measurements, apart from some impulsive types of noise when the peak value is also measured.

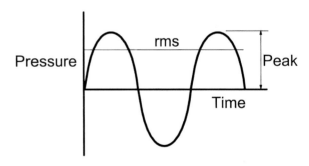

Sound waves travel through air at the **'speed of sound'** which is approximately equal to 344 m/s.

Figure 2-8-2: Rms and peak levels of a sound wave.   Source: RMS.

A sound can have a **'frequency'** or **'pitch'**, which is measured in cycles per second (Hz).

THE DECIBEL SCALE

The ear can detect pressures over a very wide range, from 20 µPa to 20 Pa (Pascals). To help deal with this wide range, the **deciBel (dB)** is used to measure noise. A decibel is a unit of sound pressure (intensity) measured on a logarithmic scale from a base level taken to be the threshold of hearing (0dB). Typical noise levels include:

Source	dB	Source	dB
Night club	110	Radio in average room	70
Smoke detector at 1 metre	105	Library	30
Machine Shop	90	Threshold of Hearing	0

A problem with decibels is that they are based on a logarithmic scale and cannot be added together in the conventional way, for example:

2 dB + 2 dB = 5 dB (deciBel Arithmetic)   and   85 dB + 85 dB = 88 dB (deciBel Arithmetic)

Weighting scales - the terms dB(A) and dB(C)

The human ear can hear sound over a range of frequencies, from 20 Hz up to approximately 20,000 Hz (20 kHz). However, the ear does not hear the same at all frequencies; it naturally reduces (attenuates) low frequencies and very high frequencies to the range of speech. To take account of the response of the human ear sound level meters use weighting scales or filters. The most widely used sound level filter is the A scale. Using this filter, the sound level meter is thus less sensitive to very high and very low frequencies. Measurements made on this scale are expressed as dB(A) or referred to as 'A weighted'. The majority of measurements are made in terms of dB(A), although there are other weightings that are used in some circumstances. One of these is the C scale, which is used to assess the acoustic emissions of machines, in the selection of hearing protectors and analysis of environmental noise. The C scale is used to determine peak sound pressure levels and is particularly useful for impact or explosive noises. It has a broader spectrum than that of the A weighted scale and is more accurate at higher levels of noise. Measurements made on this scale are expressed as dB(C). There is also a (rarely used) B weighting scale, intermediate between A and C.

The range of frequencies that we encounter is often divided into **Octave Bands**. A noise can be measured in each octave band and these levels can be used when assessing the attenuation of hearing protectors, or when diagnosing noise problems.

Other noise units

In most situations the noise level varies with time. When measuring noise we need to determine the average, or 'equivalent continuous level', over a period of time. This is known as the **Leq**. Not all noise meters include a **Leq** function. Other noise units commonly encountered are also listed below:

L_{eq} the average, or 'equivalent continuous level'.

$L_{EP,d}$ daily personal exposure level, dB(A). This is equivalent to the L_{eq} over an 8-hour working day. The
$L_{EP,d}$ is directly related to the risk of hearing damage.

L_{peak} peak pressure - pascals or dB(C). This is the peak level of the sound pressure wave with no time constant applied. For noise at work measurements the peak level should be C weighted.

The need for assessment of exposure

Employers have a duty under the Control of Noise at Work Regulations (CNWR) 2005 to reduce the risk of hearing damage to their employees by controlling exposure to noise. There is a further requirement that the employer obtain an adequate noise assessment, which will enable compliance with duties to control noise exposure.   This will also help the employer when providing suitable hearing protection, marking out ear protection zones and giving information, instruction and training to employees.

The assessment should establish which employees are at risk of hearing damage, and the level of risk. It will also identify sources of noise that particularly contribute to the noise level employees are exposed to e.g. equipment and specific activities.   This will enable analysis of the options to control the noise at source or by other means. Re-assessment should be carried out after action to control exposure, or after a reasonable time, to establish the effectiveness of the controls.

In conducting the assessment the employer should assess the level of noise the workers are exposed to by:

- Observation.
- Reference to information on expected levels for work conditions and equipment.
- If necessary by measurement of the level of noise to which their employees may be exposed.

The assessment shall include consideration of:

- Level, type and duration of exposure, including any exposure to peak sound pressure.
- Effects of exposure to **noise** on employees or groups of employees whose health is at particular risk from such exposure.
- So far as is practicable, any effects on the health and safety of employees resulting from the interaction between noise and the use of toxic substances at **work**, or between **noise** and vibration.
- Indirect effects on the health and safety of employees resulting from the interaction between noise and audible warning signals or other sounds that need to be audible in order to reduce risk at **work**.
- Information provided by the manufacturers of **work** equipment.
- Availability of alternative equipment designed to reduce the emission of **noise**.
- Any extension of exposure to noise at the workplace beyond normal **working** hours, including exposure in rest facilities supervised by the employer.
- Appropriate information obtained following health surveillance, including, where possible, published information.
- Availability of personal hearing protectors with adequate attenuation characteristics.

Employees or their representatives must be consulted and significant findings and measures taken or planned to comply with the regulations have to be recorded.

ACTION AND LIMIT VALUES

Regulation 2 of the CNWR 2005 sets out the definition of 'daily average noise exposure' as the time weighted average of the noise to which a worker is exposed over an 8 hour working day, taking account of levels of noise and duration of exposure and including impulsive noises. Weekly noise exposure means the average of daily noise exposures over a week and normalised to five working days.

	Lower exposure action values	Upper exposure action values	Exposure limit values
Daily or weekly personal noise exposure (A-weighted).	80 dB	85 dB	87 dB
Peak sound pressure (C-weighted).	135 dB	137 dB	140 dB

Under **regulation 4 of CNWR 2005** if the exposure of the employee to noise in the workplace varies greatly the employer can choose to use weekly noise exposure instead of daily noise exposure in determining if values or limits are exceeded. The exposure can take into account personal hearing protection provided to the employee.

Lower exposure action values

Where an employee is likely to be exposed to noise at or above the lower exposure action values, the daily or weekly exposure of 80dB(A) or a peak sound pressure of 135 dB(C), the employer must make hearing protection available upon request and provide the employees and their representatives with suitable and sufficient information, instruction and training. This shall include:

Figure 2-8-3: Noise hazard sign.   Source: RMS.

- Nature of risks from exposure to noise.
- Organisational and technical measures taken in order to comply.
- Exposure limit values and upper and lower exposure action values.
- Significant findings of the risk assessment, including any measurements taken, with an explanation of those findings.
- Availability and provision of personal hearing protectors and their correct use.

Figure 2-8-4: Mandatory hearing protection sign. Source: Stocksigns.

- Why and how to detect and report signs of hearing damage.
- Entitlement to health surveillance.
- Safe working practices to minimise exposure to noise.
- The collective results of any health surveillance in a form calculated to prevent those results from being identified as relating to a particular person.

Upper exposure action values

Where the noise exposure of an employee is likely to be at or above the upper exposure action values, the daily or weekly exposure of 85dB(A) or a peak sound pressure level of 137 dB(C), the employer shall:

- Provide employees with hearing protection.
- Ensure that the area is designated a hearing protection zone, fitted with mandatory hearing protection signs.
- Ensure access to the area is restricted where practicable.
- So far as reasonably practicable, ensure those employees entering the area wear hearing protection.

Exposure limit values

The employer must ensure that employees are not exposed to noise above an exposure limit value, the daily or weekly exposure of 87dB(A) or a peak sound pressure level of 140 dB(C). If an exposure limit value is exceeded the employer must immediately:

- Reduce exposure below the limit level.
- Identify the reason for the limit value being exceeded.
- Modify the organisational and technical measures to prevent a reoccurrence.

Basic noise control measures

Requirements for noise control set out in Regulation 6 of CNWR 2005 follow the general principles of prevention set out in the Management of Health and Safety at Work Regulations (MHSWR) 1999.

Employers must ensure that risk from the exposure of their employees to noise is either eliminated at source or, where this is not reasonably practicable, reduced to as low as is reasonably practicable.

Consideration should be made to:

- Other ***working*** methods which reduce exposure to noise.
- Choice of appropriate ***work*** equipment emitting the least possible ***noise***, taking account of the ***work*** to be done.
- Design and layout of workplaces, ***work*** stations and rest facilities.
- Suitable and sufficient information and training for employees, such that ***work*** equipment may be used correctly, in order to minimise their exposure to ***noise***.
- Reduction of ***noise*** by technical means.
- Appropriate maintenance programmes for ***work*** equipment, the workplace and workplace systems.
- Limitation of the duration and intensity of exposure to ***noise***.
- Appropriate ***work*** schedules with adequate rest periods.

The employer has to take care that noise levels in rest facilities are suitable for their purpose. The employer must adapt measures provided to suit a group or individual employee whose health is likely to be of particular risk from exposure to noise at work. Employees or their representatives must be consulted on the measures used.

Noise can be controlled at different points in the following 'chain':

1) The source (e.g., a noisy machine).
2) The path (e.g., through the air).
3) The receiver (e.g., the operator of a machine).

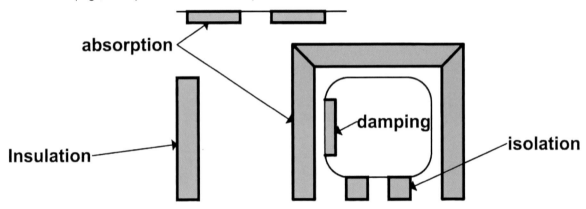

Figure 2-8-5: Basic layout of the main control methods.   *Source: RMS.*

The main methods of noise control are listed below:

Isolation	Positioning an absorbent element (e.g. rubber mount etc.) in the path of vibration can isolate a noise radiating area from a vibration input.
Absorption	When noise passes through porous materials (e.g. foam, mineral, wool etc.) some of its energy is absorbed.
Insulation	Imposing a barrier (e.g., a brick wall, lead sheet etc.) between the noise source and the receivers will provide noise insulation.
Damping	Mechanical vibration can be converted into heat by damping materials (e.g. metal/plastic/metal panels).
Silencing	Pipes/boxes can be designed to reduce air/gas noise (e.g. engine exhaust silencers, duct silencers, etc.).

Other specialist control methods (NOT examinable):

- ***Force Reduction*** - reduce impacts by using rubber pads or lower drop heights.
- ***Air exhaust and jet silencers*** - proprietary silencers can be used.
- ***Active*** - equal but opposite phase noise can cancel a problem noise.

In addition to controlling the amplitude of noise the ***exposure level*** can be reduced by minimising the amount of time an employee is exposed to noise, for example, by job rotation. Increasing the distance between noisy equipment and a work location can reduce the noise to which an employee is exposed. When buying new plant and equipment; employers should adopt a purchasing policy which results in the quietest machines being sourced.

Personal hearing protection

All types of personal ear protector should carry a CE marking.

PURPOSE

The purpose of personal hearing protection is to protect the user from the adverse effects on hearing caused by exposure to high levels of noise. All hearing protection must be capable of reducing exposure to below the upper exposure action value as required by the CNWR 2005 regulations. (85dB averaged over 8 hours).

APPLICATION AND LIMITATIONS OF VARIOUS TYPES

Earmuffs:

1) Banded.
2) Helmet mounted.
3) Communication muffs.

Application:

- Worn on the outside of the ear so less chance of infection.
- Clearly visible therefore easy to monitor.
- Can be integrated into other forms of personal protective equipment (PPE) e.g. head protection.

Limitations:

- Can be uncomfortable when worn for long periods.
- Incompatibility with other forms of PPE.
- Effectiveness may be compromised by e.g. long hair, spectacles etc.
- Requires correct storage facilities and regular maintenance.

Ear plugs:

1) Pre-moulded.
2) User formable.
3) Custom moulded.
4) Banded plugs.

Application:

- Easy to use and store - but must be inserted correctly.
- Available in many materials and designs, disposable.
- Relatively lightweight and comfortable. Can be worn for long periods.

Limitations:

- They are subject to hygiene problems unless care is taken to keep them clean.
- Correct size may be required. Should be determined by a competent person.
- Interferes with communication.
- Worn inside the ear, difficult to monitor.

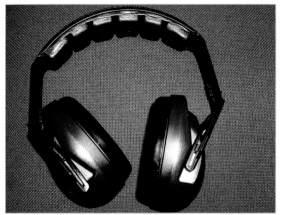

Figure 2-8-6: Ear defenders. *Source: RMS.*

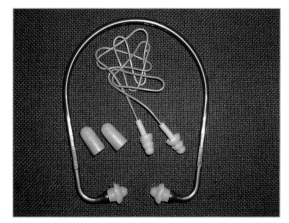

Figure 2-8-7: Disposable ear plugs. *Source: RMS.*

SELECTION

When selecting personal hearing protectors employers must take into consideration several factors, including:

- Noise attenuation (reduction) capability.
- Compatibility with other personal protective equipment.
- Suitability for the work environment.
- Readily available.
- Comfort and personal choice.
- Issue to visitors.
- Provision of information and training.
- Care and maintenance.

USE

All PPE should be used in accordance with employer's instructions, which should be based on manufacturer's instructions for use. PPE should only be used after adequate training has been given. Also, adequate supervision must be provided to ensure that training and instructions are being followed. Personal ear protection may not provide adequate protection due to any of the following reasons:

a) Long hair, spectacles, earrings etc, may cause a poor seal to occur.
b) Ear protectors are damaged, e.g., cracked.
c) Not fitted properly - due to lack of training.
d) Not wearing ear protectors all of the time.
e) Specification of protectors does not provide sufficient attenuation.

MAINTENANCE

Employers have a legal duty to ensure that any PPE is maintained in an efficient state, efficient working order and good repair. Simple maintenance can be carried out by the trained wearer, but more intricate repairs should only be done by specialist personnel. Maintenance in this context includes actions to keep personal hearing protection in use in good order. This will include the timely disposal of personal hearing protection that no longer affords adequate protection due to use.

ATTENUATION FACTORS

The attenuation (noise reduction) associated with personal hearing protectors must be supplied with the product. The information required is in terms of:

- SNR (Single Number Rating) values.
- HML (High, Medium and Low) values.
- Octave band values.

For example, a hearing protector might be designated with SNR 26, H=32, M=23, L=14. The estimated attenuation changes according to the noise spectrum of the environment in which the hearing protector is to be worn.

The SNR value is the result of a lengthy mathematical calculation; it gives a single-number rating of a hearing protector's attenuation for a specified percentage of the population. The SNR is significantly lower than the average attenuation across all of its test frequencies as the calculation contains correction factors to make it applicable to the broader population. While it is not the perfect measure of attenuation, SNR is a very useful standardised method for describing a hearing protector's attenuation in a single number. For example if an environment has a weighted noise measurement of 100dBC then by using an earplug with a SNR rating of 25dB it will reduce the noise to 75dBA.

Using HML values, H is for high-frequency noise environments, M for mid-frequency and L for low-frequency. Note that the HML designation does not refer to noise level, rather the spectrum of the noise frequencies. To determine the predicted noise attenuation (PNA) it is necessary that a noise reading be taken in both A weighting and C weighting mode, at the worker's ear. If the difference between the A weighted reading and the C weighted reading is greater than 2 a formula using the medium and low values is used; if it is less than or equal to 2 a formula using the high and medium value is used. This method enables the effects of the frequency of the noise to be taken into account by using a sound level meter with A and C weighting.

If readings have been taken using an octave band sound level meter the octave band method can be used to produce a more accurate reflection of the effectiveness of hearing protectors. This can assist with ensuring a close match of a particular hearing protector with the noise created by a particular noise source. It involves quite complicated mathematics, so to assist employers the Health and Safety Executive (HSE) has produced a calculator, which can be found at http://www.hse.gov.uk/noise/calculator.htm. Calculators are also available for SNR and HML methods.

Whichever method is used to determine the predicted noise attenuation of hearing protection, the HSE recommends the reduction of the value by 4dB to reflect what they see as 'real world factors'. This takes account of variances with fit or other user factors that may limit the effectiveness of the hearing protection.

The role of health surveillance

The role of health surveillance is to provide early detection of work-related ill-health. It will assist with the identification of noise hazards and the evaluation of noise control measures. By conducting health surveillance from the start of an employee's employment it is possible to detect early signs of hearing loss and provide early intervention to limit the continuing effects. Health surveillance can assist with confirming the success of noise controls at source and support the promotion of personal hearing protection.

Regulation 9 of the CNWR 2005 states that if a risk assessment indicates a risk to the health and safety of employees who are, or are liable to be, exposed to noise, and then they must be put under suitable health surveillance (including testing of their hearing). The employer must keep and maintain a suitable health record. The employer will, providing reasonable notice is given, allow the employee access to their health record.

Where, as a result of health surveillance, an employee is found to have identifiable hearing damage the employer shall ensure that the employee is examined by a doctor. If the doctor, or any specialist to whom the doctor considers it necessary to refer the employee, considers that the damage is likely to be the result of exposure to noise, the employer shall:

- Ensure that a suitably qualified person informs the employee accordingly.
- Review the risk assessment.
- Review any measure taken to comply with the regulations.
- Consider assigning the employee to alternative work.
- Ensure continued health surveillance.
- Provide for a review of the health of any other employee who has been similarly exposed.

Employees must, when required by the employer and at the cost of the employer, present themselves during working hours for health surveillance procedures.

Occupations with potential noise exposure problems

CONSTRUCTION SITES

Major construction sites generate significant levels of noise. Construction works include the demolition, maintenance, repair, erection, construction of buildings or roads and any work of engineering construction. Much of the noise generated is unavoidable and noise control methods are a balance between the needs of the developer to carry out the works and the rights of neighbours to quiet enjoyment of their properties.

Construction site workers are not only exposed to the noise from construction machinery but also the excessive noise levels generated by heavy traffic when work is being carried out on the side of a busy road. In addition to the nuisance to local residents, many employees have been injured from exposure to excessive noise.

Some typical decibels levels for equipment used on sites are:

- Disc cutter   99-115dB.
- Hammer drill   102-111dB.
- Breakers   103-113dB.
- Earthmover   87-94dB.

The noise levels change depending on the distance from the piece of equipment. The noise from an earthmover may be 94 decibels from 3 metres away and decreases to 82 decibels at 21 metres away.

UNIFORMED SERVICES

People serving in the military or other uniformed services, at some point, may be exposed to high-intensity noise of various types. Particularly high noise levels can be experienced if they are involved with firing weapons in practice or live firing operations. In addition, fire and rescue services may use noisy cutting gear to assist with rescue from road accidents. Many of the uniformed services operate heavy equipment and some may be maintaining noisy plant, such as engines of ships and other vessels.

Some typical decibel levels for military equipment used are:

- Apache Helicopter   Pilot 104dB, Co-pilot 101.3dB.
- M60 Machine Gun   155dB.
- Grenade at 150 metres   64.3dB.

ENTERTAINMENT

From 6th April 2008 licensees had to comply with the Control of Noise at Work Regulations (CNWR) 2005, which aims to protect workers from the effects of excessive noise. Other industry sectors had to comply with the regulations since April 2006, but all workplaces where live or recorded music is played in restaurants, bars, nightclubs etc were granted a two year transitional period, in recognition that the music in these venues is deliberately created for enjoyment and therefore different to other sectors.

Employers and employees working in pubs and clubs have responsibilities to protect the hearing of all employees, including bar staff, performers and crew and guest performers.

It is not uncommon for rock bands to generate noise levels in excess of 110 dB. However, many factors have to be taken into consideration when assessing the effects of exposure, not least of which is the size of the venue.

Measures that may can be taken include steps to reduce people's exposure to noise; acoustic controls; reducing the time employees spend in noisy areas; pointing the sound to where it is needed (e.g. the dance floor as opposed to the bar); volume control; training; hearing protection and health surveillance.

MANUFACTURING

Manufacturing processes can produce a great deal of noise as an inherent part of the process. This is particularly the case with processes involving forging, shaping, riveting, cutting or grinding. Many supplementary processes also generate noise, particularly where components are dropped from a height and where compressed air is released suddenly. With all the various types of equipment used within the manufacturing process, it is the cumulative effect of all the different noise levels and frequencies that needs to be assessed. Some typical noise levels:

- Conveyor   115dB.
- Lathe   96dB.
- Packing Machine   106dB.

CALL CENTRES

Any workplace which has a large volume of people working alongside each other engaged in speaking is at risk of exposure to noise. The level of noise will depend on the number and proximity of the people. In addition, the need to speak loudly will be influenced by the effectiveness of any headset worn.

If people cannot hear what is being said over the telephone there is a tendency for them to raise their voice to ensure they are heard and this can have a compounding effect which causes noise to increase.

HSE considers that, in general, call handlers' daily personal noise exposure is unlikely to exceed the 80 dB lower exposure action value defined in the Control of Noise at Work Regulations (CNWR) 2005, provided good practice in the management of noise risks is followed.

Figure 2-8-8: Call centre noise level.   *Source: HSE.*

There is some concern about workers being exposed to 'Acoustic shock', which is a term used in connection with incidents involving exposure to short duration, high frequency, high intensity sounds through a telephone headset, possibly due to some form of interference. Although call handlers may be shocked or startled by the sounds, exposure to them should not cause hearing damage as assessed by conventional methods. Headset 'noise limiter devices' should limit the exposure from this source to below significant noise levels.

8.2 - Vibration

The effects on the body of exposure to vibration

Occupational exposure to vibration may arise in a number of ways, often reaching workers at intensity levels disturbing to comfort, efficiency and health and safety. Long-term, regular exposure to vibration is known to lead to permanent and debilitating health effects such as vibration white finger, loss of sensation, pain, and numbness in the hands, arms, spine and joints. These effects are collectively known as hand-arm or whole body vibration syndrome.

In the case of whole body vibration it is transmitted to the worker through a contacting or supporting structure which is itself vibrating, e.g. a ship's deck, the seat or floor of a vehicle (tractor or tank), or a whole structure shaken by machinery (e.g. in the processing of coal, iron ore or concrete), where the vibration is intentionally generated for impacting.

Figure 2-8-9: Use of circular saw - vibration.   *Source: RMS.*

By far the most common route of harm to the human body is through the hands, wrists and arms of the subject - so called segmental vibration, where there is actual contact with the vibrating source.

HAND-ARM VIBRATION

Prolonged intense vibration transmitted to the hands and arms by vibrating tools and equipment can lead to a condition known as **hand-arm vibration syndrome (HAVs).** These are a range of conditions relating to long term damage to the circulatory system, nerves, soft tissues, bones and joints. Probably the best known of these conditions is known as vibration white finger (VWF). Here the fingers go white and numb (known as **Raynaud's phenomenon**), leading to sharp tingling pains in the affected area and an often painful deep red flush. This seems to occur in response to a change in metabolic demand in the fingers induced, for example, by temperature change. It seems that the blood vessels are unable to dilate either at all or rapidly enough because of the thickened tissues that then become anoxic (lacking in oxygen).

Contributory factors

As with all work-related ill health there are a number of factors which when combined result in the problem occurring. These include:

- Vibration frequency - frequencies ranging from 2- 1,500 Hz are potentially damaging but the most serious is the 5-20 Hz range.
- Duration of exposure - this is the length of time the individual is exposed to the vibration.
- Contact force - this is the amount of grip or push used to guide or apply the tools or work piece. The tighter the grip the greater the vibration to the hand.
- Factors affecting circulation - including temperature and smoking.
- Individual susceptibility.

Examples of risk activities

- The use of hand-held chain saws in forestry.
- The use of hand-held rotary tools in grinding or in the sanding or polishing of metal, or the holding of material being ground, or metal being sanded or polished by rotary tools.
- The use of hand-held percussive metal-working tools, or the holding of metal being worked upon by percussive tools in riveting, caulking, chipping, hammering, fettling or swaging.

- The use of hand-held powered percussive drills or hand-held powered percussive hammers in demolition, or on roads or footpaths, including road construction.

The medical effects are in the main more serious and permanent and are summarised below:

- Vascular changes in the blood vessels of the fingers.
- Neurological changes in the peripheral nerves.
- Muscle and tendon damage in the fingers, hands, wrists and forearms.
- Suspected bone and joint changes.
- Damage to the autonomic centres of the central nervous system in the brain influencing the endocrine, cardiac, vestibular and cochlear functions (not proven).

WHOLE BODY VIBRATION (WBV)

Whole-body vibration is vibration transmitted to the entire body via the seat or the feet, or both, often through driving or riding in motor vehicles (including fork trucks and off-road vehicles) or through standing on vibrating floors (e.g., near power presses in a stamping plant or near shakeout equipment in a foundry).

Figure 2-8-10: Dumper truck seat.   Source: RMS.

Prolonged exposure can lead to considerable back pain and time off work and may result in permanent injury and having to give up work. High-risk activities include driving site vehicles (e.g. dumper trucks) and the prolonged use of compactors.

The need for assessment of exposure, including limit and action values

RISK ASSESSMENT

Regulation 5 of CVWR 2005 requires the employer to make a suitable and sufficient assessment of the risk created by work that is liable to expose employees to risk from vibration. The assessment must observe work practices, make reference to information regarding the magnitude of vibration from equipment and, if necessary, measurement of the magnitude of the vibration.

Consideration must also be given to the type, duration, effects of exposure, exposures limit/action values, effects on employees at particular risk, the effects of vibration on equipment and the ability to use it, manufacturers' information, availability of replacement equipment, and extension of exposure at the workplace (e.g. rest facilities), temperature and information on health surveillance. The risk assessment should be recorded as soon as is practicable after it is made and be reviewed regularly.

EXPOSURE ACTION AND LIMIT VALUES

Regulation 4 of the CVWR 2005 states the personal daily exposure limits and daily exposure action values, normalised over an 8-hour reference period.

	Daily exposure action values	*Daily exposure limit values*
Hand arm vibration	2.5 m/s2	5 m/s2
Whole body vibration	0.5 m/s2	1.15 m/s2

Basic vibration control measures

PREVENTIVE AND PRECAUTIONARY MEASURES

Regulation 6 of CVWR 2005 states that the employer must seek to eliminate the risk of vibration at source or, if not reasonably practicable, reduce it to as low a level as is reasonably practicable. Where it is not reasonably practicable to take preventive measures which eliminate the risk at source and the personal daily exposure action value is likely to be reached or exceeded the employer must reduce exposure by implementing a programme of organisational and technical measures. These precautionary measures include the use of other methods of work, improved ergonomics, maintenance of equipment, design and layout, rest facilities, information, instruction and training, limitation by schedules and breaks and the provision of personal protective equipment to protect from cold and damp.

Measures must be adapted to take account of any group or individual employee whose health may be of particular risk from exposure to vibration.

The following precautionary measures should be considered when protecting people who work with vibrating equipment.

CHOICE OF EQUIPMENT

It is important to consider vibration characteristics when purchasing new equipment or selecting equipment for a task. Some equipment will provide better control of vibration at source; others will have damping measures provided to limit vibration transmission to the user. Many manufacturers claim to use composite materials that, when moulded into hand-grips and fitted onto vibrating power tools, reduce vibration by up to 45%. Some equipment may provide beneficial design that can limit the effects of vibration, such as the routing of exhaust gases of portable petrol driven equipment through the operating handles, to keep the user's hands warm.

MAINTENANCE

Equipment should be maintained to its optimum performance level, thereby reducing vibration to a minimum (e.g. the bearings of grinders).

LIMITING EXPOSURE

- Carry out a detailed assessment of hazardous tasks (e.g. breaking asphalt with a road breaker). This should include duration and frequency of the task.
- The work schedule should be examined to reduce duration of vibration exposure and magnitude, either by alternating with non-vibration work or avoiding continuous vibration by, for example, scheduling ten minute breaks every hour. Where equipment creates a high magnitude of vibration this must be clearly identified and its use by a single worker limited to short periods. Care should be taken to organise work schedules so that rest periods from this high risk work happen naturally in the process. Where they do not, it may be necessary to use reminders in the form of timed alarms or supervision.
- Wearing gloves is recommended for safety and protection against the cold by the retention of heat. Gloves of this type will not absorb a significant fraction of the vibration energy which lies within the 30-300Hz range. Care needs to be taken to select appropriate gloves, as the absorbent material in some gloves for thermal insulation may introduce a resonance frequency which may increase the total energy input to the hands (early work, Bednall, HSE).
- Warm clothing can help workers exposed to vibration to maintain a good body core temperature, which will assist circulation to the hands. It may be necessary for workers to be provided with a warm location for rest breaks or periods when cold is affecting their circulation. Workers with established HAVS should avoid exposure to cold and thus minimise the number of blanching attacks.
- Workers with advanced HAVS, which health surveillance has determined as deteriorating, should be removed from further exposure. The medical priority of this action is to prevent finger tip ulceration (tissue necrosis).

Other precautionary measures

- The vibration characteristics of hand tools should be assessed and reference made to the BSI and ISO Guidelines.
- Development of a purchasing policy to include consideration of vibration and, where necessary, vibration isolating devices.
- Training of all exposed employees on the proper use of tools and the minimisation of exposure. The greater the coupling (hand and tool interface), the more energy enters the hand. Increasing grip force increases the coupling. There are working techniques for all tools and the expertise developed over time justifies an initial training period for new starters. Operators of vibrating equipment should be trained to recognise the early symptoms of HAVS and WBV and how to report them.
- A continuous review should be conducted with regard to the redesigning tools, rescheduling work methods, or automating the process until such time as the risks associated with vibration are under control.
- As with any management system, the controls in place for vibration should be subject to audit.

Regulation 8 of CVWR 2005 states that employers must provide information, instruction and training to all employees who are exposed to risk from vibration and their representatives. This includes any organisational and technical measures taken, exposure limits and values, risk assessment findings, why and how to detect injury, entitlement to and collective results of health surveillance and safe working practices. Information, instruction and training shall be updated to take account of changes in the employer's work or methods. The employer shall ensure all persons, whether or not an employee, who carry out work in connection with the employer's duties have been provided with information, instruction and training.

Role of health surveillance

The role of health surveillance is to provide early detection of work related ill-health; it will assist with the identification of symptoms of the effects of vibration on health. By conducting health surveillance from the start of an employee's employment it is possible to detect early signs of the effects of vibration and provide early intervention to limit the continuing effects. Health surveillance can assist with confirming the success of vibration control measures. Surveillance for HAVS usually involves the worker or an occupational health specialist examining the hands to identify early signs of tingling or blanching. For whole body vibration, it can be a simple reporting method or questionnaire relating to experience of lower back discomfort or pain.

Regulation 7 of CVWR 2005 states that health surveillance must be carried out if there is a risk to the health of employees liable to be exposed to vibration. This is in order to prevent or diagnose any health effect linked with exposure to vibration. A record of health shall be kept of any employee who undergoes health surveillance. The employer shall, providing reasonable notice is given, provide the employee with access to their health records and provide copies to an enforcing officer on request.

If health surveillance identifies a disease or adverse health effect, considered by a doctor or other occupational health professional to be a result of exposure to vibration, the employer shall ensure that a qualified person informs the employee and provides information and advice. The employer must ensure they are kept informed of any significant findings from health surveillance, taking into account any medical confidentiality.

In addition the employer must also:

- Review risk assessments.
- Review the measures taken to comply.
- Consider assigning the employee to other work.
- Review the health of any other employee who has been similarly exposed and consider alternative work.

8.3 - Radiation

Differences between non-ionising and ionising radiation

Ionising radiation is that radiation, typically alpha and beta particles and gamma and x-rays, which has sufficient energy to produce ions by interacting with matter, whereas non-ionising radiation does not possess sufficient energy to cause the ionisation of matter.

Types of non-ionising radiation

Non-ionising radiation relates to the part of the electromagnetic spectrum covering two main regions, optical radiation (ultraviolet, visible and infrared) and electromagnetic fields (power frequencies, microwaves, and radio frequencies).

ULTRAVIOLET

Possible sources

There are many possible sources of Ultraviolet (UV) radiation to which people may be exposed at work:

- The sun.
- Electric arc welding.
- Insect killers.
- Sunbeds and sunlamps.
- Crack detection equipment.

- Tanning and curing equipment.
- Forgery detectors.
- Some lasers.
- Mercury vapour lamps.
- Tungsten halogen lamps.

Potential health effects

Much of the natural ultraviolet in the atmosphere is filtered out by the ozone layer. However, sufficient ultraviolet penetrates to cause sunburn and even blindness.

Its effect is thermal and photochemical, producing burns and skin thickening, and eventually skin cancer.

Electric arcs and ultraviolet lamps can produce an effect on the conjunctiva of the eyes resulting in inflammation (sometimes called "arc-eye") and cataract formation.

VISIBLE LIGHT (INCLUDING LASERS)

Possible sources

Any high intensity source of visible light can cause problems. Lasers are an obvious danger but so are light beams, powerful light bulbs and the sun. The danger is always due to direct or reflected radiation.

Potential health effects

Light in the visible frequency range can cause damage if it is present in sufficiently intense form. The eyes are particularly vulnerable but skin tissue may also be damaged. Indirect danger may also be created by employees being temporarily dazzled.

Figure 2-8-11: UV - from welding. *Source: Speedy Hire Plc.*

INFRARED

Possible sources

Anything that glows is likely to be a source of infrared radiation, for example:

- Furnaces or fires.
- Molten metal or glass.
- Burning or welding.

- Heat lamps.
- Some lasers.
- The sun.

Potential health effects

Exposure results in a thermal effect such as skin burning and loss of body fluids (heat exhaustion and dehydration). The eyes can be damaged in the cornea and lens which may become opaque (cataract). Retinal damage may also occur if the radiation is focused.

RADIO FREQUENCY AND MICROWAVES

Possible sources

This type of radiation is produced by radio/television transmitters. It is used industrially for induction heating of metals and is often found in intruder detectors.

Potential health effects

Burns can be caused if persons using this type of equipment allow parts of the body which carry jewellery to enter the radio frequency field. Intense fields at the source of transmitters will damage the body and particular precautions need to be taken to isolate radio/television transmitters to protect maintenance workers.

Microwaves can produce the same deep heating effect in live tissue as they can produce in cooking.

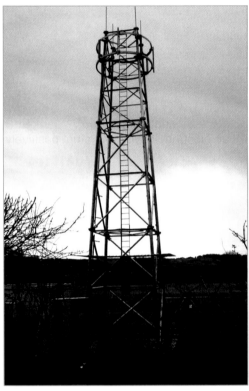

Figure 2-8-12: Radio mast.   Source: RMS.

Types of ionising radiation

Ionising radiation occurs as either electromagnetic rays, e.g. gamma rays or x-rays, or in particles, e.g. alpha and beta particles. Radiation is emitted by a wide range of sources and appliances used throughout industry, medicine and research. It is also a naturally occurring part of the environment. All matter is composed of **atoms**. Different atomic structures give rise to unique **elements**. Examples of common elements, which form the basic structure of life, are hydrogen, oxygen and carbon.

Atoms form the building blocks of nature and cannot be further sub divided by chemical means. The centre of the atom is called the **nucleus**, which consists of **protons** and **neutrons**. Electrons take up orbit around the nucleus.

Protons	-	Have a unit of mass and carry a positive electrical charge.
Neutrons	-	These also have mass but no charge.
Electrons	-	Have a mass about 2,000 times less than that of protons and carry a negative charge.

In an electrically neutral atom the number of electrons equals the number of protons (the positive and negative charges cancel out each other). If the atom loses an electron then a positively charged atom is created. The process of losing or gaining electrons is called **ionisation**.

If the matter which is ionised is a human cell, the cell chemistry will change and this will lead to functional changes in the body tissue. Some cells can repair radiation damage, others cannot. The cell's sensitivity to radiation is directly proportional to its reproductive function; bone marrow, and reproductive organs are the most vulnerable; muscle and central nervous system tissue are affected to a lesser extent.

"Ionising radiation is that radiation which has sufficient energy to produce ions by interacting with matter".

Figure 2-8-13: Ionising radiation.   Source: RMS.

Ionising radiation found in industry are alpha, beta and gamma, and X-rays. Whilst X-rays may occur in nature, generally they are created in the work place either with knowledge, e.g. X-ray machines or sometimes without knowledge from high voltage equipment. The human body absorbs radiation readily from a wide variety of sources, mostly with adverse effects.

There are a number of different types of ionising radiation each with their different powers of penetration and effects on the body. Therefore, the type of radiation will determine the type and level of protection.

ALPHA PARTICLES

Alpha particles are comparatively large. Alpha particles travel short distances in dense materials, and can only just penetrate the skin. The principal risk is through ingestion or inhalation of a source e.g. radon gas emits alpha particles. This might place the material close to vulnerable tissue such as the lungs; when this happens the high localised energy effect will destroy associated tissue of the organs affected.

BETA PARTICLES

Beta particles are much smaller and faster moving than alpha particles. They are smaller in mass than alpha particles, but have longer range, so they can damage and penetrate the skin. Whilst they have greater penetrating power than alpha particles, beta particles are less ionising and take longer to effect the same degree of damage.

GAMMA RAYS

These have great penetrating power. Gamma radiation passing through a normal atom will sometimes force the loss of an electron, leaving the atom positively charged; this is called an **ion**.

X-RAYS

X-rays are very similar in their effects to gamma rays. X-rays are produced by sudden acceleration or deceleration of a charged particle, usually when high-speed electrons strike a suitable target under controlled conditions. The electrical potential required to accelerate electrons to speeds where X-ray production will occur is a minimum of **15,000volts**. X-rays and gamma rays have **high energy**, and **high penetration** power through fairly dense material. In low density substances, including air, they may travel long distances.

RADON

Radon is a naturally occurring radioactive gas that can seep out of the ground and enter buildings. It is also the most common source of exposure to radiation in Britain, easily exceeding exposure from nuclear power stations or hospital scans and X-rays. It is the second most common cause of lung cancer in the UK, tobacco smoking being the most common cause.

It occurs naturally from decaying uranium, and it is particularly abundant in regions with granite bedrock. Exposure is high in Cornwall, Devon and Somerset, because of these counties' underlying geology, and there are also 'hotspots' in Wales, the Cotswolds and the Pennines. However, the gas disperses outdoors so levels are generally very low.

Once inhaled into the lungs, the gas decays into other radioactive isotopes of lead, bismuth and polonium, including polonium 210, the poison that was used to kill the Russian former spy Alexander Litvinenko in London in 2006. Some decay products emit alpha particles which, when breathed in, can cause harm to the sensitive cells of the lungs.

POTENTIAL HEALTH EFFECTS OF IONISING RADIATION

The effects on the body of exposure to ionising radiation will depend on the type of radiation, the frequency and duration of exposure. Acute effects will include nausea, vomiting, diarrhoea and burns (either superficial skin burns or deep, penetrating burns causing cell damage). Long-term (chronic) effects such as dermatitis, skin ulcers, cataracts and cancers can also be expected.

Typical occupational sources of non-ionising and ionising radiation

SOURCES OF NON-IONISING RADIATION

Ultraviolet

- The sun.
- Arc welding and cutting.
- Adhesive curing processes.
- Water treatment.
- Lights and torches. Ultraviolet is used to attract insects to an electric sterilising device located in areas where food preparation is carried out *(see figure ref 2-8-14)*.

Visible radiation

- Lasers, for example, in surveying or level alignment equipment.

- Other high intensity lights such as photocopiers and printers.

Figure 2-8-14: Pest control.   Source: RMS.

Infrared

- Furnaces or fires.
- Molten metal or glass.
- Burning or welding.
- Heat lamps.
- Some lasers.
- Toasters

Radio frequency

- Overhead power lines.
- Plastic welding.
- High powered transmitters.

Microwave

- Telecommunications.
- Cooking equipment.

SOURCES OF IONISING RADIATION

The most familiar examples of ionising radiation in the workplace are in hospitals, dentist surgeries and veterinary surgeries where X-rays are used extensively. X-ray machines are used for security purposes at baggage handling points in airports. In addition, gamma rays are used in non-destructive testing of metals, for example, site radiography of welds in pipelines.

In other industries ionising radiation is used for measurement, for example, in the paper industry for the thickness of paper, and in the food processing industry for measuring the contents of sealed tins.

The Health Protection Agency (HPA) and British Geological Survey have extensively surveyed the UK and the Government has defined the highest radon areas as radon affected areas.

Whilst all workplaces can be at risk from radon, workplaces at higher risk tend to be those located in affected areas. Underground workplaces such as mines and caves made available as tourist attractions are also at higher risk of increased radon levels, wherever their location might be.

The basic means of controlling exposures to ionising and non-ionising radiation

CONTROLS FOR NON-IONISING RADIATION

The Control of Artificial Optical Radiation at Work Regulations (CAOR) 2010 requires an employer to conduct a specific risk assessment and to eliminate or reduce risks. Optical radiation includes ultraviolet, visible light and infrared. Exposure limit levels are set for this form of radiation. Information and training is to be provided to those that may be affected, which includes employees and others carrying out work on behalf of the employer. Medical examination and health surveillance is to be provided for those employees that receive over exposure.

Ultraviolet

Protection from natural sources of UV is relatively simple and includes the provision of outdoor workers with barrier creams, suitable lightweight UV rated clothing and head protection, and as appropriate eye protection. In addition, workers should be encouraged to take breaks in the shade where possible and consideration should be made to adjusting work schedules so outside tasks may be conducted at times of day that are less affected by UV.

Control of artificial sources of UV includes segregation of UV emitting processes and the use of warning signs. UV radiation emitted from industrial processes can be isolated by physical shielding such as partitions or plastic curtains. It should be borne in mind that some plastic materials differ in their UV absorption abilities and care should be taken in their selection. Users of UV emitting equipment, such as welders, can protect themselves by the use of goggles and protective clothing - the latter to avoid "sunburn". Assistants in welding processes often fail to appreciate the extent of their own exposure, and require similar protection. Workers should check skin exposed to UV frequently to identify possible effects that might lead to skin cancer.

Visible light

The eye detects visible light. It has two protective control mechanisms of its own, the eyelids and the iris. These are normally sufficient to provide general protection, as the eyelid has a reaction of 150 milliseconds. However, where this is not adequate because of the intensity of light or the sustained exposure of the eye to it other precautions should be considered, including confinement of high-intensity sources, matt finishes to nearby paint-work, and provision of optically-correct protective glasses for outdoor workers in snow, sand or near large bodies of water. Where the high intensity visible light is artificially created those not involved in the process must also be protected. Warning signs should be posted and access restricted to the process area.

Infrared

Controls to limit exposure include engineered measures, such as remote controls, screening, interlocks and clamps to hold material to enable the worker to be outside the exposure area. This can be supplemented by forms of personal protective equipment where exposure cannot be prevented, for example, face shields, goggles or other protective eyewear, coveralls and gloves. The management of enforced maximum working periods should be used where exposure cannot be reduced to an acceptable level; this can include a routine change of activity/job rotation. It is important to protect others not directly involved in the process by using screens, curtains and restricted access.

Radio frequency and microwaves

Radio frequency and microwave radiation can usually be shielded at point of generation, to protect the users. If size and function prohibits this, restrictions on entry and working near an energised microwave device will be needed. Metals, tools, flammable and explosive materials should not be left in the electromagnetic field generated by microwave equipment. Appropriate warning devices should be part of the controls for each such appliance.

CONTROLS FOR IONISING RADIATION

Reduced time

Reducing the duration of exposure through redesigning work patterns; giving consideration to shift working, job rotation etc. The dose received will also depend upon the time of the exposure. These factors must be taken into account when devising suitable operator controls.

Increased distance

Radiation intensity is subject to the inverse square law. Energy received (dose) is inversely proportional to the square of the distance from the source.

Shielding

The type of shielding required giving adequate protection will depend on the penetration power of the radiation involved. For example, it may vary from thin sheets of silver paper to protect from beta particles through to several centimetres of concrete and lead for protection against gamma or X-rays. In addition to the previous specific controls, the following general principles must be observed:

■ Radiation should only be introduced to the work place if there is a positive benefit.
■ Safety information must be obtained from suppliers about the type(s) of radiation emitted or likely to be emitted by their equipment.
■ Safety procedures must be reviewed regularly.
■ Protective equipment provided must be suitable and appropriate, as required by relevant Regulations. It must be checked and maintained regularly.
■ Emergency plans must cover the potential radiation emergency.
■ Written authorisation by permit should be used to account for all purchase/use, storage, transport and disposal of radioactive substances.

The basic means of controlling exposures to radon

Control of radon exposure in new buildings can be done by installing a 'radon proof membrane' within the floor structure. In areas more seriously affected by radon it may be necessary to install a 'radon sump' to vent the gas into the atmosphere. A radon sump has a pipe connecting a space under a solid floor to the outside.

A small electric fan in the pipe continually sucks the radon from under the house and expels it harmlessly to the atmosphere.

Modern sumps are often constructed from outside the building so there is no disruption inside. In existing buildings it is not usually possible to provide a radon proof barrier, so alternative measures are used to control the build up of radon in the building and subsequent exposure to it.

Such measures include a mixture of active and passive systems such as improved under floor and indoor ventilation in the area, positive pressure ventilation of occupied areas, installation of radon sumps and extraction pipework and sealing large gaps in floors and walls in contact with the ground.

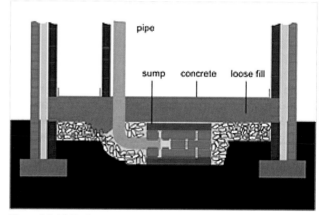

Figure 2-8-15: Radon sump.   Source: HSE

Basic radiation protection strategies

Basic radiation protection strategies include the application of the principles of time, distance and shielding. Exposure should be limited to as few people as possible and those individuals should be monitored and exposure levels maintained within limits.

Regulation 8 of the Ionising Radiation Regulations (IRR) 1999 sets out requirements for the employer to control exposure to ionising radiation:

Every radiation employer shall, in relation to any work with ionising radiation that he undertakes, take all necessary steps to restrict so far as is reasonably practicable the extent to which his employees and other persons are exposed to ionising radiation.

In the case of ionising radiation, where possible only sealed sources should be used and a system developed to minimise dose levels to individuals. This work must be under the control of a radiation protection advisor.

RADIATION PROTECTION ADVISERS (RPA)

With the exception of the operations specified in Schedule 1 of the IRR 1999, at least one radiation protection adviser (RPA) must be appointed in writing by employers using ionising radiation. The numbers of RPA appointed must be appropriate to the risk and the area where advice is needed is to be stated. Employers must consult the RPA on:

- The implementation of controlled and supervised areas.
- The prior examination of plans for installations and the acceptance into service of new or modified sources of ionising radiation in relation to any engineering controls, design features, safety features and warning devices provided to restrict exposure to ionising radiation.
- The regular calibration of equipment provided for monitoring levels of ionising radiation and the regular checking that such equipment is serviceable and correctly used.
- The periodic examination and testing of engineering controls, design features, safety features and warning devices and regular checking of systems of work provided to restrict exposure to ionising radiation.

Adequate information and facilities must be provided by the employer to the RPA in order to allow them to fulfil their functions.

RADIATION PROTECTION SUPERVISOR

A radiation employer is required to appoint one or more radiation protection supervisors for the purpose of securing compliance with the regulations in respect of work carried out in any area subject to 'local rules for work in controlled or supervised areas'. Their area of work needs to be defined and they must be trained so that they understand the requirements of legislation and local rules insofar as they affect their area of work. They also need to understand the reasons for the precautions that need to be taken in their area of work, and they should command the respect of those they supervise.

CLASSIFIED WORKERS

Persons entering a controlled area should either be classified or be entering in accordance with 'written arrangements' designed to ensure that doses will not exceed, in cases of persons over 18, levels which would otherwise require the persons to be classified. In the case of other persons the relevant dose limit is applicable.

The role of monitoring and health surveillance

Regulation 19 of the Ionising Radiation Regulations (IRR) 1999 requires every employer who designates an area as a controlled or supervised area to ensure that levels of ionising radiation are adequately monitored for each such area and that working conditions in those areas are kept under review.

The main purposes of monitoring are to:

- Check that areas have been correctly designated.
- Help determine radiation levels and contamination from particular operations, so that appropriate control measures for restricting exposure can be proposed.
- Detect breakdowns in controls or systems, so as to indicate whether conditions are satisfactory for continuing work in that area.
- Provide information on which to base estimates of personal dose for non-classified persons.

Regulation 24(2) of the Ionising Radiation Regulations (IRR) 1999 requires every employer to ensure that each of his employees affected by the regulations is under adequate health surveillance by an appointed doctor or employment medical adviser to determine their fitness for the work with ionising radiation. Fitness in this sense is not restricted to possible health effects from exposure to ionising radiation. Those conducting the health surveillance will need to take account of specific features of the work with ionising radiation, such as the fitness of the individual. This will include such things as:

- Their ability to wear any personal protective equipment (including respiratory protective equipment) required to restrict exposure.
- Whether they have a skin disease which could affect their ability to undertake work involving unsealed radioactive materials.
- Whether they have serious psychological disorders which could affect their ability to undertake work with radiation sources that involves a special level of responsibility for safety.

8.4 - Stress

Causes

"Stress is the adverse reaction people have to excessive pressures or other demands placed on them".

Figure 2-8-16: Definition of stress.   *Source: HSE.*

Stress in workers can be caused by a range of issues that relate to the organisation they work in and issues that are external to the organisation but influence the worker while they are at work, for example, personal relationship problems at home.

The issues that relate to the organisation can be considered using the structure depicted in the Health and Safety Executive (HSE) Management Standards for stress at work. The standards define the positive characteristics or culture of an organisation where stress is being managed effectively, but if these characteristics are absent they can be a cause of stress.

DEMAND

This includes issues like workload and work patterns, stress may be due to an individual not being able to cope with the demands of the job, and the work environment itself. Work patterns that could lead to stress include shift working, excessive overtime and unsocial hours. If the work pattern or job demands are such that the worker does not get adequate breaks this can also lead to stress. Typical environmental stressors are:

- Noise.
- Extremes of temperature.
- Poor lighting.

CONTROL

If an individual has little control over the pace and manner they work this can create stress. In particular, work that has repetitive or monotonous features that the worker has no ability to control or adjust may lead to stress.

SUPPORT

If a worker perceives a lack of encouragement or resources provided by the organisation, line management or co-workers a feeling of remoteness can be created.

The failure to provide support was highlighted in the landmark case, **Lancaster v Birmingham City Council (1999),** where liability was admitted when an employee had taken three periods of sick leave and had then been medically retired. She had been moved from her job as draughtswoman to work as a neighbourhood housing officer. In addition to dealing with members of the public who were often intimidating and abusive, she was not given sufficient administrative support, and had a high workload, partly as a result of an unfilled vacancy. She said she was expected to do the job without ever having been given proper training. In July 1999 she was awarded more than £67,000 in compensation.

WORK RELATIONSHIPS

As long ago as 1994, Staffordshire University Business School published the results of a survey indicating that 1 in 2 UK employees have been bullied at work during their working life.

The Manufacturing, Science and Finance Union (MSF) have identified workplace bullying as:

"Persistent, offensive, abusive, intimidating, malicious or insulting behaviour, abuse of power or unfair penal sanctions which make the recipient feel upset, threatened, humiliated, or vulnerable, which undermines their self confidence and which may cause them to suffer stress. Harassment, in general terms, is unwanted conduct affecting the dignity of men and women in the workplace. It may be related to age, sex, race, disability, religion, sexual orientation, nationality or any personal characteristic of the individual, and may be persistent or an isolated incident. The key is that the actions or comments are viewed as demeaning and unacceptable to the recipient".

Figure 2-8-17: Bullying.   Source: cipd.

If relationships with co-workers, customers or suppliers are poor, this can put the worker under pressure, which may lead to stress. This is particularly so if the relationship involves such issues as harassment, discrimination or bullying. If the relationship part of the work includes the fear of violence, this can put the worker under significant pressure when conducting their job, particularly if they feel they can do nothing to manage the risk. Poor work relationships can lead to poor communications, and visa versa, which can cause the worker to feel isolated or unprepared for the work they are doing. In the same way, if workers are not consulted or involved in processes that might affect them and their work, like risk assessment, they may feel under additional pressure because they do not understand or accept the outcomes from the process.

ROLE

If workers do not understand their role in the organisation, or have conflicting roles, this can increase the potential for stress. In particular, undertaking new or difficult work without first achieving the appropriate skills to complete it successfully or safely could put the individual under pressure.

CHANGE

If the management of organisational change is not conducted or communicated well, individuals can be confused or feel threatened by the change and this could lead to stress. Changes that cause the worker to feel their job or salary may be insecure due to re-organisation or redundancy can particularly have this effect. The absence of consultation of workers when change is considered can add to concerns about the change and lead to stress.

Effects of stress

Being exposed to stressful situations brings about changes in behaviour and also physical well being.

Physical effects

- Increased heart rate.
- Increased sweating.
- Headache.
- Dizziness.
- Blurred vision.
- Aching neck and shoulders.
- Skin rashes.
- Lowered resistance to infection.

Behavioural effects

- Increased anxiety.
- Irritability.
- Increased alcohol intake.
- Increased smoking.
- Erratic sleep patterns.
- Poor concentration.
- Feeling of inability to cope with everyday tasks.

This can result in

- Lack of motivation.
- Lack of commitment.
- Poor timekeeping.
- Increase in mistakes.

- Increase in sickness absence.
- Poor decision making.
- Poor planning.

Stress is reflected in relationships at work as

- Tension between colleagues/supervisors.
- Poor service to clients.

- Deterioration in industrial relations.
- Increase in disciplinary problems.

Control measures

The Health and Safety Executive (HSE) Management Standards for stress at work set out the positive characteristics or culture of an organisation where stress is being managed effectively. Stress, like other risks should be subject to a risk assessment in order to identify the causes of pressure that can lead to stress and to evaluate the current controls.

The HSE Management Standards are based on the 6 main stress factors of demands, control, change, relationships, role and support. Each standard defines a desired state (best practice) to be achieved in order to minimise the risk of stress in the workplace.

DEMAND

The standard is - "employees indicate they can cope with the demands of the job and there are systems in place locally to respond to any individual concerns".

Control measures to meet this include:

- Balancing the demands of the work to the agreed hours of work, consider shift working, the amount of additional hours worked and unsocial hours.
- Provision of regular and suitable breaks from work and rest periods.
- Matching worker skills and abilities to the job demands.
- Designing jobs so they are within the capability of workers.
- Minimising the work environment risks, such as noise and temperature.

CONTROL

The standard is - "employees indicate that they are able to have a say about the way they do their work and there are systems in place locally to respond to any individual concerns".

Control measures to meet this include:

- Providing, where possible, workers with control over their pace and manner of work, consider reducing the effects of repetitive and monotonous work by job rotation.
- Encouraging workers to use their skills and initiative to do the work.
- Encouraging workers to develop to enable them to do more challenging or new work.
- Providing workers with opportunity to influence when breaks are taken.
- Consulting workers regarding work patterns.

SUPPORT

The standard is - "employees indicate that they receive adequate information and support from their colleagues and superiors and there are systems in place locally to respond to any individual concerns".

Control measures to meet this include:

- Establishing policies and procedures that provide support, particularly where workers may feel other factors are putting them under pressure.
- Provide systems that enable and encourage managers to identify where workers need support, consider where workers deal with the public in demanding environments, where new workers are introduced and times of high demand.

- Provide systems that enable and encourage managers to provide support to workers, consider particularly those working remotely by virtue of their location or time of working and new workers.
- Encourage co-workers to support each other.
- Ensure workers understand what resources and support is available and how they access it.
- Provide regular constructive feedback to workers.

WORK RELATIONSHIPS

Improving work relationships and attempting to modify people's attitudes and behaviour is a difficult and time-consuming process. Effective strategies include regular communication with staff, provision of accurate and honest information on the effect of organisational changes on them, adopting partnership approaches to problems, provision of support. The onus is on employers to promote a culture that respects the dignity of others - if it is left to employees to do this it will not happen.

The standard is - "employees feel able to indicate that they are not subjected to unacceptable behaviours, e.g. bullying at work and there are systems in place locally to respond to any individual concerns".

Control measures to meet this include:

- Promote positive behaviour that avoids conflict and leads to fairness; consider co-workers, customers and suppliers.
- Establish policies and procedures that resolve unacceptable behaviour that leads to conflict.
- Encourage managers to deal with unacceptable behaviour, such as harassment, discrimination or bullying.
- Encourage workers to report unacceptable behaviour.
- Establish systems that ensure communication with managers and workers, consider timeliness of communication to those that work isolated by location or time.
- Establish systems that ensure involvement and consultation, such as regarding the process of conducting risk assessments.

ROLE

The standard is - "employees indicate that they understand their role and responsibilities and there are systems in place locally to respond to any individual concerns".

Control measures to meet this include:

- Ensure workers have the knowledge, skill and experience to conduct their role or are being supported appropriately; consider workers undertaking new or difficult work.
- Ensure role requirements are compatible, for example, that the need to manage costs does not conflict with health and safety.
- Ensure role requirements are clear.
- Ensure workers and their managers understand the roles and responsibilities.
- Provide systems to enable workers to raise concerns about role uncertainty or conflict, particularly consider the work life balance for those workers that provide care for others outside their work.

CHANGE

The standard is - "employees indicate that the organisation engages them frequently when undergoing organisational change and there are systems in place locally to respond to any individual concerns".

Control measures to meet this include:

- Provide workers with timely information to help them understand the change, reasons for it and timing of effects.
- Ensure worker consultation on proposed changes.
- Provide workers with information on likely impacts of change on their jobs.
- Provide training and support through the period of change.

In addition to the six specific factors that relate to the HSE management standards for stress at work there are a number of general control measures that should form part of a stress management strategy. These include:

- Introducing a stress policy and procedures to demonstrate to managers, workers, worker representatives and enforcing authorities that the organisation recognises stress as a serious issue worthy of a commitment to manage the risk.
- Providing training and support for workers and all levels of management in the form of stress awareness and stress management training, as appropriate.
- Addressing the issue of work-life balance, which may include consideration of job-share, part-time work, voluntary reduced hours, home-working, flexitime etc.
- Promoting general health and well-being awareness initiatives within the organisation, such as diet, exercise and fitness programmes.
- Providing access to occupational health practitioners, counselling support or assistance programmes for those that may be affected by stress.

This page is intentionally blank

Relevant Statutory Provisions

RMS Publishing's technical authors regularly review examiners reports for all NEBOSH awards to ensure that the specific publication content is in keeping with the level of study required for the award.

The review considers the core training materials, assessment criteria and relevant legislation. At each stage care is taken to pitch the level of the content to the examination requirements and, in particular, knowledge of the legislation required at this level.

The syllabus does not require knowledge of all legislation to the same depth, this is reflected in the 'relevant statutory provisions' section of the study book. Relevant statutory provisions abstracts are designed to focus on the specific aspects (often popular with the examiners) of the legislation required to meet the syllabus. The study book provides guidance in the form of 'outline of main points' enabling students to focus on the critical learning points and avoid over studying. In addition, legislation is considered in context in the relevant elements of the study book.

Students are advised to obtain or gain access to statutory documents, approved codes of practice and guidance related to the relevant statutory provisions as part of their personal development programme, for the purpose of the examination and future career development.

NEBOSH do not examine on legislation until it has been in force for 6 months. Students may show knowledge of new legislation in their answers until that point, students referring to the former legislation will not loose marks until the 6 month period has passed.

Chemicals (Hazard Information and Packaging for Supply) Regulations (CHIP 4) 2009

Considered in context in NGC2, Element 7.

Arrangement of Regulations

PART 1 - INTRODUCTION
1. Citation, commencement and extent
2. Interpretation
3. Application

PART 2 - GENERAL REQUIREMENTS
4. Classification of dangerous substances and dangerous preparations
5. Safety data sheets for substances and preparations
6. Packaging of dangerous substances, dangerous preparations and certain specified preparations
7. Labelling of dangerous substances and dangerous preparations
8. Labelling of single receptacles and receptacles in outer packagings
9. Particular labelling requirements for certain preparations
10. Methods of marking or labelling packages
11. Child resistant fastenings, tactile warning devices and other consumer protection measures
12. Retention of data for dangerous preparations
13. Transitional provisions for dangerous substances, dangerous preparations and certain specified preparations

PART 3 - MISCELLANEOUS
14. Enforcement
15. Defence
16. Extension outside Great Britain
17. Revocations and amendments

SCHEDULES
Schedule 1 - Classification of dangerous substances and dangerous preparations
Schedule 2 - Indications of danger and symbols for dangerous substances and dangerous preparations
Schedule 3 - Provisions for classifying dangerous preparations
Part 1 - General provisions
Part 2 - Concentration limits to be used in the evaluation of health hazards
Part 3 - Concentration limits to be used for the evaluation of environment hazards
Schedule 4 - Labelling particulars for dangerous substances, dangerous preparations and for certain other preparations
Part 1 - General provisions relating to labels
Part 2 - Particular provisions concerning certain preparations
Schedule 5 - British and international standards relating to child resistant fastenings and tactile warning devices
Schedule 6 - Amendments
Schedule 7 - Revocations

Outline of main points

CHIP refers to the Chemicals (Hazard Information and Packaging for Supply) Regulations 2009, which came into force on 6th April 2009. These regulations are also known as CHIP 4 and shall not extend to Northern Ireland.

CHIP is the law that applies to suppliers of dangerous chemicals. Its purpose is to protect people and the environment from the effects of those chemicals by requiring suppliers to provide information about the dangers and to package them safely.

CHIP requires the supplier of a dangerous chemical to:

- Identify the hazards (dangers) of the chemical. This is known as 'classification'.
- Give information about the hazards to their customers. Suppliers usually provide this information on the package itself (e.g. a label).
- Package the chemical safely.

Safety data sheets (SDS) are no longer covered by the CHIP regulations. The laws that require a SDS to be provided have been transferred to the European REACH Regulation.

REACH

REACH is a new European Union regulation concerning the registration, evaluation, authorisation and restriction of chemicals. It came into force on 1st June 2007 and replaces a number of European Directives and Regulations with a single system to gather hazard information, assess risks, classify, label, and restrict the marketing and use of individual chemicals and mixtures. This is known as the REACH system:

R egistration of basic information of substances to be submitted by companies, to a central database.

E valuation of the registered information to determine hazards and risks.

A uthorisation requirements imposed on the use of high-concern substances.

CH emicals.

REACH covers both "new" and "existing" substances and puts the onus on Industry to prove that chemicals it uses are safe. REACH only applies to chemicals manufactured in or imported into the EU. It does not apply to the use of chemicals in finished products. So a product like a television, or computer or shampoo made outside the EU could contain chemicals that are not registered under REACH - providing they are not banned under specific safety regulations (such as lead).

'Supply' means making a chemical available to another person. Manufacturers, importers, distributors, wholesalers and retailers are all examples of suppliers.

CHIP applies to most chemicals but not all. The details of the scope are set out in the regulations. Some chemicals, such as cosmetics and medicines, are outside the scope and have their own specific laws.

CHIP 4 arises from the need to align national legislation with the new European regulation on the Classification, Labelling and Packaging of Substances and Mixtures, known as the CLP Regulation, which will directly apply in all member states of the European Union. CHIP 4 will also put in place the necessary legal provisions to allow regulators in Great Britain to enforce the CLP Regulation.

Source: HSE.

Confined Spaces Regulations (CSR) 1997

Considered in context in NGC1, Element 4.

Arrangement of Regulations

1) Citation, commencement and interpretation.
2) Disapplication of Regulations.
3) Duties.
4) Work in confined spaces.
5) Emergency arrangements.
6) Exemption certificates.
7) Defence in proceedings.
8) Extension outside Great Britain.
9) Repeal and revocations.

Outline of main points

The Confined Spaces Regulations (CSR) 1997 repeal and replace earlier provisions contained in s.30 of the Factories Act 1961.

A failure to appreciate the dangers associated with confined spaces has led not only to the deaths of many workers, but also to the demise of some of those who have attempted to rescue them. A confined space is not only a space which is small and difficult to enter, exit or work in; it can also be a large space, but with limited/restricted access. It can also be a space which is badly ventilated e.g. a tank or a large tunnel.

The Confined Spaces Regulations (CSR) 1997, define a confined space as any place, including any chamber, tank, vat, silo, pit, pipe, sewer, flue, well, or other similar space, in which, by virtue of its enclosed nature, there is a foreseeable risk of a 'specified occurrence'.

Construction (Design and Management) Regulations (CDM) 2007

Considered in context in NGC1, Element 1 and NGC2, Element 1.

The new, simplified CDM Regulations came into force on 6th April 2007 and revised and brought together the existing CDM 1994 and the Construction (Health Safety and Welfare) (CHSWR) Regulations 1996 into a single regulatory package. They are supported by an Approved Code of Practice (ACoP) and industry-approved guidance.

The CDM 2007 regulations offer an opportunity for a step change in health and safety performance and will be used to re-emphasise the health, safety and broader business benefits of a well-managed and co-ordinated approach to the management of health and safety in construction.

Arrangement of regulations

PART 1 - INTRODUCTION

1. Citation and commencement.
2. Interpretation.
3. Application.

PART 2 - GENERAL MANAGEMENT DUTIES APPLYING TO CONSTRUCTION PROJECTS

4. Competence.
5. Co-operation.
6. Co-ordination.
7. General principles of prevention.
8. Election by clients.
9. The client's duty in relation to arrangements for managing projects.
10. Client's duty in relation to information.
11. Duties of designers.
12. Designs prepared or modified outside Great Britain.
13 Duties of contractors.

PART 3 - ADDITIONAL DUTIES WHERE PROJECT IS NOTIFIABLE

14.   Appointments by the client.
15.   Client's duty in relation to information.
16.   The client's duty in relation to the start of construction phase.
17.   The client's duty in relation to the health and safety file.
18.   Additional duties of designers.
19.   Additional duties of contractors.
20.   General duties of CDM co-ordinators.
21.   Notification of project by CDM co-ordinator.
22.   Duties of the principal contractor.
23.   Principal contractor's duties in relation to the construction phase plan.
24.   Principal contractor's duties in relation to co-operation and consultation with workers.

PART 4 - DUTIES RELATING TO HEALTH AND SAFETY ON CONSTRUCTION SITES

25.   Application of regulations 26-44.
26.   Safe places of work.
27.   Good order and site security.
28.   Stability of structures.
29.   Demolition or dismantling.
30.   Explosives.
31.   Excavations.
32.   Cofferdams and caissons.
33.   Reports of inspections.
34.   Energy distribution installations.
35.   Prevention of drowning.
36.   Traffic routes.
37.   Vehicles.
38.   Prevention of risk from fire etc.
39.   Emergency procedures.
40.   Emergency routes and exits.
41.   Fire detection and fire-fighting.
42.   Fresh air.
43.   Temperature and weather protection.
44.   Lighting.

PART 5 - GENERAL

45.   Civil liability.
46.   Enforcement in respect of fire.
47.   Transitional provision.
48.   Revocation and amendments.

SCHEDULES

Schedule 1 (regulation 21(1), (2) and (4)) - Particulars to be notified to the Executive

Schedule 2 (regulation 11, 16(I)(b)and 19(4)) - Welfare facilities

1.   Sanitary conveniences.
2.   Washing facilities.
3.   Drinking water.
4.   Changing rooms and lockers.
5.   Facilities for rest.

Schedule 3 (regulation 33(1)(b)) - Particulars to be included in a report of inspection

Schedule 4 (regulation 48(1)) - Revocation of instruments

Schedule 5 (regulation 48(2)) - Amendments

Outline of main points

PART 2 - GENERAL MANAGEMENT DUTIES

Competence

4(1)   No person on whom these regulations place a duty shall:

    (a)   Appoint or engage a co-ordinator, designer, principal contractor or contractor unless he has taken reasonable steps to ensure that he is competent.

    (b)   Accept such appointment or engagement unless he is competent.

    (c)   Arrange for or instruct a worker to carry out or manage design or construction work unless he is -

        (i) Competent.

        (ii) Under the supervision of a competent person.

Co-operation

5(1)   Every person concerned in a project on whom a duty is placed by these regulations, including paragraph (2), shall:

    (a)   Co-operate with any other person concerned in any project involving construction work at the same or an adjoining site so far as is necessary to enable the latter to perform any duty or function under these regulations.

    (b)   Seek the co-operation of any other person concerned in any project involving construction work at the same or an adjoining site so far as is necessary to enable the former to perform any duty or function under these regulations.

(2)   Every person concerned in a project who is working under the control of another person shall report to him anything which he is aware is likely to endanger the health or safety of himself or others.

Co-ordination

6   All persons shall coordinate their activities with one another in a manner which ensures, so far as is reasonably practicable, the health and safety of persons affected by the work.

General principles of prevention

7   Every person on whom a duty is placed by these regulations in relation to the design, planning and preparation of a project shall take account of the general principles of prevention in the performance of those duties during all the stages of the project.

Election by clients

8.   If, in relation to a project, one or more clients elect in writing to be treated for the purposes of these regulations as the only clients, other clients who have agreed in writing to such election shall not be subject to any duty owed by a client under these regulations after such election and consent, save the duties in regulations 5(1)(a), 10(1) so far as it relates to information in his possession, and 12(1).

The client's arrangements for managing projects

9(1)   The client shall take reasonable steps to ensure that arrangements are made, and maintained throughout the project, for managing it which are suitable to ensure:

     (a)   that -
         (i)   the construction work can be carried out; and
         (ii)   any structure to which the construction work relates, and which is designed for use as a place of work, can be used, without risk to health or safety; and

     (b)   the welfare of the persons carrying out the construction work.

(2)   The arrangements referred to in paragraph (1) shall include:

     (a)   the allocation of resources (including time) to:
         (i) the design of a structure;
         (ii) planning and preparation for construction work; and
         (iii) the construction work itself,
         which are, so far as the client in question can reasonably determine, adequate; and

     (b)   arrangements for:
         (i) review and revision of the arrangements;
         (ii) review of the suitability and compatibility of designs and for any modification;
         (iii) ensuring that persons arc appointed under regulation 8 or engaged as designers or contractors in a suitable sequence and in good time;
         (iv) the planning for and monitoring of construction work; (v) ensuring that the duties in regulations 5 and 16 are performed; and
         (vi) communication.

Client's duty in relation to information

10(1)   The client shall ensure that the persons specified in regulation 13(I)(f)(i) to (iii) are promptly provided by the co-ordinator with all the information in the client's possession, or prepared by the co-ordinator, or which is reasonably obtainable (or with such of the information as is relevant to the person to whom the co-ordinator provides it), including:

     (a)   any such information in a health and safety file;
     (b)   any such further information about or affecting the site or the construction work;
     (c)   information provided by a designer under regulation 14(5);
     (d)   the minimum notice which will be allowed to the principal contractor, and the contractors directly appointed by the client, for planning and preparation for construction work, which is relevant to the purposes specified in paragraph (2).

(2)   The purposes referred to in paragraph (1) are:

     (a)   to secure so far as is reasonably practicable the health, safety of persons engaged in the construction work and the health and safety of persons liable to be affected by the way in which it is carried out;
     (b)   without prejudice to sub-paragraph (a), to assist the persons to whom information is provided under this regulation
         (i) to perform their duties and functions under these regulations; and
         (ii) to determine the adequacy of the resources referred to in regulation 7(2) to be allocated by them.

Duties of designers

11   No designer shall commence work in relation to a project unless any client for the project is aware of his duties under these regulations.

Every designer shall in preparing or modifying a design which may be used in construction work in Great Britain avoid foreseeable risks to the health and safety of any person liable to be affected by such construction work;

In discharging these duties, the designer shall -
- Eliminate hazards which may give rise to risks.
- Reduce risks from any remaining hazards, and in so doing shall give collective measures priority over individual measures.

In designing any structure for use as a workplace the designer shall take account of the provisions of the Workplace (Health, Safety and Welfare) Regulations 1992 which relate to the design of, and materials used in, the structure.

The designer shall take all reasonable steps to provide with his design sufficient information about aspects of the design of the structure or its construction or maintenance as will adequately assist clients, other designers and contractors to comply with their duties under these Regulations.

Designs prepared or modified outside Great Britain

12.   Where a design is prepared or modified outside Great Britain for use in construction work to which these Regulations apply:
     (a)   the person who commissions it, if he is established within Great Britain; or
     (b)   if that person is not so established, the client, shall ensure that Regulation 14 is complied with.

Duties of contractors

13   No contractor shall carry out construction work in relation to a project unless any client for the project is aware of his duties under these Regulations.

Every contractor shall ensure that any contractor whom he appoints or engages in his turn in connection with a project is informed of the minimum amount of time which will be allowed to him for planning and preparation before he begins construction work

Every contractor shall provide every worker carrying out the construction work under his control with any information and training which he needs for the particular work to be carried out safely and without risk to health.

No contractor shall begin work on a construction site unless reasonable steps have been taken to prevent access by unauthorised persons to that site.

PART 3 - ADDITIONAL DUTIES FOR NOTIFIABLE PROJECTS

Appointments by the client

14(1)   The client shall:
- (a)   appoint a person ("the co-ordinator"), before design work, or planning or other preparation for construction work is begun, to perform the functions specified in regulation 13(1); and
- (b)   ensure so far as is reasonably practicable that the functions are performed.

(2)   The client shall appoint one person (in these Regulations called "the principal contractor") as soon as is practicable after the client knows enough about the project to be able to select a suitable person for such appointment, to perform the functions specified in regulations 16 to 18.

(3)   The client shall ensure that appointments under paragraphs (1) and (2) are changed or renewed as necessary to ensure that there are at all times until the end of the construction phase a co-ordinator and a principal contractor, filling them.

(4)   The client shall:
- (a)   be deemed for the purposes of these Regulations, save paragraphs (1) and (2) and regulations 14(l)(b) and 19(1) (b), to have been appointed as the co-ordinator or principal contractor for any period for which no person (including himself) has been so appointed; and
- (b)   accordingly be subject to the duty imposed by regulation 13(2) on a co-ordinator or, as the case may be, the duties imposed by regulations 16 to 18 on a principal contractor.

(5)   Any reference in this regulation to appointment is to appointment in writing.

Client's duty in relation to information where a project is notifiable

15.   Where the project is notifiable, the client shall provide the CDM co-ordinator with pre-construction information consisting of -
- Any information about or affecting the site or the construction work.
- Any information concerning the proposed use of the structure as a workplace.
- The minimum amount of time before the construction phase which will be allowed to the contractors appointed by the client for planning and preparation for construction work.
- Any information in any existing health and safety file.

The client's duty in relation to the start of construction phase

16.   The client shall ensure that the construction phase does not start unless:
- (a)   the principal contractor has prepared a construction phase plan which is sufficient to enable the construction work to start without undue risk to health or safety; and
- (b)   the requirements of Schedule 2 are complied with.

The client's duty in relation to the health and safety file

17(1)   The client shall ensure that the co-ordinator is provided with all the health and safety information likely to be needed during any subsequent works for inclusion in a record ("the health and safety file").

(1)   Where a single health and safety file relates to more than one project, site or structure, or where it includes other related information the client shall ensure that the information relating to each site or structure can be easily identified.

(2)   The client shall take reasonable steps to ensure that after the construction phase the information in the health and safety file:
- (a)   is kept available for inspection by any person who may need it to comply with the relevant statutory provisions; and
- (b)   is revised as often as may be appropriate to incorporate any relevant new information, including information specified in regulation 4(9)(c) of the Control of Asbestos at Work Regulations 2002(d) *(Now CAR 2006.)*

(3)   It shall be sufficient compliance with paragraph (3)(a) by a client who disposes of his entire interest in the site if he delivers the health and safety file to the person who acquires his interest in it and ensures that he is aware of the nature and purpose of the file.

Additional duties of designers

18(1)   No designer shall commence work in relation to a project unless:
- (a)   the client is aware of his duties under these Regulations;
- (b)   a co-ordinator has been appointed for the project; and
- (c)   notice of the project has been given to the Executive under regulation 9.

(2)   The duties in paragraphs (3) and (4) shall be performed so far as is reasonably practicable, taking due account of other relevant design considerations.

(3)   Every designer shall in preparing or modifying a design which may be used in construction work in the United Kingdom avoid risks to the health and safety of any person:
- (a)   carrying out construction work;
- (b)   cleaning or maintaining the permanent fixtures and fittings of a structure;
- (c)   using a structure designed as a place of work; or
- (d)   liable to be affected by such construction work.

(4)   In discharging the duty in paragraph (3), the designer shall:
- (a)   eliminate hazards which may give rise to risks; and
- (b)   reduce risks from any remaining hazards, and in doing so shall give collective measures priority over individual measures.

(5)   The designer shall provide with the design sufficient information about aspects of the design of a structure or its construction or maintenance as will adequately assist:

    (a)   other designers to comply with their duties under this regulation;

    (b)   contractors to comply with their duties under regulation 19.

Additional duties of contractors

19   Where a project is notifiable, no contractor shall carry out construction work in relation to the project unless -

- He has been provided with the names of the CDM co-ordinator and principal contractor.
- He has been given access to such part of the construction phase plan as is relevant to the work to be performed by him, containing sufficient detail in relation to such work.
- Notice of the project has been given to the Executive.

Every contractor shall -

- Provide the principal contractor with any information (including any relevant part of any risk assessment in his possession or control) which -
- Might affect the health or safety of any person carrying out the construction work or of any person who may be affected by it.
- Might justify a review of the construction phase plan.
- Which has been identified for inclusion in the health and safety file in pursuance of regulation 22(1)(j).
- Identify any contractor whom he appoints or engages in his turn in connection with the project to the principal contractor.
- Comply with -
- Any directions of the principal contractor given to him under regulation 22(1)(e).
- Any site rules.
- Provide the principal contractor with the information in relation to any death, injury, condition or dangerous occurrence which the contractor is required to notify or report under the Reporting of Injuries, Diseases and Dangerous Occurrences Regulations 1995.

Every contractor shall -

- Take all reasonable steps to ensure that the construction work is carried out in accordance with the construction phase plan.
- Notify the principal contractor of any significant finding which requires the construction phase plan to be altered or added to.

General duties of CDM co-ordinators

20(1)   The functions of a co-ordinator, referred to in regulation 8(l)(a), are to:

    (a)   advise and assist the client in undertaking the measures he needs to take to comply with these Regulations (including in particular, in assisting the client in complying with regulations 9 and 16);

    (b)   identify and extract the information specified in regulation 10;

    (c)   advise on the suitability and compatibility of designs and on any need for modification;

    (d)   co-ordinate design work, planning and other preparation;

    (e)   liaise with the principal contractor in relation to any design or change to a design requiring a review of the construction phase plan, during the construction phase;

    (f)   promptly provide, in a convenient form, to:

        (i) every person designing the structure;

        (ii) the principal contractor; and

        (iii) every contractor who has been or is likely to be appointed by the client, the information specified in regulation 10 (or such of it as is relevant to him);

    (g)   prepare, where none exists, and otherwise review and update the health and safety file;

    (h)   at the end of the construction phase, pass the health and safety file to the client.

(2)   A co-ordinator shall so far as is reasonably practicable perform any function specified in paragraph (1) for which he is appointed.

Notification of the project by the CDM co-ordinator

21   The CDM co-ordinator shall as soon as is practicable after his appointment ensure that notice is given to the Executive containing such of the particulars specified in Schedule 1 as are available.

Duties of the principal contractor

22   The principal contractor for a project shall -

- Plan, manage and monitor the construction phase in a way which ensures that, so far as is reasonably practicable, it is carried out without risks to health or safety, including facilitating -

    (i)   Co-operation and co-ordination between persons concerned in the project in pursuance of regulations 5 and 6; and

    (ii)   The application of the general principles of prevention in pursuance of regulation 7.

- Liaise with the CDM co-ordinator in performing his duties in regulation 20(2)(d) during the construction phase in relation to any design or change to a design.
- Ensure that sufficient welfare facilities are provided.
- Draw up rules which are appropriate to the construction site and the activities on it.
- Give reasonable directions to any contractor.
- Ensure that every contractor is informed of the minimum amount of time which will be allowed to him.
- Consult a contractor before finalising such part of the construction phase plan as is relevant to the work to be performed by him.
- Ensure that every contractor is given, access to such part of the construction phase plan as is relevant to the work to be performed by him.
- Ensure that every contractor is given, such further information as he needs to carry out the work to be performed by him without risk.
- Identify to each contractor the information relating to the contractor's activity which is likely to be required by the CDM co-ordinator for inclusion in the health and safety file.

- Ensure that the particulars required to be in the notice are displayed in a readable condition in a position where they can be read by any worker.
- Take reasonable steps to prevent access by unauthorised persons to the construction site.

The principal contractor shall take all reasonable steps to ensure that every worker carrying out the construction work is provided with -
- A suitable site induction.
- Any further information and training which he needs for the particular work to be carried out without undue risk to health or safety.

The principal contractor's duty in relation to the construction phase plan

The principal contractor shall -
- Prepare a construction phase plan.
- Update, review, revise and refine the construction phase plan.
- Arrange for the construction phase plan to be implemented in a way which will ensure so far as is reasonably practicable the health and safety of all persons carrying out construction work and all persons who may be affected by the work.

The principal contractor's duty in relation to co-operation and consultation with workers

The principal contractor shall -
- Consult those workers or their representatives on matters connected with the project which may affect their health, safety or welfare.
- Ensure that such workers or their representatives can inspect and take copies of any information except any information -
  - The disclosure of which would be against the interests of national security.
  - Which he could not disclose without contravening a prohibition imposed by or under an enactment.
  - Relating specifically to an individual, unless he has consented to its being disclosed.
  - The disclosure of which would, for reasons other than its effect on health, safety or welfare at work, cause substantial injury to his undertaking or, where the information was supplied to him by some other person, to the undertaking of that other person.
  - Obtained by him for the purpose of bringing, prosecuting or defending any legal proceedings.

Principal contractor's duties in relation to the construction phase plan

23(1) the principal contractor shall
  (a) before the start of the construction phase, prepare a sufficient health and safety plan to allow the construction phase to start, so far as is reasonably practicable, without risk to health and safety.
  (b) review, update, revise and refine the plan as necessary.
  (c) arrange for the construction phase to be implemented in such a way as to ensure, so far as is reasonably practicable, the health and safety of people carrying out the construction work.
 (2) take reasonable steps to ensure that the construction phase plan identifies all the risks arising from the construction phase.

Principal contractor's duties in relation to co-operation and consultation with workers

24 the principal contractor shall
  (a) make and maintain arrangements to ensure that workers co-operate in promoting and developing measures to ensure the health, safety and welfare of workers.
  (b) consult with workers or their representatives in good time on matters that may affect their health, safety or welfare.
  (c) ensure that relevant information is available to workers except any information which is specified in the Health and Safety (Consultation with Employees) Regulations 1996.

PART 4 - DUTIES RELATING TO HEALTH AND SAFETY ON CONSTRUCTION SITES

A general duty to ensure a safe place of work and safe means of access to and from that place of work, this Regulation sets out a general requirement which applies to all construction work. It applies equally to places of work in the ground, at ground level and at height. In essence it requires that 'reasonably practicable' steps should be taken to provide for safety and to ensure risks to health are minimised. This means that action to be taken should be proportionate to the risk involved.

Safe place of work, good order and site security (regulations 26 and 27)

- Safe access to and egress from places of work, safe and healthy places of work.
- The site should be kept in a reasonable state of cleanliness and in good order.
- Site fencing and signage to be provided in accordance with the level of risk.
- Removal of material with nails or similar objects that could be a source of danger.

Work on structures (regulations 28, 29 and 30)

- Prevent accidental collapse of new or existing structures or those under construction.
- Make sure any dismantling or demolition of any structure is planned and carried out in a safe manner under the supervision of a competent person.
- Only fire explosive charges after steps have been taken to ensure that no one is exposed to risk or injury from the explosion.

Every year there are structural collapses which have the potential to cause serious accidents. Demolition or dismantling are recognised as high risk activities. In any cases where this work presents a risk of danger to anyone, it should be planned and carried out under the direct supervision of a competent person.

Excavations, cofferdams and caissons (regulations 31 and 32)

- Prevent collapse of ground both in and above excavations.
- Identify and prevent risk from underground cables and other services.
- Ensure cofferdams and caissons are properly designed, constructed and maintained.

From the outset, and as work progresses, any excavation which has the potential to collapse unless supported, should have suitable equipment immediately available to provide such support. Underground cables and services can also be a source of danger. These should be identified before work starts and positive action taken to prevent injury.

Energy distribution installations (regulation 34)

- Where necessary to prevent danger, energy distribution installations shall be suitably located, checked and clearly indicated.
- Where there is a risk from electric power cables: they shall be directed away from the area of risk; or the power shall be cut off; or if it is not reasonably practicable to comply with these requirements:

- Suitable warning notices.
- Barriers suitable for excluding work equipment which is not needed.
- Where vehicles need to pass beneath the cables, suspended protections.
- In either case, measures providing an equivalent level of safety, shall be provided or (in the case of measures) taken.

■ No construction work which is liable to create a risk to health or safety from an underground service, or from damage to or disturbance of it, shall be carried out unless suitable and sufficient steps (including any steps required by this regulation) have been taken to prevent such risk, so far as is reasonably practicable.

Prevention or avoidance of drowning (regulation 35)

■ Take steps to prevent people from falling into water or other liquid so far as is reasonably practicable.
■ Ensure that personal protective and rescue equipment is immediately available for use and maintained, in the event of a fall.
■ Make sure safe transport by water is under the control of a competent person.

Traffic routes and vehicles (regulations 36 and 37)

■ Ensure construction sites are organised so that pedestrians and vehicles can both move safely and without risks to health.
■ Make sure routes are suitable and sufficient for the people or vehicles using them.
■ Prevent or control the unintended movement of any vehicle.
■ Make arrangements for giving a warning of any possible dangerous movement, e.g. reversing vehicles.
■ Ensure safe operation of vehicles including prohibition of riding or remaining in unsafe positions.
■ Make sure doors and gates which could present danger, e.g. trapping risk of powered doors, have suitable safeguards.

Prevention and control of emergencies (regulations 38, 39, 40 and 41)

■ Prevent risk from fire, explosion, flooding and asphyxiation.
■ Provide emergency routes and exits.
■ Make arrangements for dealing with emergencies, including procedures for evacuating the site.
■ Where necessary, provide fire-fighting equipment, fire detectors and alarm systems.

These Regulations require the prevention of risk as far as it is reasonably practicable to achieve. However, there are times when emergencies do arise and planning is needed to ensure, for example, that emergency routes are provided and evacuation procedures are in place. These particular Regulations (as well as those on traffic routes, welfare, cleanliness and signing of sites) apply to construction work which is carried out on construction sites. However, the rest of the Regulations apply to all construction work.

The HSE continues to be responsible for inspection of means of escape and fire-fighting for most sites. However, fire authorities have enforcement responsibility in many premises which remain in normal use during construction work. This continues the sensible arrangement which ensures that the most appropriate advice is given.

Site-wide issues (regulations 27, 42, 43, and 44)

■ Ensure sufficient fresh or purified air is available at every workplace, and associated plant is capable of giving visible or audible warning of failure.
■ Make sure a reasonable working temperature is maintained at indoor work places during working hours.
■ Provide facilities for protection against adverse weather conditions.
■ Make sure suitable and sufficient emergency lighting is available.
■ Make sure suitable and sufficient lighting is available, including providing secondary lighting where there would be a risk to health or safety if primary or artificial lighting failed.
■ Keep construction sites in good order and in a reasonable state of cleanliness.
■ Ensure the perimeter of a construction site to which people, other than those working on the site could gain access, is marked by suitable signs so that its extent can be easily identified.

Reports of inspections (regulation 33)

■ The person who carries out an inspection under regulations 31 or 32 must:
- Inform the person for whom the inspection was carried out if he is not satisfied that the construction work can be carried out safely at the place inspected.
- Prepare a report which includes the particulars set out in Schedule 3 and within 24 hours of completion of the inspection, to which the report relates, provide a copy to the person for whom the inspection was carried out.

■ The inspector's employer, or the person under whose control he works, shall ensure that the inspector performs his duty.
■ The person for whom the inspection was carried out must keep the report or a copy of it available for inspection at the site of the place of work until that work is completed, and after that for 3 months, and send out extracts from or copies of it as required by an inspector appointed under section 19 of The Health and Safety at Work etc. Act 1974.
■ No further inspection reports required within a 7 day period.

SCHEDULE 2 (REGULATIONS 9(1)(B), 13(7) AND 22(1)(C)) WELFARE FACILITIES

SANITARY CONVENIENCES

1. Suitable and sufficient sanitary conveniences shall be provided or made available at readily accessible places. So far as is reasonably practicable, rooms containing sanitary conveniences shall be adequately ventilated and lit.
2. So far as is reasonably practicable, sanitary conveniences and the rooms containing them shall be kept in a clean and orderly condition.
3. Separate rooms containing sanitary conveniences shall be provided for men and women, except where and so far as each convenience is in a separate room the door of which is capable of being secured from the inside.

Washing facilities

4. Suitable and sufficient washing facilities, including showers if required by the nature of the work or for health reasons, shall so far as is reasonably practicable be provided or made available at readily accessible places.
5. Washing facilities shall be provided:
   (a) in the immediate vicinity of every sanitary convenience, whether or not provided elsewhere; and
   (b) in the vicinity of any changing rooms required by paragraph 15 whether or not provided elsewhere.
6. Washing facilities shall include:

(a)   a supply of clean hot and cold, or warm, water (which shall be running water so far as is reasonably practicable); and

(b)   soap or other suitable means of cleaning; and

(c)   towels or other suitable means of drying.

7.   Rooms containing washing facilities shall be sufficiently ventilated and lit.

8.   Washing facilities and the rooms containing them shall be kept in a clean and orderly condition.

9.   Subject to paragraph 10 below, separate washing facilities shall be provided for men and women, except where and so far as they are provided in a room the door of which is capable of being secured from inside and the facilities in each such room arc intended to be used by only one person at a time.

10.   Paragraph 9 above shall not apply to facilities which are provided for washing hands, forearms and face only.

Drinking water

11.   An adequate supply of wholesome drinking water shall be provided or made available at readily accessible and suitable places.

12.   Every supply of drinking water shall be conspicuously marked by an appropriate sign where necessary for reasons of health and safety.

13.   Where a supply of drinking water is provided, there shall also be provided a sufficient number of suitable cups or other drinking vessels unless the supply of drinking water is in a jet from which persons can drink easily.

Changing rooms and lockers

14(1)   Suitable and sufficient changing rooms shall be provided or made available at readily accessible places if:

    (a)   a worker has to wear special clothing for the purposes of his work; and

    (b)   he cannot, for reasons of health or propriety, be expected to change elsewhere, being separate rooms for, or separate use of rooms by, men and women where necessary for reasons of propriety.

(2)   Changing rooms shall:

    (a)   be provided with seating;

    (b)   include, where necessary, facilities to enable a person to dry any such special clothing and his own clothing and personal effects.

(3)   Suitable and sufficient facilities shall, where necessary, be provided or made available at readily accessible places to enable persons to lock away:

    (a)   any such special clothing which is not taken home;

    (b)   their own clothing which is not worn during working hours; and

    (c)   their personal effects.

Facilities for rest

15(1)   Suitable and sufficient rest rooms or rest areas shall be provided or made available at readily accessible places.

(1)   Rest rooms and rest areas shall:

    (a)   include suitable arrangements to protect non-smokers from discomfort caused by tobacco smoke;

    (b)   be equipped with an adequate number of tables and adequate seating with backs for the number of persons at work likely to use them at any one time;

    (c)   where necessary, include suitable facilities for any person at work who is a pregnant woman or nursing mother to rest lying down;

    (d)   include suitable arrangements to ensure that meals can be prepared and eaten; and

    (e)   include the means for boiling water.

Construction (Head Protection) Regulations (CHPR) 1989

Considered in context in NGC1, Element 1.

Arrangement of Regulations

1)   Citation, commencement and interpretation.

2)   Application of these Regulations.

3)   Provision, maintenance and replacement of suitable head protection.

4)   Ensuring suitable head protection is worn.

5)   Rules and directions.

6)   Wearing of suitable head protection.

7)   Reporting the loss of, or defect in, suitable head protection.

8)   Extension outside Great Britain.

9)   Exemption certificates.

Outline of main points

ENSURING SUITABLE HEAD PROTECTION IS WORN

Reg. 4(1)   Every employer shall ensure so far as is reasonably practicable that each of his employees who is at work on operations or works to which these Regulations apply wears suitable head protection, unless there is no foreseeable risk to injury to his head other than by his falling.

4(2)   Every employer, self-employed person or employee who has control over any other person who is at work on operations or works to which these Regulations apply shall ensure so far as is reasonably practicable that each such other person wears suitable head protection, unless there is no foreseeable risk of injury to that other person's head other than by his falling.

RULES AND DIRECTIONS

Reg.5(1)   The person for the time being having control of a site where operations or works to which these Regulations apply are being carried out may, so far as is necessary to comply with regulation 4 of these Regulations, make rules regulating the wearing of suitable head protection on that site by persons at work on those operations or works.

5(2) Rules made in accordance with paragraph (1) of this regulation shall be in writing and shall be brought to the notice of persons who may be affected by them.

5(3) An employer may, so far as is necessary to comply with regulation 4(1) of these Regulations, give directions requiring his employees to wear suitable head protection.

5(4) An employer, self-employed person or employee who has control over any other self-employed person may, so far as is necessary to comply with regulation 4(2) of these Regulations, give directions requiring each such other self-employed person to wear suitable head protection.

WEARING OF SUITABLE HEAD PROTECTION

Reg.6(1) Every employee who has been provided with suitable head protection shall wear that head protection when required to do so by rules made or directions given under regulation 5 of these Regulations.

6(2) Every self-employed person shall wear suitable head protection when required to do so by rules made or directions given under regulation 5 of these Regulations.

6(3) Every self-employed person who is at work on operations or works to which these Regulations apply, but who is not under the control of another employer or self-employed person or of an employee, shall wear suitable head protection unless there is no foreseeable risk of injury to his head other than by his falling.

6(4) Every employee or self-employed person who is required to wear suitable head protection by or under these Regulations shall do so properly.

REPORTING THE LOSS OF, OR DEFECT IN, SUITABLE HEAD PROTECTION

Reg. 7 Every employee who has been provided with suitable head protection by his employer shall take reasonable care of it and shall forthwith report to his employer any loss of, or obvious defect in, that head protection.

Control of Asbestos Regulations (CAR) 2006

Considered in context in NGC2, Element 7.

Arrangement of Regulations

PART 1 - PRELIMINARY
1) Citation and commencement.
2) Interpretation.
3) Application of these Regulations.

PART 2 - GENERAL REQUIREMENTS
4) Duty to manage asbestos in non-domestic premises.
5) Identification of the presence of asbestos.
6) Assessment of work which exposes employees to asbestos.
7) Plans of work.
8) Licensing of work with asbestos.
9) Notification of work with asbestos.
10) Information, instruction and training.
11) Prevention or reduction of exposure to asbestos.
12) Use of control measures etc.
13) Maintenance of control measures etc.
14) Provision and cleaning of protective clothing.
15) Arrangements to deal with accidents, incidents and emergencies.
16) Duty to prevent or reduce the spread of asbestos.
17) Cleanliness of premises and plant.
18) Designated Areas.
19) Air Monitoring.
20) Standards for air testing and site clearance certification.
21) Standards for analysis.
22) Health records and medical surveillance.
23) Washing and changing facilities.
24) Storage, distribution and labelling of raw asbestos and asbestos waste.

PART 3 - PROHIBITIONS AND RELATED PROVISIONS
25) Interpretation of prohibitions.
26) Prohibitions of exposure to asbestos.
27) Prohibition of the importation of asbestos.
28) Prohibition of the supply of asbestos.
29) Prohibition of the use of asbestos.
30) Labelling of products containing asbestos.
31) Additional provisions in the case of exceptions and exemptions.

PART 4 - MISCELLANEOUS
32) Exemption certificates.
33) Exemptions relating to the Ministry of Defence.
34) Extension outside Great Britain.

35) Existing licences and exemption certificates.
36) Revocations, amendments and savings.
37) Defence

SCHEDULES

Schedule 1 - particulars to be included in a notification.
Schedule 2 - the labelling of raw asbestos, asbestos waste and products containing asbestos.
Schedule 3 - exceptions to the prohibitions on the importation, supply and use of chrysotile.
Schedule 4 - revocations.
Schedule 5 - amendments.

Outline of main points

SUMMARY

The Control of Asbestos Regulations 2006 came into force on 13th November 2006 (Asbestos Regulations - SI 2006/2737). These Regulations brought together the three previous sets of Regulations covering the prohibition of asbestos, the control of asbestos at work and asbestos licensing:

- Asbestos (Licensing) Regulations (ASLIC) 1983 (and as amended).
- Asbestos (Prohibitions) Regulations 1992 (and as amended).
- Control of Asbestos at Work Regulations (CAWR) 2002.

The Regulations prohibit the importation, supply and use of all forms of asbestos. They continue the ban introduced for blue and brown asbestos 1985 and for white asbestos in 1999. They also continue the ban the second-hand use of asbestos products such as asbestos cement sheets and asbestos boards and tiles; including panels which have been covered with paint or textured plaster containing asbestos.

REMEMBER: The ban applies to new use of asbestos. If existing asbestos containing materials are in good condition, they may be left in place, their condition monitored and managed to ensure they are not disturbed.

DUTY TO MANAGE ASBESTOS IN NON-DOMESTIC PREMISES (REGULATION 4)

The Asbestos Regulations also include the 'duty to manage asbestos' in non-domestic premises. Guidance on the duty to manage asbestos can be found in the 'Approved Code of Practice, The Management of Asbestos in Non-Domestic Premises', L27, ISBN 0 7176 6209 8.

INFORMATION, INSTRUCTION AND TRAINING (REGULATION 10)

The Regulations require mandatory training for anyone liable to be exposed to asbestos fibres at work. This includes maintenance workers and others who may come into contact with or who may disturb asbestos (e.g. cable installers) as well as those involved in asbestos removal work.

PREVENTION OR REDUCTION OF EXPOSURE TO ASBESTOS (REGULATION 11)

When work with asbestos or which may disturb asbestos is being carried out, the Asbestos Regulations require employers and the self-employed to prevent exposure to asbestos fibres. Where this is not reasonably practicable, they must make sure that exposure is kept as low as reasonably practicable by measures other than the use of respiratory protective equipment. The spread of asbestos must be prevented. The Regulations specify the work methods and controls that should be used to prevent exposure and spread.

CONTROL LIMITS

Worker exposure must be below the airborne exposure limit (Control Limit). The Asbestos Regulations have a single Control Limit for all types of asbestos of 0.1 fibres per cm^3. A Control Limit is a maximum concentration of asbestos fibres in the air (averaged over any continuous 4 hour period) that must not be exceeded.

In addition, short term exposures must be strictly controlled and worker exposure should not exceed 0.6 fibres per cm^3 of air averaged over any continuous 10 minute period using respiratory protective equipment if exposure cannot be reduced sufficiently using other means.

RESPIRATORY PROTECTIVE EQUIPMENT

Respiratory protective equipment is an important part of the control regime but it must not be the sole measure used to reduce exposure and should only be used to supplement other measures. Work methods that control the release of fibres such as those detailed in the **Asbestos Essentials task sheets** (available on the HSE website) for non-licensed work should be used. Respiratory protective equipment must be suitable, must fit properly and must ensure that worker exposure is reduced as low as is reasonably practicable.

ASBESTOS REMOVAL WORK UNDERTAKEN BY A LICENSED CONTRACTOR

Most asbestos removal work must be undertaken by a licensed contractor but any decision on whether particular work is licensable is based on the risk. Work is only exempt from licensing if:

- The exposure of employees to asbestos fibres is sporadic and of low intensity (but exposure cannot be considered to be sporadic and of low intensity if the concentration of asbestos in the air is liable to exceed 0.6 fibres per cm3 measured over 10 minutes); and
- It is clear from the risk assessment that the exposure of any employee to asbestos will not exceed the control limit; and
- The work involves:
  - Short, non-continuous maintenance activities. Work can only be considered as short, non-continuous maintenance activities if any one person carries out work with these materials for less than one hour in a seven-day period. The total time spent by all workers on the work should not exceed a total of two hours*.
  - Removal of materials in which the asbestos fibres are firmly linked in a matrix. Such materials include: asbestos cement; textured decorative coatings and paints which contain asbestos; articles of bitumen, plastic, resin or rubber which contain asbestos where their thermal or acoustic properties are incidental to their main purpose (e.g. vinyl floor tiles, electric cables, roofing felt) and other insulation products which may be used at high temperatures but have no insulation purposes, for example gaskets, washers, ropes and seals.

- Encapsulation or sealing of asbestos-containing materials which are in good condition, or
- Air monitoring and control, and the collection and analysis of samples to find out if a specific material contains asbestos.

It is important that the amount of time you or your employees spend working with asbestos insulation, asbestos coatings or asbestos insulating board (AIB) is managed to make sure that these time limits are not exceeded. This includes the time for activities such as building enclosures and cleaning.

Under the Asbestos Regulations, anyone carrying out work on asbestos insulation, asbestos coating or AIB needs a licence issued by HSE unless they meet one of the exemptions above.

REMEMBER: Although you may not need a licence to carry out a particular job, you still need to comply with the rest of the requirements of the Asbestos Regulations.

LICENSABLE WORK - ADDITIONAL DUTIES

If the work is licensable you have a number of additional duties. You need to:

- Notify the enforcing authority responsible for the site where you are working (for example HSE or the local authority).
- Designate the work area (see regulation 18 for details).
- Prepare specific asbestos emergency procedures.
- Pay for your employees to undergo medical surveillance.

AIR MONITORING (REGULATION 19)

The Asbestos Regulations require any analysis of the concentration of asbestos in the air to be measured in accordance with the 1997 WHO recommended method.

STANDARDS FOR AIR TESTING AND SITE CLEARANCE CERTIFICATION (REGULATION 20)

From 06 April 2007, a clearance certificate for re-occupation may only be issued by a body accredited to do so. At the moment, such accreditation can only be provided by the United Kingdom Accreditation Service (UKAS).

You can find more details of how to undertake work with asbestos containing materials, the type of controls necessary, what training is required and analytical methods in the following HSE publications:

- Approved Code of Practice Work with Materials containing Asbestos, L143, ISBN 0 7176 6206 3.
- Asbestos: the Licensed Contractors Guide, HSG 247, ISBN 0 7176 2874 4.
- Asbestos: The analysts' guide for sampling, analysis and clearance procedures, HSG 248, ISBN 0 7176 2875 2.
- Asbestos Essentials, HSG 210, ISBN 0 71761887 0. (See also the 'Asbestos Essentials task sheets' available on the HSE website).

REMEMBER: You must also comply with other health and safety legislation.

Source: HSE website: www.hse.gov.uk.

Control of Noise at Work Regulations (CNWR) 2005

Considered in context in NGC2, Element 8.

The Noise at Work Regulations was established in 1989 and had a significant effect on the reduction of exposure to workplace noise. The implementation of the European Physical Agents (Noise) Directive as the Control of Noise at Work Regulations 2005 came into force on 6th April 2006.

Arrangement of Regulations

1) Citation and commencement.
2) Interpretation.
3) Application and transition.
4) Exposure limit values and action values.
5) Assessment of the risk to health created by exposure to noise at the workplace.
6) Elimination or control of exposure to noise at the workplace.
7) Hearing protection.
8) Maintenance and use of equipment.
9) Health surveillance.
10) Information, instruction and training.
11) Exemption certificates from hearing protection.
12) Exemption certificates for emergency services.
13) Exemption relating to the Ministry of Defence etc.
14) Extension outside Great Britain.
15) Revocations, amendment and savings.

Outline of main points

CHANGES TO THE ACTION LEVELS (REGULATION 4)

The values of the actions levels associated with noise at work have been lowered and their names have been changed. The first action level is reduced from *85 dB(A) down to 80 dB(A)* and is known as the *lower exposure action value.* Meanwhile, the section level is reduced from *90 dB(A) down to 85 dB(A)* and is known as the *upper exposure action value*. The Regulations also allow the employer to average out the exposure to noise over a one week period instead of the previous normal eight hour period, in situations where the noise exposure varies on a day-to-day basis. When determining noise levels for the purposes of determining exposure action levels, the noise exposure reducing effects of hearing protection may not be taken in to account.

Where exposure is at, or above, the *lower exposure action value* (80 dB(A)) the employer has a duty to provide hearing protection to those employees that request it. The employer also has a duty to information, instruction and training on the risks posed by exposure to noise and the control measures to be used.

Where the exposure is at, or above, the ***upper exposure action value*** (85 dB(A)) the employer is also required to introduce a formal programme of control measures. The measures to be taken as part of this programme of control measures will depend on the findings of the noise risk assessment (see below).

The Control of Noise at Work Regulations 2005 also introduces a new value known as the ***exposure limit value***. These are limits set both in terms of daily (or weekly) personal noise exposure (*LEP,d* of 87 dB) and in terms of peak noise (*LCpeak* of 140 dB). The exposure action values, take account of the protection provided by personal hearing protection (unlike the two exposure limit values). *If an employee is exposed to noise at or above the exposure limit value, then the employer must take immediate action to bring the exposure down below this level.*

SUMMARY OF EXPOSURE LIMIT VALUES AND ACTION VALUES

The lower exposure action values are: A daily or weekly personal noise exposure of 80 dB (A-weighted)
A peak sound pressure of 135 dB (C-weighted)

The upper exposure action values are: A daily or weekly personal noise exposure of 85 dB (A-weighted)
A peak sound pressure of 137 dB (C-weighted)

The exposure limit values are: A daily or weekly personal exposure of 87 dB (A-weighted)
A peak sound pressure of 140 db (C-weighted)

NOISE RISK ASSESSMENT AND CONTROL MEASURES (REGULATIONS 5 AND 6)

The requirement for a noise risk assessment carries through from the Noise at Work Regulations 1989 into the Control of Noise at Work Regulations 2005. Employers are required (in accordance with the general risk assessment and general principles of prevention contained in Schedule 1 to the Management of Health and Safety at Work Regulation 1999) to ensure that the risks associated with employees' exposure to noise are eliminated where this is reasonably practicable. Where elimination is not reasonably practicable, then the employer must reduce the risks down to as low a level as is reasonably practicable.

Regulation 6(2) of the Control of Noise at Work Regulations 2005 introduces the requirement for a formal programme of control measures. If any employee is likely to be exposed to noise at or above an upper exposure action value, the employer shall reduce exposure to a minimum by establishing and implementing a programme of organisational and technical measures, excluding the provision of personal hearing protectors, which is appropriate to the activity and consistent with the risk assessment, and shall include consideration of:

(a) Other working methods which eliminate or reduce exposure to noise.
(b) Choice of appropriate work equipment emitting the least possible noise, taking account of the work to be done.
(c) The design and layout of workplaces, work stations and rest facilities.
(d) Suitable and sufficient information and training for employees, such that work equipment may be used correctly, in order to minimise their exposure to noise.
(e) Reduction of noise by technical means including:
(i) In the case of airborne noise the use of shields, enclosures, and sound-absorbent coverings.
(ii) In the case of structure-borne noise by damping and isolation.
(f) Appropriate maintenance programmes for work equipment, the workplace and workplace systems.
(g) Limitation of the duration and intensity of exposure to noise.
(h) Appropriate work schedules with adequate rest periods.

If the risk assessment indicates an employee is likely to be exposed to noise at or above an upper exposure action value, the employer shall ensure that

- The area is designated a Hearing Protection Zone.
- The area is demarcated and identified by means of the sign specified for the purpose of indicating "ear protection must be worn" (to be consistent with the Health and Safety (Safety Signs and Signals) Regulations 1996).
- The sign shall be accompanied by text that indicates that the area is a Hearing Protection Zone and that employees must wear personal hearing protectors while in that area.
- Access to the area is restricted where this is technically feasible and the risk of exposure justifies it and shall make every effort to ensure that no employee enters that area unless they are wearing personal hearing protectors.

MAINTENANCE AND USE OF EQUIPMENT (REGULATION 8)

There is a duty on the employer to maintain the control introduced to protect employees. This will include maintenance of acoustic enclosures, etc as well as the maintenance of machinery (as required under the Provision and Use of Work Equipment Regulations 1998) to control noise at source.

HEALTH SURVEILLANCE (REGULATION 9)

Under the Control of Noise at Work Regulations 2005, employees who are regularly exposed to noise levels of 85 dB(A) or higher must be subject to health surveillance, including audiometric testing. This constitutes a big change from the previous Regulations that only required an employer to carry out health surveillance where the employee was subject to noise levels of 95 dB(A) or higher. Where exposure is between 80 dB and 85 dB, or where employees are only occasionally exposed above the upper exposure action values, health surveillance will only be required if information comes to light that an individual may be particularly sensitive to noise induced hearing loss.

SUMMARY

The Control of Noise at Work Regulations 2005 became part of UK health and safety law in April 2006. They introduced levels for employees to control exposure down to, including a new exposure limit value, above which employers are obliged to take immediate action to reduce exposure. These new lower limits mean that about a further million workers will be afforded protection by these Regulations. The requirements for risk assessments, control measures and health surveillance have been updated, but are broadly similar to previous requirements.

Source: www.lrbconsulting.com and www.hse.gov.uk.

Control of Artificial Optical Radiation at Work Regulations (CAOR) 2010

Considered in context in NGC2, Element 8.

Arrangement of Regulations

1) Citation, commencement and interpretation.
2) Application of these Regulations.
3) Assessment of the risk of adverse health effects to the eyes or skin created by exposure to artificial optical radiation at the workplace.
4) Obligations to eliminate or reduce risks.
5) Information and training.
6) Health surveillance and medical examinations.
7) Extension outside Great Britain.

Outline of main points

The Regulations came into force on 27 April 2010.

The employer has duties to employees and any other person at work who may be affected by the work carried out.

ASSESSMENT OF THE RISK OF ADVERSE HEALTH EFFECTS TO THE EYES OR SKIN

The employer must make a suitable and sufficient assessment of risk for the purpose of identifying the measures it needs to take to meet the requirements of these Regulations where;

(a)   The employer carries out work which could expose any of its employees to levels of artificial optical radiation that could create a reasonably foreseeable risk of adverse health effects to the eyes or skin of the employee.

(b)   That employer has not implemented any measures to either eliminate or, where this is not reasonably practicable, reduce to as low a level as is reasonably practicable, that risk based on the general principles of prevention set out in Schedule 1 to the Ionising Radiation (IRR) Regulations 1999.

OBLIGATIONS TO ELIMINATE OR REDUCE RISKS

An employer must ensure that any risk of adverse health effects to the eyes or skin of employees as a result of exposure to artificial optical radiation which is identified in the risk assessment is eliminated or, where this is not reasonably practicable, reduced to as low a level as is reasonably practicable.

INFORMATION AND TRAINING

If the risk assessment indicates that employees could be exposed to artificial optical radiation which could cause adverse health effects to the eyes or skin of employees, the employer must provide its employees and representatives with suitable and sufficient information and training relating to the outcome of the risk assessment, and this must include the following:

(a)   The technical and organisational measures taken in order to comply with the requirements of regulation 4.

(b)   The exposure limit values.

(c)   The significant findings of the risk assessment, including any measurements taken, with an explanation of those findings.

(d)   Why and how to detect and report adverse health effects to the eyes or skin.

(e)   The circumstances in which employees are entitled to appropriate health surveillance.

(f)   Safe working practices to minimise the risk of adverse health effects to the eyes or skin from exposure to artificial optical radiation.

(g)   The proper use of personal protective equipment.

The employer must ensure that any person, whether or not that person is an employee, who carries out work in connection with the employer's duties under these Regulations has suitable and sufficient information and training.

HEALTH SURVEILLANCE AND MEDICAL EXAMINATIONS

If the risk assessment indicates that there is a risk of adverse health effects to the skin of employees, as a result of exposure to artificial optical radiation, the employer must ensure that such employees are placed under suitable health surveillance.

Control of Substances Hazardous to Health Regulations (COSHH) 2002

Considered in context in NGC2, Element 7.

Amendments to these Regulations were made by the Control of Substances Hazardous to Health (Amendment) Regulations 2004. The main change being that MELs and OESs were replaced by workplace exposure limits (WELs).

Arrangement of Regulations

1) Citation and commencement.
2) Interpretation.
3) Duties under these Regulations.
4) Prohibitions on substances.
5) Application of regulations 6 to 13.
6) Assessment of health risks created by work involving substances hazardous to health.
7) Control of exposure.
8) Use of control measures etc.
9) Maintenance of control measures.
10) Monitoring exposure.
11) Health surveillance.
12) Information etc.
13) Arrangements to deal with accidents, incidents and emergencies.
14) Exemption certificates.
15) Extension outside Great Britain.
16) Defence in proceedings for contravention of these Regulations.

17) Exemptions relating to the Ministry of Defence etc.
18) Revocations, amendments and savings.
19) Extension of meaning of "work".
20) Modification of section 3(2) of the Health and Safety at Work etc Act (HASAWA) 1974.

Schedule 1	Other substances and processes to which the definition of "carcinogen" relates.
Schedule 2	Prohibition of certain substances hazardous to health for certain purposes.
Schedule 3	Special provisions relating to biological agents.
Schedule 4	Frequency of thorough examination and test of local exhaust ventilation plant used in certain processes.
Schedule 5	Specific substances and processes for which monitoring is required.
Schedule 6	Medical surveillance.
Schedule 7	Legislation concerned with the labelling of containers and pipes.
Schedule 8	Fumigations excepted from regulation 14.
Schedule 9	Notification of certain fumigations.
Appendix 1	Control of carcinogenic substances.
Annex 1	Background note on occupational cancer.
Annex 2	Special considerations that apply to the control of exposure to vinyl chloride.
Appendix 2	Additional provisions relating to work with biological agents.
Appendix 3	Control of substances that cause occupational asthma.

NOTE the main impact to the latest version of the COSHH Regs concern the control of substances that cause occupational asthma.

Outline of main points

REGULATIONS

Reg. 2 **Interpretation**

"Substance hazardous to health" includes:

1) Substances which under The Chemicals (Hazard Information and Packaging) Regulations (CHIP 3) 2002 are in categories of very toxic, toxic, harmful, corrosive or irritant.

2) A substance listed in Schedule 1 to the Regulations or for which the HSE (*formerly HSC*) have approved a maximum exposure limit or an occupational exposure standard.

3) A biological agent.

4) Dust in a concentration in air equal to or greater than:

■ 10 mg/m3 inhalable dust as an 8hr TWA.

■ 4mg/m3 respirable dust as an 8hr TWA.

SCHEDULE 3 Any other substance which creates a health hazard comparable with the hazards of the substances in the other categories above.

Reg. 3 **Duties**

Are on employer to protect:

■ Employees.

Any other person who may be affected, except:

■ Duties for health surveillance do not extend to non-employees.

■ Duties to give information may extend to non-employees if they work on the premises.

Reg. 4 **Prohibitions on substances**

Certain substances are prohibited from being used in some applications. These are detailed in Schedule 2.

Reg. 5 **Application of regulations 6-13**

Regulations 6-13 are made to protect a person's health from risks arising from exposure. They do not apply if:

The following Regulations already apply:

■ The Control of Lead at Work Regulations (CLAW) 2002.

■ The Control of Asbestos at Work Regulations (CAWR) 2002.

The hazard arises from one of the following properties of the substance:

■ Radioactivity, explosive, flammable, high or low temperature, high pressure.

■ Exposure is for medical treatment.

■ Exposure is in a mine.

Reg. 6 **Assessment**

Employers must not carry out work that will expose employees to substances hazardous to health unless they have assessed the risks to health and the steps that need to be taken to meet the requirements of the Regulations. The assessment must be reviewed if there are changes in the work and at least once every 5 years.

A suitable and sufficient assessment should include:

■ An assessment of the risks to health.

■ The practicability of preventing exposure.

■ Steps needed to achieve adequate control.

An assessment of the risks should involve:

■ Types of substance including biological agents.

■ Where the substances are present and in what form.

■ Effects on the body.

■ Who might be affected?

■ Existing control measures.

Reg. 7 **Control of exposure**

1) Employer shall ensure that the exposure of employees to substances hazardous to health is either prevented or, where this is not reasonably practicable, adequately controlled.

2) So far as is reasonably practicable (1) above except to a carcinogen or biological agent shall be by measures other than personal protective equipment (PPE).

SCHEDULE 3 Where not reasonably practicable to prevent exposure to a carcinogen by using an alternative substance or process, the following measure shall apply:

- Total enclosure of process.
- Use of plant, process and systems which minimise generation of, or suppress and contain, spills, leaks, dust, fumes and vapours of carcinogens.
- Limitation of quantities of a carcinogen at work.
- Keeping of numbers exposed to a minimum.
- Prohibition of eating, drinking and smoking in areas liable to contamination.
- Provision of hygiene measures including adequate washing facilities and regular cleaning of walls and surfaces.
- Designation of areas/installations liable to contamination and use of suitable and sufficient warning signs.
- Safe storage, handling and disposal of carcinogens and use of closed and clearly-labelled containers.

4) If adequate control is not achieved, then employer shall provide suitable PPE to employees in addition to taking control measures.

SCHEDULE 3 PPE provided shall comply with The Personal Protective Equipment at Work Regulations (PPER), 2002 (dealing with the supply of PPE).

6&7) For substances which have a maximum exposure limit (MEL), control of that substance shall, so far as inhalation is concerned, only be treated if the level of exposure is reduced as far as is reasonably practicable and in any case below the MEL.

Where a substance has an occupational exposure standard (OES), control of that substance shall, so far as inhalation is concerned, only be treated as adequate if the OES is not exceeded or if it is, steps are taken to remedy the situation as soon as reasonably practicable.

8) Respiratory protection must be suitable and of a type or conforming to a standard approved by the HSE.

9) In the event of failure of a control measure which may result in the escape of carcinogens, the employer shall ensure:

- Only those who are responsible for repair and maintenance work are permitted in the affected area and are provided with PPE.
- Employees and other persons who may be affected are informed of the failure forthwith.

Reg. 8 Employer shall take all reasonable steps to ensure control measures, PPE, etc. are properly used/applied.

Employee shall make full and proper use of control measures, PPE etc. and shall report defects to employer.

Reg. 9 **Maintenance of control measures**

Employer providing control measures to comply with Reg.7 shall ensure that it is maintained in an efficient state, in efficient working order and in good repair and in the case of PPE in a clean condition, properly stored in a well-defined place checked at suitable intervals and when discovered to be defective repaired or replaced before further use.

- Contaminated PPE should be kept apart and cleaned, decontaminated or, if necessary destroyed.
- Engineering controls - employer shall ensure thorough examination and tests.
- Local exhaust ventilation (LEV) - Once every 14 months unless process specified in Schedule 4.
- Others - At suitable intervals.
- Respiratory protective equipment - employer shall ensure thorough examination and tests at suitable intervals.
- Records of all examinations, tests and repairs kept for 5 years.

Reg. 10 **Monitoring exposure**

Employer shall ensure exposure is monitored if:

- Needed to ensure maintenance of adequate control.
- Otherwise needed to protect health of employees.
- Substance/process specified in Schedule 5.

Records kept if:

- There is an identified exposure of identifiable employee - 40 years.
- Otherwise - 5 years.

Reg. 11 **Health surveillance**

1) Where appropriate for protection of health of employees exposed or liable to be exposed, employer shall ensure suitable health surveillance.

2) Health surveillance is appropriate if:

- Employee exposed to substance/process specified in Schedule 6.
- Exposure to substance is such that an identifiable disease or adverse health effect can result, there is a reasonable likelihood of it occurring and a valid technique exists for detecting the indications of the disease or effect.

3) Health records kept for at least 40 years.

4) If employer ceases business, HSE notified and health records offered to HSE.

5) If employee exposed to substance specified in Schedule 6, then health surveillance shall include medical surveillance, under Employment Medical Adviser (EMA) at 12 monthly intervals - or more frequently if specified by EMA.

6) EMA can forbid employee to work in process, or specify certain conditions for him to be employed in a process.

7) EMA can specify that health surveillance is to continue after exposure has ceased. Employer must ensure.

8) Employees to have access to their own health record.

9) Employee must attend for health/medical surveillance and give information to EMA.

10) EMA entitled to inspect workplace.

11) Where EMA suspends employee from work exposing him to substances hazardous to health, employer of employee can apply to HSE in writing within 28 days for that decision to be reviewed.

Reg. 12 **Information etc**

Employer shall provide suitable and sufficient information, instruction and training for him to know:

■ Risks to health.
■ Precautions to be taken.

This should include information on:

■ Results of monitoring of exposure at workplace.
■ Results of collective health surveillance.

If the substances have been assigned a maximum exposure limit, then the employee/Safety Representative must be notified forthwith if the MEL has been exceeded.

Reg. 13 **Arrangements to deal with accidents, incidents and emergencies**

To protect the health of employees from accidents, incidents and emergencies, the employer shall ensure that:

■ Procedures are in place for first aid and safety drills (tested regularly).
■ Information on emergency arrangements is available.
■ Warning, communication systems, remedial action and rescue actions are available.
■ Information made available to emergency services: external and internal.
■ Steps taken to mitigate effects, restore situation to normal and inform employees.
■ Only essential persons allowed in area.

These duties do not apply where the risks to health are slight or measures in place Reg 7(1) are sufficient to control the risk. The employee must report any accident or incident which has or may have resulted in the release of a biological agent which could cause severe human disease.

NOTE the main impact to the latest version of the COSHH Regs concern the control of substances that cause occupational asthma.

APPENDIX 3 CONTROL OF SUBSTANCES THAT CAUSE OCCUPATIONAL ASTHMA

This relates certain regulations specifically to substances with the potential to cause asthma.

■ Regulation 6 - assessment of risk to health created by work involving substances hazardous to health, (i.e. substances that may cause asthma).
■ Regulation 7 - prevention or control of exposure to substances hazardous to health, (i.e. substances that may cause occupational asthma).
■ Regulation 11 - health surveillance, (for employees who are or may be exposed to substances that may cause occupational asthma).
■ Regulation 12 - information, instruction and training for persons who may be exposed to substances hazardous to health, to include: typical symptoms of asthma, substances that may cause it, the permanency of asthma and what happens with subsequent exposures, the need to report symptoms immediately and the reporting procedures.

Training should be given, including induction training before they start the job.

SCHEDULE 3 ADDITIONAL PROVISIONS RELATING TO WORK WITH BIOLOGICAL AGENTS

Regulation 7(10)

Part I Provision of general application to biological agents

1 Interpretation.

2 Classification of biological agents.

The HSC shall approve and publish a "Categorisation of Biological Agents according to hazard and categories of containment" which may be revised or re-issued. Where no approved classification exists, the employer shall assign the agent to one of four groups according to the level of risk of infection.

Group 1 - unlikely to cause human disease.
Group 2 - can cause human disease.
Group 3 - can cause severe disease and spread to community.
Group 4 - can cause severe disease, spread to community and there is no effective treatment.

3 **Special control measures for laboratories, animal rooms and industrial processes**

Every employer engaged in research, development, teaching or diagnostic work involving Group 2, 3 or 4 biological agents; keeping or handling laboratory animals deliberately or naturally infected with those agents, or industrial processes involving those agents, shall control them with the most suitable containment.

4 **List of employees exposed to certain biological agents**

The employer shall keep a list of employees exposed to Group 3 or 4 biological agents for at least 10 years. If there is a long latency period then the list should be kept for 40 years.

5 **Notification of the use of biological agents**

Employers shall inform the HSE at least 20 days in advance of first time use or storage of Group 2, 3 or 4 biological hazards. Consequent substantial changes in procedure or process shall also be reported.

6 **Notification of the consignment of biological agents**

The HSE must be informed 30 days before certain biological agents are consigned.

Part II Containment measures for health and veterinary care facilities, laboratories and animal rooms.

Part III Containment measures for industrial processes.

Part IV Biohazard sign.

The biohazard sign required by regulation 7(6) (a) shall be in the form shown.

Part V Biological agents whose use is to be notified in accordance with paragraph 5(2) of Part I of this Schedule.

- Any Group 3 or 4 agent.
- Certain named Group 2 agents.

Figure RSP-1: Biohazard sign. *Source: COSHH 2002.*

Control of Vibration at Work Regulations (CVWR) 2005

Considered in context in NGC2, Element 8.

Hand-arm vibration (HAV) and whole body vibration (WBV) are caused by the use of work equipment and work processes that transmit vibration into the hands, arms and bodies of employees in many industries and occupations. Long-term, regular exposure to vibration is known to lead to permanent and debilitating health effects such as vibration white finger, loss of sensation, pain, and numbness in the hands, arms, spine and joints. These effects are collectively known as hand-arm or whole body vibration syndrome. These Regulations introduce controls, which aim substantially to reduce ill health caused by exposure to vibration. These Regulations came into force on 6th July 2005.

Arrangement of Regulations

1) Citation and commencement.
2) Interpretation.
3) Application and transition.
4) Exposure limit values and action values.
5) Assessment of the risk to health created by vibration at the workplace.
6) Elimination or control of exposure to vibration at the workplace.
7) Health surveillance.
8) Information, instruction and training for persons who may be exposed to risk from vibration.
9) Exemption certificates for emergency services.
10) Exemption certificates for air transport.
11) Exemption relating to the Ministry of Defence etc.
12) Extension outside Great Britain.
13) Amendment.

Outline of main points

Regulation 3 makes provision for transition arrangements affecting equipment provided for use before 6th July 2007 and does not permit compliance with the exposure limits, taking into account technical advances and organisational measures to respond to the regulations, the regulations shall not apply until 6th July 2010. Duties under most of these regulations extend not only to employees but to others, whether or not at work, that may be affected. The duty does not include regulation 7 (health surveillance) or regulation 8 (information instruction and training), these are limited to employees.

Regulation 4 states the personal daily exposure limits and daily exposure action values, normalised over an 8-hour reference period.

	Daily exposure action values	Daily exposure limits
Hand arm vibration	2.5 m/s^2	5 m/s^2
Whole body vibration	0.5 m/s^2	1.15 m/s^2

Regulation 5 requires the employer to make a suitable and sufficient assessment of the risk created by work that is liable to expose employees to risk from vibration. The assessment must observe work practices, make reference to information regarding the magnitude of vibration from equipment and if necessary measurement of the magnitude of the vibration.

Consideration must also be given to the type, duration, effects of exposure, exposures limit/action values, effects on employees at particular risk, the effects of vibration on equipment and the ability to use it, manufacturers' information, availability of replacement equipment, and extension of exposure at the workplace (e.g. rest facilities), temperature and information on health surveillance. The risk assessment should be recorded as soon as is practicable after the risk assessment is made and reviewed regularly.

Regulation 6 states that the employer must seek to eliminate the risk of vibration at source or, if not reasonably practicable, reduce it to as low a level as is reasonably practicable. Where the personal daily exposure limit is exceeded the employer must reduce exposure by implementing a programme of organisational and technical measures. Measures include the use of other methods of work, ergonomics, maintenance of equipment, design and layout, rest facilities, information, instruction and training, limitation by schedules and breaks and the provision of personal protective equipment to protect from cold and damp.

Measures must be adapted to take account of any group or individual employee whose health may be of particular risk from exposure to vibration.

Regulation 7 states that health surveillance must be carried out if there is a risk to the health of employees liable to be exposed to vibration. This is in order to prevent or diagnose any health effect linked with exposure to vibration. A record of health shall be kept of any employee who undergoes health surveillance. The employer shall, providing reasonable notice is given, provide the employee with access to their health records and provide copies to an enforcing officer on request. If health surveillance identifies a disease or adverse health effect, considered by a doctor or other occupational health professional to be a result of exposure to vibration, the employer shall ensure that a qualified person informs the employee and provides information and advice. The employer must ensure they are kept informed of any significant findings from health surveillance, taking into account any medical confidentiality.

In addition the employer must also:

- Review risk assessments.
- Review the measures taken to comply.
- Consider assigning the employee to other work.
- Review the health of any other employee who has been similarly exposed and consider alternative work.

Regulation 8 states that employers must provide information, instruction and training to all employees who are exposed to risk from vibration and their representatives. This includes any organisational and technical measures taken, exposure limits and values, risk assessment findings, why and how to detect injury, entitlement to and collective results of health surveillance and safe working practices. Information instruction and training shall be updated to take account of changes in the employers work or methods. The employer shall ensure all persons, whether or not an employee, who carries out work in connection with the employer's duties has been provided with information, instruction and training.

Corporate Manslaughter and Corporate Homicide Act (CMCHA) 2007

Considered in context in NGC1, Elements 1 and 3.

Arrangement of Act

Section 1: The offence
Section 2: Meaning of "relevant duty of care"
Section 3: Public policy decisions, exclusively public functions and statutory inspections
Section 4: Military activities
Section 5: Policing and law enforcement
Section 6: Emergencies
Section 7: Child-protection and probation functions
Section 8: Factors for jury
Section 9: Remedial Orders
Section 10: Power to order conviction etc to be publicised
Section 11: Application to Crown bodies
Section 12: Application to armed forces
Section 13: Application to police forces
Section 14: Application to partnerships
Section 15: Procedure, evidence and sentencing
Section 16: Transfer of functions
Section 17: DPP's consent required for proceedings
Section 18: No individual liability
Section 19: Convictions under this Act and under health and safety legislation
Section 20: Abolition of liability of corporations for manslaughter at common law
Section 21: Power to extend section 1 to other organisations
Section 22: Power to amend Schedule 1
Section 23: Power to extend section 2(2)
Section 24: Orders
Section 25: Interpretation
Section 26: Minor and consequential amendments
Section 27: Commencement and saving
Section 28: Extent and territorial application
Section 29: Short title
Schedule 1: List of Government departments etc
Schedule 2: Minor and consequential amendments

Outline of main points

The Corporate Manslaughter and Corporate Homicide Act introduced a new offence, across the UK, for prosecuting companies and other organisations where there has been a gross failing in the management of health and safety, with fatal consequences.

Section 1 defines the offence and identifies the sorts of organisation to which the Act applies. The offence only applies in circumstances where an organisation owed a duty of care to the victim under the law of negligence. This reflects the position under the common law offence of gross negligence manslaughter and, by defining the necessary relationship between the defendant organisation and victim, sets out the broad scope of the offence. Duties of care commonly owed by corporations include the duty owed by employers to their employees to provide a safe system of work and by an occupier of buildings and land to people in or on, or potentially affected by, the property. Duties of care also arise out of the activities that are conducted by corporations, such as the duty owed by transport companies to their passengers.

Section 5 provides an exemption that applies to the police and other law enforcement bodies in respect of all categories of duty of care referred to in section 2, i.e., including those duties of care owed by an organisation as an employer or the occupier of premises. But this wide exemption is available only in limited circumstances, specifically operations dealing with terrorism, civil unrest or serious disorder in which an authority's officers or employees come under attack or the threat of attack; or where the authority in question is preparing for or supporting such operations; or where it is carrying on training with respect to such operations.

Section 6 clarifies that the offence does not apply to the emergency services when responding to emergencies. This does not exclude the responsibilities these authorities owe to provide a safe system of work for their employees or to secure the safety of their premises. Emergency circumstances are defined in terms of those that are life-threatening or which are causing, or threaten to cause, serious injury or illness or serious harm to the environment or buildings or other property. However, the exemption does not extend to medical treatment itself, or to decisions about this (other than decisions that establish the priority for treating patients).

Section 8 outlines factors for the jury to consider when assessing an organisation's culpability. This sets out the test for assessing whether the breach of duty involved in the management failure was gross. The test asks whether the conduct that constitutes this failure falls far below what could reasonably have been expected. The jury is directed by the Act to consider the extent to which the evidence shows that there were "attitudes, policies, systems or accepted practices within the organisation that were likely to have encouraged any such failure... or to have produced tolerance of it".

Sections 9 and 10 make provision for remedial orders and publicity orders to be made on conviction.

Sections 11 to 13 deal with the application of the offence to the Crown and police forces, where a number of provisions are required to reflect the particular status of Crown bodies and police forces. Section 14 makes provision to accommodate the application of the offence to partnerships. Section 15 makes further supplemental provision to ensure that rules of procedure, evidence and sentencing apply to Crown bodies, police forces and those unincorporated bodies to which the offence applies. Section 16 sets out where liability will fall following machinery of Government changes or other cases where functions are transferred.

Section 19 clarifies that a conviction for corporate manslaughter would not preclude an organisation being convicted for a health and safety offence on the same facts if this were in the interests of justice. It would therefore also be possible to convict an individual on a secondary basis for such an offence under provisions such as section 37 of the Health and Safety at Work etc. Act 1974. This does not impose any new liabilities on individuals but ensures that existing liabilities are not reduced as an unintended consequence of the new offence.

The Schedules to the Act set out the Government departments and other similar bodies to which the offence will apply and make a number of minor and consequential amendments.

Dangerous Substances and Explosive Atmospheres Regulations (DSEAR) 2002

Considered in context in NGC2, Element 6.

Arrangement of Regulations

1) Citation and commencement.
2) Interpretation.
3) Application.
4) Duties under these Regulations.
5) Risk assessment.
6) Elimination or reduction of risks from dangerous substances.
7) Places where explosive atmospheres may occur.
8) Arrangements to deal with accidents, incidents and emergencies.
9) Information, instruction and training.
10) Identification of hazardous contents of containers and pipes.
11) Duty of co-ordination.
12) Extension outside Great Britain.
13) Exemption certificates.
14) Exemptions for Ministry of Defence etc.
15) Amendments.
16) Repeals and revocations.
17) Transitional provisions.
Schedule 1. General safety measures.
Schedule 2. Classification of places where explosive atmospheres may occur.
Schedule 3. Criteria for the selection of equipment and protective systems.
Schedule 4. Warning sign for places where explosive atmospheres may occur.
Schedule 5. Legislation concerned with the marking of containers and pipes.
Schedule 6. Amendments.
Schedule 7. Repeal and revocation.

Outline of main points

These regulations aim to protect against risks from fire, explosion and similar events arising from dangerous substances that are present in the workplace.

DANGEROUS SUBSTANCES

These are any substances or preparations that due to their properties or the way in which they are being used could cause harm to people from fires and explosions. They may include petrol, liquefied petroleum gases, paints, varnishes, solvents and dusts.

APPLICATION

DSEAR applies in most workplaces where a dangerous substance is present. There are a few exceptions where only certain parts of the regulations apply, for example:

- Ships.
- Medical treatment areas.
- Explosives/chemically unstable substances.
- Mines.
- Quarries.
- Boreholes.
- Offshore installations.
- Means of transport.

MAIN REQUIREMENTS

You must:

- Conduct a risk assessment of work activities involving dangerous substances.
- Provide measures to eliminate or reduce risks.
- Provide equipment and procedures to deal with accidents and emergencies.

- Provide information and training for employees.
- Classify places into zones and mark zones where appropriate.

The risk assessment should include:

- The hazardous properties of substance.
- The way they are used or stored.
- Possibility of hazardous explosive atmosphere occurring.
- Potential ignition sources.
- Details of zoned areas
- Co-ordination between employers.

SAFETY MEASURES

Where possible eliminate safety risks from dangerous substances or, if not reasonably practicable to do this, control risks and reduce the harmful effects of any fire, explosion or similar event.

Substitution - Replace with totally safe or safer substance (best solution).

Control measures - If risk cannot be eliminated apply the following control measures in the following order:

- Reduce quantity.
- Avoid or minimise releases.
- Control releases at source.
- Prevent formation of explosive atmosphere.
- Collect, contain and remove any release to a safe place e.g. ventilation.
- Avoid ignition sources.
- Avoid adverse conditions e.g. exceeding temperature limits.
- Keep incompatible substances apart.

Mitigation measures - Apply measures to mitigate the effects of any situation.

- Prevent fire and explosions from spreading to other plant, equipment or other parts of the workplace.
- Reduce number of employees exposed.
- Provide process plant that can contain or suppress an explosion, or vent it to a safe place.

ZONED AREAS

In workplaces where explosive atmospheres may occur, areas should be classified into zones based on the likelihood of an explosive atmosphere occurring. Any equipment in these areas should ideally meet the requirements of the Equipment and Protective Systems Intended for Use in Potentially Explosive Atmospheres Regulations (ATEX) 1996. However equipment in use before July 2003 can continue to be used providing that the risk assessment says that it is safe to do so. Areas may need to be marked with an 'Ex' warning sign at their entry points. Employees may need to be provided with appropriate clothing e.g. anti static overalls. Before use for the first time, a person competent in the field of explosion protection must confirm hazardous areas as being safe.

ACCIDENTS, INCIDENTS AND EMERGENCIES

DSEAR builds on existing requirements for emergency procedures, which are contained in other regulations. These may need to be supplemented if you assess that a fire, explosion or significant spillage could occur, due to the quantities of dangerous substances present in the workplace. You may need to arrange for:

- Suitable warning systems.
- Escape facilities.
- Emergency procedures.
- Equipment and clothing for essential personnel who may need to deal with the situation.
- Practice drills.
- Make information, instruction and training available to employees and if necessary liaise with the emergency services.

Electricity at Work Regulations (EWR) 1989

Considered in context in NGC2, Element 5.

Arrangement of Regulations

PART I - INTRODUCTION
1)   Citation and commencement.
2)   Interpretation.
3)   Persons on whom duties are imposed by these Regulations.

PART II - GENERAL
4)   Systems, work activities and protective equipment.
5)   Strength and capability of electrical equipment.
6)   Adverse or hazardous environments.
7)   Insulation, protection and placing of conductors.
8)   Earthing or other suitable precautions.
9)   Integrity of referenced conductors.
10)   Connections.
11)   Means for protecting from excess of current.
12)   Means for cutting off the supply and for isolation.
13)   Precautions for work on equipment made dead.
14)   Work on or near live conductors.
15)   Working space, access and lighting.
16)   Persons to be competent to prevent danger and injury.

PART III - REGULATIONS APPLYING TO MINES ONLY

17) Provisions applying to mines only.
18) Introduction of electrical equipment.
19) Restriction of equipment in certain zones below ground.
20) Cutting off electricity or making safe where firedamp is found either below ground or at the surface.
21) Approval of certain equipment for use in safety-lamp mines.
22) Means of cutting off electricity to circuits below ground.
23) Oil-filled equipment.
24) Records and information.
25) Electric shock notices.
26) Introduction of battery-powered locomotives and vehicles into safety-lamp mines.
27) Storage, charging and transfer of electrical storage batteries.
28) Disapplication of section 157 of the Mines and Quarries Act 1954.

PART IV - MISCELLANEOUS AND GENERAL

29) Defence.
30) Exemption certificates.
31) Extension outside Great Britain.
32) Disapplication of duties.
33) Revocations and modifications.

Schedule 1.   Provisions applying to mines only and having effect in particular in relation to the use below ground in coal mines of film lighting circuits.

Schedule 2.   Revocations and modifications.

Outline of main points

SYSTEMS, WORK ACTIVITIES AND PROTECTIVE EQUIPMENT (REGULATION 4)

The system and the equipment comprising it must be designed and installed to take account of all reasonably foreseeable conditions of use.

- The system must be maintained so as to prevent danger.
- All work activities must be carried out in such a manner as to not give rise to danger.
- Equipment provided to protect people working on live equipment must be suitable and maintained.

STRENGTH AND CAPABILITY OF ELECTRICAL EQUIPMENT (REGULATION 5)

Strength and capability refers to the equipment's ability to withstand the effects of its load current and any transient overloads or pulses of current.

ADVERSE OR HAZARDOUS ENVIRONMENTS (REGULATION 6)

This regulation requires that electrical equipment is suitable for the environment and conditions that might be reasonably foreseen. In particular, attention should be paid to:

- Mechanical damage caused by for example; vehicles, people, vibration, etc.
- Weather, natural hazards, temperature or pressure. Ice, snow, lightning, bird droppings, etc.
- Wet, dirty, dusty or corrosive conditions. Conductors, moving parts, insulators and other materials may be affected by the corrosive nature of water, chemicals and solvents. The presence of explosive dusts must be given special consideration.
- Flammable or explosive substances. Electrical equipment may be a source of ignition for liquids, gases, vapours etc.

INSULATION, PROTECTION AND PLACING OF CONDUCTORS (REGULATION 7)

The purpose of this regulation is to prevent danger from direct contact. Therefore, if none exists, no action is needed. Conductors though will normally need to be insulated and also have some other protection to prevent mechanical damage.

EARTHING OR OTHER SUITABLE PRECAUTIONS (REGULATION 8)

The purpose of this regulation is to prevent danger from indirect contact. Conductors such as metal casings may become live through fault conditions. The likelihood of danger arising from these circumstances must be prevented by using the techniques described earlier in this section i.e. earthing, double insulation, reduced voltages etc.

INTEGRITY OF REFERENCED CONDUCTORS (REGULATION 9)

In many circumstances the reference point is earthed because the majority of power distribution installations are referenced by a deliberate connection to earth at the generators or distribution transformers. The purpose of this regulation is to ensure that electrical continuity is never broken.

CONNECTIONS (REGULATION 10)

As well as having suitable insulation and conductance, connections must have adequate mechanical protection and strength. Plugs and sockets must conform to recognised standards as must connections between cables. Special attention should be paid to the quality of connections on portable appliances.

MEANS FOR PROTECTING FROM EXCESS CURRENT (REGULATION 11)

Faults or overloads can occur in electrical systems and protection must be provided against their effects. The type of protection depends on several factors but usually rests between fuses and circuit breakers.

MEANS FOR CUTTING OFF THE SUPPLY AND FOR ISOLATION (REGULATION 12)

Means must be provided to switch off electrical supplies together with a means of isolation so as to prevent inadvertent reconnection.

PRECAUTIONS FOR WORK ON EQUIPMENT MADE DEAD (REGULATION 13)

Working dead should be the norm. This regulation requires that precautions be taken to ensure that the system remains dead and to protect those at work on the system. Any or all of the following steps should be considered:

- Identify the circuit. Never assume that the labelling is correct.
- Disconnection and isolation. These are the most common methods: isolation switches, fuse removal and plug removal.
- Notices and barriers.
- Proving dead. The test device itself must also be tested before and after testing.
- Earthing.
- Permits to work.

WORK ON OR NEAR LIVE CONDUCTORS (REGULATION 14)

Live work must only be done if it is unreasonable for it to be done dead. If live work must be carried out then any or all of the following precautions should be taken:

- Competent staff (see reg. 16).
- Adequate information.
- Suitable tools. Insulated tools, protective clothing.
- Barriers or screens.
- Instruments and test probes. To identify what is live and what is dead.
- Accompaniment.
- Designated test areas.

WORKING SPACE, ACCESS AND LIGHTING (REGULATION 15)

Space. Where there are dangerous live exposed conductors, space should be adequate to:

- Allow persons to pull back from the hazard.
- Allow persons to pass each other.

Lighting. The first preference is for natural lighting then for permanent artificial lighting.

PERSONS TO BE COMPETENT TO PREVENT DANGER AND INJURY (REGULATION 16)

The object of this regulation is to 'ensure that persons are not placed at risk due to a lack of skills on the part of themselves or others in dealing with electrical equipment'.

In order to meet the requirements of this regulation a competent person would need:

- An understanding of the concepts of electricity and the risks involved in work associated with it.
- Knowledge of electrical work and some suitable qualification in electrical principles.
- Experience of the type of system to be worked on with an understanding of the hazards and risks involved.
- Knowledge of the systems of work to be employed and the ability to recognise hazards and risks.
- Physical attributes to be able to recognise elements of the system e.g. colour blindness and wiring.

Advice and queries regarding qualifications and training can be directed to the IEE - Institute of Electrical Engineers, London.

DEFENCE (REGULATION 29)

In any Regulation where the absolute duty applies, a defence in any criminal proceedings shall exist where a person can show that: *"He took all reasonable steps and exercised due diligence to avoid the commission of the offence"*.

Is there a prepared procedure (steps), is the procedure being followed (diligence) and do you have the records or witness to prove it retrospectively?

Employers' Health and Safety Policy Statements (Exception) Regulations (EHSPS) 1975

Considered in context in NGC1, Element 2.

The Employers' Health and Safety Policy Statements (Exception) Regulations (EHSPS) 1975 which exempt "any employer who carries on an undertaking in which for the time being he employs less than five employees".

All the employees of an undertaking count for the purposes of this exemption, whether they are employed in one or several sites or establishments. It should also be noted that, for the purposes of these and other health and safety requirements, trainees count as employees of the immediate provider of their workplace training or work experience (unless this is a college or other educational establishment, and the training or work experience is provided on a course run by the college or educational establishment).

Fire Safety (Scotland) Regulations (FSSR) 2006

Considered in context in NGC2, Element 6.

The Fire Safety (Scotland) Regulations 2006 ("FSSR") are regulations that were made by Scottish Ministers under the powers contained in the Fire (Scotland) Act 2005, and further build upon the requirements of that act.

Arrangement of regulations

PART 1 - PRELIMINARY

1. Citation and commencement
2. Interpretation

PART 2 - ASSESSMENTS

3. Duty to review
4. Duty in respect of young persons
5. Assessment and review duty in respect of young persons
6. Assessment and review duty in respect of dangerous substances
7. New work activities where dangerous substances are present
8. Duty to record information
9. Specified information

PART 3 - FIRE SAFETY

10. Fire safety arrangements
11. Elimination or reduction of risks from dangerous substances

12. Means for fighting fire and means for giving warning in the event of fire
13. Means of escape
14. Procedures for serious and imminent danger from fire and for danger areas
15. Additional emergency measures in respect of dangerous substances
16. Maintenance
17. Safety assistance
18. Provision of information to employees
19. Provision of information to employers and the self-employed from outside undertakings
20. Training
21. Co-operation and co-ordination
22. Duties of employees

PART 4 - MISCELLANEOUS
23. Maintenance of measures provided in relevant premises for protection of fire fighters
24. Maintenance of measures provided in the common areas of private dwellings for protection of fire-fighters
25. Arrangements with the Office of Rail Regulation
26. Nominated person's act or omission not to afford employer defence
27. Service of documents: further provision
28. Disapplication of certain provisions
Schedule - Measures to be taken in respect of dangerous substances

Please refer to the Regulatory Reform (Fire Safety) Order 2005 for the equivalent legislation for England and Wales.

Fire (Scotland) Act (FSA) 2005

Considered in context in NGC2, Element 6.

Arrangement of Act

PART 1 - FIRE AND RESCUE AUTHORITIES
Fire and rescue authorities.
Joint fire and rescue boards.
Meaning of "relevant authority".

PART 2 - FIRE AND RESCUE SERVICES
Chapter 1	Appointment of chief officer.
Chapter 2	Principal fire and rescue functions.
Chapter 3	Ancillary functions.
Chapter 4	Water supply.
Chapter 5	Powers of employees and constables.
Chapter 6	Mutual assistance etc.
Chapter 7	Assaulting or impeding employees and others.
Chapter 8	Central supervision and support.
Chapter 9	Employment.
Chapter 10	Interpretation.

PART 3 - FIRE SAFETY
Chapter 1	Fire safety duties.
Chapter 2	Enforcement.
Chapter 3	Miscellaneous.
Chapter 4	Offences.
Chapter 5	General.

PART 4 - MISCELLANEOUS
Inquiries.
Consultation requirements.
Pre-commencement consultation.
Advisory bodies.
Payments in respect of advisory bodies.
Abolition of Scottish Central Fire Brigades Advisory Council.
False alarms.
Disposal of land.

PART 5 - GENERAL
Ancillary provision.
Orders and regulations.
Minor and consequential amendments and repeals.
Commencement.
Short title.
Schedule 1	Joint fire and rescue boards: supplementary provision.
Schedule 2	Fire safety measures.
Schedule 3	Minor and consequential amendments.
Schedule 4	Repeals.

Outline of main points

The Act is targeted at reducing the number of workplace fires by imposing far reaching responsibilities on all employers, as well as those who have control to any extent of non-domestic premises, to assess and reduce the risks from fire.

Fire certificates were abolished under the Act and have been replaced by a new fire safety regime based upon the principles of risk assessment and the requirement to take steps to mitigate the detrimental effects of a fire on relevant premises. The new regime applies to all employers as well as to anyone who has control of non-domestic premises to any extent including building owners, tenants, occupiers and factors.

The overriding duty is to ensure, so far as is reasonably practicable, safety in respect of harm caused by fire in the workplace and is supplemented by a number of prescriptive duties:

- To carry out a fire safety risk assessment of the premises. If you have 5 or more employees, the risk assessment must be recorded in writing.
- Not to employ a young person (a person under 18) unless an assessment of the risks of fire to young persons has been undertaking.
- To appoint a competent person to assist with the discharge of fire safety duties.
- To identify the fire safety measures necessary.
- To put in place arrangements for the planning, organisation, control, monitoring and review of the fire safety measures that are put in place.
- To implement these fire safety measures using risk reduction principles.
- To inform employees of the fire safety risks and provide fire safety training.
- To co-ordinate and co-operate with other duty holders in the same premises.
- To review the risk assessment.

Hazardous Waste (England and Wales) Regulations (HWR) 2005 (as amended)

INTRODUCTION

Considered in context in NGC2, Element 7.

These regulations replaced the Special Waste Regulations 1996 (as amended); the regulations came into force from 16[th]July 2005 and were subsequently amended by the Hazardous Waste (England and Wales) (Amendment) Regulations 2009 SI 507, which came into force in England on 6th April 2009. The regulations are outlined in their amended form.

Outline of main points

1. The term "special waste" has been replaced by "hazardous waste".

2. The European Waste Catalogue (EWC) and the Hazardous Waste List (part of the EWC) have been formally transposed into UK legislation. All wastes need to be characterised by their EWC code. *(See following section on the List of Wastes (England) Regulations 2005).*

3. Some wastes which were not classified as special waste will now be classified as hazardous waste by virtue of their EWC code, as a result more waste will need to be consigned.

4. Hazardous waste movements will continue to require a consignment note. However, additional information will be required.

5. 200 additional wastes have been added to the Hazardous Waste List. Among them are everyday items such as fluorescent tubes, fridges, TVs, computer monitors and end of life vehicles. There are new requirements on hazardous waste producers (registration, inspections, consignment notes, record keeping):

   - All producers of hazardous waste are required to annually register each of their sites with the Environment Agency, for which there is a fee.
   - Some sites will be exempt from registration such as those producing less than 500kg (200kg before amendment) of hazardous waste per annum.
   - The requirement to pre-notify the Environment Agency for every consignment of hazardous waste will be abolished, as will the consignment note charge.
   - Consignees, disposal and transfer sites, are required to provide quarterly returns that will form the basis of the new consignment charge.

7. Mixing of hazardous wastes with other hazardous wastes and with non-hazardous wastes is not permitted, except under license.

8. Fixed penalty charges of £300.00 for minor offences.

All Hazardous Waste producers must be registered; it will be an offence for companies to move the waste if the producers are not registered.

From 16th July 2005 all treated hazardous waste accepted into hazardous or special 'cells' of a non-hazardous landfill site must comply with the full Waste Acceptance Criteria (WAC), as required by the Landfill Regulations 2002.

EXCLUSIONS

The only hazardous waste type excluded from the regulations will be 'domestic wastes', arising from households. If you are a contractor dealing with asbestos waste from domestic premises the regulations affect you, but not the occupier.

THE NEED TO REGISTER WITH THE ENVIRONMENT AGENCY AS A HAZARDOUS WASTE PRODUCER

If hazardous waste is produced (as defined in the Hazardous Waste List of the EWC) the production site will be classed as a producer of hazardous waste. Each hazardous waste production site must be registered annually with the Environment Agency.

Registration applies to sites where separately collected fractions of domestic waste are bulked up (CA site, transfer station, etc).

These sites are classed as sites of production with appropriate notification fees.

THE RULES FOR NOTIFICATION AND RECORD KEEPING

1. Consignment Notes are used as before under the Special Waste Regulations, but a 72 hour pre-notification to the Environment Agency will be required before hazardous waste is moved.

2. Quarterly consignee returns have replaced the system of the consignee copying each Consignment Note to the Environment Agency. Electronic transfer is encouraged.

3. Sites exempt from waste management licensing need to send quarterly returns to the Environment Agency.

4.　The consignee must send returns to waste producers notifying them of the receipt of their wastes.　It is an offence to collect hazardous waste from non-notified premises if the producer is not exempt.

HOW THE CHANGES AFFECT THE COLLECTION OF WASTE

Waste producers cannot mix different categories of hazardous waste or mix hazardous waste with non-hazardous waste, except under license.

If multiple hazardous waste streams from industrial or commercial premises are deposited within a single container, all the individual EWC codes must accompany the consignment note, which must contain the relevant EWC codes.

Both individual and multiple collections of hazardous wastes can be arranged.　There is one consignment note for multiple collections with space in an annex for the details of individual loads rather than completely separate consignment notes for each collection.

For waste collections using multi-lift vehicles and single compartment tankers, a transfer note will exist for each waste producer. Differences in the contents of the individual containers must be recorded in the individual written descriptions.

DUTIES RELATING TO THE WASTE ACCEPTANCE CRITERIA

From 16th July 2005 all hazardous and non hazardous wastes destined for disposal in landfill have to meet the WAC before they can be deposited.　WAC contain the 'quality standards' wastes have to comply with before they are allowed to be placed in inert, non hazardous or hazardous landfills.

The waste producer is under a duty of care to ensure the characterisation of the waste to establish its main characteristics as specified in the Regulations.　That is, to assess the physical and chemical properties to identify if they classify as hazardous, non hazardous or inert waste.　In particular, details of the chemical composition and leaching behaviour of the waste are required.　This assessment takes the form of sample testing, whereby a representative sample of waste arising is sent away for scientific analysis.

THE INSPECTION REGIME

The Environment Agency will periodically inspect hazardous waste producing premises and assess the following:

a.　Does the site produce hazardous waste?
b.　Has the site been notified (i.e. registered)?
c.　Is mixing carried out?
d.　Are the Consignment Note records complete?
e.　Is the waste moved by a registered carrier …
f.　… and taken to a permitted consignee?
g.　If going to landfill how are the Waste Acceptance Criteria being met?

The Environment Agency issues fixed penalties (spot fines) for:

■　Failing to notify premises.
■　Failing to complete consignment notes.
■　Failing to apply for review of existing permit.

Source: www.sita.co.uk. Document code M141, Review of the Hazardous Waste (England) Regulations 2005 and the introduction of the Waste Acceptance Criteria.

List of Wastes (England) Regulations (LoWR) 2005

Considered in context in NGC2, Element 7.

OUTLINE OF MAIN POINTS

Includes the European Waste Catalogue (EWC) and the Hazardous Waste List (part of the EWC); all wastes need to be characterised by their EWC code.

These regulations include Chapters of the List numbered 01-20.　The Chapters are broken down into specific materials or substances which are further identified as 'wastes' or 'hazardous wastes'; *a waste marked with an asterisk in the List of Wastes is considered listed as a hazardous waste*, whereas those without an asterisk are considered as a waste.

The different types of wastes in the List of Wastes are fully defined by the six-digit code for the waste and the respective two-digit and four-digit chapter headings, and accordingly, for purposes connected with the regulation of waste or hazardous waste -

(a)　Any reference to a waste by its six-digit code as specified in the List of Wastes is to be treated as a reference to that waste.

(b)　A reference to wastes by the respective two-digit or four-digit chapter heading is a reference to the wastes listed in the List of Wastes under that chapter heading.

Source: The List of Wastes (England) Regulations 2005.

The regulations set out a list of hazardous waste properties, wastes on the List of Wastes are hazardous if they have one or more of the listed hazardous properties, for example:

H1	**Explosive:** substances and preparations which may explode under the effect of flame or which are more sensitive to shocks or friction than dinitrobenzene.
H2	**Oxidizing:** substances and preparations which exhibit highly exothermic reactions when in contact with other substances, particularly flammable substances.
H3A	**Highly flammable:** ■ Liquid substances and preparations having a flash point below 21C (including extremely flammable liquids). ■ Substances and preparations which may become hot and finally catch fire in contact with air at ambient temperature without any application of energy. ■ Solid substances and preparations which may readily catch fire after brief contact with a source of ignition and which continue to burn or to be consumed after removal of the source of ignition. ■ Gaseous substances and preparations which are flammable in air at normal pressure. ■ Substances and preparations which, in contact with water or damp air, evolve highly flammable gases in dangerous quantities.

Figure RSP-2: Hazardous properties.   *Source: Environment Agency, HWR01, What is a Hazardous Waste?*

See the Regulations for specific details.

Health and Safety (Consultation with Employees) Regulations (HSCER) 1996

Considered in context in NGC1, Element 3.

Arrangement of Regulations

1) Citation, extent and commencement.
2) Interpretation.
3) Duty of employer to consult.
4) Persons to be consulted.
5) Duty of employer to provide information.
6) Functions of representatives of employee safety.
7) Training, time off and facilities for representatives of employee safety and time off for candidates.
8) Amendment of the Employment Rights Act 1996.
9) Exclusion of civil liability.
10) Application of health and safety legislation.
11) Application to the Crown and armed forces.
12) Disapplication to sea-going ships.
13) Amendment of the 1977 Regulations.

Outline of main points

1) The HSCER 1996 came into force on 1st October 1996 and were made under the European Communities Act 1972.

2) "Employees" do not include persons employed in domestic service in private households. Workplaces are defined as "any place where the employee is likely to work, or which he is likely to frequent in the course of his employment or incidentally to it".

3) Where there are employees not represented by the Safety Representatives and Safety Committee Regulations (SRSCR), the employer shall consult those employees in good time on matters relating to their health & safety at work. In particular, they must be consulted on:

   ■ The introduction of any new measures which may affect their safety and health.
   ■ Arrangements made by the employer for appointing or nominating competent persons in accordance with regs. 6(1) and 7(1) of the Management of Health and Safety at Work Regs (MHSWR) 1999.
   ■ Any safety information the employer is legally obliged to provide to workers.
   ■ The planning and organisation of any health and safety training required under particular health and safety laws.
   ■ The health and safety consequences for employees of the introduction of new technologies into the workplace.

4) Employers can consult either directly with employees or, in respect of any group of employees, one or more elected representatives of that group. These are referred to as "representatives of employee safety" (RES). If the latter option is chosen, then employers must tell the employees the name of the representative and the group he/she represents. An employer which has been consulting a representative may choose to consult the whole workforce. However, the employer must inform the employees and the representatives of that fact.

5) If the employer consults employees directly then it must make available such information, within the employers' knowledge, as is necessary to enable them to participate fully and effectively in the consultation. If a representative is consulted, then the employer must make available all necessary information to enable them to carry out their functions, and of any record made under the Reporting of Injuries, Diseases and Dangerous Occurrences Regulations (RIDDOR) 1995 which relates to the represented group of employees.

6) Representatives of employee safety have the following functions:

   ■ To make representations to the employer on potential hazards and dangerous occurrences at the workplace which affect, or could affect the represented employees.
   ■ Make representations to the employer on general matters of health and safety.
   ■ To represent the employees in workplace consultations with HSE or local authority inspectors.

7) Representatives of employee safety must be given reasonable training in order to carry out their duties. Employers must meet the costs of the training and any travel and subsistence. They must also permit the representatives to take time off with pay during working hours in order for them to carry out their functions. Time off shall also be given, with pay, where this is required for any person standing as a candidate for election as a representative. Employers must also provide suitable facilities for the representatives to carry out their duties.

8) The Employment Rights Act 1996, which gives protection against unfair dismissal or discrimination on grounds of health and safety, is amended to protect representatives of employee safety and candidates for their election.

9) A breach of the HSCER 1996 does not confer any right of action in any civil proceedings.

10) Ensures that certain provisions of health and safety legislation (including enforcement provisions) operate in respect of the HSCER 1996. The Regulations are made under the European Communities Act 1972. Enforcement is by the enforcing authorities appointed under the Health & Safety at Work Act (HASAWA) 1974.

11) The HSCER 1996 will apply in respect of the armed forces. However, the representatives of employee safety will be appointed by the employer, rather than elected. Furthermore, representatives in the armed forces will not be entitled to time off with pay under reg.7.

12) The HSCER 1996 do not apply to the master or crew of a seagoing ship.

13) The SRSC 1977 are amended so that they now include employees of coal mines.

Health and Safety (Display Screen Equipment) Regulations (DSE) 1992

Considered in context in NGC2, Element 3.

Arrangement of Regulations

2) Every employer shall carry out suitable and sufficient analysis of workstations.
3) Employers shall ensure that equipment provided meets the requirements of the schedule laid down in these Regulations.
4) Employers shall plan activities and provide such breaks or changes in work activity to reduce employees' workload on that equipment.
5) For display screen equipment (DSE) users, the employer shall provide, on request, an eyesight test carried out by a competent person.
6 & 7) Provision of information and training.

Outline of main points

WORKSTATION ASSESSMENTS (REG 2)

Workstation assessments should take account of:

- Screen   -   positioning, character definition, character stability etc.
- Keyboard   -   tilt able, character legibility etc.
- Desk   -   size, matt surface etc.
- Chair   -   adjustable back and height, footrest available etc.
- Environment -   noise, lighting, space etc.
- Software   -   easy to use, work rate not governed by software.

INFORMATION AND TRAINING (REGS 6 & 7)

Information and training should include:

- Risks to health.
- Precautions in place (e.g. the need for regular breaks).
- How to recognise problems.
- How to report problems.

Health and Safety (First-Aid) Regulations (FAR) 1981

Considered in context in NGC2, Element 3.

Arrangement of Regulations

1) Citation and commencement.
2) Interpretation.
3) Duty of employer to make provision for first-aid.
4) Duty of employer to inform his employees of the arrangements.
5) Duty of self-employed person to provide first-aid equipment.
6) Power to grant exemptions.
7) Cases where these Regulations do not apply.
8) Application to mines.
9) Application offshore.
10) Repeals, revocations and modification.
Schedule 1   Repeals.
Schedule 1   Revocations.

Outline of main points

2) Regulation 2 defines first aid as: '…treatment for the purpose of preserving life and minimising the consequences of injury or illness until medical (doctor or nurse) help can be obtained. Also, it provides treatment of minor injuries which would otherwise receive no treatment, or which do not need the help of a medical practitioner or nurse'.

3) Requires that every employer must provide equipment and facilities which are adequate and appropriate in the circumstances for administering first-aid to his employees.

4) Employer must inform their employees about the first-aid arrangements, including the location of equipment, facilities and identification of trained personnel.

5) Self-employed people must ensure that adequate and suitable provision is made for administering first-aid while at work.

Health and Safety Information for Employees Regulations (IER) 1989

Considered in context in NGC2, Element 3.

Arrangement of Regulations

1) Citation and commencement.
2) Interpretation and application.
3) Meaning of and revisions to the approved poster and leaflet.
4) Provision of poster or leaflet.
5) Provision of further information.
6) Exemption certificates.
7) Defence.
8) Repeals, revocations and modifications.
The Schedule - Repeals, revocations and modifications.
Part I - Repeals.
Part II - Revocations.
Part III - Modifications.

Outline of main points

The Health and Safety (Information for Employees) Regulations (IER) 1989 require that information relating to health and safety at work to be furnished to all employees by means of posters or leaflets in a form approved by the Health and Safety Executive.

The Health and Safety Information for Employees (Modifications and Repeals) Regulations 1995 amended these regulations; this allows the HSE to approve an alternative poster to the basic 'Health and Safety Law' poster. The Health and Safety Executive (HSE) may approve a particular form of poster or leaflet for use in relation to a particular industry or employment and, where any such form has been approved, the HSE shall publish it. If a poster is used, the information must be legible and up to date. The poster must be prominently located in an area which all employees have access. If a leaflet is used, revised leaflets must be issued to employees when any similar changes occur.

The HSE has published a new, simplified version of the *Health and Safety Law Poster; the 2009 poster.* It tells workers what they and their employers need to do in simple terms, using numbered lists of basic points. The employer is required by law to either display the HSE-approved poster in a prominent position or to provide each of their workers with the equivalent 'leaflet'.

MODIFICATION TO THE REGULATIONS

It is no longer a requirement for the employer to add the contact details of the enforcing authority and the HSE's Employment Medical Advisory Service. Details may be added of any employee safety representatives or other health and safety contacts, but this is not compulsory.

The existing *"Health and Safety Law - what you should know"* poster can continue to be displayed until 5th April 2014, so long as they are readable and contain up-to-date contact details. Workers can be given copies of the equivalent 1999 leaflet until 5th April 2014. After this date, the 2009 approved poster must be displayed or workers must be provided with personal copies of the 2009 equivalent.

Health and Safety (Miscellaneous Amendments) Regulations (MAR) 2002

See also - FAR 1981, DSE 1992, MHOR 1992, PPER 1992, WHSWR 1992, PUWER and LOLER.

These Regulations made minor amendments to UK law to come into line with the requirements of the original Directives and came into force on 17th September 2002. In relation to this publication, the Regulations that are affected by the amendments are:

- Health and Safety (First-Aid) Regulations (FAR) 1981.
- Health and Safety (Display Screen Equipment) Regulations (DSE) 1992.
- Manual Handling Operations Regulations (MHOR) 1992.
- Personal Protective Equipment at Work Regulations (PPER) 1992.
- Workplace (Health, Safety and Welfare) Regulations (WHSWR) 1992.
- Provision and Use of Work Equipment Regulations (PUWER) 1998.
- Lifting Operations and Lifting Equipment Regulations (LOLER) 1998.

Arrangement of Regulations

1) Citation and commencement.
2) Amendment of the Health and Safety (First-Aid) Regulations 1981.
3) Amendment of the Health and Safety (Display Screen Equipment) Regulations 1992.
4) Amendment of the Manual Handling Operations Regulations 1992.
5) Amendment of the Personal Protective Equipment at Work Regulations 1992.
6) Amendment of the Workplace (Health, Safety and Welfare) Regulations 1992.
7) Amendment of the Provision and Use of Work Equipment Regulations 1998.
8) Amendment of the Lifting Operations and Lifting Equipment Regulations 1998.
9) Amendment of the Quarries Regulations 1999.

Outline of main points

REGULATION 3 - AMENDMENT OF THE HEALTH AND SAFETY (FIRST AID) REGULATIONS 1981

The Health and Safety (First Aid) Regulations 1981 are amended by adding the additional requirements that any first-aid room provided under requirements of these regulations must be easily accessible to stretchers and to any other equipment needed to convey patients to and from the room and that the room be sign-posted by use of a sign complying with the Health and Safety (Safety Signs and Signals) Regulations 1996.

REGULATION 3 - AMENDMENT OF THE HEALTH AND SAFETY (DISPLAY SCREEN EQUIPMENT) REGULATIONS 1992

The Health and Safety (Display Screen Equipment) Regulations 1992 were amended to cover workstations "used for the purposes of" an employer's undertaking, which includes workstations provided by the employer and others.

The Health and Safety (Display Screen Equipment) Regulations 1992 were amended to provide for people that are users of display screen equipment in an employers undertaking but are not employees of the employer, for example staff provided through an employment agency. This extension of duty relates to requests for eye site tests from the person. The employer who carries on the undertaking must ensure an eyesight test is carried out, as soon as is practicable after the request for those currently a user and before they become a user for those who become users.

The Health and Safety (Display Screen Equipment) Regulations 1992 were similarly amended with regard to health and safety training for users.

REGULATION 4 - AMENDMENT OF THE MANUAL HANDLING OPERATIONS REGULATIONS 1992

Regulation 4 of the Manual Handling Operations Regulations 1992 were amended by adding the requirement to, when determining whether manual handling operations at work involve a risk of injury and the appropriate steps to reduce that risk, have regard to:

- Physical suitability of the employee to carry out the operations.
- Clothing, footwear or other personal effects they are wearing.
- Knowledge and training.
- Results of any relevant risk assessment conducted for the Management of Health and Safety at Work Regulations.
- Whether the employee is within a group of employees identified by that assessment as being especially at risk.
- Results of any health surveillance provided under the Management of Health and Safety Regulations.

REGULATION 5 - AMENDMENT OF THE PERSONAL PROTECTIVE EQUIPMENT AT WORK REGULATIONS 1992

The Personal Protective Equipment at Work Regulations 1992 were amended so that personal protective equipment (PPE) must also be suitable for the period for which it is worn and account is taken of the characteristics of the workstation of each person.

Provision of personal issue of PPE needs to take place in situations where it is necessary to ensure it is hygienic and free of risk to health.

Where an assessment of PPE is made this must consider whether it is compatible with other personal protective equipment that is in use and which an employee would be required to wear simultaneously.

The amendments require that information provided to satisfy regulation 9 for the provision of information, instruction and training must be kept available to employees. A new, additional duty is created requiring the employer, where appropriate, and at suitable intervals, to organise demonstrations in the wearing of PPE.

REGULATION 6 - AMENDMENT OF THE WORKPLACE (HEALTH, SAFETY AND WELFARE) REGULATIONS 1992

The Workplace (Health, Safety and Welfare) Regulations 1992 have been amended to improve clarity, include additional regulations and make provision for the disabled.

An additional regulation (4A) sets out a requirement where a workplace is in a building, the building shall have a stability and solidity appropriate to the nature of the use of the workplace. The range of things requiring maintenance under these regulations is extended to equipment and devices intended to prevent or reduce hazards. A new duty requires workplaces to be adequately thermally insulated where it is necessary, having regard to the type of work carried out and the physical activity of the persons carrying out the work. In addition, excessive effects of sunlight on temperature must be avoided.

The regulations were amended with regard to facilities for changing clothing in that the facilities need to be easily accessible, of sufficient capacity and provided with seating. Requirements were amended such that rest rooms and rest areas must include suitable arrangements to protect non-smokers from discomfort caused by tobacco smoke. They also must be equipped with an adequate number of tables and adequate seating with backs for the number of persons at work likely to use them at any one time and seating which is adequate for the number of disabled persons at work and suitable for them.

A new regulation (25A) was added requiring, where necessary, those parts of the workplace (including in particular doors, passageways, stairs, showers, washbasins, lavatories and workstations) used or occupied directly by disabled persons at work to be organised to take account of such persons.

AMENDMENT OF THE PROVISION AND USE OF WORK EQUIPMENT REGULATIONS 1998

The regulations have a small number of amendments affecting 3 main regulations. Regulation 10, which deals with equipment's conformity with community requirements, is amended such that the requirement to conform to 'essential requirements' is no longer limited to the point at which the equipment was designed and constructed - equipment must now conform at 'all times'. The 'essential requirements' are those that were applicable at the time it was put into first service. Regulation 11 was amended to remove the opportunity of reliance on information, instruction, training and supervision as a separate option in the hierarchy of control of dangerous parts of machinery. The requirement to provide information, instruction, training and supervision is now amended to apply to each stage of the dangerous parts of machinery control hierarchy. Regulation 18, which deals with control systems, carries a small but important amendment which means the requirement that all control systems of work equipment are "chosen making due allowance for the failures, faults and constraints to be expected in the planned circumstances of use" is modified from an absolute duty to one of so far as is reasonably practicable.

AMENDMENT OF THE LIFTING OPERATIONS AND LIFTING EQUIPMENT REGULATIONS 1998

Minor changes to the definitions in the Lifting Operations and Lifting Equipment Regulations 1998 were made by these regulations.

(a)   In the definition of "accessory for lifting" in regulation 2(1), by substituting for the word "work" the word "lifting";

(b)   In regulation 3(4), by substituting for the words "(5)(b)" the words "(3)(b)".

Health and Safety (Safety Signs and Signals) Regulations (SSSR) 1996

Considered in context in NGC2, Element 1.

Arrangement of Regulations

1)   Citation and commencement.
2)   Interpretation.
3)   Application.
4)   Provision and maintenance of safety signs.
5)   Information, instruction and training.
6)   Transitional provisions.
7)   Enforcement.
8)   Revocations and amendments.

Outline of main points

The Regulations require employers to provide specific safety signs whenever there is a risk which has not been avoided or controlled by other means, e.g. by engineering controls and safe systems of work. Where a safety sign would not help to reduce that risk, or where the sign is not significant, there is no need to provide a sign.

They require, where necessary, the use of road traffic signs within workplaces to regulate road traffic.

They also require employers to:

■   Maintain the safety signs which are provided by them.
■   Explain unfamiliar signs to their employees and tell them what they need to do when they see a safety sign.

The Regulations cover 4 main types of signs:

1)   *PROHIBITION* - circular signs, prime colours red and white, e.g., no pedestrian access.
2)   *WARNING* - triangular signs, prime colours black on yellow, e.g., overhead electrics.
3)   *MANDATORY* - circular signs, prime colours blue and white, e.g., safety helmets must be worn.
4)   *SAFE CONDITION* - oblong/square signs, prime colours green and white, e.g., fire assembly point, first aid etc.

Supplementary signs provide additional information.

Supplementary signs with yellow/black or red/white diagonal stripes can be used to highlight a hazard, but must not substitute for signs as defined above.

Fire fighting, rescue equipment and emergency exit signs have to comply with a separate British Standard.

Health and Safety at Work etc. Act (HASAWA) 1974

Considered in context in NGC1, Element 1.

Arrangement of Act

PRELIMINARY

1)   Preliminary.

GENERAL DUTIES

2)   General duties of employers to the employees.
3)   General duties of employers and self-employed to persons other than their employees.
4)   General duties of persons concerned with premises to persons other than their employees.
5)   [repealed].
6)   General duties of manufacturers etc. as regards articles and substances for use at work.
7)   General duties of employees at work.
8)   Duty not to interfere with or misuse things provided pursuant to certain provisions.
9)   Duty not to charge employees for things done or provided pursuant to certain specific requirements.

THE HEALTH AND SAFETY COMMISSION AND THE HEALTH AND SAFETY EXECUTIVE

10)   Establishment of the Commission and the Executive.
11)   General functions of the Commission and the Executive.
12)   Control of the Commission by the Secretary of State.
13)   Other powers of the Commission.
14)   Power of the Commission to direct investigations and Inquiries.

HEALTH AND SAFETY REGULATIONS AND APPROVED CODES OF PRACTICE

15)   Health and safety regulations.
16)   Approval of codes of practice by the Commission.
17)   Use of approved codes of practice in criminal proceedings.

ENFORCEMENT

18)   Authorities responsible for enforcement of the relevant statutory provisions.
19)   Appointment of inspectors.
20)   Powers of inspectors.
21)   Improvement notices.
22)   Prohibition notices.
23)   Provisions supplementary toss. 21 and 22.
24)   Appeal against improvement or prohibition notice.
25)   Power to deal with cause of imminent danger.

26)	Power of enforcing authorities to indemnify their inspectors.

OBTAINING AND DISCLOSURE OF INFORMATION

27)	Obtaining of information by the Commission, the Executive, enforcing authorities etc.
28)	Restrictions on disclosure of information.

SPECIAL PROVISIONS RELATING TO AGRICULTURE

29-32)	[repealed].

PROVISIONS AS TO OFFENCES

33)	Offences.
34)	Extension of time for bringing summary proceedings.
35)	Venue.
36)	Offences due to fault of other person.
37)	Offences by bodies corporate.
38)	Restriction on institution of proceedings in England and Wales.
39)	Prosecutions by inspectors.
40)	Onus of proving limits of what is practicable etc.
41)	Evidence.
42)	Power of court to order cause of offence to be remedied or, in certain cases, forfeiture.

FINANCIAL PROVISION

43)	Financial provisions.

MISCELLANEOUS AND SUPPLEMENTARY

44)	Appeals in connection with licensing provisions in the relevant statutory provisions.
45)	Default powers.
46)	Service of notices.
47)	Civil liability.
48)	Application to Crown.
49)	Adaptation of enactments to metric units or appropriate metric units.
50)	Regulations under the relevant statutory provisions.
51)	Exclusion of application to domestic employment.
52)	Meaning of work and at work.
53)	General interpretation of Part I.
54)	Application of Part I to Isles of Scilly.

Outline of main points

OVERALL AIMS OF THE ACT

1)	To protect people.
2)	To protect the public from risks which may arise from work activities.

THE MAIN PROVISIONS - SECTION 1

a)	Securing the health, safety and welfare of people at work.
b)	Protecting others against risks arising from workplace activities.
c)	Controlling the obtaining, keeping, and use of explosive and highly flammable substances.
d)	Controlling emissions into the atmosphere of noxious or offensive substances.

Duties are imposed on:

a)	The employer.
b)	The self-employed.
c)	Employees.
d)	Contractors and subcontractors.
e)	Designers, manufacturers, suppliers, importers and installers.
f)	Specialists - architects, surveyors, engineers, personnel managers, health and safety practitioners, and many more.

EMPLOYER'S DUTIES - [TO EMPLOYEES]

Section 2(1)

To ensure, so far as *reasonably practicable*, the health, safety and welfare at work of employees.

Section 2(2)

Ensuring health, safety and welfare at work through:

- Safe plant and systems of work e.g. provision of guards on machines.
- Safe use, handling, storage and transport of goods and materials e.g. good manual handling of boxes.
- Provision of information, instruction, training and supervision e.g. provision of induction training.
- Safe place of work including means of access and egress e.g. aisles kept clear.
- Safe and healthy working environment e.g. good lighting.

Further duties are placed on the employer by:

Section 2(3)

Prepare and keep up to date a written safety policy supported by information on the organisation and arrangements for carrying out the policy. The safety policy has to be brought to the notice of employees. If there are fewer than five employees, this section does not apply.

Section 2(4)

Recognised Trade Unions have the right to appoint safety representatives to represent the employees in consultations with the employer about health and safety matters.

Section 2(6)

Employers must consult with any safety representatives appointed by recognised Trade Unions.

Section 2(7)

To establish a safety committee if requested by two or more safety representatives.

EMPLOYER'S DUTIES - [TO PERSONS NOT HIS EMPLOYEES]

Section 3

a)   Not to expose them to risk to their heath and safety e.g. contractor work barriered off.

b)   To give information about risks which may affect them e.g. location induction for contractors.

SELF EMPLOYED DUTIES

Section 3

a)   Not to expose themselves to risks to their health and safety e.g. wear personal protection.

b)   Not to expose other persons to risks to their health and safety e.g. keep shared work area tidy.

Some of the practical steps that an organisation might take in order to ensure the safety of visitors to its premises are:

- Identify visitors by signing in, badges etc.
- Provide information regarding the risks present and the site rules and procedures to be followed, particularly in emergencies.
- Provide escorts to supervise visitors throughout the site.
- Restrict access to certain areas.

Figure RSP-3: Risks from roadside work.   *Source: RMS.*

Figure RSP-4: Risks from street light repairing or tree felling.
Source: RMS.

CONTROL OF PREMISES

Section 4

This section places duties on anyone who has control to any extent of non-domestic premises used by people who are not their employees. The duty extends to the provision of safe premises, plant and substances, e.g. maintenance of a boiler in rented out property.

MANUFACTURERS, DESIGNERS, SUPPLIERS, IMPORTERS, INSTALLERS

Section 6

This section places specific duties on those who can ensure that articles and substances are as safe and without risks as is reasonably practicable. The section covers:

- Safe design, installation and testing of equipment (including fairground equipment).
- Safe substances tested for risks.
- Provision of information on safe use and conditions essential to health and safety.
- Research to minimise risks.

EMPLOYEES' DUTIES

Section 7

a)   To take reasonable care for themselves and others that may be affected by their acts/omissions e.g. wear eye protection, not obstruct a fire exit.

b)   To co-operate with the employer or other to enable them to carry out their duty and/or statutory requirements e.g. report hazards or defects in controls, attend training, provide medical samples.

Additional duties created by the Management of Health and Safety at Work Regulations 1999 employees' duties:

- Every employee shall use any equipment, material or substance provided to them in accordance with any training and instruction.
- Every employee shall inform (via supervisory staff) their employer of any (a) risk situation or (b) shortcoming in the employer's protection arrangements.

OTHER DUTIES

Section 8

No person to interfere with or misuse anything provided to secure health and safety - e.g. wedge fire door open, remove first aid equipment without authority, breach lock off systems.

Section 9

Employees cannot be charged for anything done or provided to comply with a specific legal obligation e.g. personal protective equipment, health surveillance or welfare facilities.

OFFENCES COMMITTED BY OTHER PERSONS

Section 36

- Where the commission by any person of the breach of legislation is due to the act or default of some other person, that other person shall be guilty of the offence and may be charged with and convicted of the offence whether or not proceedings are taken against the first mentioned person.
- Case law indicates that 'other person' refers to persons lower down the corporate tree than mentioned in section 37, e.g. middle managers, safety advisors, training officers; and may extend to people working on contract e.g. architects, consultants or a planning supervisor.

OFFENCES COMMITTED BY THE BODY CORPORATE

Section 37

Where there has been a breach of legislation on the part of a body corporate (limited company or local authority) and the offence can be proved to have been committed with the consent or connivance of or to be attributable to any neglect on the part of any director, manager, secretary or similar officer of the body corporate, he, as well as the body corporate, can be found guilty and punished accordingly.

ONUS OF PROOF

Section 40

In any proceedings for an offence under any of the relevant statutory involving a failure to comply with a duty or requirement:

- To do something so far as is practicable.
- To do something so far as is reasonably practicable.
- It shall be for the accused to prove that the requirements were met rather than for the prosecution to prove that the requirements were not met.

Interpretation Act (IA) 1978

Considered in context in NGC1, Element 1.

Arrangement of Act

GENERAL PROVISIONS AS TO ENACTMENT AND OPERATION

1. Words of enactment.
2. Amendment or repeal in same Session.
3. Judicial notice.
4. Time of commencement.

INTERPRETATION AND CONSTRUCTION

5. Definitions.
6. Gender and number.
7. References to service by post.
8. References to distance.
9. References to time of day.
10. References to the Sovereign.
11. Construction of subordinate legislation.

STATUTORY POWERS AND DUTIES

12. Continuity of powers and duties.
13. Anticipatory exercise of powers.
14. Implied power to amend.

REPEALING ENACTMENTS

15. Repeal of repeal.
16. General savings.
17. Repeal and re-enactment.

MISCELLANEOUS

18. Duplicated offences.
19. Citation of other Acts.
20. References to other enactments.
20A. References to Community instruments.

SUPPLEMENTARY

21. Interpretation etc.
22. Application to Acts and Measures.
23. Application to other instruments.
23A. Acts of the Scottish Parliament etc.
23B. Measures and Acts of the National Assembly for Wales etc.

Outline of main points

The Interpretation Act 1978 came into force on 1st January 1979 and is an Act of the Parliament that governs the interpretation of terms within Acts of Parliament and other statutory documents.

Section 6 of the Act establishes that if, in any Act of Parliament or other Statutory Instrument, there are words importing the masculine gender, the words should be construed to incorporate the feminine and vice versa. Also, words in the singular include the plural and words in the plural include the singular.

Ionising Radiations Regulations (IRR) 1999

Considered in context in NGC2, Element 8.

Arrangement of Regulations

PART I - INTERPRETATION AND GENERAL
1.   Citation and commencement.
2.   Interpretation.
3.   Application.
4.   Duties under the Regulations.

PART II - GENERAL PRINCIPLES AND PROCEDURES
5.   Authorisation of specified practices.
6.   Notification of specified work.
7.   Prior risk assessment etc.
8.   Restriction of exposure.
9.   Personal protective equipment.
10.   Maintenance and examination of engineering controls etc. and personal protective equipment.
11.   Dose limitation.
12.   Contingency plans.

PART III - ARRANGEMENTS FOR THE MANAGEMENT OF RADIATION PROTECTION
13.   Radiation protection adviser.
14.   Information, instruction and training.
15.   Co-operation between employers.

PART IV - DESIGNATED AREAS
16.   Designation of controlled or supervised areas.
17.   Local rules and radiation protection supervisors.
18.   Additional requirements for designated areas.
19.   Monitoring of designated areas.

PART V - CLASSIFICATION AND MONITORING OF PERSONS
20.   Designation of classified persons.
21.   Dose assessment and recording.
22.   Estimated doses and special entries.
23.   Dosimetry for accidents etc.
24.   Medical surveillance.
25.   Investigation and notification of overexposure.
26.   Dose limitation for overexposed employees.

PART VI - ARRANGEMENTS FOR THE CONTROL OF RADIOACTIVE SUBSTANCES, ARTICLES AND EQUIPMENT
27.   Sealed sources and articles containing or embodying radioactive substances.
28.   Accounting for radioactive substances.
29.   Keeping and moving of radioactive substances.
30.   Notification of certain occurrences.
31.   Duties of manufacturers etc. of articles for use in work with ionising radiation.
32.   Equipment used for medical exposure.
33.   Misuse of or interference with sources of ionising radiation.

PART VII - DUTIES OF EMPLOYEES AND MISCELLANEOUS
34.   Duties of employees.
35.   Approval of dosimetry services.
36.   Defence on contravention.
37.   Exemption certificates.
38.   Extension outside Great Britain.
39.   Transitional provisions.
40.   Modifications relating to the Ministry of Defence.
41.   Modification, revocation and saving.

SCHEDULES

Schedule 1.   Work not required to be notified under regulation 6.

Schedule 2.   Particulars to be provided in a notification under regulation 6(2).

Schedule 3.   Additional particulars that the Executive may require.

Schedule 4.   Dose limits.

Schedule 5.   Matters in respect of which radiation protection adviser must be consulted by a radiation employer.

Schedule 6.   Particulars to be entered in the radiation passbook.

Schedule 7.   Particulars to be contained in a health record.

Schedule 8.   Quantities and concentrations of radionuclides.

Schedule 9.   Modifications.

Outline of main points

The Regulations supersede and consolidate the Ionising Radiations Regulations 1985 and the Ionising Radiation (Outside Workers) Regulations 1993.

They impose duties on employers to protect employees and other persons against ionising radiation arising from work with radioactive substances and other sources of ionising radiation; and also impose certain duties on employees.

Lifting Operations and Lifting Equipment Regulations (LOLER) 1998

Considered in context in NGC2, Element 3.

Arrangements of Regulations

1)   Citation and commencement.

2)   Interpretation.

3)   Application.

4)   Strength and stability.

5)   Lifting equipment for lifting persons.

6)   Positioning and installation.

7)   Marking of lifting equipment.

8)   Organisation of lifting operations.

9)   Thorough examination and inspection.

10)   Reports and defects.

11)   Keeping of information.

12)   Exemption for the armed forces.

13)   Amendment of the Shipbuilding and Ship-repairing Regulations 1960.

14)   Amendment of the Docks Regulation 1988.

15)   Repeal of provisions of the Factories Act 1961.

16)   Repeal of section 85 of the Mines and Quarries Act 1954.

17)   Revocation of instruments.

Schedule 1.   Information to be contained in a report of a thorough examination.

Schedule 2.   Revocation of instruments.

Outline of main points

The Lifting Operations and Lifting Equipment Regulations (LOLER) 1998 impose health and safety requirements with respect to lifting equipment (as defined in regulation 2(1)). They are not industry specific and apply to almost all lifting operations.

The Regulations place duties on employers, the self-employed, and certain persons having control of lifting equipment (of persons at work who use or supervise or manage its use, or of the way it is used, to the extent of their control (regulation 3(3) to (5)).

The Regulations make provision with respect to:

- The strength and stability of lifting equipment (regulation 4).
- The safety of lifting equipment for lifting persons (regulation 5).
- The way lifting equipment is positioned and installed (regulation 6).
- The marking of machinery and accessories for lifting, and lifting equipment which is designed for lifting persons or which might so be used in error (regulation 7).
- The organisation of lifting operations (regulation 8).
- The thorough examination (defined in (regulation 2(1)) and inspection of lifting equipment in specified circumstances, (regulation 9(1) to (3)).
- The evidence of examination to accompany it outside the undertaking (regulation 9(4)).
- The exception for winding apparatus at mines from regulation 9 (regulation 9(5)).
- Transitional arrangements relating to regulation 9 (regulation 9(6) and (7)).
- The making of reports of thorough examinations and records of inspections (regulation 10 and Schedule 1).
- The keeping of information in the reports and records (regulation 11).

Management of Health and Safety at Work Regulations (MHSWR) 1999

Considered in context in NGC1, Element 1.

Arrangement of Regulations

1)   Citation, commencement and interpretation.

2)   Disapplication of these Regulations.

3)   Risk assessment.

4)   Principles of prevention to be applied.

5)   Health and safety arrangements.

6)   Health surveillance.

7) Health and safety assistance.
8) Procedures for serious and imminent danger and for danger areas.
9) Contacts with external services.
10) Information for employees.
11) Co-operation and co-ordination.
12) Persons working in host employers' or self-employed persons' undertakings.
13) Capabilities and training.
14) Employees' duties.
15) Temporary workers.
16) Risk assessment in respect of new or expectant mothers.
17) Certificate from a registered medical practitioner in respect of new or expectant mothers.
18) Notification by new or expectant mothers.
19) Protection of young persons.
20) Exemption certificates.
21) Provisions as to liability.
22) Exclusion of civil liability.
23) Extension outside Great Britain.
24) Amendment of the Health and Safety (First-Aid) Regulations 1981.
25) Amendment of the Offshore Installations and Pipeline Works (First-Aid) Regulations 1989.
26) Amendment of the Mines Miscellaneous Health and Safety Provisions Regulations 1995.
27) Amendment of the Construction (Health, Safety and Welfare) Regulations 1996.
28) Regulations to have effect as health and safety regulations.
29) Revocations and consequential amendments.
30) Transitional provision.
Schedule 1.   General principles of prevention.
Schedule 2.   Consequential amendments.

Outline of main points

Management of Health and Safety at Work Regulations (MHSWR) 1999 set out some broad general duties that apply to almost all kinds of work.   They are aimed mainly at improving health and safety management.   The Regulations work in a similar way to the broad health and safety requirements set out in the Health and Safety at Work Act (HASAWA) 1974, and can be seen as a way of fleshing out what is already in the HASAWA 1974.   The 1999 Regulations replace the Management of Health and Safety at Work Regulations 1992, the Management of Health and Safety at Work (Amendment) Regulations 1994, the Health and Safety (Young Persons) Regulations 1997 and Part III of the Fire Precautions (Workplace) Regulations 1997.   The principal Regulations are discussed below.

RISK ASSESSMENT (REGULATION 3)

The regulations require employers (and the self-employed) to assess the risk to the health and safety of their employees and to anyone else who may be affected by their work activity.   This is necessary to ensure that the preventive and protective steps can be identified to control hazards in the workplace.

Where an employer is employing or about to employ young persons (under 18 years of age) he must carry out a risk assessment which takes particular account of:

■ The inexperience, lack of awareness of risks and immaturity of young persons.
■ The layout of the workplace and workstations.
■ Exposure to physical, biological and chemical agents.
■ Work equipment and the way in which it is handled.
■ The extent of health and safety training to be provided.
■ Risks from agents, processes and work listed in the Annex to Council Directive 94/33/EC on the protection of young people at work.

Where 5 or more employees are employed, the significant findings of risk assessments must be recorded in writing (the same threshold that is used in respect of having a written safety policy).   This record must include details of any employees being identified as being especially at risk.

PRINCIPLES OF PREVENTION TO BE APPLIED (REGULATION 4)

Regulation 4 requires an employer to implement preventive and protective measures on the basis of general principles of prevention specified in Schedule 1 to the Regulations.   These are:

1) Avoiding risks.
2) Evaluating the risks which cannot be avoided.
3) Combating the risks at source.
4) Adapting the work to the individual, especially as regards the design of workplaces, the choice of work equipment and the choice of working and production methods, with a view, in particular, to alleviating monotonous work and work at a predetermined work-rate and to reducing their effect on health.
5) Adapting to technical progress.
6) Replacing the dangerous by the non-dangerous or the less dangerous.
7) Developing a coherent overall prevention policy which covers technology, organisation of work, working conditions, social relationships and the influence of factors relating to the working environment.
8) Giving collective protective measures priority over individual protective measures.
9) Giving appropriate instructions to employees.

HEALTH AND SAFETY ARRANGEMENTS (REGULATION 5)

Appropriate arrangements must be made for the effective planning, organisation, control, monitoring and review of preventative and protective measures (in other words, for the management of health and safety).

Again, employers with five or more employees must have their arrangements in writing.

HEALTH SURVEILLANCE (REGULATION 6)

In addition to the requirements of other specific regulations, consideration must be given to carrying out health surveillance of employees, where there is a disease or adverse health condition identified in risk assessments.

HEALTH AND SAFETY ASSISTANCE (REGULATION 7)

The employer must appoint one or more competent persons to assist him in complying with the legal obligations imposed on the undertaking. The number of persons appointed should reflect the number of employees and the type of hazards in the workplace.

If more than one competent person is appointed, then arrangements must be made for ensuring adequate co-operation between them. The competent person(s) must be given the necessary time and resources to fulfil their functions. This will depend on the size the undertaking, the risks to which employees are exposed and the distribution of those risks throughout the undertaking.

The employer must ensure that competent person(s) who are not employees are informed of the factors known (or suspected) to affect the health and safety of anyone affected by business activities.

Competent people are defined as those who have sufficient training and experience or knowledge and other qualities to enable them to perform their functions.

Persons may be selected from among existing employees or from outside. Where there is a suitable person in the employer's employment, that person shall be appointed as the 'competent person' in preference to a non-employee.

PROCEDURES FOR SERIOUS AND IMMINENT DANGER AND FOR DANGER AREAS (REGULATION 8)

Employers are required to set up emergency procedures and appoint **competent persons** to ensure compliance with identified arrangements, to devise control strategies as appropriate and to limit access to areas of risk to ensure that only those persons with adequate health and safety knowledge and instruction are admitted.

The factors to be considered when preparing a procedure to deal with workplace emergencies such as fire, explosion, bomb scare, chemical leakage or other dangerous occurrence should include:

- The identification and training requirements of persons with specific responsibilities.
- The layout of the premises in relation to escape routes etc.
- The number of persons affected.
- Assessment of special needs (disabled persons, children etc.).
- Warning systems.
- Emergency lighting.
- Location of shut-off valves, isolation switches, hydrants etc.
- Equipment required to deal with the emergency.
- Location of assembly points.
- Communication with emergency services.
- Training and/or information to be given to employees, visitors, local residents and anyone else who might be affected.

CONTACTS WITH EXTERNAL SERVICES (REGULATION 9)

Employers must ensure that, where necessary, contacts are made with external services. This particularly applies with regard to first-aid, emergency medical care and rescue work.

INFORMATION FOR EMPLOYEES (REGULATION 10)

Employees must be provided with relevant information about hazards to their health and safety arising from risks identified by the assessments. Clear instruction must be provided concerning any preventative or protective control measures including those relating to serious and imminent danger and fire assessments. Details of any competent persons nominated to discharge specific duties in accordance with the regulations must also be communicated as should risks arising from contact with other employer's activities (see Regulation 11).

Before employing a child (a person who is not over compulsory school age) the employer must provide those with parental responsibility for the child with information on the risks that have been identified and preventative and protective measures to be taken.

CO-OPERATION AND CO-ORDINATION (REGULATION 11)

Employers who work together in a common workplace have a duty to co-operate to discharge their duties under relevant statutory provisions. They must also take all reasonable steps to inform their respective employees of risks to their health or safety which may arise out of their work. Specific arrangements must be made to ensure compliance with fire legislation.

PERSONS WORKING IN HOST EMPLOYERS' OR SELF EMPLOYED PERSONS' UNDERTAKINGS (REGULATION 12)

This regulation extends the requirements of regulation 11 to include employees working as sole occupiers of a workplace under the control of another employer. Such employees would include those working under a service of contract and employees in temporary employment businesses under the control of the first employer.

CAPABILITIES AND TRAINING (REGULATION 13)

Employers need to take into account the capabilities of their employees before entrusting tasks. This is necessary to ensure that they have adequate health and safety training and are capable enough at their jobs to avoid risk. To this end, consideration must be given to recruitment including job orientation when transferring between jobs and work departments. Training must also be provided when other factors such as the introduction of new technology and new systems of work or work equipment arise.

Training must:

- Be repeated periodically where appropriate.
- Be adapted to take account of any new or changed risks to the health and safety of the employees concerned.
- Take place during working hours.

EMPLOYEES' DUTIES (REGULATION 14)

Employees are required to follow health and safety instructions by using machinery, substances, transport etc. in accordance with the instructions and training that they have received.

They must also inform their employer (and other employers) of any dangers or shortcoming in the health and safety arrangements, even if there is no risk of imminent danger.

TEMPORARY WORKERS (REGULATION 15)

Consideration is given to the special needs of temporary workers. In particular to the provision of particular health and safety information such as qualifications required to perform the task safely or any special arrangements such as the need to provide health screening.

RISKS ASSESSMENT IN RESPECT OF NEW OR EXPECTANT MOTHERS (REGULATION 16)

Where the work is of a kind which would involve risk to a new or expectant mother or her baby, then the assessment required by regulation 3 should take this into account.

If the risk cannot be avoided, then the employer should take reasonable steps to:

- Adjust the hours worked.
- Offer alternative work.
- Give paid leave for as long as is necessary.

CERTIFICATE FROM A REGISTERED MEDICAL PRACTITIONER IN RESPECT OF NEW OR EXPECTANT MOTHERS (REGULATION 17)

Where the woman is a night shift worker and has a medical certificate identifying night shift work as a risk then the employer must put her on day shift or give paid leave for as long as is necessary.

NOTIFICATION BY NEW OR EXPECTANT MOTHERS (REGULATION 18)

The employer need take no action until he is notified in writing by the woman that she is pregnant, has given birth in the last six months, or is breastfeeding.

PROTECTION OF YOUNG PERSONS (REGULATION 19)

Employers of young persons shall ensure that they are not exposed to risk as a consequence of their lack of experience, lack of awareness or lack of maturity.

No employer shall employ young people for work which:

- Is beyond his physical or psychological capacity.
- Involves exposure to agents which chronically affect human health.
- Involves harmful exposure to radiation.
- Involves a risk to health from extremes of temperature, noise or vibration.
- Involves risks which could not be reasonably foreseen by young persons.

This regulation does not prevent the employment of a young person who is no longer a child for work:

- Where it is necessary for his training.
- Where the young person will be supervised by a competent person.
- Where any risk will be reduced to the lowest level that is reasonably practicable.

(Note: Two HSE publications give guidance on these topics. HSG122 - New and expectant mothers at work: a guide for employers and HSG165 - Young people at work: a guide for employers).

EXEMPTION CERTIFICATES (REGULATION 20)

The Secretary of State for Defence may, in the interests of national security, by a certificate in writing exempt the armed forces, any visiting force or any headquarters from certain obligations imposed by the Regulations.

PROVISIONS AS TO LIABILITY (REGULATION 21)

Employers cannot submit a defence in criminal proceedings that contravention was caused by the act or default either of an employee or the competent person appointed under Regulation 7.

EXCLUSION OF CIVIL LIABILITY (REGULATION 22)

Breach of a duty imposed by these Regulations shall not confer a right of action in any civil proceedings for those other than employees.

REVOCATIONS AND AMENDMENTS (REGULATIONS 24-29)

The Regulations:

- Revoke regulation 6 of the Health and Safety (First-Aid) Regulations (FAR) 1981 which confers power on the Health and Safety Executive to grant exemptions from those Regulations.
- Amend the Offshore Installations and Pipeline Works (First-Aid) Regulations 1989.
- Amend the Mines Miscellaneous Health and Safety Provisions Regulations 1995.

The Regulations also make amendments to the statutory instruments as specified in Schedule 2.

Manual Handling Operations Regulations (MHOR) 1992

Considered in context in NGC2, Element 3.

Arrangement of Regulations

1)	Citation and commencement.
2)	Interpretation.
3)	Disapplication of Regulations.
4)	Duties of employers.

5) Duty of employees.
6) Exemption certificates.
7) Extension outside Great Britain.
8) Repeals and revocations.

Outline of main points

CITATION AND COMMENCEMENT (1)

INTERPRETATION (2)

"Injury" does not include injury caused by toxic or corrosive substances which:
- Have leaked/spilled from load.
- Are present on the surface but not leaked/spilled from it.
- Are a constituent part of the load.

"Load" includes any person or animal.

"Manual Handling Operations" means transporting or supporting a load including:
- Lifting and putting down.
- Pushing, pulling or moving by hand or bodily force.
- Shall as far as is reasonably practicable.

DISAPPLICATION OF REGULATIONS (3)

DUTIES OF EMPLOYERS (4)

AVOIDANCE OF MANUAL HANDLING (4) (1)(A)

The employer's duty is to avoid the need for manual handling operations which involve a risk of their employees being injured - as far as is reasonably practicable.

ASSESSMENT OF RISK (4) (1)(B)(I)

Where not reasonably practicable make a suitable and sufficient assessment of all such manual handling operations.

REDUCING THE RISK OF INJURY (4) (1)(B)(II)

Take appropriate steps to reduce the risk of injury to the lowest level reasonably practicable.

THE LOAD - ADDITIONAL INFORMATION (4) (1)(B)(III)

Employers shall provide information on general indications or where reasonably practicable precise information on:
- The weight of each load.
- The heaviest side of any load whose centre of gravity is not central.

REVIEWING THE ASSESSMENT (4) (2)

Assessment review:
- Where there is reason to believe the assessment is no longer valid.
- There is sufficient change in manual handling operations.

DUTY OF EMPLOYEES (5)

Employees shall make full and proper use of any system of work provided for his use by his employer.

EXEMPTION CERTIFICATES (6)

EXTENSION OUTSIDE GREAT BRITAIN (7)

REPEALS AND REVOCATIONS (8)

SCHEDULES

Schedule 1 - Factors to which the employer must have regard and questions he must consider when making an assessment of manual handling operations.

Schedule 2 - Repeals and revocations.

Appendix 1 - Numerical guidelines for assessment.

Appendix 2 - Example of an assessment checklist.

Thus the Regulations establish a clear hierarchy of measures:

1. Avoid hazardous manual handling operations so far as is reasonably practicable.
2. Make a suitable and sufficient assessment of any hazardous manual handling operations that cannot be avoided.
3. Reduce the risk of injury so far as is reasonably practicable.

Personal Protective Equipment at Work Regulations (PPER) 1992 (as amended)

Considered in context in NGC1, Element 4 and NGC2, Elements 7 and 8.

Arrangement of Regulations

1) Citation and commencement.
2) Interpretation.
3) Disapplication of these Regulations.
4) Provision of personal protective equipment.
5) Compatibility of personal protective equipment.
6) Assessment of personal protective equipment.
7) Maintenance and replacement of personal protective equipment.
8) Accommodation for personal protective equipment.

9)   Information, instruction and training.
10)   Use of personal protective equipment.
11)   Reporting loss or defect.
12)   Exemption certificates.
13)   Extension outside Great Britain.
14)   Modifications, repeal and revocations directive.

Schedule 1   Relevant Community.
Schedule 2   Modifications.
 Part I   Factories Act 1961.
 Part II   The Coal and Other Mines (Fire and Rescue) Order 1956.
 Part III   The Shipbuilding and Ship-Repairing Regulations 1960.
 Part IV   The Coal Mines (Respirable Dust) Regulations 1975.
 Part V   The Control of Lead at Work Regulations 1980.
 Part VI   The Ionising Radiations Regulations 1985.
 Part VII   The Control of Asbestos at Work Regulations 1987.
 Part VIII   The Control of Substances Hazardous to Health Regulations 1988.
 Part IX   The Noise at Work Regulations 1989.
 Part X   The Construction (Head Protection) Regulations 1989.
Schedule 3   Revocations.

Outline of main points

2)   Personal protective equipment (PPE) means all equipment (including clothing provided for protection against adverse weather) which is intended to be worn or held by a person at work and which protects him against risks to his health or safety.

3)   These Regulations do not apply to:
- Ordinary working clothes/uniforms.
- Offensive weapons.
- Portable detectors which signal risk.
- Equipment used whilst playing competitive sports.
- Equipment provided for travelling on a road.

The Regulations do not apply to situations already controlled by other Regulations i.e.
- Control of Lead at Work Regulations 2002.
- Ionising Radiation Regulations 1999.
- Control of Asbestos at Work Regulations 2002.
- CoSHH Regulations 2002 (as amended).
- Noise at Work Regulations 2005.
- Construction (Head Protection) Regulations 1989.

4)   Suitable PPE must be provided when risks cannot be adequately controlled by other means. Reg. 4 requires that PPE will not be suitable unless it:
- Is appropriate for the risk and conditions.
- It takes account of ergonomic requirements.
- It takes account of the state of health of users.
- It takes account of the characteristics of the worker's workstation.
- Is capable of fitting the wearer, if required after adjustment.
- Is effective in controlling risks, without increase in overall risk.
- Complies with EU directives.

Where it is necessary to ensure hygiene or prevention of health risk personal issue will be made.

5)   Equipment must be compatible with any other PPE which has to be worn.

6)   Before issuing PPE, the employer must carry out a risk assessment to ensure that the equipment is suitable.
- Assess risks not avoided by other means.
- Define characteristics of PPE and of the risk of the equipment itself.
- Compare characteristics of PPE to defined requirement.
- Repeat assessment when no longer valid, or significant change has taken place.

7)   PPE must be maintained.
- In an efficient state.
- In efficient working order.
- In good repair.

8)   Accommodation must be provided for equipment when it is not being used.

9)   Information, instruction and training must be given on:
- The risks PPE will eliminate or limit.
- Why the PPE is to be used.
- How the PPE is to be used.
- How to maintain the PPE.

Information and instruction must be comprehensible to the wearer/user and kept available to them.

10)   Employers shall take reasonable steps to ensure PPE is worn.
- Every employee shall use PPE that has been provided.
- Every employee shall take reasonable steps to return PPE to storage.

11)   Employees must report any loss or defect.

The Guidance on the Regulations points out:

"Whatever PPE is chosen, it should be remembered that, although some types of equipment do provide very high levels of protection, none provides 100%".

Provision and Use of Work Equipment Regulations (PUWER) 1998

Considered in context in NGC2, Element 1.

Arrangement of Regulations

PART I - INTRODUCTION
1) Citation and commencement.
2) Interpretation.
3) Application.

PART II - GENERAL
4) Suitability of work equipment.
5) Maintenance.
6) Inspection.
7) Specific risks.
8) Information and instructions.
9) Training.
10) Conformity with Community requirements.
11) Dangerous parts of machinery.
12) Protection against specified hazards.
13) High or very low temperature.
14) Controls for starting or making a significant change in operating conditions.
15) Stop controls.
16) Emergency stop controls.
17) Controls.
18) Control systems.
19) Isolation from sources of energy.
20) Stability.
21) Lighting.
22) Maintenance operations.
23) Markings.
24) Warnings.

PART III - MOBILE WORK EQUIPMENT
25) Employees carried on mobile work equipment.
26) Rolling over of mobile work equipment.
27) Overturning of fork-lift trucks.
28) Self-propelled work equipment.
29) Remote-controlled self-propelled work equipment.
30) Drive shafts.

PART IV - POWER PRESSES
31) Power presses to which Part IV does not apply.
32) Thorough examination of power presses, guards and protection devices.
33) Inspection of guards and protection devices.
34) Reports.
35) Keeping of information.

PART V - MISCELLANEOUS
36) Exemption for the armed forces.
37) Transitional provision.
38) Repeal of enactment.
39) Revocation of instruments.
Schedule 1   Instruments which give effect to Community directives concerning the safety of products.
Schedule 2   Power presses to which regulations 32 to 35 do not apply.
Schedule 3   Information to be contained in a report of a thorough examination of a power press, guard or protection device.
Schedule 4   Revocation of instruments.

Outline of main points

GENERAL REQUIREMENTS

These Regulations impose health and safety requirements with respect to the provision and use of work equipment, which is defined as 'any machinery, appliance, apparatus, tool or installation for use at work (whether exclusively or not)'. These regulations:

- Place general duties on employers.
- Certain persons having control of work equipment, of persons at work who use or supervise or manage its use or of the way it is used, to the extent of their control.
- List minimum requirements for work equipment to deal with selected hazards whatever the industry.
- 'Use' includes any activity involving work equipment and includes starting, stopping, programming, setting, transporting, repairing, modifying, maintaining, servicing and cleaning.

The general duties require the employer to:

- Make sure that equipment is suitable for the use that will be made of it.
- Take into account the working conditions and hazards in the workplace when selecting equipment.
- Ensure equipment is used only for operations for which, and under conditions for which, it is suitable.
- Ensure that equipment is maintained in an efficient state, in efficient working order and in good repair.

- Ensure the inspection of work equipment in specified circumstances by a competent person; keep a record of the result for specified periods; and ensure that evidence of the last inspection accompany work equipment used outside the undertaking.
- Give adequate information, instruction and training.
- Provide equipment that conforms with EU product safety directives.

SPECIFIC REQUIREMENTS COVER

- Guarding of dangerous parts of machinery.
- Protection against specified hazards i.e. articles and substances falling/ejected, rupture/disintegration of work equipment parts, equipment catching fire or overheating, unintended or premature discharge of articles and substances, explosion.
- Work equipment parts and substances at high or very low temperatures.
- Control systems and control devices.
- Isolation of equipment from sources of energy.
- Stability of equipment.
- Lighting.
- Maintenance operations.
- Warnings and markings.

MOBILE WORK EQUIPMENT

Mobile work equipment must have provision as to:

- Its suitability for carrying persons and its safety features.
- Means to minimise the risk to safety from its rolling over.
- Means to reduce the risk to safety from the rolling over of a fork-lift truck.
- The safety of self-propelled work equipment and remote-controlled self propelled work equipment.
- The drive shafts of mobile work equipment.

POWER PRESSES

The Regulations provide for:

- The thorough examination (defined in regulation 2(1)) of power presses and their guards and protection devices (regulation 32).
- Their inspection after setting, re-setting or adjustment of their tools, and every working period (regulation 33).
- The making (regulation 34 and Schedule 3) and keeping (regulation 35) of reports.
- The regulations implement an EU directive aimed at the protection of workers. There are other directives setting out conditions which new equipment (especially machinery) will have to satisfy before it can be sold in EU member states.

Regulatory Reform (Fire Safety) Order (RRFSO) 2005

Considered in context in NGC2, Element 6.

INTRODUCTION

The amount of legislation covering the risk of fire has grown considerably over time. The situation was identified as unwieldy, many different regulations existed, often with conflicting definitions and requirements. In order to simply this and remove confusion the Regulatory Reform (Fire Safety) Order 2005 was introduced.

There were 4 principal pieces of legislation that covered fire safety in the workplace that have been affected by the RRFSO:

- Fire Precautions Act (FPA).
- Fire Precautions (Workplace) Regulations (FPWR).
- Management of Health and Safety at Work Regulations (MHSWR).
- Dangerous Substances & Explosive Atmosphere Regulations (DSEAR).

FIRE PRECAUTIONS ACT

This legislation is has been repealed by the RRFSO 2005.

FIRE PRECAUTIONS WORKPLACE REGULATIONS

These regulations outlined the fire safety measures that need to be achieved via the risk assessment of fire and management of fire safety within a workplace. These regulations have been repealed by the implementation of the RRFSO, however their content has been incorporated within the RRFSO 2005.

MANAGEMENT OF HEALTH AND SAFETY AT WORK REGULATIONS

It is this regulation that makes the legal requirement for risk assessments. In addition, it made various requirements for the management of fire safety within workplaces, which have now been revoked. This regulation will continue as a stand alone health and safety regulation as the relevant fire aspects of this regulation have been incorporated within the RRFSO 2005.

DANGEROUS SUBSTANCES & EXPLOSIVE ATMOSPHERE REGULATIONS

This regulation outlines the safety and control measures that need to be taken if dangerous or flammable/explosive substances are present. This regulation will continue as a stand alone health and safety regulation. Again the relevant fire aspects of this regulation have been incorporated within the RRFSO 2005.

REGULATORY REFORM (FIRE SAFETY) ORDER 2005

This is a new, all encompassing, fire safety order, which came into force in England and Wales on 01 October 2006. As shown above it has aspects of other legislation within it and has been compiled in such a way as to present a cohesive structure for fire safety legislation.

The order is split into 5 parts, each part is then subdivided into the individual points, or articles as they are called in the order:

- Part 1   General.
- Part 2   Fire Safety Duties.
- Part 3   Enforcement.
- Part 4   Offences and appeals.
- Part 5   Miscellaneous.

Outline of main points

PART 1 - GENERAL

This part covers various issues such as the interpretation of terminology used, definition of responsible person, definition of general fire precautions, duties under the order, and its application.

PART 2 - FIRE SAFETY DUTIES

This part imposes a duty on the responsible person to carry out a fire risk assessment to identify what the necessary general fire precautions should be. It also outlines the principles of prevention that should be applied and the necessary arrangements for the management of fire safety.

The following areas are also covered:

- Fire-fighting and fire detection.
- Emergency routes and exits.
- Procedures for serious and imminent danger and for danger areas.
- Additional emergency measures re dangerous substances.
- Maintenance.
- Safety assistance.
- Provision of information to employees, employers and self employed.
- Capabilities and training.
- Co-operation and co-ordination.
- General duties of employees.

PART 3 - ENFORCEMENT

This part details who the enforcing authority is, (which in the main is the Fire Authority), and it states they must enforce the order. It also details the powers of inspectors. It also details the different types of enforcement that can be taken:

- Alterations notice.
- Enforcement notice.
- Prohibition notice.

PART 4 - OFFENCES AND APPEALS

This part details the 13 offences that may occur and the subsequent punishments and appeals procedure. It also explains that the legal onus for proving that an offence was not committed is on the accused. A new disputes procedure is also outlined within this part.

PART 5 - MISCELLANEOUS

Various matters are covered within this part, the principal points being:

- 'Fire-fighters switches' for luminous tube signs etc.
- Maintenance of measures provided for the protection of fire-fighters.
- Civil liability.
- Duty to consult employees.
- Special provisions for licensed premises.
- Application to crown premises.

There is then a schedule that covers the risk assessment process.

Reporting of Injuries, Diseases and Dangerous Occurrences Regulations (RIDDOR) 1995

Considered in context in NGC1, Element 5.

Arrangement of Regulations

1) Citation and commencement.
2) Interpretation.
3) Notification and reporting of injuries and dangerous occurrences.
4) Reporting of the death of an employee.
5) Reporting of cases of disease.
6) Reporting of gas incidents.
7) Records.
8) Additional provisions relating to mines and quarries.
9) Additional provisions relating to offshore workplaces.
10) Restrictions on the application of regulations 3, 4 and 5.
11) Defence in proceedings for an offence contravening these Regulations.
12) Extension outside Great Britain.
13) Certificates of exemption.
14) Repeal and amendment of provisions in the Regulation of Railways Act 1871, the Railway Employment (Prevention of Accidents) Act 1900 and the Transport and Works Act 1992.
15) Revocations, amendments and savings.

Schedule 1   Major Injuries.
Schedule 2   Dangerous Occurrences.
Schedule 3   Reportable Diseases.
Schedule 4   Records.
Schedule 5   Additional provisions relating to mines and quarries.
Schedule 6   Additional provisions relating to offshore workplaces.
Schedule 7   Enactments or instruments requiring the notification of events which are not required to be notified or reported under these Regulations.
Schedule 8   Revocations and amendments.

Outline of main points

The Reporting of Injuries, Diseases and Dangerous Occurrences Regulations (RIDDOR) 1995 cover the requirement to report certain categories of injury and disease sustained at work, along with specified dangerous occurrences and gas incidents, to the relevant enforcing authority. These reports are used to compile statistics to show trends and to highlight problem areas in particular industries or companies.

REPORTING

1) When a person *dies or suffers any serious condition* specified in Schedule 1 *(Reporting of Injuries)* and Schedule 2 *(Reporting of Dangerous Occurrences)* a responsible person is to notify by the quickest possible means (usually by telephone) the enforcing authorities and must send them a written report within 10 days (F2508).

2) In cases of diseases which are linked to work activities listed in Schedule 3 *(Reporting of Diseases)* a responsible person is required to notify by the quickest possible means (usually by telephone) the enforcing authorities and must send them a written report forthwith (F2508A).

3) If personal injury results in *more than 3 days incapacity* from work off from normal duties, but does not fall in the category of "major", the written report alone is required. The day of the accident is not counted.

4) The enforcing authority is either the Health and Safety Executive or the Local Authority. The approved form for reporting is F2508 for injuries and dangerous occurrences and F2508A for diseases.

"Accident" includes:

- An act of non-consensual physical violence done to a person at work.
- An act of suicide which occurs on or in the course of the operation of a relevant transport system.

ROAD TRAFFIC ACCIDENTS

Road traffic accidents only have to be reported if:

- Death or injury results from exposure to a substance being conveyed by a vehicle.
- Death or injury results from the activities of another person engaged in the loading or unloading of an article or substance.
- Death or injury results from the activities of another person involving work on or alongside a road.
- Death or injury results from an accident involving a train.

NON EMPLOYEE

The responsible person must not only report non-employee deaths, but also cases that involve major injury or hospitalisation.

RECORDING

In the case of an accident at work, the following details must be recorded:

- Date.
- Name.
- Nature of injury.
- Brief description of the event.

- Time.
- Occupation.
- Place of accident.

Copies of F2508, or suitable alternative records, must be kept for at least 3 years. This may be held electronically provided it is printable.

DEFENCES

A person must prove that he was not aware of the event and that he had taken all reasonable steps to have such events brought to his notice.

Typical examples of major injuries, diseases and dangerous occurrences

MAJOR INJURIES (RIDDOR - SCHEDULE 1)

The list of major injuries includes:

- Any fracture, other than the finger or thumbs or toes.
- Any amputation.
- Dislocation of the shoulder, hip, knee or spine.
- Permanent or temporary loss of sight.
- Chemical, hot metal or penetrating eye injury.
- Electrical shock, electrical burn leading to unconsciousness or resuscitation or admittance to hospital for more than 24 hours.
- Loss of consciousness caused by asphyxia or exposure to a harmful substance or biological agent.
- Acute illness or loss of consciousness requiring medical attention due to any entry of substance by inhalation, ingestion or through the skin.
- Acute illness where there is a reason to believe that this resulted from exposure to a biological agent or its toxins or infected material.
- Any other injury leading to hypothermia, heat-induced illness or unconsciousness requiring resuscitation, hospitalisation greater than 24 hours.

DISEASES (RIDDOR - SCHEDULE 3)

Conditions due to physical agents and the physical demands of work

- Inflammation, ulceration or malignant disease of the skin due to ionising radiation.
- Decompression illness.
- Subcutaneous cellulitis of the hand (beat hand).
- Carpal tunnel syndrome.
- Hand-arm vibration syndrome.

Infections due to biological agents

- Anthrax.
- Hepatitis.
- Legionellosis.
- Leptospirosis.
- Tetanus.

Conditions due to chemicals and other substances

- Arsenic poisoning.
- Ethylene Oxide poisoning.
- Cancer of a bronchus or lung.
- Folliculitis.
- Acne.
- Pneumoconiosis.
- Asbestosis.
- Occupational dermatitis.

DANGEROUS OCCURRENCES (RIDDOR - SCHEDULE 2)

Dangerous occurrences are events that have the potential to cause death or serious injury and so must be reported whether anyone is injured or not. Examples of dangerous occurrences that must be reported are:

- The failure of any load bearing part of any lift, hoist, crane or derrick etc.
- The failure of any pressurised closed vessel.
- The failure of any freight container in any of its load bearing parts.
- Any unintentional incident in which plant or equipment either comes into contact with an uninsulated overhead electric line causes an electrical discharge from such an electric line by coming into close proximity to it.
- Electrical short circuit or overload attended by fire or explosion which results in the stoppage of the plant involved for more than 24 hours.

Note: This information is a brief summary only. For full details consult HSE document L73 A Guide to RIDDOR 95.

Road Traffic Act (RTA)1991

Considered in context in NGC2, Element 2.

Arrangement of main part of Act

PART 1 - GENERAL

DRIVING OFFENCES

1. Offences of dangerous driving.
2. Careless, and inconsiderate, driving.

DRINK AND DRUGS

3. Causing death by careless driving when under influence of drink or drugs.
4. Driving under influence of drink or drugs.

MOTORING EVENTS

5. Disapplication of sections 1 to 3 of the Road Traffic Act 1988 for authorised motoring events.

DANGER TO ROAD-USERS

6. Causing danger to road-users.

CYCLING

7. Cycling offences.

CONSTRUCTION AND USE

8. Construction and use of vehicles.
9. Vehicle examiners.
10. Testing vehicles on roads.
11. Inspection of vehicles.
12. Power to prohibit driving of unfit vehicles.
13. Power to prohibit driving of overloaded vehicles.
14. Unfit and overloaded vehicles: offences.
15. Removal of prohibitions.
16. Supply of unroadworthy vehicles etc.

LICENSING OF DRIVERS

17. Requirement of licence.
18. Physical fitness.
19. Effects of disqualification.

INSURANCE

20. Exception from requirement of third-party insurance.

INFORMATION

21. Information as to identity of driver etc.

TRIAL

22. Amendment of Schedule 1 to the Road Traffic Offenders Act 1988.
23. Speeding offences etc: admissibility of certain evidence.

PENALTIES

MISCELLANEOUS

Outline of main points

SECTION 2 - CARELESS, AND INCONSIDERATE, DRIVING

"If a person drives a vehicle on a road or other public place without due care and attention, or without reasonable consideration for other persons using the road or place, he is guilty of an offence".

SECTION 3 - DRINK AND DRUGS

Causing death by careless driving when under influence of drink or drugs - if a person causes the death of another person by driving a vehicle on a road or other public place without due care and attention, or without reasonable consideration for other persons using the road or place, and

- At the time of driving is unfit to drive through drink or drugs, or
- Has consumed so much alcohol that the proportion of it in his breath, blood or urine at that time exceeds the prescribed limit, or
- Is within 18 hours after that time, required to provide a specimen in pursuance of section 7 of this Act, but without reasonable excuse fails to provide it, he is guilty of an offence.

For the purposes of this section a person shall be taken to be unfit to drive at any time when his ability to drive properly is impaired.

SECTION 6 - DANGER TO ROAD-USERS

Causing danger to road-users - a person is guilty of an offence if he intentionally and without lawful authority or reasonable cause.

- Causes anything to be on or over a road, or
- Interferes with a motor vehicle, trailer or cycle, or
- Interferes (directly or indirectly) with traffic equipment, in such circumstances that it would be obvious to a reasonable person that to do so would be dangerous.

SECTION 8 - CONSTRUCTION AND USE OF VEHICLES

A person is guilty of an offence if he uses, or causes or permits another to use, a motor vehicle or trailer on a road when:

- The condition of the motor vehicle or trailer, or
- Its accessories or equipment, or
- The purpose for which it is used, or
- The number of passengers carried by it, or the manner in which they are carried, or
- The weight, position or distribution of its load, or the manner in which it is secured

…..is such that the use of the motor vehicle or trailer involves a danger of injury to any person.

Breach of requirement as to weight (goods and passenger vehicles) - a person who:

- Contravenes or fails to comply with a construction and use requirement as to any description of weight applicable to
- A goods vehicle, or
- A motor vehicle or trailer adapted to carry more than eight passengers, or
- Uses on a road a vehicle which does not comply with such a requirement, or causes or permits a vehicle to be so used, is guilty of an offence.

SECTION 21 - INFORMATION AS TO THE DRIVER ETC

Where the driver of a vehicle is alleged to be guilty of an offence to which this section applies:

- The person keeping the vehicle shall give such information as to the identity of the driver as he may be required to give by or on behalf of a chief officer of police, and
- Any other person shall if required as stated above give any information which it is in his power to give and may lead to identification of the driver.

Safety Representatives and Safety Committees Regulations (SRSC) 1977

Considered in context in NGC1, Element 3.

Arrangement of Regulations

1) Citation and commencement.
2) Interpretation.
3) Appointment of safety representatives.
4) Functions of safety representatives.
5) Inspections of the workplace.
6) Inspections following notifiable accidents, occurrences and diseases.
7) Inspections of documents and provision of information.
8) Cases where safety representatives need not be employees.
9) Safety committees.
10) Power of Health and Safety Commission to grant exemption.
11) Provision as to industrial tribunals.

Outline of main points

The Safety Representatives and Safety Committees Regulations (SRSC) 1977 are concerned with the appointment by recognised trade unions of safety representatives, the functions of the representatives and the establishment of safety committees.

Representatives are appointed when a recognised trade union notifies the employer in writing. Representatives must have been employed throughout the preceding 2 years or, where this is not reasonably practicable, have had at least 2 years' experience in similar employment. Similarly, employees cease to be representatives when:

- The employer has been notified in writing by the trade union.
- The representative ceases to be employed.
- The representative resigns.

FUNCTIONS OF TRADE UNION - APPOINTED SAFETY REPRESENTATIVES

The SRSC 1977 grant safety representatives certain functions as outlined below.

Functions are activities that safety representatives are permitted to carry out by legislation, but do not have a 'duty' to perform and therefore are treated as advisory actions. As a consequence the representatives cannot be held accountable for failing to carry out these activities or for the standard of the advice given, when performing their functions. They are, however, still employees and have the same consequent duties as any other employee (for example their duties under HASAWA Ss 7 and 8). Their functions as safety representatives are:

a) To take all reasonably practical steps to keep themselves informed of:
- The legal requirements relating to the health and safety of persons at work, particularly the group or groups of persons they directly represent.
- The particular hazards of the workplace and the measures deemed necessary to eliminate or minimise the risk deriving from these hazards and the health and safety policy of their employer and the organisation and arrangements for fulfilling that policy.
b) To encourage co-operation between their employer and his employees in promoting and developing essential measures to ensure the health and safety of employees, and in checking the effectiveness of these measures.
c) To carry out investigations into:
- Hazards and dangerous occurrences (incl. accidents) at the workplace.
- Complaints, by any employee he represents, relating to that employee's health, safety or welfare.
d) To carry out inspections of the workplace.
e) To bring to the employer's notice, normally in writing, any unsafe or unhealthy conditions, or unsafe working practices, or unsatisfactory arrangements for welfare at work, which comes to their attention whether during an inspection/investigation or day to day observation.

The report does not imply, that all other conditions and working practices are safe and healthy or that the welfare arrangements are satisfactory in all other respects. Making a written report does not preclude the bringing of such matters to the attention of the employer or his representative by a direct oral approach in the first instance, particularly in situations where speedy remedial action is necessary. It will also be appropriate for minor matters to be the subject of direct discussion, without the need for a formal written approach.

f) To represent the employees they were appointed to represent in consultation at the workplace with inspectors of the Health and Safety Executive and of any other enforcing authority within the Act.
g) To receive information from inspectors in accordance with section 28(8) of the HASAWA.
h) To attend meetings of safety committees during which he/she attends in his capacity as a safety representative in connection with any of the above conditions.

EMPLOYERS' DUTIES

The Regulations require employers to make any known information available to safety representatives which is necessary to enable them to fulfil their functions. This should include:

a) Information about the plans and performances of the undertaking and any changes proposed, in so far as they affect the health and safety at work of their employees.
b) Information of a technical nature about hazards to health and safety and precautions deemed necessary to eliminate or minimise them, in respect of machinery, plant, equipment, processes, systems of work and substances in use at work. This should include any relevant information provided by consultants or designers or by the manufacturer, importer or supplier of any article or substance used, or proposed to be used, at work by their employees.
c) Information which the employer keeps relating to the occurrence of any accidents, dangerous occurrences or notifiable industrial disease and any statistical records relating to such accidents, dangerous occurrences or cases of notifiable industrial disease.

d) Any other information specifically related to matters affecting the Health and Safety at work of his employees, including the result of any measurements taken by persons acting on his behalf in the course of checking the effectiveness of his health and safety arrangements.

e) Information on articles or substances which an employer issues to homeworkers.

f) Any other suitable and relevant reasonable facility to enable the representatives to carry out their functions.

TRAINING

The basis of Trades Union Congress (TUC) policy is that the union appointed safety representative will be trained on TUC approved courses. However, there is much to be gained by the employer approaching the trades unions active in his workplace with the objective of holding joint company/industry based courses. In any event it is prudent for the employer to carry out company/industry orientated training to supplement the wide industry based TUC course. The functions and training of the safety representatives should be carried out during normal working hours. The representative must receive normal earnings, this taking into consideration any bonuses which would have been earned if carrying out their normal work activities.

HEALTH AND SAFETY COMMITTEES

If two or more appointed safety representatives request in writing the formation of a health and safety committee, the employer must implement this request within three months. Consultation must take place with the representatives making the request and the appointing trade union. A basic requirement for a successful health and safety committee is the desire of both employee and management to show honest commitment and a positive approach to a programme of accident prevention and the establishment of a safe and healthy environment and systems of work.

The membership and structure of the health and safety committee should be settled in consultation between management and the trade union representatives concerned. This should be aimed at keeping the total size as compact as possible, compatible with the adequate representation of the interests of management and employees. Management representatives will naturally be appointed by the management. Employee representatives will either be appointed by a recognised Trade Union (HASAWA 1974 Section 2(4)) or, in a non-union company, elected by their colleagues.

The committee suggested in HASAWA 1974 section 2 (7) would probably be one serving the whole organisation. There is nothing to prevent the formation of local committees, as required, in order to maintain the company safety committee at a reasonable size.

Special Waste Regulations (SWR)1996

Considered in context in NGC2, Element 7.

Arrangement of Regulations

1. Citation, commencement, extent, application and interpretation.
2. Meaning of special waste.
3. Certain radioactive waste to be special waste.
4. Coding of consignments.
5. Consignment notes: standard procedure.
6. Consignment notes: cases in which pre-notification is not required.
7. Consignment notes: procedure where pre-notification is not required.
8. Consignment notes: carrier's rounds.
9. Consignment notes: removal of ships' waste to reception facilities.
10. Consignment notes etc.: duty of consignee not accepting delivery of a consignment.
11. Consignment notes: duties of the Agencies.
12. Consignment notes: provisions as to furnishing.
13. Consignment notes: importers and exporters.
14. Fees.
15. Registers.
16. Site records.
17. Restrictions on mixing special waste.
18. Offences.
19. Responsibilities of the Agencies.
20. Transitional provisions for certificates of technical competence.
21. Amendment of regulations relating to the assessment of environmental effects.
22. Amendment of the Controlled Waste (Registration of Carriers and Seizure of Vehicles) Regulations 1991.
23. Amendment of the Environmental Protection (Duty of Care) Regulations 1991.
24. Amendment of the Controlled Waste Regulations 1992.
25. Amendment of the Waste Management Licensing Regulations 1994.
26. Revocations and savings.

SCHEDULES

1 - Forms of consignment note and schedule.
2 - Special waste.
3 - Amendments to the Waste Management Licensing Regulations 1994.

Outline of main points

The Special Waste Regulations 1996 were used to implement the European Hazardous Waste Directive 91/689/EEC. They provide an effective system of control for wastes that are dangerous and have special requirements placed on their handling. The Regulations ensure sound management of waste from production to final disposal or recovery.

Special Waste Amendment (Scotland) Regulations (SWASR) 2004

Considered in context in NGC2, Element 7.

The Special Waste Amendment (Scotland) Regulations amend the Special Waste Regulations 1996 SI 972 as it relates to storing and disposing of 'special waste' in Scotland.

Special waste is hazardous waste which may be harmful to human health or the environment. Examples include asbestos, lead acid batteries, electrical equipment containing hazardous components such as cathode ray tubes, oily sludge, solvents, fluorescent light tubes, chemical wastes and pesticides. The regulations apply in Scotland only.

Arrangement of Regulations

Citation and commencement

1) These Regulations may be cited as the Special Waste Amendment (Scotland) Amendment Regulations 2004 and shall come into force on 21st May 2004.

Amendment of the Special Waste Amendment (Scotland) Regulations 2004

2) In regulation 2(10) of the Special Waste Amendment (Scotland) Regulations 2004(2), in regulation 15A(5) (Registers: special waste producers) as inserted into the Special Waste Regulations 1996(3), omit, "together with the producer return detailing that consignment".

Outline of main points

These Regulations amend the Special Waste (Scotland) Regulations 1996 (S.I. 1996/972) ("the principal Regulations"), which make provision for handling special waste and for implementing Council Directive 91/689/EEC on hazardous waste (O.J. No. L 377, 31.12.1991, p.20) ("the Hazardous Waste Directive").

Supply of Machinery (Safety) Regulations (SMSR) 1992
Considered in context in NGC2, Element 4.

Outline of main points

GENERAL ADVICE

The Supply of Machinery (Safety) Regulations (SMSR) 1992 came into force on 1st January 1993 and implement the EU Machinery Directive (89/392/EEC) and its first amendment (91/368/EEC). Duties are placed upon those who supply machinery. 'Supply' is given a broad definition and those covered by the Regulations include manufacturers, importers and others in the supply chain. Machinery first supplied after 1st January 1995 must comply with these Regulations. These Regulations are mirrored in other EU countries and also those not in the EU but within the European Economic Area (EEA) (EU and EFTA countries except Switzerland), so that there is uniformity in legislation, and legal barriers to trade within the EEA will be removed. The machinery covered by the regulations is very wide ranging. There are some exclusions, however, such as most manually powered machines, machinery for medical use and most means of transport (see Schedule 5 of the Regulations). Machinery whose risks are mainly electrical are also excluded.

AMENDING REGULATIONS

In 1994 the Supply of Machinery (Safety) Regulations were extended to implement two more European Directives. The principal effect of this has been to apply the above requirements, as from 1st January 1995, to safety components, as defined, and widens the scope to include a greater range of lifting machines (but not classical passenger lifts and other specified exclusions). There was a further two year transitional period from January 1995, during which time compliance with the new requirements was optional, with certain conditions.

MEETING THE REQUIREMENTS

The duty to meet the requirements mainly falls to the 'responsible person' who is defined as the manufacturer or the manufacturer's representative. If the manufacturer is not established in the EEA, the person who first supplies the machinery in the EEA may be the responsible person, which can be a user who manufactures or imports a machine for their own use.

Conformity assessment

The responsible person should ensure that machinery and safety components satisfy the essential health and safety requirements (EHSRs), and that appropriate conformity assessment procedures have been carried out. The EHSRs are laid out in the Directive and repeated in the Regulations (Schedule 3). This can be done either by reference directly to these requirements or to a relevant transposed harmonised standard where one exists. Harmonised standards are currently being prepared by the European Standards Organisations, CEN and CENELEC, before formal adoption by the European Commission. Harmonised standards will be available for a wide range of industrial machinery, including agricultural, textiles, engineering, construction, machinery. In addition, the responsible person must draw up a technical file (see below).

For certain classes of dangerous machine and safety component, a more rigorous procedure is required. Such products are listed in Annex 4 of the Directive and reproduced in Schedule 4 of the Regulations. In additional to the above requirements, the responsible person must arrange for type-examination of these produces by an approved body if there are no harmonised standards formally adopted by the EU for them, or if they are not manufactured to such standards. The Department of Trade and Industry (DTI) has appointed approved bodies in the UK for this purpose.

Declaration procedure

The responsible person must issue one of two forms of declaration.

Declaration of conformity

This declaration should be issued with the finished product so that it is available to the user. It will contain various details such as the manufacturer's address, the machinery type and serial number, and Harmonised European or other Standards used in design.

Declaration of Incorporation

Where machinery is intended for incorporation into other machinery, the responsible person can draw up a declaration of incorporation. This should state that the machinery must not be put into service until the machinery into which it is to be incorporated has been given a Declaration of Conformity. A CE mark is not affixed at this intermediate stage.

Marking

When the first two steps have been satisfactorily completed, the responsible person or the person assembling the final product should affix the CE mark.

ENFORCEMENT

In the UK the Health and Safety Executive is responsible for enforcing these Regulations in relation to machinery and safety components designed for use at work. Trading Standards Officers are responsible for enforcing these Regulations in relation to consumer goods. *After 1st January 1995 it is an offence for the responsible person to supply machinery or safety components which do not comply with these requirements. It is also an offence for any supplier to supply machinery which is not safe (and which was not first supplied before 1st January 1995).*

DETAILED ADVICE FOR THE DESIGNER AND MANUFACTURER.

Technical file contents

The responsible person (defined above) is required to draw up a technical file for all machinery and safety components covered by these Regulations. The file or documents should comprise:

a) An overall drawing of the product together with the drawings of the control circuits.

b) Full detailed drawings, accompanied by any calculation notes, test results etc. required to check the conformity of the product with the essential health and safety requirements.

c) A list of the essential health and safety requirements, transposed harmonised standards, national standards and other technical specifications which were used when the product was designed.

d) A description of methods adopted to eliminate hazards presented by the machinery or safety component.

e) If the responsible person so desires, any technical report or certificate obtained from a component body or laboratory.

f) If the responsible person declares conformity with a transposed harmonised standard, any technical report giving the results of tests.

g) A copy of the instructions for the product.

For series manufacture, the responsible person must also have available documentation on the necessary administrative measures that the manufacturer will take to ensure that the product meets requirements.

Technical file procedure

The technical file document need not be on a permanent file, but it should be possible to assemble and make them available to an enforcement authority. The technical file documents should be retained and kept available for at least ten years following the date of manufacture of the product or of the last unit produced, in the case of a series manufacture. If the technical file documents are drawn up in the United Kingdom, they should be in English unless they are to be submitted to an Approved/Notified Body in another Member State, in which case they should be in a language acceptable to that approved Body. In all cases the instructions for the machinery should be in accordance with the language requirements of the EHSRs.

Work at Height Regulations (WAH) 2005

Considered in context in NGC2, Element 1. See also - PUWER 1998 and WHSWR 1992.

Arrangement of Regulations

1) Citation and commencement.
2) Interpretation.
3) Application.
4) Organisation and planning.
5) Competence.
6) Avoidance of risks from work at height.
7) Selection of work equipment for work at height.
8) Requirements for particular work equipment.
9) Fragile surfaces.
10) Falling objects.
11) Danger areas.
12) Inspection of work equipment.
13) Inspection of places of work at height.
14) Duties of persons at work.
15) Exemption by the Health and Safety Executive.
16) Exemption for the Armed Forces.
17) Amendment to the Provision and Use of Work Equipment Regulations (PUWER) 1998.
18) Repeal of section 24 of the Factories Act 1961.
19) Revocation of instruments.

SCHEDULES

Schedule 1	Requirements for existing places of work and means of access or egress at height.
Schedule 2	Requirements for guard-rails, toe-boards, barriers and similar collective means of protection.
Schedule 3	Requirements for working platforms.
	Part 1 Requirements for all working platforms.
	Part 2 Additional requirements for scaffolding.
Schedule 4	Requirements for collective safeguards for arresting falls.
Schedule 5	Requirements for personal fall protection systems.
	Part 1 Requirements for all personal fall protection systems.
	Part 2 Additional requirements for work positioning systems.
	Part 3 Additional requirements for rope access and positioning techniques.
	Part 4 Additional requirements for fall arrest systems.
	Part 5 Additional requirements for work restraint systems.
Schedule 6	Requirements for ladders.
Schedule 7	Particulars to be included in a report of inspection.
Schedule 8	Revocation of instruments.

Amendments to other regulations as a result of the Work at Height Regulations 2005

These regulations make an amendment to the Provision and Use of Work Equipment Regulations 1998, and replace certain parts of the Workplace (Health and Safety) Regulations:

Regulation 17 - amendment of the Provision and Use of Work Equipment Regulations (PUWER) 1998. There shall be added to regulation 6(5) of the Provision and Use of Work Equipment Regulations 1998 the following sub-paragraph:

(f)   "Work equipment to which regulation 12 of the Work at Height Regulations 2005 applies".

Schedule 8 - revocation of instruments
Workplace (Health and Safety) Regulations 1992 - extent of revocation: regulation 13(1) to (4).

Outline of main points

Under these Regulations the interpretation of 'work at height' includes any place of work at ground level, above or below ground level that a person could fall a distance liable to cause personal injury and includes places for obtaining access or egress, except by staircase in a permanent workplace.

Regulation 4 states that all work at height must be properly planned, supervised and be carried out so far as is reasonably practicable safe. Planning must include the selection of suitable equipment, take account of emergencies and give consideration to weather conditions impacting on safety.

Regulation 5 states that those engaged in any activity in relation to work at height must be competent; and, if under training, be supervised by a competent person.

Regulation 6 states that work at height must only be carried out when it is not reasonably practicable to carry out the work otherwise. If work at height does take place, suitable and sufficient measures must be taken to prevent a fall of any distance, to minimise the distance and the consequences of any fall liable to cause injury. Employers must also make a risk assessment, as required by regulation 3 of the Management of Health and Safety at Work Regulations.

Regulation 7 states that when selecting equipment for use in work at height the employer shall take account of working conditions and any risk to persons in connection with the place where the equipment is to be used. The selection of work equipment must have regard in particular to the purposes specified in regulation 6.

Regulation 8 sets out requirements for particular equipment to conform to standards expressed in schedules to the regulations. It includes guard-rails, toe-boards, working platforms, nets, airbags, personal fall arrest equipment rope access and ladders.

Regulation 9 states that every employer shall ensure that suitable and sufficient steps are taken to prevent any person at work falling through any fragile surface; and that no work may pass across or near, or work on, from or near, fragile surfaces when it is reasonably practicable to carry out work without doing so. If work has to be from a fragile roof then suitable and sufficient means of support must be provided that can sustain foreseeable loads. No person at work should be allowed to pass or work near a fragile surface unless suitable and sufficient guard rails and other means of fall protection is in place. Signs must be situated at a prominent place at or near to works involving fragile surfaces, or persons are made aware of the fragile roof by other means.

Regulation 10 states that every employer shall take reasonably practicable steps to prevent injury to any person from the fall of any material or object; and where it is not reasonably practicable to do so, to take similar steps to prevent any person being struck by any falling material or object which is liable to cause personal injury. Also, that no material is thrown or tipped from height in circumstances where it is liable to cause injury to any person. Materials and objects must be stored in such a way as to prevent risk to any person arising from the collapse, overturning or unintended movement of the materials or objects.

Regulation 11 states that every employer shall ensure that where an area presents a risk of falling from height or being struck from an item falling at height that the area is equipped with devices preventing unauthorised persons from entering such areas and the area is clearly indicated.

Regulation 12 states that every employer shall ensure that, where the safety of work equipment depends on how it is installed or assembled, it is not used after installation or assembly in any position unless it has been inspected in that position.

Also, that work equipment is inspected at suitable intervals and each time that exceptional circumstances which are liable to jeopardise the safety of the work equipment occur. Specific requirements exist for periodic (every 7 days) inspection of a working platform where someone could fall 2 metres or more.

Regulation 13 states that every employer shall ensure that fall protection measures of every place of work at height are visually inspected before use.

Regulation 14 states the duties of persons at work to report defects and use equipment in accordance with training/instruction.

Workplace (Health, Safety and Welfare) Regulations (WHSWR) 1992

Considered in context in NGC2, Element 1.

Arrangement of Regulations

1)   Citation and commencement.
2)   Interpretation.
3)   Application of these Regulations.
4)   Requirements under these Regulations.
5)   Maintenance of workplace, and of equipment, devices and systems.
6)   Ventilation.
7)   Temperature in indoor workplaces.
8)   Lighting.
9)   Cleanliness and waste materials.
10)   Room dimensions and space.
11)   Workstations and seating.
12)   Condition of floors and traffic routes.

13) Falls or falling objects (*Revoked in part by WAH 2005*).
14) Windows, and transparent or translucent doors, gates and walls.
15) Windows, skylights and ventilators.
16) Ability to clean windows etc. safely.
17) Organisation etc. of traffic routes.
18) Doors and gates.
19) Escalators and moving walkways.
20) Sanitary conveniences.
21) Washing facilities.
22) Drinking water.
23) Accommodation for clothing.
24) Facilities for changing clothing.
25) Facilities for rest and to eat meals.
26) Exemption certificates.
27) Repeals, saving and revocations.
Schedule 1   Provisions applicable to factories which are not new workplaces, extensions or conversions.
Schedule 2   Repeals and revocations.

Outline of main points

SUMMARY

The main requirements of the Workplace (Health, Safety and Welfare) Regulations (WHSWR) 1992 are:

1) *Maintenance* of the workplace and equipment.
2) *Safety* of those carrying out maintenance work and others who might be at risk (e.g. segregation of pedestrians and vehicles, provision of handrails etc).
3) Provision of *welfare* facilities (e.g. rest rooms, changing rooms etc).
4) Provision of a safe *environment* (e.g. lighting, ventilation etc).

ENVIRONMENT

Reg 1   New workplaces, extensions and modifications must comply now. Older workplaces have until 01 January 1996 to get up to standard.

Reg 4   Requires employers, persons in control of premises and occupiers of factories to comply with the regulations.

Reg 6   Ventilation - enclosed workplaces should be ventilated with a sufficient quantity of fresh or purified air (5 to 8 litres per second per occupant).

Reg 7   Temperature indoors - This needs to be reasonable and the heating device must not cause injurious fumes. Thermometers must be provided. Temperature should be a minimum of 16°C or 13°C if there is physical effort.

Reg 8   Lighting - must be suitable and sufficient. Natural light if possible. Emergency lighting should be provided if danger exists.

Reg 10   Room dimensions and space - every room where persons work shall have sufficient floor area, height and unoccupied space (min 11 cu. m per person).

Reg 11   Workstations and seating have to be suitable for the person and the work being done.

SAFETY

Reg 12   Floors and traffic routes must be of suitable construction. This includes absence of holes, slope, uneven or slippery surface. Drainage where necessary. Handrails and guards to be provided on slopes and staircases.

Reg 13   Tanks and pits containing dangerous substances to be covered or fenced where people could fall into them and traffic routes fenced.

Reg 14   Windows and transparent doors, where necessary for health and safety, must be of safety material and be marked to make it apparent.

Reg 15   Windows, skylights and ventilators must be capable of opening without putting anyone at risk.

Reg 17   Traffic routes for pedestrians and vehicles must be organised in such a way that they can move safely.

Reg 18   Doors and gates must be suitably constructed and fitted with any necessary safety devices.

Reg 19   Escalators and moving walkways shall function safely, be equipped with any necessary safety devices and be fitted with emergency stop.

HOUSEKEEPING

Reg 5   Workplace and equipment, devices and systems must be maintained in efficient working order and good repair.

Reg 9   Cleanliness and waste materials - workplaces must be kept sufficiently clean. Floors, walls and ceilings must be capable of being kept sufficiently clean. Waste materials shall not be allowed to accumulate, except in suitable receptacles.

Reg 16   Windows etc. must be designed so that they can be cleaned safety.

FACILITIES

Reg 20   Sanitary conveniences must be suitable and sufficient and in readily accessible places. They must be adequately ventilated, kept clean and there must be separate provision for men and women.

Reg 21   Washing facilities must be suitable and sufficient. Showers if required (a table gives minimum numbers of toilets and washing facilities).

Reg 22   Drinking water - an adequate supply of wholesome drinking water must be provided.

Reg 23   Accommodation for clothing must be suitable and sufficient.

Reg 24   Facilities for changing clothes must be suitable and sufficient, where a person has to use special clothing for work.

Reg 25   Facilities for rest and eating meals must be suitable and sufficient.

Assessment

Content

Written assessments - Papers NGC1 and NGC2

At every examination a number of candidates - including some good ones - perform less well than they might because of poor examination technique. It is essential that candidates practice answering both essay-type and short answer questions and learn to budget their time according to the number of marks allocated to questions (and parts of questions) as shown on the paper.

Each written paper is 2 hours duration and contains 2 sections:

Section 1 has one question carrying 20 marks requiring quite an 'in-depth' answer. This question should be allocated 30 minutes in total. If time (e.g. 5 minutes) is given to reading, planning and checking, the time available for writing is 25 minutes. Two pages are allowed for this answer; candidates should produce approximately 1½ sides for an average answer.

Section 2 has 10 questions each carrying 8 marks. If time (e.g. 10 minutes) is allowed for reading, planning and checking then there are 8 minutes to answer each question. One page is allowed for each of these answers, candidates should produce approximately ½ a side for an average answer.

A common fault is that candidates may fail to pay attention to the action verb in each question. The most common 'action verbs' used in Certificate examination questions are:

Define   provide a generally recognised or accepted definition

State   a less demanding form of 'define', or where there is no generally recognised definition

Sketch   provide a simple line drawing using labels to call attention to specific features

Explain   give a clear account of, or reasons for

Describe   give a word picture

Outline   give the most important features of (less depth than either 'explain' or 'describe', but more depth than 'list')

List   provide a list without explanation

Give   provide without explanation (used normally with the instruction 'give an example [or examples] of...)

Identify   select and name

NEBOSH questions have progressively changed to reflect practical issues that need to be managed in the workplace. Questions have increasingly reflected more than one element of knowledge, for example "electrical fires" which could require an understanding of Unit NGC2 - Elements 5 and 6 to answer adequately. We have chosen example questions of this type to enable you to better apply your knowledge and approach to meet the future requirements. The need to understand the meaning of the 'action verb' and to read the question carefully is emphasised in the comments below that are taken from some recent examiner's reports:

"... Many answers were too brief to satisfy the requirement for an outline or description. Points made should have been supported by sufficient reasoning to show their relevance to the question".

"Some candidates, even though they identified many of the relevant factors, could not be awarded the full range of marks available because they produced a truncated list that did not properly outline the relationship between each factor and the corresponding risks".

"It was disappointing to note that some candidates again misread the question and provided outlines of the duties of employers rather than employees".

"While answers to this question were generally to a reasonable standard, many were too brief to attract all the marks that were available".

"In answering questions on Paper NGC2, practical issues should be addressed. It is not sufficient in questions such as this merely to refer to generic issues such as risk assessment and safe systems of work without providing further detail of the controls that a risk assessment might show to be necessary or the elements of a safe system of work".

"Weaker answers tended to be those that provided insufficient detail - for example, mention of "PPE" or "edge protection" should have been accompanied by some examples of what might be required and reference to the purpose that they serve".

"Some answers were extremely brief and candidates should remember that one-fifth of the marks for the entire paper are available for answers to this question (question 1). Answers are expected to be proportionate to the marks available".

NEBOSH sample questions

Unit NGC1 - Management of health and safety

ELEMENT 1

1. Replacement or repair of damaged plant and equipment is a cost that an organisation may face following a workplace accident.

   List **EIGHT** possible costs to the organisation following a workplace accident. **(8)**

   Mar 2005 Paper A1 Question 11

2. **Identify** the **TWO** types of enforcement notice that may be served by an inspector, stating the conditions that must be satisfied before **EACH** type of notice is served. **(8)**

   Dec 2001 Paper A2 Question 5

3. **Explain** the meaning, status and roles of:

   (i) Health and safety regulations. **(3)**

   (ii) HSC Approved Codes of Practice. **(3)**

   (iii) HSE guidance. **(2)**

   Dec 2004 Paper A1 Question 4

4. (a) **Give** the meaning of the term 'negligence'. **(2)**

   (b) **Give** an example of a negligent act by an employer. **(2)**

   (c) **Outline** the role of the civil courts with respect to health and safety matters. **(4)**

   Jun 2009 Paper NGC1 Question 10

5. (a) **Draw** a flowchart to show the relationships between the six elements of the health and safety management system model in HSE's "Successful Health and Safety Management' (HSG65). **(4)**

   (b) **Outline** the part that EACH element of the HSG65 model plays within the health and safety management system. **(12)**

   (c) **Outline** the economic benefits that an organisation may obtain by implementing a successful health and safety management system. **(4)**

   Jun 2004 Paper A1 Question 1

ELEMENT 2

1. (a) **Outline** the requirements of section 2(3) of the Health and Safety at Work etc Act 1974 in relation to an employer's duty to prepare a health and safety policy. **(2)**

   (b) **Explain** the purposes of the following sections of a health and safety policy:

   (i) 'Statement of intent'. **(2)**

   (ii) 'Organisation'. **(2)**

   (iii) 'Arrangements'. **(2)**

   Mar 2005 Paper A1 Question 8

2. (a) **Identify** the legal requirements whereby employers must prepare a written statement of their health and safety policy. **(2)**

   (b) **Identify SIX** categories of persons who may be shown in the 'organisation' section of a health and safety policy document **AND state** their likely general or specific health and safety responsibilities. **(6)**

   Jun 2006 Paper A1 Question 9

ELEMENT 3

1. (a) **Outline** the benefits to an organisation of having a health and safety committee. **(4)**

   (b) **Outline** the reasons why a health and safety committee may prove to be ineffective in practice. **(8)**

   (c) **Identify** a range of methods that an employer can use to provide health and safety information directly to individual employees. **(8)**

   Jun 2005 Paper A1 Question 1

2. An organisation occupying an office block is to use a contractor to carry out extensive refurbishment.

   (a) **Outline** checks that the organisation should make when assessing the health and safety competence of the contractor. **(6)**

   (b) **Outline** the duties placed on the contractor's employees by the Health and Safety at Work etc Act 1974. **(4)**

   (c) **Outline** procedural measures that the organisation should take to help reduce the risk to the health and safety of their own employees whilst the contractors are carrying out this work. **(10)**

   Jun 2009 Paper NGC1 Question 1

3. (a) **Identify** the **TWO** means by which employers may provide information to employees in order to comply with the Health and Safety Information for Employees Regulations 1989. **(2)**

   (b) **Outline** the categories of information provided to employees by the means identified in (a). **(6)**

   Jun 2006 Paper A1 Question 7

4. **Identify** the main health and safety issues to be included in an induction training programme for goods delivery drivers using small vehicles, both on and off-site. **(8)**

   Mar 2009 Paper NGC1 Question 4

5. (a) **Identify** the 'five' steps involved in the assessment of risk from workplace activities (as described in HSE's "Five steps to risk assessment" (INDG 163)). **(5)**

   (b) **Explain** the criteria that should be applied to help develop an action plan to prioritise the control of health and safety risks in the workplace. **(3)**

   Sep 2006 Paper A1 Question 10

ELEMENT 4

1. **Identify EIGHT** sources of information that might usefully be consulted when developing a safe system of work. **(8)**

   Jun 2001 Paper A2 Question11

2. (a) **Identify TWO** situations where a permit-to-work system might be considered appropriate. **(2)**

   (b) **Outline** the key elements of a permit-to-work system. **(6)**

   Dec 2000 Paper A2 Question 9

3. **Outline** the precautions to ensure the health and safety of persons engaged in paint-spraying in a motor vehicle repair workshop. **(8)**

   Dec 2002 Paper A2 Question 5

ELEMENT 5

1. **Identify FOUR** active and **FOUR** reactive means by which an organisation can monitor its health and safety performance. **(8)**

   Mar 2006 Paper A1 Question 11

2. **Identify** the advantages **AND** disadvantages of carrying out a health and safety audit of an organisation's activities by:

   (i) An internal auditor. **(4)**

   (ii) An external auditor. **(4)**

   Jun 2006 Paper A1 Question 2

3. (a) An employee has been seriously injured after being struck by a reversing vehicle in a loading bay.

   (i) Give **FOUR** reasons why the accident should be investigated by the person's employer. **(4)**

   (ii) **Outline** the information that should be included in the investigation report. **(8)**

   (b) Outline **FOUR** possible immediate causes and **FOUR** possible underlying (root) causes of the accident. **(8)**

   Dec 2001 Paper A2 Question 1

4. (a) **Identify FOUR** reasons why accidents should be reported and recorded within a workplace. **(4)**

    (b) **Outline** factors that might discourage employees from reporting workplace accidents. **(4)**

Sep 2001 Paper A1 Question 9

5. With reference to the Reporting of Injuries, Diseases and Dangerous Occurrences Regulations 1995:

    (i) **State** the legal requirements for reporting a fatality resulting from an accident at work to an enforcing authority. **(5)**

    (ii) **Outline THREE** further categories of work-related injury (other than fatal injuries) that are reportable. **(3)**

Dec 2002 Paper A1 Question 5

Unit NGC2 - Controlling workplace risks

ELEMENT 1

1. The water main supplying a school is to be repaired. The work will be carried out in a 1.5 metre deep excavation, which will be supported in order to ensure the safety of the employees working in the excavation.

    (i) **Identify** when the **THREE** statutory inspections of the supported excavation must be carried out by the competent person. **(3)**

    (ii) **State** the information that should be recorded in the excavation inspection report. **(5)**

    (iii) Other than the provision of supports for the excavation, **outline** additional precautions to be taken during the repair work in order to reduce the risk of injury to the employees and others who may be affected by the work. **(12)**

Mar 2006 Paper A2 Question 1

2. Excluding welfare facilities, **Identify** issues associated with the workplace that should addressed to ensure that it meets the requirements of the Workplace (Health, Safety and Welfare) Regulations 1992. **(8)**

Dec 2008 Paper MGC2 Question 4

3. **Outline** the measures an employer might consider to minimise the risk of violence against employees. **(8)**

Jun 2009 Paper NGC1 question 8

ELEMENT 2

1. **Outline** measures to be taken to prevent accidents when pedestrians are required to work in vehicle manoeuvring areas. **(8)**

Jun 2001 Paper A1 Question 2

2. **Outline** the means by which the risk of accidents from reversing vehicles within a workplace can be reduced. **(8)**

Dec 2002 Paper A2 Question 2

ELEMENT 3

1. **Identify EIGHT** rules to follow when a fork-lift truck is left unattended during a driver's work break. **(8)**

Jun 2006 Paper A2 Question 11

2. **Outline** the issues to consider when undertaking a manual handling assessment of a task that involves lifting buckets of water out of a sink. **(8)**

Sep 2001 Paper A1 Question 4

3. **Outline** the precautions to be taken when using a mobile elevating work platform (MEWP) to reach a high point such as a streetlight. **(8)**

Dec 2002 Paper A2 Question 8

ELEMENT 4

1. A local authority employee uses a petrol-driven strimmer to maintain roadside grass verges.

    (i) **Describe** the possible hazards faced by the employee in carrying out this task. **(10)**

    (ii) **List FIVE** items of personal protective equipment that should be provided to, and used by, the employee. **(5)**

    (iii) **Outline** measures other than the use of personal protective equipment that might be necessary to ensure the health and safety of the employee. **(5)**

Dec 2000 Paper A1 Question 1

2.   In relation to the ill-health effects from the use of vibrating hand-held tools:

   (a) **Identify** the health effects associated with exposure to vibration. **(4)**

   (b) **Outline** the control measures that may be used to minimise the risk of such effects. **(4)**

Sept 2009 Paper NGC2 Question11

3.   (a)   **Identify:**

   (i)   **TWO** mechanical hazards associated with moving parts of machinery. **(2)**

   (ii)   **TWO** non-mechanical hazards to which a machine operator may be exposed. **(2)**

   (b)   **Outline** a hierarchy of control measures that may be used to reduce the risk of injury from dangerous parts of machinery. **(4)**

Dec 2002 Paper A2 Question 3

ELEMENT 5

1.   With respect to the use of portable electrical appliances in the workplace, **identify EIGHT** examples of faults and bad practices that could contribute to electrical accidents. **(8)**

Sept 2009 Paper NGC2 Question 3

2.   In relation to the use of electrical cables and plugs in the workplace:

   (i)   **Identify FOUR** examples of faults and bad practices that could contribute to electrical accidents. **(4)**

   (ii)   **Outline** the corresponding precautions that should be taken for **EACH** of the examples identified in (i). **(4)**

Mar 2000 Paper A1 Question 10

3.   In relation to electrical safety, **explain** the meaning of the following terms:

   (i)   'Isolation'. **(2)**

   (ii)   'Earthing'. **(2)**

   (iii) 'Reduced low voltage'. **(2)**

   (iv) 'Overcurrent protection'. **(2)**

Dec 2002 Paper A2 Question 4

ELEMENT 6

1.   **List EIGHT** ways of reducing the risk of a fire starting in a workplace. **(8)**

Jun 2001 Paper A1 Question 11

2.   (a)   **Explain**, using a suitable sketch, the significance of the 'fire triangle'. **(4)**

   (b)   **Identify TWO** methods of heat transfer and **explain** how **EACH** method can contribute to the spread of fire in work premises. **(4)**

Dec 2005 Paper A2 Question 3

ELEMENT 7

1.   (a)   **State** the primary effect on the body of the following types of hazardous substance:

   (i)   'Irritant'. **(1)**

   (ii)   'Corrosive'. **(1)**

   (iii) 'Toxic'. **(1)**

   (iv) 'Carcinogenic'. **(1)**

   (b)   **Describe** the differences between acute and chronic health effects. **(4)**

Dec 2002 Paper A2 Question 7

2.   A company produces a range of solid and liquid wastes, both hazardous and non-hazardous. **Outline** the arrangements that should be in place to ensure the safe storage of the wastes prior to their collection and disposal. **(8)**

Dec 2004 Paper A2 Question 4

3. For each of the following agents, **outline** the principal health and safety effects **AND identify** a typical workplace situation in which a person might be exposed:

   (i) Isocyanates. **(2)**

   (ii) Asbestos. **(2)**

   (iii) Leptospira bacteria. **(2)**

   (iv) Lead. **(2)**

   Mar 2005 Paper A2 Question 3

ELEMENT 8

1. In relation to the ill-health effects from the use of vibrating hand-held tools:

   (i) **Identify** the typical symptoms that might be shown by affected individuals. **(4)**

   (ii) **Outline** the control measures that may be used to minimise the risk of such effects. **(4)**

   Mar 2006 Paper A2 Question 5

2. (a) **Identify TWO** types of non-ionising radiation **AND give** an occupational source of **EACH**. **(4)**

   (b) **Outline** the health effects associated with exposure to non-ionising radiation. **(4)**

   Jun 2009 Paper NGC2 Question 7

3. (a) **Explain** the following terms in relation to noise exposure at work:

   (i) 'Noise-induced hearing loss'. **(2)**

   (ii) 'Tinnitus'. **(2)**

   (b) **Identify FOUR** limitations of personal hearing protection as a means of protecting against the effects of noise. **(4)**

   Dec 2002 Paper A2 Question 10

QUESTIONS REQUIRING KNOWLEDGE FROM MORE THAN ONE ELEMENT

1. Due to an increase in knife related accidents amongst hotel kitchen staff that use the sharp tools in the preparation of food for the restaurant, a safe system of work is to be developed to minimise the risk of injury to this group of employees.

   (i) **Identify** the legal requirement under which the employer must provide a safe system of work. **(2)**

   (ii) **Describe** the issues to be addressed when developing the safe system of work for the hotel kitchen staff who use the knives as part of their work. **(10)**

   (iii) **Outline** the ways in which the employer could motivate the hotel kitchen staff to follow the safe system of work. **(8)**

   Sep 2006 Paper A1 Question 1

2. (a) **Give TWO** reasons why visitors to a workplace might be at greater risk of injury than an employee. **(2)**

   (b) **Outline** measures to be taken to ensure the health and safety of visitors to the workplace. **(6)**

   Mar 2007 Paper NGC1 Question 4

PLEASE REFER TO BACK OF THIS SECTION FOR ANSWERS

Health and safety practical application - Unit NGC3

The practical assessment is intended to test candidates' abilities to apply their knowledge of health and safety to a practical situation, to demonstrate their understanding of key issues and to communicate findings in an effective way. The practical assessment require candidates to carry out unaided a safety inspection of a workplace and then prepare a management report. Completion of study for both NGC1 and NGC2 is recommended in order to undertake the practical application unit.

It should be carried out under the control of the accredited centre and be invigilated (supervised) by a safety professional or a senior manager. The assessment must take place within 14 days of (before or after) the date of the written papers (date of the examination). Please make sure you are clear about when you will carry out the assessment and that your assessment invigilator has set the time aside.

Procedure

Copies of the observation sheet should be used during your inspection. There are four columns on the form; observations, priority / risk, timescales; and brief notes on actions. The forms must be completed during the inspection and must be included with your covering management report for marking by the assessor.

The maximum time allocated to the practical assessment is 2 hours. You should spend no more than 45 minutes making an assessment of your workplace, covering as wide a range of hazards as possible. The remaining time should be allocated to writing a report to management in your own handwriting, you should use lined paper to produce a report, consulting your own (and only your own) notes made during the inspection.

The whole assessment must be carried out under as near examination conditions as possible and you must not use anything previously prepared or company check lists, nor any other aids which would give you an advantage over other candidates at other centres. You must sign the declaration form that the submission is your own work, failure to submit this with the submission may result in the practical application being declared as void.

You are expected to recognise physical, health and environmental hazards - good, as well as bad, work practices. While only short notes on each hazard are required, it is important that the assessor is able to subsequently identify the following:

- Where the hazard was located.
- The nature of the hazard.
- In what way, if any, the hazard is being controlled.
- The remedial action, where appropriate.
- Preventative action required.

You should, however, note that the assessment is not intended to be a pure hazard spotting exercise and consideration should be given to other matters such as:

- Availability and standard of washing and toilet facilities.
- Adequacy of heating, lighting and ventilation.
- General condition of floors and gangways.
- Cleanliness of structures.
- If staff are present, are they aware of the actions to take in the event of an emergency?

Sample practical assessment

NEBOSH NATIONAL GENERAL CERTIFICATE
Unit NGC3 – Health and safety practical application

Candidate's observation sheet

Sheet No 1 of 6

Candidates Name: _____ And number: _____ *c*

Place inspected: _____ *Company Offices* _____ Date of Inspection: _____ *Mon 4 Dec xx* _____

No	Observations — List hazards, unsafe practices and good practice	Priority /risk (H,M,L)	Action to be taken (if any) — List any immediate or longer-term action required		Timescale (immediate, 1 week, etc.)
1	Risk of slips and trips due to loose and worn carpets in office generally	M	I	Alert staff to hazards and fix/tape down most hazardous areas	Immediate
			M	Replace carpets (worst should be replaced first)	1 Week
			L	Monitor to ensure no recurrence of problem	Monthly
2	Reduce risk of falls due to incorporation of window cleaners fixings at each window	M	I	No immediate action.	
			M	Ensure window cleaners are using harness and fixings	1 Week
			L	Ensure fixings tested regularly (British Standard required)	3 Monthly
3	Increased risk of fire / smoke speed, due to fire doors being wedged open & propped open with fire extinguishers	M	I	Close fire doors (remove wedges, etc.)	Immediate
			M	Inform / train staff	1 Day
			L	Monitor and remind staff. Consider installing hold open devices linked to fire alarms	6 Months
4	Risk of falls due to possible failure of loose balustrade (at 2 locations on main staircase)	M	I	Inform staff or risk and effect a temporary repair (boarding fixed across balusters or similar)	3 Days
			M	Effect permanent repair (replacement steel balusters fixed to floor etc)	1 Month
			L	Monitor for recurrence	3 Monthly

NEBOSH NATIONAL GENERAL CERTIFICATE
Unit NGC3 – Health and safety practical application

Candidate's observation sheet

Candidates Name: _____ And number: *C*

Place inspected: *Company Offices* Date of Inspection: *Mon 4 Dec xx*

No	Observations List hazards, unsafe practices and good practice	Priority /risk (H,M,L)		Action to be taken (if any) List any immediate or longer-term action required	Timescale (immediate, 1 week, etc.)
5	Risk of electric shock due to broken plastic casing on electric fan in project management office	H	I	Isolate from electricity and remove from service	Immediate
			M	Replace plastic casing	1 Week
			L	Monitor as part of standard procedure	Weekly
6	Reduce risk of injury (cuts, amputation) from guillotine (for paper and card cutting) with fixed guard	M	I	No action required at present	
			M	Maintain on regular basis	1 week
			L	Ensure guard is not removed and inform/train staff	1 month
7	Generally good lighting risk of trips, eye strain, prevented	L	I	Nil	1 week
			M	Maintain luminaries'	3 months
			L	Assess requirements and provide additional lighting if work practices change	annual
8	Risk of trips and slips due to trailing cables in project management and drawing offices	M	I	Fix cover over cables or tape down	Immediate
			M	Re-route cables, re locate desk / drawing boards or provide flexi sockets	1 Month
			L	Review office layouts Train staff in awareness of hazards	3 Monthly

NEBOSH NATIONAL GENERAL CERTIFICATE
Unit NGC3 – Health and safety practical application

Candidate's observation sheet

Candidates Name: _____ And number: *C*

Place inspected: *Company Offices* Date of Inspection: *Mon 4 Dec xx*

No	Observations List hazards, unsafe practices and good practice	Priority /risk (H,M,L)		Action to be taken (if any) List any immediate or longer-term action required	Timescale (immediate, 1 week, etc.)
9	Risk of electric shock due to frayed power cable on draughtsman's hand held erasing machine (in drawing office)	H	I	Isolate electrical supply and remove machine from service	Immediate
			L	Replace damaged cable	1 Week
			M	Monitor equipment on a regular basis and train staff in awareness	Monthly
10	Risk of injury and damage due to collapse of shelving over drawing boards as a result of loose brackets (faulty fixings) (drawing office)	L	I	Remove shelving	Immediate
			L	Refit shelving securely (establishing reason for failure)	1 Week
			M	Monitor for possible recurrence	1 Month
11	Risk of work-related upper limb disorder, back and neck pain, eye strain, fatigue, stress etc, due to poorly laid out work stations with computers, inappropriate chairs, etc (secretarial, computer drafting, etc) Noted generally	M	I	Assess each users workstation	1 Month
			M	Adjust layouts and provide appropriate equipment as necessary	3 Months
			L	Reassess at regular intervals and monitor Display Screen Equipment Regs	Annual
12	Risk of lacerations and / or falls due to low sill to window at top of stair flight on landing,	H	I	Fix temporary protection	1 Week
			M	Fix permanent protection barrier (metal bar or similar) across window and apply safety film to glazing	1 Month
			L	Monitor	3 Monthly

NEBOSH NATIONAL GENERAL CERTIFICATE
Unit NGC3 – Health and safety practical application

Candidate's observation sheet

Sheet No 4 of 6

Candidates Name: _____ And number: _____ C _____

Place inspected: _____ Company Offices _____ Date of Inspection: _____ Mon 4 Dec xx _____

No	Observations List hazards, unsafe practices and good practice	Priority /risk (H,M,L)	Action to be taken (if any) List any immediate or longer-term action required		Timescale (immediate, 1 week, etc.)
13	Risk of confusion etc in the event of fire due to missing fire exit sign at ground floor (people not knowing direction of escape	H	I	Inform staff of escape requirements	1 week
			M	Fix up new fire exit sign as soon as possible	2 Week
			L	Train staff and have fire drills	Monthly
14	Risk of strains / injury due to moving of large boxes of photocopy paper stored on floor near to photocopier	L	I	Inform staff to move small amounts at a time	Immediate
			M	Fix shelves at appropriate height for paper storage.	1 Week
			L	Train staff in manual handling and use of shelves	3 Months
15	Risk of falls and strains due to heavy articles on high shelves, with no adequate means of access (general office)	M	I	Remove articles form high shelves	Immediate
			M	Supply means of access (steps etc) and store small items at high level.	1 Week
			L	Monitor situation and train staff	1 Month
16	Risk of fire and possible reduced means of escape due to papers and files stored under fire escape stair at basement level	H	I	Remove papers, etc	Immediate
			M	Inform / train staff	1 Month
			L	Monitor situation to ensure situation does not recur	On going

NEBOSH NATIONAL GENERAL CERTIFICATE
Unit NGC3 – Health and safety practical application

Candidate's observation sheet

Candidates Name: _____ And number: _____ C_____

Place inspected: _Company Offices_____ Date of Inspection: _Mon 4 Dec xx_____

No	Observations List hazards, unsafe practices and good practice	Priority /risk (H,M,L)	Action to be taken (if any) List any immediate or longer-term action required		Timescale (immediate, 1 week, etc.)
17	Location of first aid box and names and locations of appropriate persons (First Aid) prominently displayed Risk of delay in first aid treatment reduced / controlled	M	I M	No immediate action Ensure all staff kept informed (including changes) and monitor	Monthly
18	Risk of injury due to impact of forward opening door into small utility room (sink and kettle immediately behind door)	L	I M L	Put warning sign on outside of door and inform staff Fit inside panel into door (fire resisting) Monitor	Immediate 1 Week 1 Month
19	Risk of electric shock due to electrical socket (for kettle) within 1M of sink (utility room) reduced by provision residual current device (RCD)	M	I M L	Inform staff of risk and controls. Monitor staff usage and remind them to keep all surfaces free from water prior to use of kettle. Relocate socket, but retain RCCB	Immediate 1 Month 3 Monthly
20	Risk of laceration due to breakage of glass in glazed screen at entrance reduced / controlled by application of protective clear plastic film (Workplace (HSW) Regs 92	M	I M L	No immediate action Check that appropriate type of film approved Monitor condition at regular intervals	1 Week 1 Month

<u>Management Report</u>

<u>Introduction</u>

This report identifies good and poor practices within the head office of Pristine Tiles Plc., Northampton. The office is a modern two storey building, with basement, situated on a small business park adjacent to a main trunk road. The building consists of a reception, kitchen and toilet facilities on the ground floor together with three small offices. The second floor is reached by a central stair well and this leads to six further offices. The nature of the work carried out in the building includes sales, customer support, finance, human resources and a design department. Work involves telephone calls, use of computers for data entry and design. There are 26 employees located within the building. The purpose of the report is to highlight the main findings of a workplace inspection carried out on the 4th December xx. It covers hazards and office related welfare matters. A number are considered in detail and the full observation list is included in the appendix.

1. <u>Executive Summary</u>

    I was impressed to find a high level of housekeeping, the floor areas and corridors were clear of obstructions and the lighting levels were appropriate to the work being carried out. Unfortunately a number of items were noticed on further inspection which required rectification to prevent the risk of serious injury or ill health. Detailed consideration is given to faulty balustrades, a defective electric fan, fire precautions, the potential danger from a first floor window and the need to carry out Display Screen Equipment assessments for computer users. Urgent repairs/replacement is recommended to the balustrade and fan, improved management systems for fire prevention and remedial measures to the window. Approximate costs are given under each heading.

2. <u>Main Findings</u>

    The general the level of housekeeping was maintained to a high standard, the floor areas and corridors were clear of obstructions and the lighting levels were appropriate to the work being carried out.

2.1   Observation No 4 - Loose balustrades on main stair

Two sections of balustrade are loose and likely to fail if leaned against heavily. Any fall could be serious or fatal. Apart from the cost in human terms and loss of professional time of such an accident, the defective balustrades breaches legislation: the Workplace (Health Safety and Welfare) Regulations (WHSW) which require all traffic routes to be kept free from obstruction. Since the stair is in constant use, I recommend immediate temporary repair using boarding, quickly followed by permanent repair comprising replacement steel balusters fixed to floor and handrail. I assess cost of repairs at £650 + VAT.

The balustrades should be inspected regularly in future.

2.2   Observation No 5 - Faulty electric fan in sales office

A section of the plastic cover was found to be broken exposing electrically conductive parts to the rear of the fan motor, which were accessible to the touch. Accidental electrocution could easily occur, so the fan should be taken out of service and the cover replaced. If parts are not available, the whole fan should be replaced. Cost off repair is £10 (carried out by our own staff) and replacement is £55 (incl.VAT). Action should be taken immediately to avoid a serious/fatal accident, lost time and to comply with the Provision and Use of Work Equipment Regulations. (PUWER) which require all dangerous parts of machinery to be adequately guarded.

Portable appliance testing should be reviewed and carried out at least annually. Cost £2.5 per item.

2.3   Observation No 16 - Basement fire escape exit stair

Documents are stored under the fire escape exit stair. This is a fire hazard and in the event of fire the only escape route would be cut off from the basement. This could lead to fatalities and is a contravention of the Regulatory Reform (Fire Safety) Order since adequate escape routes are not provided. The situation is remedied, at almost no cost, by removing the documents. I recommend, this is done immediately and management procedures adopted to prevent reoccurrence. This should include immediate provision of corrective action information to staff, and further staff training on fire prevention.

2.4   Observation No 12 - Stair windows with low sill

This first floor landing window has a very low sill and is unprotected from impact. If someone trips and falls against it, they could break the glass and cut themselves badly and possibly fall through to the outside. To prevent a fall the glazing should be protected by applying plastic safety film and fixing a bar or hand rail across the opening should be installed for further protection, this will then comply with the WHSW Regulations which state that large areas of glass should be clearly marked.

Costs would be approx £450 (+VAT).

2.5   Observation No 11 - Display screen equipment

Risk of work-related upper limb disorder, back and neck pain, eye strain, fatigue, stress etc, due to poorly laid out work stations with computers, inappropriate chairs, Noted generally. An assessment of each user's workstation should be carried out. Employers must carry out workstation assessments in order to comply with the Display Screen Equipment Regulations.

Whilst the above are the most critical issues there are a number of items requiring attention and reference should be made to the observation sheets in the appendix.

3.   Conclusion

Defective balustrades' and a damaged eclectic fan were observed indicating that routine maintenance and portable appliance testing was not being carried out. Maintenance schedules and routine electrical testing of equipment should be established to prevent a reoccurrence of similar issues in future.

Computer workstations were not correctly adjusted for users and many chairs were inadequate for this type of work. DSE assessments should be reviewed as a priority and new chairs purchased as necessary to reduce the risk of muscular skeletal injury to operators.

Fire precautions were inadequate in the basement and accumulated files under the exit staircase should be removed. Staff should be instructed not to store such materials under the stairway in the future; this will avoid the risk of a blocked escape in the event of a fire in the basement.

Occupational health and safety is a subject which needs to be managed properly. Failure to do this might result in prosecution in a criminal court or civil claims for compensation. The attendant costs and adverse publicity could have a significant impact on profitability.

Accidents have to be investigated by management and when time is lost from work, workloads have to be reorganised and sometimes re-training has to take place. These issues cause disruption and have an economic impact.

Accidents that result in personal injury will cause pain and suffering to the victim. More serious accidents affect a wider circle of family and friends. Witnesses to serious accidents may also suffer. It is my belief that people have a right to be protected from the hazards that are present in the workplace and that managers have a duty to ensure this protection is in place.

It is my conclusion that if my recommendations are not accepted, we are not fulfilling our legal and moral obligations as an employer and that profitability could be adversely affected.

Recommendations

Ref. No.	Recommendations	Likely resource implications	Priority	Review Date
3.1 (Item 4)	Fit temporary boards to stairwell Replace defective balustrades'	£100 £650.00	3 days 1 month	3 monthly
3.2 (Item 5)	Take out of service Repair replace electric fan Implement portable appliance testing	 £10 to £55 £150	Immediate 1 week 3 months	Annual
3.3 (Item 16)	Remove files from beneath basement fire exit stairway Inform/train staff not to store files under stairwell	£0 £300	Immediate 1 week	Monthly
3.4 (Item 12)	Apply plastic safety film to window Fit hand rail in front f window	£50 £450	1 week 1 month	3 monthly
3.5 (Item 11)	Carry out DSE risk assessments Provide replacement chairs	£400 £600 – 800	1 month 3 month	Annual

End

NEBOSH sample questions - answers

Unit NGC1 - Management of health and safety

ELEMENT 1

1. Replacement or repair of damaged plant and equipment is a cost that an organisation may face following a workplace accident.

   List **EIGHT** possible costs to the organisation following a workplace accident. **(8)**

There are many possible responses to this question and a long list of possible costs. They include:

- *Costs associated with lost production.*
- *Damage to materials.*
- *First-aid.*
- *Investigation and remedial action.*
- *Additional administration incurred.*
- *Replacement staff.*
- *Increases in insurance premiums as well as criminal and civil actions (the imposition of fines, parts of compensation payments not covered by insurance and legal representation).*

There may also be intangible costs following an accident arising from a poor corporate image and a possible detrimental effect on employee morale resulting in reduced productivity.

2. **Identify** the **TWO** types of enforcement notice that may be served by an inspector, stating the conditions that must be satisfied before **EACH** type of notice is served. **(8)**

This question requires candidates to identify, and distinguish between, improvement and prohibition notices. An improvement notice may be served where an inspector is of the opinion that there is a breach of a statutory health and safety duty, or that there has been such a breach which is likely to continue or be repeated; a prohibition notice may be served only where, in the inspector's opinion, there is a risk of serious personal injury. In the latter case, a breach need not have occurred for the notice to be served. As a point of accuracy, a number of answers have included the phrase 'imminent risk' even though the word 'imminent' does not appear in the relevant section of the Act.

3. **Explain** the meaning, status and roles of:

   (i) Health and safety regulations. **(3)**

   (ii) HSC Approved Codes of Practice. **(3)**

   (iii) HSE guidance. **(2)**

For part (i), regulations contain requirements that lay down minimum legal standards. Breaches of regulations constitute criminal offences that can lead to enforcement action, with the possibility of prosecution and the imposition of fines; that most health and safety regulations are made under the Health and Safety at Work etc Act by the Secretary of State after consultation with HSC; and that they often implement EC Directives that are aimed at protecting employees and others.

For part (ii), duty holders must comply with the requirements of an ACOP or be able to show that the chosen means of control are equally effective. ACOPs are approved by the HSC with the consent of the Secretary of State and that their purpose is to provide practical interpretation of legal requirements in specific areas.

For part (iii) HSE guidance has no formal legal standing, is generally more informative and practical than an ACOP, and is intended to give advice on good practice.

4. (a) **Give** the meaning of the term 'negligence'. **(2)**

   (b) **Give** an example of a negligent act by an employer. **(2)**

   (c) **Outline** the role of the civil courts with respect to health and safety matters. **(4)**

In answering part (a) of the question, candidates should say that negligence is a civil wrong (tort) involving unreasonable careless conduct, or a breach of the common law duty of care, resulting in loss, damage or injury.

An example of a negligent act by an employer can include a failure to provide a safe system of work, a failure to provide safe means of access or egress or a failure to provide safe plant and equipment.

The role of the civil courts with respect to health and safety matters is to adjudicate on actions for damages relating to personal injury arising from breaches of a common law or statutory duty, to establish liability and to award compensation where this is appropriate. There is a hierarchy of appeal involving firstly a Court of Appeal which hears cases referred from the County and/or High Courts. Finally, appeals from the Court of Appeal are heard by the House of Lords whose decisions importantly set a binding precedent for all courts below it.

5. (a) **Draw** a flowchart to show the relationships between the six elements of the health and safety management system model in HSE's "Successful Health and Safety Management' (HSG65). **(4)**

(b) **Outline** the part that EACH element of the HSG65 model plays within the health and safety management system. **(12)**

(c) **Outline** the economic benefits that an organisation may obtain by implementing a successful health and safety management system. **(4)**

For part (a), a flow chart should show the six elements of the health and safety management system model (i.e. 'policy', 'organising', 'planning and implementation', 'measuring performance', 'reviewing performance' and 'audit'} in their correct sequence. The relationships with one another should then have been indicated by arrows to show how one element progresses to the next and how performance review should feed back into the other elements. The flowchart should show clearly the role of auditing in examining each of the five main elements and then feeding back into the review process.

For part (b), outline the part played by each of the six elements of the management system. It starts with establishing a policy that states management's intentions and sets clear aims, objectives and targets. This is followed by organising for health and safety by allocating responsibilities and establishing effective communication and commitment at all levels established. The next stage involves planning and implementing, where practical plans are developed to meet the objectives and effective control measures introduced based on risk assessment. Proactive and reactive monitoring systems should be introduced to measure performance in health and safety and a system of review established to evaluate the performance against the objectives and targets, to consider options for improvement and to reset targets. The review would be reinforced by an independent and structured audit of all parts of the system, which would assess compliance with health and safety management procedures and identify where existing standards are inadequate or deficient.

In answering part (c), a number of appropriate economic benefits from achieving high standards of health and safety may include: increased productivity with improved morale and a reduction in downtime; an improvement in product quality and reduced wastage; a reduction in the costs associated with accidents; reduced insurance premiums; an enhanced corporate image; and lower staff turnover involving a reduction in recruitment and training costs.

ELEMENT 2

1. (a) **Outline** the requirements of section 2(3) of the Health and Safety at Work etc Act 1974 in relation to an employer's duty to prepare a health and safety policy. **(2)**

(b) **Explain** the purposes of the following sections of a health and safety policy:

(i) 'Statement of intent'. **(2)**

(ii) 'Organisation'. **(2)**

(iii) 'Arrangements'. **(2)**

In answering part (a) of the question, candidates can outline that an employer has a duty to prepare a written statement of his general policy with respect to health and safety together with the organisation and arrangements for carrying out the policy. An exception to the requirement for the policy to be in writing exists in cases where there are fewer than five employees.

Part (b) the 'statement of intent' should both demonstrate management's commitment to health and safety and set goals and objectives for the organisation; the purpose of the section of the policy on 'organisation' is to identify health and safety responsibilities and reporting lines within the company; and the section on 'arrangements' is intended to set out in detail the specific systems and procedures that aim to assist in the implementation of the general policy.

2. (a) **Identify** the legal requirements whereby employers must prepare a written statement of their health and safety policy. **(2)**

(b) **Identify SIX** categories of persons who may be shown in the 'organisation' section of a health and safety policy document **AND state** their likely general or specific health and safety responsibilities. **(6)**

There are two particular circumstances when section 2(3) of the Health and Safety at Work etc Act 1974 applies - i.e. when there is an employer, and when that employer employs five or more persons.

Part (b) requires candidates both to identify six categories of persons who might appear in the "organisation" section of a policy document and also to state their likely general or specific health and safety responsibilities. Categories identified with their responsibilities could have included: directors and senior managers (setting general policy and objectives); supervisors (checking day-to-day compliance with the policy); safety advisers (advising the company on accident and compliance issues); safety representatives (representing employees in consultation on health and safety matters with the employers); employees (responsible for their own general health and safety and that of others); fire marshals (to evacuate buildings safely in the event of an emergency) and trained first-aid personnel (to provide first-aid to injured persons).

ELEMENT 3

1. (a) **Outline** the benefits to an organisation of having a health and safety committee. **(4)**

(b) **Outline** the reasons why a health and safety committee may prove to be ineffective in practice. **(8)**

(c) **Identify** a range of methods that an employer can use to provide health and safety information directly to individual employees. **(8)**

Benefits which can be outlined include: it demonstrates management commitment and compliance with the legal requirement to consult with employees; it facilitates consultation and communication with the workforce via employee representatives; it provides a means of recording discussions that have taken place on health and safety matters and it may help to foster a positive health and safety culture by encouraging employee involvement and ownership.

Identify reasons such as: a lack of management commitment; no terms of reference for the committee; no agenda and/or minutes of the meetings being produced; an uneven balance between management and employee representatives; poor chairmanship; no access to the decision making processes; infrequent meetings; inappropriate topics for discussion and no access to health and safety expertise.

A range of valid methods such as: notice boards; team briefings; training sessions including induction and tool box talks; news letters and the inclusion of messages with wage/pay slips; posters, competitions and signs; and one to one briefing such as in appraisal sessions.

2.   An organisation occupying an office block is to use a contractor to carry out extensive refurbishment.

    (a)   **Outline** checks that the organisation should make when assessing the health and safety competence of the contractor. **(6)**

    (b)   **Outline** the duties placed on the contractor's employees by the Health and Safety at Work etc Act 1974. **(4)**

    (c)   **Outline** procedural measures that the organisation should take to help reduce the risk to the health and safety of their own employees whilst the contractors are carrying out this work. **(10)**

For part (a) outline checks such as the contractor's previous experience with the type of work to be carried out; the reputation amongst previous or current clients; the content and quality of the health and safety policy and the systems in place for its implementation including the preparation of risk assessments, monitoring and consultation with the workforce; the level of training and qualifications of staff, including those with health and safety responsibilities; membership of a trade organisation or professional body; the safety of equipment to be used on site, its maintenance and its examination in accordance with statutory requirements; procedures for the selection and monitoring of sub-contractors; and the detailed proposals, such as method statements, for the work to be carried out.

For part (b), the duties placed upon the contractor's employees by the Health and Safety at Work etc Act 1974 are those contained in Section 7 and 8. Section 7 requires an employee to take reasonable care for their own health and safety and that of others who might be affected by acts or omissions at work, and to co-operate with their employer or any other person so far as is necessary to enable them to comply with any statutory duty or requirement placed upon them. Additionally, Section 8 places a duty on the employee to refrain from intentionally or recklessly interfering with or misusing anything provided in the interests of health, safety or welfare.

The last part of the question requires candidates to outline procedural measures that the organisation should take to help reduce the risk to the health and safety of their own employees whilst the contractors were at work. These include the appointment of a contact person with whom the contractor should communicate in the event of a problem, incident or emergency; regular contact and consultation between both parties to aid the transfer of relevant information; informing employees on the work to be completed, its likely duration, the contractors involved and any new hazards that might be introduced by the work; procedures for entry to restricted areas and the use of permit-to-work systems for certain operations; procedures for the delivery of materials, the handling, storage and disposal of waste and for the management of the traffic involved; procedures to be followed in the event of an emergency and the introduction of monitoring systems to ensure the contractor's compliance with the standards of health and safety that had been agreed.

3.   (a)   **Identify** the **TWO** means by which employers may provide information to employees in order to comply with the Health and Safety Information for Employees Regulations 1989. **(2)**

    (b)   **Outline** the categories of information provided to employees by the means identified in (a). **(6)**

Candidates should identify the approved poster and the approved leaflet and then outline the categories of information they contain such as a resume of the duties both of employers and employees; the name and address of the enforcing authority for the workplace together with the address of the Employment Medical Advisory Service; consultation arrangements on health and safety issues; co-operation with other employers sharing the same premises; emergency procedures; the provision of personal protective equipment and duties under RIDDOR.

4.   **Identify** the main health and safety issues to be included in an induction training programme for goods delivery drivers using small vehicles, both on and off-site. **(8)**

In answering this question, candidates should identify issues such as the health and safety policy of the company and its culture; the employees' legal duties as contained in the Health and Safety at Work etc Act and the Management of Health and Safety at Work Regulations; information on the internal traffic routes and site rules including speed limits together with the signage and markings used; the specific workplace hazards such as restricted areas, the presence of hazardous materials and load security; the precautions to be taken in the manual handling of goods; the need to carry out periodic checks of the vehicle and the procedures for the reporting of defects and unsafe conditions; the wearing of personal protective equipment such as gloves and hi-visibility clothing; the procedures to be followed in the event of an accident or emergency; the company's policy with respect to alcohol or substance misuse, smoking, the use of mobile phones and the carrying of passengers; lone working issues including security, communication and the need to check in on return to base; and information on the arrangements for first aid and welfare.

5   (a)   **Identify** the 'five' steps involved in the assessment of risk from workplace activities (as described in HSE's "Five steps to risk assessment" (INDG 163)). **(5)**

    (b)   **Explain** the criteria that should be applied to help develop an action plan to prioritise the control of health and safety risks in the workplace. **(3)**

Candidates should show a good understanding of the risk assessment process by being able to describe the "five" steps as identifying the hazards associated with the activities and tasks performed at the workplace; identifying who might be harmed (including operators, maintenance staff, cleaners, visitors, etc); evaluating the likelihood and probable severity of the harm that might be caused and assessing the adequacy of existing control measures; recording the significant findings of the assessment and carrying out a review at a later date and revising the findings when necessary.

Once a risk assessment has been completed, an action plan will need to be developed to prioritise the suggested remedial measures. Criteria which may be applied to assist with the prioritisation include legal requirements, the likelihood and severity of the risk, the number of persons who might be affected, the speed of the action required (whether long or short term), the possibility of enforcement action and publicity affecting the reputation of the company.

ELEMENT 4

1.   **Identify EIGHT** sources of information that might usefully be consulted when developing a safe system of work. **(8)**

A selection can be made from sources such as:

- *Statutory instruments.*
- *ACOPs.*
- *HSE guidance.*
- *Manufacturers' information.*
- *European and other official standards.*
- *Industry or trade literature.*
- *Results of risk assessments.*
- *Accident statistics and health/medical surveillance records, the employees involved, and enforcement agencies and other experts.*

2.   (a)   **Identify TWO** situations where a permit-to-work system might be considered appropriate. **(2)**

    (b)   **Outline** the key elements of a permit-to-work system. **(6)**

In answering part (a), the types of situation that candidates can identify include:

- *Work in confined spaces.*
- *Work in flammable atmospheres.*
- *Work on electrical equipment.*
- *Work on dangerous plant such as conveyors and hot work.*

For part (b), the key elements that should be outlined include:

- *A description of the task to be performed.*
- *An indication of the duration of the validity of the permit.*
- *The isolations that have been made and the additional precautions required.*
- *Details and signature of the person authorising the work.*
- *An acknowledgement of acceptance by the employee carrying out the task, who would then need to indicate on the permit that the work has been completed and the area made safe in order for the permit to be cancelled.*

3.   **Outline** the precautions to ensure the health and safety of persons engaged in paint-spraying in a motor vehicle repair workshop. **(8)**

This question presents a particular scenario and requires candidate to outline the precautions that should be taken to ensure the health and safety of those involved in the activity described.

Outline such precautions as:

- *Segregation of the activity, typically by means of a spray booth fitted with local exhaust ventilation and protected electrical equipment.*
- *Suitable storage and fire precautions for flammable paints and solvents.*
- *The provision and use of personal protective equipment (clothing, respiratory protection, etc).*
- *Monitoring employees' exposures to airborne substances.*
- *Ensuring the examination and maintenance of control measures.*
- *Providing appropriate training to employees; and maintaining welfare and hygiene facilities.*

ELEMENT 5

1.   **Identify FOUR** active and **FOUR** reactive means by which an organisation can monitor its health and safety performance. **(8)**

Active methods of monitoring might include:

- *Safety audits involving comprehensive and independently executed examinations of all aspects of an organisation's health and safety performance against stated objectives.*
- *Safety surveys focusing on a particular activity such as manual handling, training programmes and employees' attitudes towards health and safety.*

- *Sampling where specific areas of occupational health and safety are targeted.*
- *Tours involving unscheduled workplace inspections to check on issues such as wearing of PPE and housekeeping.*
- *Benchmarking where an organisation's performance in certain areas is compared with that of other organisations with similar processes.*
- *Risks and health surveillance using techniques such as audiometry.*

Reactive methods of monitoring might include:

- *An analysis of statistics on accidents, dangerous occurrences, near misses and cases of occupational ill-health.*
- *Assessment of the cost of these incidents including damage to property.*
- *The number of enforcement actions such as prosecutions and notices taken against the organisation.*
- *The number of civil claims for damages pursued on behalf of its employees.*

Avoid confusion between 'active' and 'reactive' methods of monitoring.

2. **Identify** the advantages **AND** disadvantages of carrying out a health and safety audit of an organisation's activities by:

    (i)   An internal auditor. **(4)**

    (ii)   An external auditor. **(4)**

(Advantages in one type of audit are often mirrored by disadvantages in the other).

*The possible advantages of using an **internal auditor** for a safety audit of an organisation would include familiarity with the workplace, its tasks and processes and an awareness of what might be practicable for the industry; familiarity with members of the workforce including knowledge of an individual's qualities and attitude; and an audit which was relatively less costly and easier to arrange. On the other hand, an internal auditor may not be in possession of recognised auditing skills, may not be up to date with legal requirements and be less likely to be aware of best practice in other organisations. They may be subject to pressure from management and the workforce and have time constraints imposed upon him.*

*Conversely an **external auditor** is more likely to posses the necessary auditing skills and credibility; will not be inhibited from criticising members of management or the workforce; is more likely to be up to date with legal requirements and best practice in other companies and will view the organisation's performance with a fresh pair of eyes. However, he will be disadvantaged in that he is unlikely to be familiar with the workplace, tasks and processes; may have difficulty in obtaining the full cooperation of the workforce; may be unfamiliar with the industry and seek unrealistic standards and may well be more costly than an internal member of staff.*

3. (a)   An employee has been seriously injured after being struck by a reversing vehicle in a loading bay.

            (i)   Give **FOUR** reasons why the accident should be investigated by the person's employer. **(4)**

            (ii)   **Outline** the information that should be included in the investigation report. **(8)**

    (b)   Outline **FOUR** possible immediate causes and **FOUR** possible underlying (root) causes of the accident. **(8)**

For part (i), candidates should recognise that the primary purpose of investigating an accident is to identify the immediate and root causes in order to prevent similar accidents occurring in the future. In this respect, the main reasons for investigation relate to the identification of possible weaknesses in risk assessment processes and other aspects of safety management systems. Other reasons relate to:

- *Facilitating compliance with legal obligations (including the requirements of the Reporting of Injuries, Diseases and Dangerous Occurrences Regulations 1995 and social security legislation).*
- *Collecting evidence to defend a civil claim.*
- *Determining economic loss.*
- *Demonstrating management commitment to occupational health and safety.*

Part (ii) requires an outline of a sufficient range of information to gain the eight marks available. This should include reference to information such as:

- *The personal details of the injured party.*
- *The date, time and location of the accident.*
- *Environmental conditions, the work activity at the time of the accident.*
- *The control measures in place.*
- *The precise circumstances of the accident.*
- *The type and extent of injury sustained.*
- *Details of witnesses and copies of their statements where taken.*
- *Drawings and photographs.*
- *Immediate and root causes identified.*
- *Possible breaches of the law.*
- *The recommendations of the investigation team in relation to remedial action required.*

In answering part (iii), marks are available for outlining possible immediate causes such as:

- *Human error or failure to comply with procedures.*
- *Mechanical failure.*
- *Poor visibility in the loading bay (e.g. absence of lighting).*
- *Restricted view for the driver.*
- *Environmental conditions such as high noise levels.*

Underlying causes could include:

- *Lack of driver and/or other employee training.*
- *Lack of supervision.*

- *Absence of site rules or procedures for the control of reversing vehicles.*
- *Failure to separate vehicular and pedestrian traffic.*
- *Lack of maintenance of vehicles and/or the workplace.*

4.   (a)   **Identify FOUR** reasons why accidents should be reported and recorded within a workplace. **(4)**

         (b)   **Outline** factors that might discourage employees from reporting workplace accidents. **(4)**

For part (a), candidates should identify that accidents should be reported and recorded in order to comply with legislative requirements, to enable an accident investigation to take place (with the aim of preventing accidents of a similar type) and to identify accident trends from later statistical analysis. Marks are also available for identifying that accident reporting and recording can also lead to a useful review of risk assessments and can assist in the consideration of any civil claims that may arise.

In answering part (b), outline factors such as:
- *Ignorance of the reporting procedures.*
- *The possibility of retribution (particularly within a 'blame culture').*
- *Peer pressure.*
- *A previous lack of management response.*
- *An aversion to form filling.*

Other factors include:
- *A reluctance to lose time from the job in hand.*
- *The trivial nature of any injury sustained.*
- *A desire to preserve the company's, the department's or the individual's personal safety record, particularly where bonus payments are affected by it.*

5.   With reference to the Reporting of Injuries, Diseases and Dangerous Occurrences Regulations 1995:

         (i)   **State** the legal requirements for reporting a fatality resulting from an accident at work to an enforcing authority. **(5)**

         (ii)   **Outline THREE** further categories of work-related injury (other than fatal injuries) that are reportable. **(3)**

Part (i) identify the requirement to notify the enforcing authority by the quickest practicable means and then to report the death formally within ten days by an approved means (e.g. on form F2508). The responsible person under the Regulations has the duty to submit the report and fewer still knew that delayed deaths, up to one year after the original accident, have to be reported whether or not they have been previously reported under another category.

For part (ii), identify 'major injury' as a category but then went on to list types of injury within this category (fracture of bone, amputation, 24-hours hospitalisation, etc.) and ignored other categories completely. They could additionally have referred to injuries that result in the injured person being away from work, or unable to do normal work, for more than three consecutive days, and injuries to non-employees who are taken to hospital for treatment.

Unit NGC2 - Controlling workplace risks

ELEMENT 1

1.   The water main supplying a school is to be repaired. The work will be carried out in a 1.5 metre deep excavation, which will be supported in order to ensure the safety of the employees working in the excavation.

         (i)   **Identify** when the **THREE** statutory inspections of the supported excavation must be carried out by the competent person. **(3)**

         (ii)   **State** the information that should be recorded in the excavation inspection report. **(5)**

         (iii)   Other than the provision of supports for the excavation, **outline** additional precautions to be taken during the repair work in order to reduce the risk of injury to the employees and others who may be affected by the work. **(12)**

For part (i), specific occasions when inspections must be carried out by law are at the start of every shift before work commences, after any event likely to affect the strength or stability of the excavation, and after any accidental fall of rock or earth or other material.

For part (ii) gain marks by stating the information that should be contained in an inspection report. What is needed is reference to information such as the name and address of the person for whom the inspection is carried out, the location of the place of work, a description of the place of work inspected, details of any matters identified that could lead to risks to the health or safety of any person, the action taken to reduce the risk, any further action that might be needed, the name and position of the person making the report, and the date and time of the inspection.

For part (iii), precautions that should be taken to reduce the risk of injury to employees include the detection of underground services, safe digging, preferably by hand, near to the services and the provision of adequate support for them once exposed; the isolation of the water supply to reduce the risk of flooding the excavation; ensuring the stability of adjacent buildings if this was thought to be necessary; the provision of safe access in and out of the excavation and placing stop blocks to prevent plant from approaching too close to its edge; and using appropriate personal protective equipment such as head protection, ear defenders and safety footwear. As for the possible risk of injury to others who might be affected by the work, there would initially need to be close liaison between the contractors and the school authorities to ensure, whenever possible, that work in the excavation was carried out outside school hours. Additionally, barriers would need to be erected to provide a safe walkway for teachers and children and other members of the public and precautions would also have to be taken to ensure that materials and equipment were stored in a safe compound and plant immobilised when not in actual use.

2.	Excluding welfare facilities, **Identify** issues associated with the workplace that should addressed to ensure that it meets the requirements of the Workplace (Health, Safety and Welfare) Regulations 1992. **(8)**

Identify issues such as:

■	*Availability of natural lighting.*
■	*Adequacy of the artificial lighting provided particularly for specific areas such as stairs and corridors.*
■	*Arrangements for the provision of emergency lighting in the event of failure of the primary supply.*
■	*The provision of effective and sufficient ventilation.*
■	*An adequate heating system to provide and maintain a reasonable temperature throughout the building.*
■	*The condition of floors which should be suitable for the purpose and well maintained.*
■	*The provision of suitable workstations and the avoidance of space constraints.*
■	*The construction of transparent or translucent doors with safety glass and ensuring they were appropriately marked.*
■	*Ensuring that windows and skylights, designed to open do not project into an area where persons are likely to collide with them.*
■	*Ensuring that adequate arrangements are in place for cleaning windows and skylights in safety.*
■	*Checking that provision had been made to deal with the needs of disabled employees.*

3.	**Outline** the measures an employer might consider to minimise the risk of violence against employees. **(8)**

Possible measures include:

■	*The completion of a workplace risk assessment which would identify vulnerable members of staff.*
■	*The design and layout of the workplace with the use of physical barriers and restricting access to buildings, particularly in the case of known offenders.*
■	*Good standards of lighting in vulnerable areas such as car parks.*
■	*The employment of trained security staff.*
■	*The use of security equipment such as alarms, panic buttons and closed circuit television.*
■	*Ensuring adequate staffing levels.*
■	*The provision of training in dealing with confrontation.*

Additional measures that could be mentioned include:

■	*The relevance of consultation with the police.*
■	*The introduction of procedures for lone working, working out of hours and for home or other off site visits.*
■	*Reducing the need for handling money.*
■	*Introducing procedures for the reporting of incidents involving violence or attempted violence to staff members.*
■	*The use of disciplinary procedures when violence occurred in-house amongst employees.*

ELEMENT 2

1.	**Outline** measures to be taken to prevent accidents when pedestrians are required to work in vehicle manoeuvring areas. **(8)**

Answers should generally include:

■	*References to segregated systems for vehicular and pedestrian traffic.*
■	*Appropriate road markings.*
■	*Maintaining good visibility (mirrors, transparent doors, provision of lighting etc).*
■	*Audible warnings on vehicles.*

Other relevant measures that should be mentioned include:

■	*The drawing up and enforcement of site rules.*
■	*The provision of refuges.*
■	*The wearing of high-visibility clothing.*
■	*A good standard of housekeeping.*
■	*Training for, and supervision of, all concerned.*

2.	**Outline** the means by which the risk of accidents from reversing vehicles within a workplace can be reduced. **(8)**

Present a hierarchical range, from avoiding the need for vehicles to reverse (one-way and 'drive-through' systems, turning circles, etc), through the separation of vehicles and pedestrians (barriers, signs, etc) and aspects of vehicle and workplace design (audible alarms, mirrors on vehicles and at blind corners, refuges, lighting, etc), to procedural measures (use of banksman, site rules, driver training, etc).

ELEMENT 3

1.	**Identify EIGHT** rules to follow when a fork-lift truck is left unattended during a driver's work break. **(8)**

Identify rules such as the return of the fork-lift truck to a designated area on firm level ground with the mast tilted forward and the forks resting on the floor; the isolation of the power with the ignition key removed and returned to a responsible person; and the need to park the truck away from other vehicles and in a position that did not block emergency exits.

2.	**Outline** the issues to consider when undertaking a manual handling assessment of a task that involves lifting buckets of water out of a sink. **(8)**

The main elements to be considered in a manual handling assessment are task, individual, load and environment.

Under the heading 'task', there a range of issues to be considered such as:

- *Frequency of the activity.*
- *Vertical and horizontal distances to be lifted/transported.*
- *Distance of the load from the body.*
- *Awkward body movements and so on.*

Similarly, under 'individual' - the physical capabilities and limitations of the individual concerned should be considered.

Under 'load' - factors such as the type/size of bucket and water temperature. Under 'environment' - wet floors, space constraints and ambient temperature.

3. **Outline** the precautions to be taken when using a mobile elevating work platform (MEWP) to reach a high point such as a streetlight. **(8)**

Outline precautions such as:

- *The need to inspect the equipment before use and to ensure it is in a good state of repair.*
- *Using only competent workers.*
- *Using outriggers and brakes.*
- *Erecting warning signs and barriers to avoid collisions.*
- *Ensuring the platform is not overloaded.*
- *Avoiding overhead obstructions.*
- *Wearing a harness.*

ELEMENT 4

1. A local authority employee uses a petrol-driven strimmer to maintain roadside grass verges.

   (i) **Describe** the possible hazards faced by the employee in carrying out this task. **(10)**

   (ii) **List FIVE** items of personal protective equipment that should be provided to, and used by, the employee. **(5)**

   (iii) **Outline** measures other than the use of personal protective equipment that might be necessary to ensure the health and safety of the employee. **(5)**

For part (i) describe the possible hazards faced by employees using a petrol-driven strimmer on grass verges on the roadside. These include:

- *Contact with the moving parts of the strimmer.*
- *The possibility of being struck by flying stones or other material.*
- *Slips/trips/falls.*
- *Manual handling hazards.*
- *The danger posed by moving traffic, noise and vibration, dust and fumes.*
- *The hazards associated with the storage and transfer of petrol.*

For part (ii), include reference to:

- *Ear defenders.*
- *Eye protection.*
- *Respiratory protection (dust mask).*
- *Gloves.*
- *Safety footwear.*
- *Gaiters.*
- *High visibility clothing that also afforded protection against the weather.*

For part (iii) outline measures such as:

- *The use of traffic control or barriers.*
- *The selection and maintenance of equipment to reduce to a minimum the levels of noise and vibration.*
- *The provision of information, instruction, training and supervision, and health surveillance.*

2. In relation to the ill-health effects from the use of vibrating hand-held tools:

   (a) **Identify** the health effects associated with exposure to vibration. **(4)**

   (b) **Outline** the control measures that may be used to minimise the risk of such effects. **(4)**

In answering part (a) identify effects such as:
- *Numbness and blanching of the fingers.*
- *Swollen and painful joints.*
- *A reduction in strength, grip and dexterity and in sensory perception.*
- *Involuntary muscular movement and carpal tunnel syndrome.*

For part (b), outline a hierarchy of control measures such as:
- *Elimination by mechanisation or automation.*
- *Substituting the tools with lower vibration equipment.*
- *Reducing the time of exposure of the operatives by providing frequent breaks and/or job rotation.*
- *Modifying the equipment to improve the grip on the tools.*
- *Introducing a planned maintenance programme for the tools.*
- *Providing appropriate personal protective equipment such as gloves to keep the hands warm.*

- *Introducing a programme of health surveillance.*
- *Providing the employees with information, instruction and training on the hazards associated with the use of the tools and the control measures that should be taken.*

3. (a) **Identify:**

   (i) **TWO** mechanical hazards associated with moving parts of machinery. **(2)**

   (ii) **TWO** non-mechanical hazards to which a machine operator may be exposed. **(2)**

   (b) **Outline** a hierarchy of control measures that may be used to reduce the risk of injury from dangerous parts of machinery. **(4)**

Distinguish clearly between 'mechanical' and 'non-mechanical' hazards. Mechanical hazards (i.e. those from moving parts of machinery and/or the material being worked) include impact, entanglement, crushing, shearing, ejection, cutting and abrasion, whereas a list of non-mechanical machinery hazards includes noise, vibration, electricity, hazardous substances, radiation, extremes of temperature and ergonomic issues. Such concepts are fundamental to an understanding of machinery safety.

Draw on their knowledge of the Provision and Use of Work Equipment Regulations 1998 and base answers on the requirements of Regulation 11. Answers that refer to fixed guards, other types of guards or protective devices, safety aids such as jigs, holders and push-sticks, and the provision of information, instruction, training and supervision - in this preferred order but not mutually exclusive - will be well rewarded.

ELEMENT 5

1. With respect to the use of portable electrical appliances in the workplace, **identify EIGHT** examples of faults and bad practices that could contribute to electrical accidents. **(8)**

Faults and bad practices that should be identified include:
- *An initial failure to select the right equipment for the job and/or environment.*
- *Inadequate checks on the equipment before use to ensure it was not damaged.*
- *A lack of procedures for its regular maintenance.*
- *Incorrect fuse rating and a failure to use residual current devices.*
- *Poor earth protection.*
- *The overloading of sockets.*
- *The use of cables which are split, twisted, kinked or jointed.*
- *Poor cable management resulting in trailing cables.*
- *The use of coiled extension cables and cables that are insufficiently protected and liable to damage particularly in workshop or construction environments.*
- *Plugs with bent pins or broken cases.*
- *Unauthorised repairs to the appliance.*
- *Misuse and abuse of the equipment by employees.*

2. In relation to the use of electrical cables and plugs in the workplace:

   (i) **Identify FOUR** examples of faults and bad practices that could contribute to electrical accidents. **(4)**

   (ii) **Outline** the corresponding precautions that should be taken for **EACH** of the examples identified in (i). **(4)**

For part (i), examples include:
- *Failure to select the right equipment for the environment (e.g. armoured or heat resistant cable might be required in arduous conditions).*
- *Incorrect rating of fuses.*
- *Ineffective or discontinuous earthing.*
- *Overloading of socket outlets.*
- *Cables unnecessarily long (or short).*
- *The use of coiled extension leads.*
- *Poorly wired plugs (e.g. wires under tension or outer protective sheath not clamped).*
- *The use of defective cables and plugs.*

For part (ii) an outline of relevant precautions for the examples identified are required:
- *Earthing.*
- *Calculate correct rating for a fuse.*
- *Residual current device (RCD).*
- *Reduce voltage.*
- *Battery powered.*
- *Double Insulation.*

3. In relation to electrical safety, **explain** the meaning of the following terms:

   (i) 'Isolation'. **(2)**

   (ii) 'Earthing'. **(2)**

   (iii) 'Reduced low voltage'. **(2)**

   (iv) 'Overcurrent protection'. **(2)**

- 'Isolation' refers to shutting off the electrical supply to an item of equipment or part of an electrical system and preventing inadvertent reconnection in order, for instance, to carry out maintenance work.
- 'Earthing' is a means whereby electrical equipment and conductive items are connected to earth by a cable or metal pipework such that the route to earth provides the path of least resistance to a current flowing under fault conditions.
- 'Reduced low voltage', commonly used on construction sites, involves the reduction of mains voltage by a transformer to a lower, safer voltage - typically 110 or 55 volts.
- "Overcurrent protection' is a method of preventing the flow of excess current by cutting the supply under fault conditions by means of a fuse or circuit breaker.

ELEMENT 6

1. **List EIGHT** ways of reducing the risk of a fire starting in a workplace. **(8)**

Choose from a list including:

- *The control of smoking and smoking materials.*
- *Good housekeeping to prevent the accumulation of waste paper and other combustible materials.*
- *Regular lubrication of machinery.*
- *Frequent inspection of electrical equipment for damage.*
- *Ensuring ventilation outlets on equipment are not obstructed.*
- *Controlling hot work.*
- *The provision of proper storage facilities for flammable liquids and the segregation of incompatible chemicals.*

2. (a) **Explain**, using a suitable sketch, the significance of the 'fire triangle'. **(4)**

    (b) **Identify TWO** methods of heat transfer and **explain** how **EACH** method can contribute to the spread of fire in work premises. **(4)**

For part (a) explain, with a clearly labelled diagram, that each side of the fire triangle represents one of the three elements - namely, fuel, oxygen and a source of ignition - that must be present for combustion to occur.

For part (b), choose two methods of heat transfer from the following:

- *Conduction (where, for example, heat can travel through metal beams between separate compartments).*
- *Radiation (where heat is radiated through the air and affects material at a distance).*
- *Convection (the upward transfer of heat by gases such as air).*
- *Contact or direct burning (where a heat source comes into direct contact with combustible material causing ignition).*

ELEMENT 7

1. (a) **State** the primary effect on the body of the following types of hazardous substance:

    (i) 'Irritant'. **(1)**

    (ii) 'Corrosive'. **(1)**

    (iii) 'Toxic'. **(1)**

    (iv) 'Carcinogenic'. **(1)**

    (b) **Describe** the differences between acute and chronic health effects. **(4)**

In answering part (a), identify that irritants cause inflammation on contact with the skin, eyes or mucous membranes, and that corrosive substances cause the destruction of living tissue at the point of contact - for example, the skin, respiratory tract or digestive tract. Toxic substances have a poisonous effect on body organs or systems, affecting normal metabolic functions, while carcinogens have the ability to alter the genetic material in living cells and to cause cancer.

For part (b), describe how acute health effects appear after a single or short term exposure, usually with a rapid or immediate response, whereas chronic effects are normally produced following prolonged or repeated exposures to an agent, appear gradually, may go unrecognised for long periods of time and may be progressive even without further exposure.

2. A company produces a range of solid and liquid wastes, both hazardous and non-hazardous. **Outline** the arrangements that should be in place to ensure the safe storage of the wastes prior to their collection and disposal. **(8)**

Refer to arrangements such as:

- *The completion of risk assessments that address the nature, properties and quantities of the wastes likely to be stored.*
- *Minimising the quantities stored by organising regular collections.*
- *Ensuring the separation of incompatible wastes.*
- *Providing appropriate means for containing the wastes in secure storage facilities (e.g. protected against unauthorised persons, weather, vehicles, etc).*
- *Installing and maintaining fire protection and fire-fighting systems in the case of flammable or combustible wastes.*
- *Installing bunds and drawing up procedures to deal with spillages that might present environmental risks.*
- *Providing safe means of transport and access to the storage site.*
- *Ensuring that wastes are accurately identified and that warning signs are in place where appropriate.*
- *Training employees in the precautions to be taken.*

- *Ensuring that they are provided with, and use, appropriate personal protective equipment, such as gloves, overalls and eye protection.*

3.   For each of the following agents, **outline** the principal health and safety effects **AND identify** a typical workplace situation in which a person might be exposed:

   (i)   Isocyanates. **(2)**

   (ii)   Asbestos. **(2)**

   (iii)   Leptospira bacteria. **(2)**

   (iv)   Lead. **(2)**

Isocyanates are a respiratory sensitiser and may also cause dermatitis. Persons carrying out work involving the use of isocyanate-based printing inks, adhesives or paints would be at risk.

Exposure to asbestos may cause asbestosis, lung cancer or mesothelioma (a rare cancer that is associated almost exclusively with asbestos). Carrying out maintenance work on, or the demolition of, a building where asbestos is contained in the fabric of the structure could lead to the inhalation of airborne fibres.

An infection caused by exposure to the leptospira bacterium is called leptospirosis, with symptoms that resemble influenza (fever, chills, muscular aches and pains, etc). In rare cases, a severe form of the condition known as Weil's disease can develop and this is characterised by symptoms that include bruising of the skin, anaemia, sore eyes, nose bleeds and jaundice. Serious damage to internal organs can result, which often proves fatal. The bacterium is carried by animals, particularly rats and cattle, and exposure to the urine of infected animals can put people such as sewer workers, farm workers and vets at particular risk. While there were some good accounts given for this part of the question, Examiners were disturbed to find that many candidates confused 'leptospira' with 'legionella'.

The health effects of exposure to lead are many and varied but principally include anaemia, fertility problems and damage to the kidneys, the nervous and muscular systems and, particularly in children, the brain. Signs and symptoms of lead poisoning include irritability, lethargy, memory and concentration problems, muscle and joint pain, 'wrist drop' and a blue line on the gums. Those engaged in any activity that involves lead and produces fume, vapour or dust (such as in battery manufacture, lead crystal glass-making or the removal of lead paint) are at risk.

ELEMENT 8

1.   In relation to the ill-health effects from the use of vibrating hand-held tools:

   (i)   **Identify** the typical symptoms that might be shown by affected individuals. **(4)**

   (ii)   **Outline** the control measures that may be used to minimise the risk of such effects. **(4)**

In answering part (i) identify symptoms such as numbness and blanching of the fingers and swollen and painful joints in addition to a reduction in dexterity, strength and sensory perception.

For part (ii), outline a hierarchy of control measures such as elimination by mechanisation or automation; substituting the tools with lower vibration equipment; reducing the time of vibration exposure to the operatives; introducing a planned maintenance programme for the tools and providing appropriate personal protective equipment such as gloves to keep hands warm.

2.   (a)   **Identify TWO** types of non-ionising radiation **AND give** an occupational source of **EACH. (4)**

   (b)   **Outline** the health effects associated with exposure to non-ionising radiation. **(4)**

In answering part (a) two examples of non-ionising radiation can be chosen from the following list:

- *Ultraviolet light (welding or excessive exposure to the sun).*
- *Infra-red (lasers).*
- *Microwave (ovens, radar or mobile phones).*
- *Radio wave (communications transmitter).*
- *Electromagnetic radiation (high voltage sources).*

Health effects associated with exposure to non-ionising radiation include:

- *Photokeratitis or arc eye from welding.*
- *Retinal burns, corneal damage and cataracts from exposure to infra-red radiation.*
- *Burns to the skin from exposure to ultra violet or infra-red radiation, the heating of, and damage to, skin and internal organs by radio frequencies, particularly microwaves and the possibility of skin cancer.*

3.   (a)   **Explain** the following terms in relation to noise exposure at work:

   (i)   'Noise-induced hearing loss'. **(2)**

   (ii)   'Tinnitus'. **(2)**

   (b)   **Identify FOUR** limitations of personal hearing protection as a means of protecting against the effects of noise. **(4)**

For part (a), a general understanding of the effects of noise on hearing is required. Noise-induced hearing loss is normally caused by prolonged exposure to high noise levels causing damage to the hair cells of the inner ear and leading to a permanent threshold shift at particular frequencies, which worsens with continued exposure both in terms of the extent of the threshold shift and of the frequencies affected. Tinnitus, on the other hand, is typified by a ringing or similar sound in the ears caused by over-stimulation of the hair cells. It can be acute or chronic, permanent or intermittent.

The main limitations of hearing protection, for part (b), are:

- Poor fit.
- Resistance to use.
- Comfort factors.
- Incompatibility with other protective equipment.
- Costly in terms of replacement and maintenance.
- Interference with communication.
- Hygiene problems.
- The need for constant supervision and attention (unlike some engineering solutions to noise problems).

QUESTIONS REQUIRING KNOWLEDGE FROM MORE THAN ONE ELEMENT

1. Due to an increase in knife related accidents amongst hotel kitchen staff that use the sharp tools in the preparation of food for the restaurant, a safe system of work is to be developed to minimise the risk of injury to this group of employees.

    (i)   **Identify** the legal requirement under which the employer must provide a safe system of work. **(2)**

    (ii)   **Describe** the issues to be addressed when developing the safe system of work for the hotel kitchen staff who use the knives as part of their work. **(10)**

    (iii) **Outline** the ways in which the employer could motivate the hotel kitchen staff to follow the safe system of work. **(8)**

In answering part (i) identify the requirement for a safe system of work under the Health and Safety at Work etc Act 1974, referring to the relevant section of the Act i.e. Section 2 and consider the employer's common law duty to provide a safe system of work.

Part (ii) of the question requires an understanding of the issues that would need to be considered in the development of a safe system of work for the hotel kitchen staff who use knives in the preparation of food for the restaurant. These include environmental issues such as noise, light, humidity and the condition of the floors; the suitability of the type of knife used; ergonomic issues such as space constraints and the design of working areas and surfaces; the provision of suitable personal protective equipment including gloves and non slip footwear; working patterns to avoid the possibility of fatigue and the competence, knowledge and experience of the staff involved.

Answers to part (iii) include issues such as senior management commitment, consultation and involvement during the development stage; provision of training and information; improving environmental conditions; provision of incentives; monitoring and supervision.

2. (a)   **Give TWO** reasons why visitors to a workplace might be at greater risk of injury than an employee. **(2)**

    (b)   **Outline** measures to be taken to ensure the health and safety of visitors to the workplace. **(6)**

Answers to part (a) include visitors unfamiliarity with the processes carried out in the workplace, the hazards they present and their associated risks and the fact that they may not have been issued with personal protective equipment; their lack of knowledge of the site layout and the fact that pedestrian routes might be inadequate or unsigned; their unfamiliarity with the emergency procedures and their vulnerability particularly if they were disabled or very young.

In answer to part (b), the range of management procedures that should be in place to deal with visitors to a workplace include measures such as visitor identification, for example, by the issue of badges with a routine for signing in and out; prior notification to those members of staff to be involved in the visit; the provision of information to the visitors on hazards and emergency procedures; an explanation of specific site rules, for example, the wearing of personal protective equipment; the clear marking of pedestrian routes and the need for visitors to be escorted by a member of management or supervisory staff.

This page is intentionally blank

Index